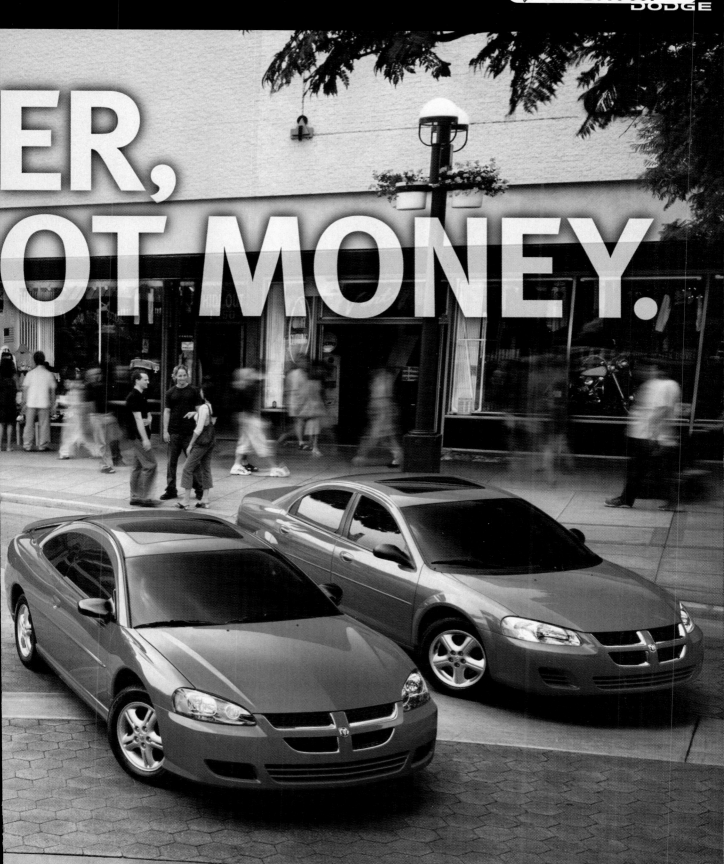

AMERICA'S BEST
GRADUATE
SCHOOLS

PLUS:

A DIRECTORY OF BUSINESS, EDUCATION,

ENGINEERING, LAW, AND MEDICAL SCHOOLS

HOW TO ORDER: Additional copies of the 2004 edition of *U.S.News & World Report*'s *Best Graduate Schools* guidebook are available for purchase by phone at (800) 836-6397, Ext. 904, and online at *www.usnews.com/grad/*. For inquiries regarding bulk pricing, please call (800) 836-6397.

2004 EDITION

www.usnews.com

ART AT CARNEGIE MELLON; TAKING
A BREAK FROM ED SCHOOL AT THE
UNIVERSITY OF CONNECTICUT; PUBLIC
HEALTH AT JOHNS HOPKINS

Becoming a grad student

BY RACHEL HARTIGAN SHEA

ou don't have to go.

That's the thing about graduate school. Your parents (and the law) make you trudge off to elementary school, and anyone who hopes for more from life than minimum-wage drudgery should finish high school. Without college, it's increasingly difficult to afford that roomy house in the suburbs with the two-car garage. But graduate school? You just don't have to do it.

So why go? Well, first off, there's the economy. More people signed up for the GMAT, the business school entrance exam, last year than in any previous year in its history, while 10 percent more law school hopefuls suffered through the LSAT this past December than did in 2001. Seeking refuge in grad school during an inhospitable job market is a time-tested strategy. When work was scarce in the mid-1980s, graduate applications rose about 7 percent a year. "It's a respectable thing to do," says Susan Krinsky, dean of admissions at the Tulane School of Law in New Orleans. "It's even a productive thing to do."

And then there's the money. The lifetime income of those holding master's degrees surpasses those who received only a bachelor's by about $335,000, while professional and doctoral graduates earn $890,000 more than the bachelor's holders, according to the Employment Policy Foundation, a Washington, D.C., think tank. But those figures can be misleading. Just ask one of the hundreds of deep-in-debt humanities Ph.D.'s barely scraping by with part-time teaching gigs. And some unknown part of the income differential between those with bachelor's and master's degrees can be attributed to the personal ambition that pushes people to sign up for graduate school in the first place.

What's more, graduate school requires too much intellectual rigor, spiritual fortitude, and financial commitment for students to be motivated solely by future job prospects and a theoretical increase in lifetime income. For one thing, it will consume at least one year of your life—and most likely much longer. Doctoral candidates and future physicians face a combination of schooling and apprenticeships that can last a decade or more. And these are years of work more demanding and competitive than college ever was.

Graduate school isn't the place for people who are trying to "find themselves," either. You don't go to explore different career options or even a wide variety of subjects, really. That's what college—and real life—are for. If you are still casting about for your life's goals, don't hide on campus. Take a stab at a career or two. Embrace your inner dilettante. And then go to graduate school if and when inspiration hits.

Because graduate school is for people who are obsessed. It's for people who don't mind living in a cheap Vicksburg motel for the summer while they sift through the probate records of Mississippi slave owners looking for key dissertation material. Or those who relish reading tax textbooks into the night so they can stun their law professor with a cogent response to a trick question in class the next morning. It's for people who like the smell of chemicals, the sight of blood, or a rowdy debate on middle school pedagogy.

Sound like you? Then get thee to grad school. Life won't offer you this luxury again.

The following pages will help you think about what you want in a school. Are you looking for a business school that specializes in internal auditing or supply-chain management or just business in general? How about a political science department focused on rational choice theory—or feminist scholarship? If you're thinking of education school, do you want to learn how people learn, or would you rather a little bit of that plus a full year of apprentice teaching at an elementary school?

Perhaps you are thinking that you can't possibly figure out the best place for you. Perhaps you are even tempted to rush to the rankings pages in this book and ignore everything else. But before you do, consider this: At this moment you have the great privilege of delving into a field that fascinates you. You can read about all its interesting permutations on university Web sites, in scholarly journals, and in books like this. And then *you*—not your parents, not your high school guidance counselor, and not anybody else who tells you that graduate degrees are good for you—can choose where to let your academic passions run free. ●

Paying for it

BY KRISTIN DAVIS

I f the prospect of paying for a grad school education seems intimidating, imagine financing two graduate degrees in one family. When Heather Hay was accepted into the master's program in marriage and family therapy at Syracuse University, her husband, Jonathan, landed a job as a writer for the school's publications department. That allowed Heather to take advantage of a partial tuition waiver for employees and their spouses. But now she's a Ph.D. candidate—and he's a master's student in Syracuse's School of Education. They both have graduate assistantships that pay for their coursework and provide a small stipend, but because he's no longer employed, they're also taking out a modest amount of subsidized student loans to cover living expenses. "We would love to have started a family or have a house by now," Jonathan says.

Thanks to the Hays' careful financial planning, however, their goal is in sight: "In a couple of years we can have those things without having the stresses of big debt," says Jonathan. If so, they're lucky; with average graduate school costs for tuition and living expenses topping $26,000 a year, it can be tough to assemble a patchwork of loans, grants, work, and other resources to get the bills paid. For students who can't pay out of pocket or use parental sup-

FIRST-YEAR ENGINEERING GRADUATE STUDENTS STUDY NUMERICAL METHODS AT THE UNIVERSITY OF CALIFORNIA–SAN DIEGO.

port, here are the top five ways to scramble together the money.

Snag a fellowship or assistantship. This is where the money is for many graduate students, especially those seeking Ph.D.'s. While undergraduates generally receive grants based on need, at the graduate level such awards are usually merit based. At elite and wealthy institutions like Cornell and Yale, virtually all Ph.D. candidates are awarded a fellowship or assistantship that covers tuition and fees, pays a stipend, and provides health insurance coverage. At other schools, top students are awarded funding when admitted, but others need to knock on doors to line up an assistantship and may not secure a position until the second semester or second year. (Fellowships usually have no work requirement, while graduate assistants typically work up to 15 hours a week teaching, grading papers, leading discussion groups, supervising lab courses, or assisting faculty with research.)

How much fellowship and assistantship aid is available varies widely depending on your field. In engineering, computer science, and math, 82 percent of full-time Ph.D. candidates and 55 percent of master's degree students are awarded assistantships, many funded with federal and corporate dollars. Fellowships are also more plentiful in engineering and the sciences—and often more generous than in other fields. Alik Widge, a Ph.D. student in robotics at Carnegie Mellon University, earns $23,000 from a National Defense Science and Engineering Fellowship, but stipends of $15,000 are more typical. In the humanities, only about half of full-time Ph.D. students and 40 percent of full-time master's degree students have assistantships, and stipends are often lower.

Comparatively few assistantships and fellowships are available for those studying law, medicine, and business, which explains why so many professional-school students borrow heavily. Master's degree candidates in education also tend to finance their degrees with savings or loans, because a majority earn their degrees part time while continuing to work full time, which makes assistantships impractical (and also typically disqualifies them for subsidized student loans).

The first step toward getting a fellowship or assistantship is to indicate on your admissions

KENNETH JARECKE—CONTACT FOR *USN&WR*

application that you want to be considered for all forms of financial aid. The choicest awards are often made by departmental committees on the basis of application materials and sometimes supplemental recommendations. Several government agencies and private organizations also sponsor outside fellowships that students can apply for on their own. Some of the more prestigious (and competitive) programs include National Science Foundation fellowships in the sciences, social sciences, and engineering; Mellon fellowships in the humanities; Ford Foundation fellowships for minorities (blacks, Hispanics, and American Indians); and American Association of University Women fellowships and grants for women. Two good online resources are Cornell University's free Graduate School Fellowship Notebook (at *cuinfo.cornell.edu/Student/GRFN*) and GrantSelect (*www.grantselect.com*), which offers a free one-week trial.

Borrow wisely. Even with a steady stream of assistantships, J. Briggs Cormier, a fifth-year Ph.D. theater student at Ohio State University, has taken out close to $100,000 in student loans, including debt for his undergraduate and master's degrees. "When you add up rent, utilities, car insurance, and health insurance, you can't live on your stipend," says Cormier, who currently receives $1,191 a month as president of the university's Council of Graduate Students.

While six-figure debt is more typical of law and medical school students, 54 percent of full-time graduate students and 80 percent of full-time professional students find they need to borrow to cover their expenses, according to the National Center for Education Statistics. Average debt, including undergraduate loans, tops $29,000 for master's degree students and $80,000 for professional-degree students.

Subsidized Stafford loans are generally the cheapest around. Rates currently are just above 4 percent, and you can borrow up to $8,500 per year ($65,000 overall). The federal government pays the interest on your loan while you're in school and for six months after you graduate or drop below half-time status. Even if interest rates rise significantly by the time you need to repay, they can't exceed 8.25 percent.

Students qualify based on financial need, so it's necessary to file federal aid forms (the FAFSA, or Free Application for Federal Student Aid) to get subsidized loans. If your need is high, you may also be offered a subsidized Perkins loan, with an interest rate of 5 percent. You can borrow an additional $10,000 a year in unsubsidized Stafford loans (and up to $138,500 in Stafford loans overall). Rates are the same as for the subsidized Stafford, and you can defer making payments, but interest begins accruing right away.

If your school participates in the Federal Direct Loan program, you'll borrow directly from the federal government. Otherwise, you can choose your own lender. Rates and fees are usually the same no matter where you go, but some

MARK POWERS, A UNIVERSITY OF TEXAS–AUSTIN PH.D. CANDIDATE IN CLINICAL PSYCHOLOGY, HELPS A STUDENT OVERCOME HER FEAR OF SNAKES.

lenders offer attractive repayment incentives that make loans even cheaper. Student loan giant Sallie Mae, for instance, shaves a quarter point off your interest rate if you sign up for automatic payments and then rebates 3.3 percent of your loan amount after you make 33 on-time payments.

For students who own a home, a home-equity loan or line of credit is another attractive choice. Many banks were recently offering lines of credit at 5 percent or less, and the interest you pay is generally tax deductible. (So is up to $2,500 a year in student loan interest if you earn less than $50,000 as a single taxpayer and $100,000 if you file a joint return. A lesser amount of interest is deductible if you earn up to $65,000 or $130,000, respectively.)

If those options don't give you enough borrowing power, private lenders typically offer higher loan ceilings, at rates only slightly higher than those on Stafford loans. Sallie Mae, Nellie Mae, and Key Bank, for instance, all offer specialized loans for business, law, and medical students.

Some doctors, lawyers, and teachers may be able to have their debt forgiven. Teachers who work for five years in high-poverty schools, for instance, can have up to $5,000 of Stafford loans or all of their Perkins loans canceled. Fifty-six law schools, six states, and 40 employers offer loan repayment assistance to lawyers who practice public-interest law. And through the federal National Health Service Corps, healthcare workers who work in underserved areas can have up to $50,000 in debt repaid on their behalf.

Let your employer pick up the tab. Don't overlook your employer as a source of tuition funds. About 38 percent of employees at private firms have a benefit that helps finance job-related educational expenses, and 9 percent can tap their employer's pocket for courses that aren't job related. The percentages are about twice as high for professional and technical employees and for employees of large and medium-sized firms. (This is an especially popular way to fund an M.B.A.: Forty-three percent of M.B.A. students receive some kind of employer aid.) At FedEx Express, for instance, about 10 percent of employees take advantage of tuition reimbursement of up to $3,500 a year for work-related courses. Thanks to a change in the tax laws in 2002, employer-provided tuition reimbursement for graduate-level study is tax free up to $5,250 per year.

Naturally, colleges and universities tend to offer the most generous tuition benefits for employees—so much so that some prospective grad students seek out university employment to help fund their degrees. "This is a big reason many people come to work here," says Ellen Mayou, a spokeswoman for Southern Methodist University in Dallas, where full-time employees can take up to 18 hours of coursework a year in any field at no cost. Some schools, like Georgia State University in Atlanta, restrict the benefit to job-related courses or career-related degree programs.

Don't miss these tax breaks. For students paying out of pocket for tuition and fees, tax breaks for grad-school expenses received a boost in 2002 and 2003. This year, the maximum value of the Lifetime Learning tax credit rises from $1,500 to $2,000. The credit now is worth 20 percent of the first $10,000 you spend in tuition and fees each year. A tax credit reduces your tax bill dollar for dollar.

Thanks to federal legislation passed in 2001,

THE STATE OF STATE SCHOOLS

BY JUSTIN EWERS

It's a rough time to be a state-school number cruncher. Take California, facing a deficit of as much as $35 billion in the next 17 months. Proposals are on the table to pass nearly half a billion of that on to the University of California and Cal State systems. At the University of California–Los Angeles alone, that amounts to a $69 million cut. "It's not in my nature to be catastrophic," says Claudia Mitchell-Kernan, UCLA's vice chancellor for graduate studies, "but just saying that number gives me the chills."

Budget deficits exist in nearly 40 states. What does this mean for grad students? "At this critical moment," says Joan Lorden, dean of the grad school at the University of Al-abama–Birmingham, "when jobs aren't that plentiful and students are showing more interest in graduate school, we have less capacity to support them."

Sixteen states have raised tuition by more than 10 percent in the past year, a handful by as much as 20 percent. Only a third of full-time master's students can cover the cost of tuition through teaching or research assistantships—and the vast majority of those are in engineering and the sciences. "So if you're a full-time master's student in history or English," says Jacqueline King, director of the American Council on Education's center for policy analysis, "you get hit by budget deficits the same way an undergraduate would." And while most undergrads can offset the cost of tuition through need-based aid, grad students are generally awarded only merit-based aid.

On top of that, North Carolina State, facing an estimat-

UC–SAN DIEGO
COMPUTER
SCIENCE AND
ENGINEERING
STUDENT NEIL
MCCURDY HAS
COMPANY WHILE
HE STUDIES.

a new tax deduction is also available for higher-ed expenses in 2002 through 2005. This year, expenditures for tuition and fees up to $3,000 are eligible. (The amount rises to $4,000 in 2004 and 2005). Both the credit and the deduction are available whether or not you itemize deductions.

But you can't take advantage of both at once, so you'll probably have to do some number-crunching to figure out which one is more valuable to you. If you're fully eligible for either tax benefit and have $2,000 in tuition and fees, for

instance, the deduction is worth $540 if you're in the 27 percent tax bracket, while the credit is worth just $400. But if you have $10,000 or more in eligible expenses, the credit is worth $2,000 while the deduction (in the 27 percent bracket) is worth $810.

Because the tax credit and the deduction are phased out at different income levels, some students will qualify for the deduction and not the credit. If you file a single return, you're eligible for the full tax credit if your income is $41,000 or less, and for a partial credit up to $51,000. The

ed $18 million cut in state funds, plans to accept only a quarter as many out-of-state graduate students as it did last year. At UCLA, the number of fellowships and teaching assistantships has been reduced by a few dozen—bad news for master's students who already get the scraps from the doctoral student table. And the University of Kansas, which has been forced to cut $19 million, plans to reduce faculty hiring by around 30 percent.

Things may be even worse for med students. About half of medical school funding comes from professional fees physicians charge at university-affiliated hospitals, and this is where schools have taken the biggest hit. The Association of American Medical Colleges estimates that cuts in Medicare reimbursement will cost the nation's teaching hospitals $4.2 billion over the next five years. The situation is grave for the University of Iowa's Carver College of Medi-

cine. This year Carver will receive fewer total state dollars than it did six years ago—while the cost of healthcare in that period has gone up 36 percent. "We just can't raise tuition anymore and be competitive," says Robert Kelch, the school's former dean. Less money and more medical responsibilities, he says, mean "we have to give less attention to our core missions of education and social services."

For doctoral students, budget cuts have provided less of

a jolt (at least until it comes time to go on the job market). Most schools, up to this point, have been able to keep doctoral fellowship money off the chopping block. But, says Suzanne Ortega, dean of the graduate school of the University of Missouri–Columbia, which has lost $65 million over the past two years, "I doubt we'll be able to do it through another round of cuts." And how likely are those? Says Ortega, "We're almost certain of it." ●

deduction is available if you earn no more than $65,000. For married couples filing jointly, the tax credit is fully available with income up to $82,000, and partially available up to $102,000. You can earn up to $130,000 before you're disqualified from the tax deduction.

Use a 529 plan for savings. If you're looking ahead to graduate study in the next couple of years, consider state-sponsored 529 plans as a tax-advantaged way to save for your own educational expenses. While they're generally promoted as a way to sock away savings for a child's future undergrad career, most 529 plans allow you to name yourself as beneficiary.

The advantage to 529s is that your earnings are tax free when withdrawals are used for qualified educational expenses (including tuition, fees, room and board, and books). Plus, residents of 24 states and the District of Columbia get a state tax deduction for their contributions, too.

Most 529 plans offer investments suitable for those who'll need to tap the money soon. Many plans include bond and money market funds, for instance, and some have added a "stable value" option that is essentially an interest-bearing account, often with a guaranteed minimum return of around 3 percent. Many were recently paying returns of 4 percent to 5 percent—a healthy tax-free return in today's low-rate environment. ●

PART-TIME OR FULL-TIME?

BY ALICIA ABELL

When Chicago tech consultant Jeff Schlitt decided to pursue a master's in computer science, he thought about going full time—but only briefly. "I was being paid too much," says the 29-year-old. Not only did DePaul University's part-time program allow him to keep his income *and* pocket tuition reimbursement from his employer, but it also let him spread out his costs over time—key advantages since he'd just bought his first house.

According to the latest data, the average graduate student is 33 years old. Over half are married; about a third have children. Often, a full-time graduate program doesn't make sense: Only 36 percent of master's students and 61 percent of doctoral students go to school full time. But figuring out the financial part of the equation can be a challenge, says Sandy Baum, an economics professor at Skidmore College. Many decide against full-time study because they need to

keep their salaries. And yet, borrowing money to attend full time may be a good idea, depending on how much you think you'll earn once you finish, says Baum: The greater the jump in anticipated income, the better an idea it is to attend school full time.

And remember, many loans, grants, and scholarships are only for full-time students, and only full-time Ph.D. students are eligible for teaching and research assistantships. Benefits, such as student housing and health insurance, usually aren't offered to part-timers, either. On the other hand, many employers will pay for all or part of your degree if you continue to work while going to school.

If your aim is changing fields, full-time study often makes the most sense. That's in part because people with day jobs can't take internships with potential employers. Also, recruiters tend to favor full-timers. By contrast, part-time study often is best for people whose goal is advancing within their company or their field because they can maintain their network of professional contacts while

polishing their credentials.

Prospective students should look into how welcoming a school is to part-timers. Are Saturday and evening classes offered? Do libraries, labs, and other facilities have extended hours? Who's teaching the part-time classes? One hallmark of quality is whether part-timers sit in the same classes as full-timers. Easy transfer of credits between full- and part-time programs is another good indicator.

Family support—from a spouse or partner in particular—is a crucial determiner of success in a part-time program. "You need to have a relationship with your partner where you can trade off responsibility," says Ellen Ostrow, a Silver Spring, Md., psychologist. And your expectations for the grad school experience are also worth considering. If you have a job, partaking of daytime events at the school may be difficult. As will socializing with professors and fellow students. When you go part time, says Jeff Kyle, 29, a part-time M.B.A. student at the University of Michigan–Ann Arbor, "there's less camaraderie." ●

BRIDGET BESAW GORMAN—AURORA FOR *USN&WR*

SOME EDUCATION GRADUATE STUDENTS ALSO WORK AS RESIDENTIAL ADVISERS AT THE UNIVERSITY OF CONNECTICUT.

For your health

BY LYNN ROSELLINI

Christopher Phipps didn't think much about health insurance when he applied to graduate school in linguistics at the University at Buffalo in New York. He didn't even bother reading the student insurance policy. Then one day he felt a numbness in his fingers that later developed into severe pains. He was diagnosed with an aneurysm, requiring two bypass operations and five hospital stays. "I never dreamed I'd have this kind of problem," says Phipps, whose policy paid just $25,000 of the $90,000 bill. With a yearly income from part-time teaching of only $20,000, Phipps says there was no way he could have paid off his debt. He declared bankruptcy last October.

When choosing a grad school, most students rank health insurance somewhere between proximity to an all-night diner and access to cheap on-campus housing. Accustomed to good health and their parents' insurance, younger students don't read the fine print on the policies offered by schools they're considering or even purchase insurance once they've enrolled. (In fact, most get kicked off their parents' policies between the ages of 23 and 25.) "Graduate students are all broke and struggling," says Doris Dirks, past president of the National Association of Graduate-Professional Students. "They consider health insurance a luxury. You're gambling that you're not gonna get sick."

In 2000, the American College Health Association, an organization that promotes healthcare on campus, issued guidelines recommending that schools make insurance a mandatory condition of enrollment. But while 90 percent of private universities now do that, 3 out of 4 public universities still do not. Moreover, even schools that require students to get insurance don't necessarily offer decent policies. "It's a huge spectrum," says Stephen Beckley, a student healthcare management consultant who helped draw up the ACHA guidelines.

Generally, private universities offer better health policies, as do many of the major public universities. The University of Minnesota–Twin Cities has a basic plan that caps students' yearly out-of-pocket payments at just $2,000 and has no limit on preventive care received through the student health service. But the vast University of Texas system's plan has a lifetime cap of just $100,000. It covers only $500 worth of prescriptions a year and includes a clause limiting some coverage of catastrophic injury or illness suffered by a student prior to enrolling in the plan.

Some schools offer different plans to different categories of student. At the University at Buffalo, a blue-ribbon, university-subsidized policy is available to grad students with research and teaching assistantships at only about $126 a year. Two years ago when Erin Murphy, now 28, was a research assistant and Ph.D. student in microbiology at Buffalo, she was diagnosed with endometrial cancer and had a total hysterectomy. "My insurance was exceptional," she says. "The surgery and hospitalization ended up costing me $1,000."

Because university health centers provide many basic services, it is especially important that students review the level of coverage for major injuries or illnesses when picking a plan. With hospitalization costs and doctors' fees rising, many experts believe that $500,000 of lifetime coverage should be the minimum. "Bare-bones plans are not doing a service to anyone," says Edward Ehlinger, director and chief health officer for the student health center at the University of Minnesota.

Prescription drug coverage is particularly impor-

GRADUATE STUDENTS IN BIOENGINEERING AND MECHANICAL AND AEROSPACE ENGINEERING AT THE UNIVERSITY OF CALIFORNIA–SAN DIEGO

tant for those with chronic conditions, although even healthy students can suddenly find themselves needing drug benefits. Daryl Arkwright-Keeler, 42, a doctoral candidate in biological sciences at Western Michigan University in Kalamazoo, came down with Crohn's disease, an autoimmune disorder. Her then $646-a-year student insurance policy had a $500 yearly cap on prescriptions, so she moved up her wedding by two years to get on her husband's plan, which covered the $30,000-a-year drug regimen her doctor recommended.

Another important consideration is whether a policy includes mental health benefits. Graduate school, with its heavy workload and competitive environment, can be a time of considerable stress for students. Students also should check whether a policy excludes pre-existing medical conditions and find out the size of the annual deductible (which can range from nothing to several hun-

dred dollars). And remember that a top-notch plan doesn't usually come cheap: Students at Harvard pay $1,770 a year for their insurance plan ($1,020 of that is included in their tuition). University of Minnesota–Twin Cities students pay $1,028 for the basic plan, in addition to the $180 annual health services fee in their tuition. Coverage for spouses and children further inflates the bill.

On the bright side, some university administrators are improving their health plans. Western Michigan, for one, now subsidizes insurance for grad students who have jobs as teaching or research assistants. "It was one way we could make ourselves more competitive," says Kevin Vichcales, who administers the plan. If two schools have similar programs at the same cost, but one provides a good health package, "it's pretty easy to figure out where you'll go," he says. ●

THE RANKING METHODOLOGY

BY ROBERT J. MORSE
AND SAMUEL M.
FLANIGAN

Each year, *U.S. News* ranks graduate programs in the areas of business, education, engineering, law, and medicine. These rankings are based on two types of data: expert opinion about program quality and statistical indicators that measure the quality of a school's faculty, research, and students. For the rankings in all five areas, indicator and opinion data come from surveys of more than 1,000 programs and nearly 7,000 academics and other professionals conducted in the fall of 2002.

This year, we also produced new rankings of graduate programs in selected health fields and the fine arts, surveying nearly 2,000 faculty and administrators. The rankings in these fields, plus those from previous years in health-related fields,

humanities, sciences, social sciences, and public affairs, are based solely on the ratings of academic experts.

To gather the opinion data, we asked deans, program directors, and senior faculty to judge the overall academic quality of programs in their field on a scale of 1 ("marginal") to 5 ("outstanding"). In business, education, engineering, law, and medicine, we also surveyed professionals in the field who are part of the hiring process.

The statistical indicators used in our rankings of business, education, engineering, law, and medical schools fall into two broad categories: inputs, or measures of the qualities that students and faculty bring to the educational experience; and outputs, measures of graduates' achievements that can be credited to their educational experience.

Different output measures are available for different

fields, and, as a result, the indicators we use in our models vary. In business, the immediate impact of students' education can be gauged by their salaries after graduation and by how much time it takes them to find jobs. In law, we also look at how long it takes grads to land jobs, plus their bar exam passage rates. In the other fields we rank, job placement data aren't tracked as rigorously, so in our calculations we use data like—for one example— the percentage of graduates entering the field in primary-care medicine.

To arrive at a school's rank, we examined the distribution of the data for each quality indicator. Where the data deviated significantly from the normal distribution, we used standard statistical techniques to make the distribution of the values closer to that of a normal curve. We then standardized the value of these indicators about its mean. The weights applied to the indicators reflect the relative importance

of the indicators, as developed in consultation with experts in each field. (Detailed information about the weights and indicators appears with the tables.) The final scores were rescaled: The highest-scoring school was assigned 100, and the other schools' scores were recalculated as a percentage of that top score. The scores were then rounded to the nearest whole number and schools placed in descending order. Every school's performance is presented relative to the other schools with which it is being compared. So a school with an overall score of 100 did not necessarily top out on every indicator; rather it accumulated the highest composite score. A school's rank reflects the number of schools that sit above it; if three schools are tied at 1, the next school will be numbered 4, not 2. Schools that are tied are listed in alphabetical order.

More information about the methodology can be found at *www.usnews.com*. ●

The Professional Schools

You're looking to make it big in business, or you aim to change the world by becoming a teacher. You want to study the ins and outs of the human body—or the intricacies of nanotechnology. Or maybe you're just thinking about joining the rest of the world in law school. This chapter will give you information about business, law, medicine, education, engineering, public affairs, and journalism programs—plus the exclusive *U.S. News* rankings.

BUSINESS

A dose of ethics

BY JUSTIN EWERS

T hink of it this way, says Rushworth Kidder, president of the Institute for Global Ethics: "If the Dallas Cowboys folded in an ethics scandal, there'd be no question that football as a game would continue. Fans would think, 'One bad apple; let's get rid of 'em.' " But, he says, "suppose fans discovered that in the last 10 years, there had been no honest calls by a referee in any game ever. People would be appalled; they'd walk away from the sport." Enron, says Kidder, is the Dallas Cowboys. And Arthur Andersen is the crooked refs.

Ethics scandals come and ethics scandals go, but there is a growing perception in the business-school community that this one is simply too big to overlook. And as M.B.A.'s continue to pour into the highest echelons of business—a recent poll found that 38 percent of CEOs in the *Forbes* 500 now have M.B.A.'s—more and more business schools are scrambling to add ethics to their curricula. "It sounds funny now," says Ed Petry, executive director of the Ethics Officer Association, a group of industry compliance officers, "but 'business ethics' used to be considered an oxymoron." The field didn't exist on a large scale until the Watergate era in the 1970s. It received a boost in the late '80s amid the insider trading and savings and loan scandals but "was sort of on hiatus in the '90s," says Kirk Hanson, who runs the Markkula Center for Applied Ethics at Santa Clara University. Indeed, a pre-Enron survey of M.B.A. programs found that only a third of B-schools had a required ethics class.

"We were taught that Enron was the way to do business," recalls Brian Cruver, who graduated from the University of Texas–Austin with an M.B.A. in 1999. In the case of a company that found a product flaw, for example, he says students were told to think in terms of cost-benefit analysis: the cost of litigation versus the cost of redoing the product. "We learned to look straight ahead at shareholder value and nothing else," says Cruver, who went to work for Enron in 2001 and recently published *Anatomy of Greed: The Unshredded Truth From an Enron Insider.* His ethics prof at Texas, Steve Salbu,

concurs: Students, he writes in the book's foreword, "routinely recount . . . being rebuffed, or even ridiculed for so much as raising ethical questions in some finance, marketing, and accounting classes."

After Enron's collapse, of course, M.B.A. programs suddenly had a mandate for change. Even President Bush weighed in: "Our schools of business," he declared in a speech last July on Wall Street, "must be principled teachers of right and wrong." But for many experts, that is easier said than done. "Ethics is a tricky area to cover; it's not

like teaching statistics," says Jerry Trapnell, chairman of the Association to Advance Collegiate Schools of Business, the accrediting body for M.B.A. programs (which still does not require schools to have an ethics course). And there are plenty of business professors who hesitate to teach it. "While it is relatively clear what economics dictate and even what the law requires," says Amitai Etzioni, professor of ethics at George Washington University, "what is 'ethical' is far from obvious."

So what are business schools doing about it? "We're not trying to change sinners into saints," says John Dienhart, professor of ethics at Seattle University's Albers School of Business and Economics. Instead of defining what is right and wrong, he says, M.B.A. programs are trying to make students more aware of questions of right vs. right: the more routine decisions in which several courses of action are professionally justifiable, whether it's tabulating sales numbers or writing up a marketing pitch.

"Before Enron, you'd hear about something like [the dangers of] earnings manipulation in a chapter or a lecture," says Denis Shmuler, now in his third year at Rutgers Business School, "but now there's whole classes dedicated to it." At the University of California–Irvine Graduate School of Management, for example, students last year took an entire course on the Enron case, dissecting the carcass to see where and why the company went wrong. Penn's Wharton School now requires all first-years to take a class called "Ethics and Responsibility." Students discuss difficult decisions, like whether employees hired in an up market should be abandoned when the economy goes sour. "This is the kind of question that business leaders face every day," says Thomas Donaldson, the professor of ethics who teaches the course. Rutgers and the University of Maryland have upped the ante: Their M.B.A. students not only have ethics classes, but they now go on a mandatory class trip to a prison to talk with white-collar criminals. "They get to see how easy it is to end up there," says Edwin Hartman, director of Rutgers's Prudential Business Ethics Center. "It only takes one bad decision."

Will this renewed focus help clean up the business world? No, says Richard McKenzie, a management and economics professor at UC–Irvine. He points to a study published in 1985 showing that four years later, it's nearly impossible to distinguish those who took courses in ethics from those who didn't. He argues that the window of opportunity for learning ethics has long passed by the time a student enrolls in an M.B.A. program.

Others are more optimistic. "I learned ethics at my mother's knee," says Wharton's Donaldson, "but she didn't tell me about highly leveraged derivatives or off-book transactions." At least, they say, a grounding in ethics will allow M.B.A. grads to verbalize moral qualms. "When you stand up in a meeting about whether to build a sweatshop in Asia," says Richard Shreve, professor of ethics at Dartmouth's Tuck School of Business, "you can't say, 'I don't want to do it because it's just not right.'" Ethics courses, he says, can teach students to articulate their argument in the language of business. ●

EVAN KAFKA FOR *USN&WR*

WHARTON STUDENTS GATHER IN PENN'S NEW JOHN M. HUNTSMAN HALL.

A TYPICAL M.B.A. GRAD EARNED $48,000 BEFORE THE M.B.A.; THE AVERAGE NEW M.B.A. HIRE'S ANNUAL BASE SALARY IS $75,000.

The way to an M.B.A.

Business school education has come a long way. "M.B.A. programs in the 1950s [generally] provided people with a narrow set of applied skills," says Gilbert Whitaker, dean of the Jesse H. Jones Graduate School of Management at Rice. "It was sort of a 'how to run a shoe store' mentality." Today's B-schools, however, are extraordinarily diverse, with a range of concentrations—from E-commerce to environmental management—as well as a wealth of learning opportunities, like group projects that solve real companies' problems. A few issues to consider before drawing up your short list (and tips on how to get in):

What would you like to learn? At some schools, like Dartmouth, everyone earns an M.B.A. in general management. If you aren't sure what skills you're looking to develop, you might focus on these institutions. If you have a specific subfield in mind, however, look for schools with well-respected programs in that area. The E. J. Ourso College of Business Administration at Louisiana State, for example, has one of the premier internal auditing programs; its grads are heavily recruited nationwide.

Part time vs. full time? In the past, part-time M.B.A. programs have been criticized for a lack of rigor, but the gap in quality between part- and full-time programs has shrunk substantially. At Berkeley's Haas School of Business, part-time applicants are subject to the same test-score and work-experience requirements as their full-time counterparts. Part-time students also are taught by the same faculty and are offered many of the same study-abroad options.

Where do grads go to work? Even if you don't know where you want to work after school, you should think about how marketable you'll be. For starters, many schools have a regional focus when it comes to placing students in jobs. If you're considering Rice's Jones School of Management, for instance, you should be aware that 71 percent of its students last year found their

THE BIZ OF BIZ JOBS

There's no sense beating around the bush: The M.B.A. job market has been hit much harder than the economy at large. "It may not be any worse than last year," says Randy Williams, director of the M.B.A. career center at the University of California–Irvine's Graduate School of Management, "but it doesn't look any better, either." Even so, many companies are still hungry for the skills that M.B.A. grads offer. Some of the most promising fields:

Consulting. Management consulting was the first to be hurt by the economic slump. Two years ago at schools like UC–Irvine, 40 percent of M.B.A. grads found jobs in consulting. Now, that number is closer to 10 percent. But, says Mindy Storrie, vice president of the M.B.A. Career Services Council, salaries have stayed fairly steady at consulting firms (2002 M.B.A. grads from the University of North Carolina–Chapel Hill, for example, where Storrie works, pulled in an average base salary of $99,000 at consulting firms, down less than 2 percent from 2001).

STUDENTS DURING AN OPERATIONS-MANAGEMENT CLASS AT PENN'S WHARTON SCHOOL

And, she says, these companies are usually the first to recover when the economy bounces back.

Finance. Hiring has slowed dramatically at banking and venture capital firms. But there's more to finance than investment banking: Many *Fortune* 500 companies need staff skilled in fi-

first jobs in Texas, 37 percent in the energy industry.

Get work experience. Once you've chosen your dream school, brace yourself for a few weeks of cramming for the Graduate Management Admission Test, or GMAT. A good score on this exam, which tests basic verbal, math, and writing skills, can help grease the skids for your application. But, admissions officers insist, there is something even more essential: work experience. Most M.B.A. programs require at least two years, and successful applicants at top schools should also demonstrate a track record of advancement within a particular company, says Marci Armstrong, an associate dean at Southern Methodist University's Cox School of Business. But job hopping is typically frowned on. "Less than 18 months at any one company is going to be a bit of a red flag," says Armstrong, unless you can show that you switched

WHARTON STUDENTS WORK HARD WHEN PLAYING IN THE M.B.A. PUB IN VANCE HALL AT THE UNIVERSITY OF PENNSYLVANIA.

jobs to move ahead within your industry.

Show them that you care. Even if a program doesn't require an interview, try to schedule one. It's your best opportunity to show the fire in your belly for a B-school education. Be specific about how their M.B.A. is going to help you reach your particular goals. Most schools don't expect you to know exactly what you'll study, but "it helps to have an industry you're particularly interested in or a passion for a certain kind of business," says Dan Dalton, dean of Indiana University's B-school. ●

MORE THAN HALF OF M.B.A. STUDENTS ARE BETWEEN THE AGES OF 28 AND 34.

nancial modeling and cash-flow analysis. Health-care and pharmaceutical companies especially are ripe for the plucking, says Jeff Beavers, director of M.B.A. career services at the University of Illinois–Urbana-Champaign. But, says Beavers, large-scale hiring of M.B.A.'s for Wall Street could still be as much as two years off.

Marketing. The tech wreck may have finally shuddered to a halt, but marketing grads will still do better at tried-and-true consumer-products companies. "People are always going to be buying the essentials: toothpaste, shampoo, and cereal," says Erik Gordon, director of M.B.A. programs at the University of Florida in Gainesville. For example, Cincinnati-based Procter & Gamble, which makes everything from Tide to Tampax, hasn't missed a beat in its hiring of M.B.A.'s.

Entrepreneurship. The era of the M.B.A. millionaire entrepreneur is on the wane, but that doesn't mean the end of entrepreneuring. William Sahlman, professor of business administration at Harvard Business School, believes would-be entrepreneurs will simply return to their pre-dot-com

ways, when they slaved away at salaried jobs for a decade or so acquiring the money and know-how for their dreams. Budding entrepreneurs who can't wait should try innovative departments of big companies, such as IBM's Extreme Blue program, which offers M.B.A.'s the chance to try their hand at everything from strategic planning to technical research.

Supply-chain management. M.B.A. grads who have studied supply-chain management know how to streamline the process of moving products from the factory to the market. In a down economy, their expertise is at a premium: Working the kinks of out a distribution system is the cheapest way to save money, says Jackie Wilbur, director of the M.B.A. career development office at MIT's biz school. When A. J. Gardner graduated last year from Michigan State's Eli Broad Graduate School of Management with a supply-chain concentration, he was inundated with offers from across the business spectrum. He took a job at Raytheon, where he joined the supply-chain-management team. And last fall, he was already back on campus, recruiting for more supply-chain M.B.A.'s. ●

Schools of Business

THE TOP SCHOOLS

Rank/School	Overall score	Peer assessment score (5.0 highest)	Recruiter assessment score (5.0 highest)	'02 average undergrad GPA	'02 average GMAT score	'02 acceptance rate	'02 average starting salary and bonus	'02 graduates employed at graduation	Employed 3 months after graduation	'02 out-of-state tuition and fees	'02 total full-time enrollment
1. Harvard University (MA)	100	4.8	4.7	3.60	705	9.7%	$109,587	77.7%	88.9%	$31,800	1,808
2. Stanford University (CA)	97	4.8	4.4	3.58	716	7.9%	$108,840	78.4%	81.7%	$33,300	749
University of Pennsylvania (Wharton)	97	4.8	4.6	3.49	711	13.1%	$107,047	74.0%	89.7%	$33,269	1,601
4. Massachusetts Institute of Technology (Sloan)	94	4.8	4.6	3.50	707	13.7%	$101,922	72.9%	82.9%	$32,470	744
Northwestern University (Kellogg)(IL)	94	4.8	4.7	3.45	700	13.0%	$102,102	64.1%	87.8%	$32,040	1,058
6. Columbia University (NY)	91	4.4	4.3	3.50	711	10.6%	$112,045	71.1%	84.1%	$33,054	1,188
7. Duke University (Fuqua)(NC)	90	4.4	4.1	3.59	701	18.1%	$105,874	76.1%	89.0%	$32,252	697
University of California–Berkeley (Haas)	90	4.6	4.2	3.55	703	11.2%	$95,621	70.2%	88.5%	$21,753	496
9. University of Chicago	88	4.7	4.5	3.44	687	15.0%	$101,975	68.5%	77.9%	$32,602	990
10. Dartmouth College (Tuck)(NH)	84	4.4	4.4	3.40	695	14.4%	$103,413	68.9%	75.6%	$32,490	463
11. University of Virginia (Darden)	83	4.2	4.1	3.34	683	17.9%	$99,216	80.9%	89.8%	$31,343	564
12. New York University (Stern)	81	4.3	3.8	3.40	700	15.2%	$99,439	72.7%	83.3%	$32,280	817
13. University of Michigan–Ann Arbor	80	4.5	4.2	3.40	681	19.0%	$100,645	58.8%	69.7%	$32,686	862
14. University of California–Los Angeles (Anderson)	79	4.3	3.9	3.60	699	15.1%	$92,337	55.7%	74.1%	$22,952	670
Yale University (CT)	79	4.1	4.1	3.50	698	15.1%	$99,767	60.5%	75.5%	$31,650	481
16. Cornell University (Johnson)(NY)	77	4.2	4.2	3.35	673	22.2%	$99,384	62.7%	73.8%	$32,016	572
17. Carnegie Mellon University (PA)	72	4.1	3.8	3.30	672	25.9%	$92,101	67.4%	78.8%	$29,960	469
University of Texas–Austin (McCombs)	72	4.0	3.8	3.37	678	29.3%	$84,002	70.3%	81.5%	$25,005	804
19. Ohio State University (Fisher)	71	3.7	3.7	3.37	655	25.3%	$87,279	71.6%	93.1%	$23,466	289
20. University of Southern California (Marshall)	70	3.9	3.8	3.35	684	21.3%	$81,219	60.7%	83.7%	$31,680	581
21. Emory University (Goizueta)(GA)	67	3.7	3.7	3.40	675	24.0%	$84,888	60.3%	80.4%	$29,408	388
Univ. of North Carolina–Chapel Hill (Kenan-Flagler)	67	4.1	3.8	3.20	671	30.1%	$93,045	59.1%	70.2%	$28,929	560
23. Indiana University–Bloomington (Kelley)	66	3.9	3.8	3.35	651	22.4%	$88,121	57.0%	71.9%	$23,391	547
24. Georgetown University (McDonough)(DC)	64	3.4	3.8	3.35	663	22.8%	$92,159	53.9%	77.2%	$29,976	528
Purdue University–West Lafayette (Krannert)(IN)	64	3.7	3.8	3.23	651	26.7%	$90,243	66.4%	73.1%	$23,582	295
26. University of Minnesota–Twin Cities (Carlson)	63	3.6	3.5	3.20	645	39.6%	$85,589	76.5%	86.3%	$25,000	237
27. Rice University (Jones)(TX)	62	3.3	3.7	3.30	630	39.0%	$84,540	60.6%	95.5%	$24,080	359
University of Florida (Warrington)	62	3.4	4.1	3.30	658	22.9%	$65,757	56.5%	91.3%	$668 *	114
29. Brigham Young University (Marriott)(UT)	61	3.1	3.6	3.62	650	43.9%	$67,657	64.8%	89.0%	$9,270	265
University of Iowa (Tippie)	61	3.2	3.3	3.30	638	37.5%	$83,817	75.0%	94.4%	$18,211	152
University of Notre Dame (Mendoza)(IN)	61	3.4	3.4	3.40	668	22.8%	$79,243	59.2%	82.2%	$26,485	322
Washington University in St. Louis (Olin)	61	3.7	3.7	3.26	651	35.0%	$87,811	55.6%	69.9%	$30,260	308
33. Penn State University–University Park (Smeal)	60	3.5	3.4	3.35	645	24.0%	$83,592	51.2%	85.7%	$20,256	199
University of Illinois–Urbana-Champaign	60	3.7	3.4	3.30	640	31.3%	$74,809	61.1%	84.7%	$24,254	365
35. University of California–Davis	59	3.2	3.7	3.30	669	23.6%	$71,595	59.6%	84.6%	$22,224	121
University of Washington	59	3.4	2.9	3.46	671	31.2%	$73,856	63.4%	87.8%	$17,569	258
37. Arizona State University–Main Campus	58	3.5	2.9	3.42	654	29.2%	$80,026	54.5%	85.5%	$20,105	296
Michigan State University (Broad)	58	3.5	3.3	3.30	639	22.0%	$82,640	66.7%	77.4%	$19,416	218
University of Rochester (Simon)(NY)	58	3.6	3.5	3.20	649	26.9%	$90,782	58.2%	69.3%	$30,660	417
Wake Forest University (Babcock)(NC)	58	3.2	3.6	3.20	639	47.1%	$77,929	73.2%	87.6%	$25,125	225
41. Boston College (Carroll)	57	3.3	3.3	3.33	658	14.8%	$81,449	62.1%	76.8%	$874 *	252
42. Tulane University (Freeman)(LA)	56	3.1	3.1	3.30	663	54.3%	$81,932	78.8%	80.8%	$966 *	203
University of Georgia (Terry)	56	3.3	3.6	3.29	658	26.6%	$72,637	59.3%	77.8%	$15,618	169
University of Maryland–College Park (Smith)	56	3.6	3.1	3.35	656	23.3%	$81,864	54.4%	71.2%	$22,257	419
45. Vanderbilt University (Owen)(TN)	55	3.6	3.5	3.29	648	46.1%	$80,688	47.2%	65.8%	$30,018	445
46. University of California–Irvine	54	3.3	3.6	3.34	682	30.7%	$71,695	36.4%	70.7%	$22,780	231
University of Wisconsin–Madison	54	3.5	3.3	3.30	632	27.0%	$75,798	65.6%	72.0%	$24,272	355
48. Babson College (Olin)(MA)	53	3.3	3.2	3.12	643	39.2%	$78,650	61.3%	84.0%	$27,912	440
49. University of Arizona (Eller)	52	3.5	3.3	3.34	636	58.7%	$67,851	50.0%	76.7%	$20,114	67
50. University of Pittsburgh (Katz)	51	3.4	3.2	3.16	613	54.0%	$74,539	60.9%	82.6%	$35,168 **	162

Sources: *U.S. News* and the schools. Assessment data collected by Synovate.
* Tuition is per credit. ** Tuition is reported for the entire program.

More at **www.usnews.com**

Specialties

THE TOP PICKS OF BUSINESS SCHOOL DEANS AND M.B.A. DIRECTORS

ACCOUNTING
1. U. of Pennsylvania (Wharton)
2. University of Chicago
   University of Illinois–Urbana-Champaign
4. U. of Texas–Austin (McCombs)
5. U. of Michigan–Ann Arbor
6. Stanford University (CA)
7. U. of Southern Calif. (Marshall)
8. New York University (Stern)
9. Northwestern U. (Kellogg) (IL)
10. Univ. of North Carolina–Chapel Hill (Kenan-Flagler)

FINANCE
1. U. of Pennsylvania (Wharton)
2. University of Chicago
3. New York University (Stern)
4. Stanford University (CA)
5. Massachusetts Institute of Technology (Sloan)
6. Columbia University (NY)
7. Northwestern U. (Kellogg) (IL)
   University of California–Los Angeles (Anderson)
9. Harvard University (MA)
   University of California–Berkeley (Haas)

MANAGEMENT
1. Harvard University (MA)
2. Stanford University (CA)
3. Northwestern U. (Kellogg) (IL)
4. U. of Michigan–Ann Arbor
5. U. of Pennsylvania (Wharton)
6. Dartmouth College (Tuck) (NH)
7. University of Virginia (Darden)
8. Duke University (Fuqua) (NC)
9. Columbia University (NY)
10. University of California–Berkeley (Haas)

INFORMATION SYSTEMS
1. Massachusetts Institute of Technology (Sloan)
2. Carnegie Mellon U. (PA)
3. U. of Texas–Austin (McCombs)
4. University of Arizona (Eller)
5. University of Minnesota–Twin Cities (Carlson)
6. U. of Pennsylvania (Wharton)
7. Stanford University (CA)
8. University of Maryland–College Park (Smith)
9. New York University (Stern)
10. Georgia State Univ. (Robinson)

INTERNATIONAL
1. Thunderbird Grad. Sch. (AZ)
2. U. of South Carolina (Moore)
3. Columbia University (NY)
   U. of Pennsylvania (Wharton)
5. New York University (Stern)
6. U. of Michigan–Ann Arbor
7. Harvard University (MA)
8. Duke University (Fuqua) (NC)
9. University of California–Berkeley (Haas)
10. University of California–Los Angeles (Anderson)

ENTREPRENEURSHIP
1. Babson College (Olin) (MA)
2. U. of Pennsylvania (Wharton)
3. Stanford University (CA)
4. Harvard University (MA)
5. U. of Southern Calif. (Marshall)
6. Massachusetts Institute of Technology (Sloan)
7. U. of Texas–Austin (McCombs)
8. University of California–Los Angeles (Anderson)
9. University of California–Berkeley (Haas)
10. U. of Michigan–Ann Arbor

EXECUTIVE M.B.A.
1. Northwestern U. (Kellogg) (IL)
2. U. of Pennsylvania (Wharton)
3. University of Chicago
4. Columbia University (NY)
5. Duke University (Fuqua) (NC)
6. New York University (Stern)
7. University of California–Los Angeles (Anderson)
8. Stanford University (CA)
9. U. of Michigan–Ann Arbor
10. U. of Southern Calif. (Marshall)

MARKETING
1. Northwestern U. (Kellogg) (IL)
2. U. of Pennsylvania (Wharton)
3. Harvard University (MA)
4. Duke University (Fuqua) (NC)
5. U. of Michigan–Ann Arbor
6. Columbia University (NY)
7. Stanford University (CA)
8. University of California–Berkeley (Haas)
9. University of California–Los Angeles (Anderson)
10. University of Chicago
    University of Texas–Austin (McCombs)

PRODUCTION/OPERATIONS
1. Massachusetts Institute of Technology (Sloan)
2. Purdue University–West Lafayette (Krannert) (IN)
3. Carnegie Mellon Univ. (PA)
4. U. of Pennsylvania (Wharton)
5. Stanford University (CA)
6. U. of Michigan–Ann Arbor
7. Harvard University (MA)
8. Northwestern U. (Kellogg) (IL)
9. University of California–Los Angeles (Anderson)
10. Georgia Inst. of Tech. (DuPree)

NONPROFIT
1. Yale University (CT)
2. Stanford University (CA)
3. Harvard University (MA)
4. Northwestern U. (Kellogg) (IL)
5. University of California–Berkeley (Haas)
6. U. of Michigan–Ann Arbor
7. Case Western Reserve University (Weatherhead) (OH)
8. Columbia University (NY)
9. Duke University (Fuqua) (NC)
   U. of Pennsylvania (Wharton)

PART-TIME M.B.A.
1. New York University (Stern)
2. University of Chicago
3. Northwestern U. (Kellogg) (IL)
4. University of California–Los Angeles (Anderson)
5. Georgia State Univ. (Robinson)
6. U. of Southern Calif. (Marshall)
7. University of California–Berkeley (Haas)
8. U. of Michigan–Ann Arbor
9. DePaul University (Kellstadt) (IL)
10. University of Minnesota–Twin Cities (Carlson)

SUPPLY CHAIN/LOGISTICS
1. Massachusetts Institute of Technology (Sloan)
2. Michigan State Univ. (Broad)
3. U. of Pennsylvania (Wharton)
4. Stanford University (CA)
5. Arizona St. U.–Main Campus
   Carnegie Mellon Univ. (PA)
7. Penn State–Univ. Park (Smeal)
8. Ohio State University (Fisher)
9. Purdue University–West Lafayette (Krannert) (IN)
10. Northwestern U. (Kellogg) (IL)

METHODOLOGY

All 365 accredited master's programs in business were surveyed (284 responded; 165 provided the data needed to calculate rankings based on a weighted average of the eight quality indicators described below). All schools appear in the directory starting on Page 93. More on the methodology appears on Page 16.

Quality assessment (weighted by .40): Two surveys were conducted in the fall of 2002. Business school deans and directors of accredited programs were asked to rate programs on a scale from "marginal" (1) to "outstanding" (5); 56 percent responded, and the resulting score accounts for a quarter of the overall score. Corporate recruiters who hire from previously ranked programs were also asked to rate programs; 26 percent responded, and their ratings are weighted by .15 in the model.

Placement success (.35): This is measured by mean starting salary and bonus (40 percent) and employment rates for 2002 graduates, computed at graduation (20 percent) and three months later (40 percent). Those not seeking jobs are excluded. Salary figures are based on the number of graduates reporting data. Since not everyone who reported a base salary reported a signing bonus, mean signing bonus is weighted by the proportion who do.

Student selectivity (.25): The strength of full-time students entering in the fall of 2002 was measured by mean GMAT (65 percent), mean undergraduate GPA (30 percent), and the proportion of applicants accepted by the school (5 percent).

Overall rank: Data were standardized about their means, and standardized scores were weighted, totaled, and rescaled so that the top school received 100; others received their percentage of the top score.

Specialty rankings: These rankings are based solely on ratings by educators at peer schools. Business school deans and program heads were asked to nominate up to 10 programs for excellence in each of the areas listed. The 10 schools receiving the most votes appear.

LAW

Profiles in justice

BY ULRICH BOSER

Going beyond basic criminal law and contracts classes, specialization is the name of the game at many law schools today. Schools like the University of Pittsburgh (civil litigation) and the University of Missouri–Columbia (dispute resolution, tax, and electronic, commercial, and intellectual-property law) have created new certificate programs in the past few years. Others are focusing on practical skills in new clinics and classes. Vanderbilt University Law School, for instance, opened a domestic violence clinical training program this year. To get a sense of the diversity of programs out there, we looked at three students with three very different law school experiences.

AAYESHA GAISI IS IN THE THICK OF A LEGAL BATTLE. For the past year, Gaisi has been fighting for a victim of domestic violence who is seeking custody of her two children. On her client's behalf, Gaisi has filed child-support orders, written briefs in favor of a relocation of the trial, and argued with opposing lawyers in front of a judge. Not bad for someone who isn't even a lawyer—yet.

Gaisi, 26, is in her third year at the City University of New York School of Law. Like a growing number of law schools, CUNY offers legal clinics that give second- and third-year law students hands-on legal experience. But few schools have yearlong, 16-credit clinics like the one Gaisi is taking. She says that she works over 30 hours a week in the Family Law Clinic, and with two other law school classes in her schedule, she often finds herself in the clinic on weekends and holidays. "For me the real learning is practical learning," she says. "Textbooks don't tell you what clients are going to be like or how to be in front of a judge . . . but that's what you need for the real world."

While it's not likely that Gaisi's lengthy custody fight will end before she graduates, she plans to continue defending indigent clients at a legal aid clinic

in New York City when she finishes school in May. "I have cried with my clients, tears of joy, tears of sadness," she says. "It gives me a purpose in life."

IT WAS LENNETTE LEE'S FIRST DAY OF CLASS AT THE University of Chicago Law School, and she was sitting in the back row. The professor began the class by explaining a contracts case. She then asked Lee, 23, what questions she would have asked the client had she been the attorney on the case.

At first Lee thought the professor had mistaken her for someone else. "Are you sure you are calling on me?" she asked. The professor assured her that she was. "My stomach did a flip," says Lee. "Time slows down when you are called on; what seems like two minutes is like five seconds." Lee tried her best and just "threw something out there," she says. The professor nodded at her answer, asked a follow-up question, and then moved on to the next student.

Called the Socratic method, this teaching style has been around since, well, Socrates. In law school, the practice includes professors peppering individual students with questions about assigned legal readings and making them think on their feet—and in front of their peers. (Think *The Paper Chase.*) While the practice has been supplanted by more-collaborative teaching styles at many universities, some schools, like the University of Chicago, still pride themselves on the tough-love teaching approach. "It's the best way to learn on

TAKING A BREAK AND LETTING OFF STEAM AT THE UNIVERSITY OF CHICAGO LAW SCHOOL CAFE

SCOTT GOLDSMITH FOR *USN&WR*

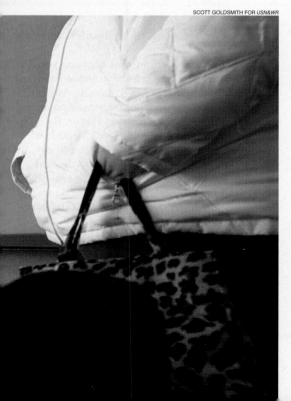

your feet and to argue," says Lee. "You get to see both sides of the argument." Emily Buss, a law professor at the University of Chicago who "cold-calls" in almost all of her classes, agrees. "Part of what makes a good lawyer is being able to make a compelling argument in front of a court without any advanced preparation time," she says.

Professors like Buss don't typically include classroom participation in their grades for first-year students. "The biggest punishment is obvious humiliation," says Lee, who does her reading almost every night. The Socratic method "really does keep you on your toes," she says. "It's better than coffee."

THERE WAS NEVER ANY QUESTION ABOUT WHAT TYSON Smith would study in law school. His earliest memories are of exploring bayous and digging for frogs and crayfish in his rural hometown of West Memphis, Ark., and his first job—at 14—was surveying land for a local engineering company. With undergraduate and graduate degrees in environmental engineering, "I didn't want to spend all my energy studying wills or corporate securities," says Smith, 28. "I wanted to study environmental law."

While schools have always tried to distinguish themselves by excelling in specialties, some schools have recently begun offering certificates for students who complete a specific set of courses in a given concentration. Smith found his program at Lewis and Clark Law School in Portland, Ore. One of the first schools to offer a certificate in environmental law, Lewis and Clark began its program in Environmental and Natural Resources Law in 1981. It now offers over 40 different classes in the area, from an environmental law insurance seminar to a course in hazardous-waste law.

Besides taking basic courses like contracts and property, Smith enrolled in nine environmental classes and participated in environmental moot court, leading the team to victory in last year's national championships. Such experiences helped him land a coveted second-year summer job in the Sierra Club's legal department, he says. In his interview with the environmental nonprofit, he was able to talk in detail about how citizens can file lawsuits under the Clean Water Act.

But what about learning the breadth of skills of a general-practice lawyer? "Basic lawyering skills are important," says Peter Devlin, president of Fish & Richardson, a high-tech law firm based in Boston, but "concentrations can offer a competitive advantage for job applicants." The Nuclear Regulatory Commission seems to agree—it hired Smith to work on environmental issues, and he will begin at the agency's Washington, D.C., office next fall. ●

ONLY 29.2% OF LAWYERS ARE WOMEN, 4.8% ARE AFRICAN-AMERICAN, AND 2.8% ARE HISPANIC; 92.6% ARE WHITE.

Getting in the door

aw school admission, in contrast to the practice of law, is mainly about numbers—two numbers, in fact: the Law School Admission Test score and the undergraduate grade-point average. By the time you've decided to go to law school, there probably isn't much you can do about your college GPA, except to know that it matters a lot. (As does the prestige of your undergraduate institution, by the way.) Half of the students admitted to the law school at Southern Methodist University in 2002, for instance, had between a 3.0 and 3.6 undergraduate GPA; at Yale Law, three quarters of the students had over a 3.77.

There are, however, ways to increase your score on the LSAT, a half-day exam that tests reading comprehension, verbal reasoning, and writing. Of course, you should start by studying the exam's format; the Law School Admissions Council sells a prep book for $17 that includes old tests (*www.lsac.org*). Much more expensive, at around $1,000 or more, are intensive prep classes offered by companies like Princeton Review and Kaplan. Some schools also have their own test classes; the University of Arizona's law school, for example, gives a free four-day class to students who demonstrate that they can't afford a commercial one.

For students who don't have stellar LSAT numbers, there is still hope. More than ever, law schools are considering other factors in admissions, including work experience and professional interests. Many schools have started new specialty pro-grams and are looking for students with a demonstrated passion in those areas. Last year, for instance, the University of California–Los Angeles began a joint degree program in law and African-American studies; after four years, graduates earn a J.D. and a master's degree.

Work experience is often the best way to show interest in a specific topic—and increase your chance of admission. So, if politics are your passion, work on Capitol Hill before you go to law school. If you're interested in kids or family issues, consider being a counselor or teacher. When Cindy Avitia, 32, applied to law school a year and a half ago, she focused her essay on her experiences as an immigration paralegal. "Law school for me is really completing the circle of what I wanted to be doing," she

IN THE REAL WORLD...

You know the economy is shaky when big-name firms lay off lawyers. Miami-based Holland & Knight, one of the largest firms in the country, handed out pink slips to over 60 attorneys last year. More recently, Pittsburgh firm Buchanan Ingersoll and Boston firm Testa, Hurwitz & Thibeault saw layoffs. Even partners haven't been spared.

But there's still work to be had. Many law schools, including the University of Michigan–Ann Arbor and the University of Southern California in Los Angeles, report the same number of recruiters coming to campus this year as last year. (Even Holland & Knight will hire some 40 new associates this year in an effort to get fresh blood.) Still, third-year students will not receive as many offers as in previous years, says Michael Schiumo, an assistant dean for career planning at Fordham Law School in New York City. Some students with subpar grades might not get any.

In a way, the most important decision you'll make is to choose what type of practice you want to go into. Working at a big firm will probably get you the most money, but your passion may take you into the public-interest sector. Remember, too, that geography will play a key role in what kind of work you do. The larger the city, the more specialized the law tends to be, and some cities dominate certain practice areas. New York, not surprisingly, is big in corporate work. Austin and San Francisco are hot for intellectual-property lawyers.

As far as weathering the economic downturn goes, consider specializing in any of the following fields of law:

Litigation. "In a bad economy, people are much more likely to litigate," says Jacki Burt, assistant dean of career services at the Ben-

PROF. CASS SUNSTEIN AT THE UNIVERSITY OF CHICAGO LAW SCHOOL, WHICH PRIDES ITSELF ON A TOUGH-LOVE TEACHING STYLE

Finally, among all the application hustle, remember that you are choosing a law school as much as the law school is choosing you. Schools vary greatly in their missions and atmosphere. Some, like the University of New Mexico in Albuquerque and the University of Maryland–Baltimore, require all students to participate in a clinic, while others have extensive study-abroad programs.

Which law school you attend will also help determine which jobs you're offered when you first get out. If you're looking to go to a top-flight corporate law firm (and rake in six digits a year), then attending a law school with a premium reputation is key. One of the top corporate firms in New York, Cravath, Swaine & Moore, visits only 20 top law schools in its on-campus interviewing program. But if you are planning to stay local, consider a state school. Smaller firms tend to hire from regional law schools. Plus, you could save upwards of $75,000—and even a lawyer can't argue with those numbers. ●

94% OF STUDENTS BORROW MONEY FOR LAW SCHOOL. THE TYPICAL LAW STUDENT GRADUATES WITH MORE THAN $84,000 IN DEBT.

says. Although her LSAT scores were average, the Santa Clara (Calif.) University School of Law gave her a $12,000 scholarship.

You can talk about these interests in your application's personal statement. But don't just review your accomplishments. Focus on your values and interests, with supporting evidence from your résumé and college experiences. " 'Been there, done that' isn't as important as what you've learned," says Donna Mancusi, a law school admissions consultant based in Boston. Give the people writing your recommendations a copy of your essay, too. Not only can they provide feedback, but it will give them some talking points.

jamin N. Cardozo School of Law of Yeshiva University in New York City. Since last year, the school has seen a 12 percent increase in the number of recruiters on campus, in part because of growth in the litigation field.

Intellectual property. Although the field has been hurt by the downturn in the Internet economy, "intellectual property is still very hot," says Kathleen Call, executive director of the Affiliates, a legal-staffing firm in Menlo Park, Calif. In IP, "you are always dealing with something complex and new," says Douglas Wilson, who graduated from the University of Texas School of Law in Austin in 2002 and recently signed on with the Houston-based firm of Conley Rose. "You are jumping from new technology to new technology."

Bankruptcy. "There are some huge bankruptcies out there, and they get very complicated and very complex, and they need a lot of attorneys," says Fordham's Schiumo. But you might want to explore this specialty even if the economy improves; companies fail and people lose their shirt even in the brightest of times.

Trust and estate. This field is expanding as the older baby boomers enter their late 50s. "People want to make sure their kids get their hard-earned money," says Eric Janson, an adjunct professor at Vermont Law School in South Royalton, Vt., who also has his own private practice.

Employment. "Whether you are hiring or firing, a company needs lawyers," says Susan Guindi, assistant dean for career services at the University of Michigan Law School.

Tax. "Tax is always solid," says Merv Loya, assistant dean at the University of Oregon School of Law in Eugene. But often, he adds, students need to get a master's degree in tax law to set themselves apart. Be prepared to spend most of your workday poring over financial forms, legal documents, and, of course, the tax code. ●

Schools of Law

THE TOP 100 SCHOOLS

Rank/School	Overall score	Peer assessment score (5.0 highest)	Assessment score by lawyers/judges (5.0 highest)	'02 undergrad GPA 25th-75th percentile	'02 LSAT score 25th-75th percentile	'02 acceptance rate	'02 student/ faculty ratio	'01 grads employed at graduation	Employed 9 months after graduation	School's bar passage rate in jurisdiction	Jurisdiction overall bar passage rate
1. Yale University (CT)	100	4.8	4.7	3.75-3.97	168-174	7.1%	7.5	98.5%	98.9%	97.9%/NY	76%
2. Stanford University (CA)	93	4.8	4.8	3.67-3.93	166-170	9.1%	12.6	98.9%	98.9%	92.4%/CA	66%
3. Harvard University (MA)	92	4.8	4.8	3.76-3.94	167-173	12.6%	13.0	98.9%	99.0%	95.5%/NY	76%
4. Columbia University (NY)	90	4.7	4.6	3.51-3.85	166-173	14.5%	13.2	99.5%	100.0%	93.2%/NY	76%
5. New York University	88	4.5	4.4	3.50-3.81	168-172	18.4%	11.4	98.1%	100.0%	95.5%/NY	76%
6. University of Chicago	85	4.7	4.7	3.54-3.76	167-171	16.4%	10.8	98.5%	99.5%	98.4%/IL	83%
7. University of Michigan–Ann Arbor	83	4.6	4.6	3.43-3.77	163-168	21.4%	14.0	95.4%	98.7%	89.7%/NY	76%
University of Pennsylvania	83	4.3	4.3	3.37-3.76	165-168	16.4%	13.0	99.6%	100.0%	95.9%/NY	76%
9. University of Virginia	82	4.4	4.5	3.49-3.78	164-168	22.3%	13.9	97.7%	99.7%	88.3%/VA	73%
10. Cornell University (NY)	81	4.2	4.2	3.50-3.79	164-166	19.2%	10.9	100.0%	100.0%	96.4%/NY	76%
University of California–Berkeley	81	4.5	4.4	3.68-3.90	161-168	11.5%	18.9	96.8%	98.3%	89.7%/CA	66%
12. Duke University (NC)	80	4.2	4.3	3.34-3.76	164-169	20.5%	12.9	96.1%	99.5%	93.0%/NY	76%
Northwestern University (IL)	80	4.2	4.2	3.30-3.70	165-169	17.4%	12.3	96.3%	98.6%	95.3%/IL	83%
14. Georgetown University (DC)	79	4.2	4.4	3.48-3.79	165-169	17.8%	15.9	94.8%	98.6%	95.3%/NY	76%
15. University of Texas–Austin	76	4.2	4.1	3.39-3.81	160-165	20.9%	16.4	91.3%	99.3%	91.0%/TX	81%
16. University of California–Los Angeles	75	4.0	4.0	3.52-3.80	162-167	14.5%	14.4	92.1%	96.9%	90.8%/CA	66%
17. Vanderbilt University (TN)	73	3.9	4.0	3.45-3.81	161-165	22.3%	15.4	87.6%	95.7%	87.2%/TN	80%
18. University of Southern California	72	3.7	3.6	3.41-3.70	163-166	20.9%	14.3	95.3%	100.0%	81.7%/CA	66%
19. University of Minnesota–Twin Cities	70	3.7	3.8	3.42-3.86	160-165	32.5%	13.6	85.3%	97.5%	93.9%/MN	90%
Washington and Lee University (VA)	70	3.3	3.7	3.28-3.78	163-166	21.0%	10.8	82.1%	95.3%	87.8%/VA	73%
21. University of Iowa	68	3.5	3.7	3.25-3.75	157-163	28.0%	11.0	83.1%	99.0%	86.4%/IA	86%
22. Boston College	67	3.4	3.6	3.39-3.74	160-165	18.4%	12.4	93.9%	97.6%	94.1%/MA	81%
George Washington University (DC)	67	3.4	3.7	3.31-3.68	161-165	15.0%	17.9	96.3%	98.6%	89.9%/NY	76%
University of Notre Dame (IN)	67	3.3	3.7	3.32-3.82	160-165	19.6%	15.2	79.6%	96.6%	97.9%/IL	83%
25. University of Illinois–Urbana-Champaign	66	3.5	3.6	3.15-3.60	159-163	25.6%	14.3	81.0%	98.9%	93.9%/IL	83%
Washington University in St. Louis	66	3.5	3.6	3.20-3.70	162-165	25.8%	14.3	87.3%	98.7%	73.7%/MO	80%
27. Emory University (GA)	65	3.3	3.6	3.37-3.75	160-165	28.7%	18.8	80.3%	98.0%	93.8%/GA	85%
28. Boston University	64	3.4	3.5	3.17-3.55	163-166	18.6%	10.7	74.3%	99.7%	88.4%/MA	81%
College of William and Mary (VA)	64	3.3	3.5	3.26-3.75	160-165	20.3%	16.5	81.3%	98.3%	82.5%/VA	73%
University of North Carolina–Chapel Hill	64	3.6	3.8	3.39-3.79	157-163	18.1%	15.4	69.2%	97.6%	87.4%/NC	95%
31. Brigham Young University (J. Reuben Clark) (UT)	63	2.9	3.4	3.48-3.82	160-166	27.4%	16.8	87.4%	97.4%	93.1%/UT	91%
Fordham University (NY)	63	3.2	3.4	3.32-3.76	162-166	20.8%	18.7	79.9%	94.9%	91.5%/NY	76%
University of California–Davis	63	3.4	3.6	3.28-3.68	157-163	23.1%	14.9	73.6%	93.8%	88.5%/CA	66%
University of Georgia	63	3.0	3.3	3.30-3.81	158-164	20.6%	19.8	85.0%	97.0%	92.1%/GA	85%
University of Wisconsin–Madison	63	3.7	3.5	3.04-3.58	155-162	32.1%	13.7	80.6%	96.9%	100.0%/WI	75%
36. University of California (Hastings)	61	3.4	3.8	3.35-3.70	159-164	23.1%	20.7	65.2%	94.4%	82.2%/CA	66%
Wake Forest University (NC)	61	3.1	3.4	3.14-3.69	158-163	28.0%	12.2	69.2%	97.7%	90.7%/NC	95%
38. Indiana University–Bloomington	60	3.2	3.5	3.03-3.73	156-163	33.5%	13.4	82.2%	94.1%	90.0%/IN	79%
Ohio State University (Moritz)	60	3.2	3.4	3.36-3.78	156-163	28.0%	14.6	70.1%	93.8%	88.5%/OH	80%
40. George Mason University (VA)	59	2.7	3.2	3.21-3.72	159-164	13.2%	14.7	92.1%	98.5%	69.0%/VA	73%
University of Colorado–Boulder	59	3.1	3.1	3.44-3.80	159-165	22.3%	13.4	54.9%	92.1%	91.2%/CO	78%
University of Connecticut	59	2.8	3.0	3.22-3.66	159-162	26.9%	11.9	74.3%	98.0%	90.4%/CT	80%
University of Utah (S. J. Quinney)	59	2.8	3.4	3.32-3.77	156-161	31.6%	13.0	77.6%	95.3%	94.8%/UT	91%
44. University of Arizona (Rogers)	58	3.1	3.1	3.23-3.78	157-164	18.4%	14.3	66.2%	93.7%	91.3%/AZ	78%
45. Tulane University (LA)	57	3.2	3.3	3.20-3.65	156-161	31.2%	22.8	69.9%	93.1%	88.0%/NY	76%
University of Alabama	57	2.7	3.0	3.10-3.63	157-162	33.1%	11.3	74.1%	98.3%	87.9%/AL	69%
University of Florida (Levin)	57	3.1	3.1	3.31-3.79	154-162	17.6%	16.4	64.4%	97.2%	86.3%/FL	79%
University of Maryland	57	2.9	2.8	3.29-3.71	155-162	13.0%	12.5	81.3%	97.4%	75.7%/MD	72%
University of Washington	57	3.2	3.4	3.46-3.79	160-165	20.0%	11.6	76.8%	75.0%	82.4%/WA	76%
50. Southern Methodist University (TX)	56	2.7	3.4	3.17-3.70	155-162	27.1%	17.6	69.6%	95.1%	87.3%/TX	81%

(CONTINUED ON PAGE 30)

Source: *U.S. News* and the schools. Assessment data collected by Synovate

More at **www.usnews.com**

Specialties

PROGRAMS RANKED BEST BY FACULTY WHO TEACH IN THE FIELD

CLINICAL TRAINING
Ranked in 2002
1. Georgetown University (DC)
2. New York University
3. American University (DC)
4. CUNY–Queens College
   Yale University (CT)
6. Washington Univ. in St. Louis
7. Univ. of Michigan–Ann Arbor
8. University of Maryland
9. Northwestern University (IL)
10. University of New Mexico

DISPUTE RESOLUTION
Ranked in 2003
1. Pepperdine University (CA)
   Univ. of Missouri–Columbia
3. Harvard University (MA)
4. Ohio State University (Moritz)
5. Hamline University (MN)
6. Cardozo-Yeshiva Univ. (NY)
   Georgetown University (DC)
8. Northwestern University (IL)
   Stanford University (CA)
10. Willamette University (OR)

ENVIRONMENTAL LAW
Ranked in 2003
1. Vermont Law School
2. Lewis and Clark
   College (Northwestern) (OR)
3. Pace University (NY)
4. University of Maryland
5. Tulane University (LA)
6. George Washington Univ. (DC)
   Univ. of Colorado–Boulder

8. Georgetown University (DC)
9. New York University
   Univ. of California–Berkeley

HEALTHCARE LAW
Ranked in 2003
1. University of Houston
2. St. Louis University
3. Loyola University Chicago
   University of Maryland
5. Boston University
6. Seton Hall University (NJ)
   Widener University (DE/PA)
8. Case Western Reserve U. (OH)
   Indiana Univ.–Indianapolis
10. DePaul University (IL)

INTELLECTUAL PROPERTY LAW
Ranked in 2002
1. Univ of California–Berkeley
2. George Washington Univ. (DC)
3. Franklin Pierce Law Ctr. (NH)
4. New York University
5. Cardozo-Yeshiva Univ. (NY)
   University of Houston
7. Columbia University (NY)
8. Stanford University (CA)
9. Santa Clara University (CA)
10. Boston University

INTERNATIONAL LAW
Ranked in 2002
1. New York University
2. Columbia University (NY)
3. Harvard University (MA)
4. Georgetown University (DC)

5. Yale University (CT)
6. George Washington
   University (DC)
7. American University
   (Washington College of Law) (DC)
8. Univ. of Michigan–Ann Arbor
9. University of Virginia
10. Univ. of California–Berkeley

TRIAL ADVOCACY
Ranked in 2003
1. Stetson University (FL)
   Temple University (Beasley) (PA)
3. Georgetown University (DC)
4. Northwestern University (IL)
   South Texas College of Law
6. New York University

Samford Univ. (Cumberland) (AL)
8. John Marshall Law School (IL)
9. University of Notre Dame (IN)
   University of Texas–Austin

TAX LAW
Ranked in 2002
1. New York University
2. University of Florida (Levin)
3. Georgetown University (DC)
4. Harvard University (MA)
5. Yale University (CT)
6. University of Texas–Austin
7. University of Miami (FL)
8. University of Virginia
9. Stanford University (CA)
10. University of Chicago

METHODOLOGY

The rankings of 177 accredited law schools are based on a weighted average of the 12 measures of quality described here. Specialty rankings are based on nomination by legal educators at peer institutions. More on our methods appears on Page 16.

Quality assessment (weighted by .40): Measured by two surveys conducted in fall 2002. The dean and three faculty members at each school were asked to rate schools from "marginal" (1) to "outstanding" (5); 70 percent voted. Their average rating for a school counts for a quarter of its overall score. Lawyers and judges also rated schools; the response was 34 percent. Their rating is weighted by .15.

Selectivity (.25): Combines median LSAT scores (50 percent), median undergrad GPA (40 percent), and proportion of applicants accepted for fall 2002 (10 percent).

Placement success (.20): Employment rates at graduation for 2001 graduates (30 percent) and nine months after (60 percent), and bar passage rate (10 percent). Employed graduates includes those reported as working or pursuing graduate degrees; for the nine-

month rate only, 25 percent of those whose status is unknown are also counted as working. Those not seeking jobs are excluded. Bar passage rate indicator is the ratio of a school's rate in the cited jurisdiction to the overall state rate, computed for first-time test takers in summer 2001 and winter 2002. The jurisdiction cited is the state where the largest number of 2001 grads first took the test.

Faculty resources (.15): Based on average 2001 and 2002 expenditures per student for instruction, library, and supporting services (65 percent); student/teacher ratio (20 percent); average per-student spending in 2001 and 2002 on all other items, including financial aid (10 percent); and total number of volumes and titles in library (5 percent).

Overall rank: A school's score on each indicator was standardized. Then scores were weighted, totaled, and rescaled so that the top school received 100 and other schools received a percentage of the top score.

Specialty rankings: Legal educators nominated up to 15 schools in each field. Those voted the top 10 appear.

UNIVERSITY OF CHICAGO LAW SCHOOL STUDENTS AT A DINNER AND DISCUSSION AT THE HOME OF DEAN SAUL LEVMORE

Rank School	Overall score	Peer assessment score (5.0 highest)	Assessment score by lawyers/judges (5.0 highest)	'02 undergrad GPA 25th-75th percentile	'02 LSAT score 25th-75th percentile	'02 acceptance rate	'02 student/ faculty ratio	'01 grads employed at graduation	Employed 9 months after graduation	School's bar passage rate in jurisdiction	Jurisdiction[1] overall bar passage rate
				THE TOP 100							
51. Baylor University (TX)	55	2.4	3.1	3.45-3.84	157-162	34.9%	17.9	72.6%	97.1%	96.1%/TX	81%
University of Cincinnati	55	2.6	3.0	3.20-3.72	156-162	31.8%	12.6	72.2%	96.7%	90.3%/OH	80%
University of Kentucky	55	2.6	2.9	3.34-3.73	156-161	33.7%	14.4	76.6%	100.0%	91.7%/KY	82%
University of Pittsburgh	55	2.8	3.1	3.05-3.60	155-161	34.8%	13.7	90.9%	97.5%	75.3%/PA	76%
55. American Univ. (Wash. Col. of Law) (DC)	54	2.9	3.1	3.24-3.62	156-160	30.4%	16.7	82.0%	94.6%	69.6%/MD	72%
University of Tennessee–Knoxville	54	2.7	2.8	3.25-3.76	155-160	28.0%	14.1	71.0%	94.8%	88.7%/TN	80%
57. Cardozo-Yeshiva University (NY)	53	2.7	2.7	3.20-3.67	158-163	27.0%	19.1	79.6%	97.9%	81.9%/NY	76%
Case Western Reserve University (OH)	53	2.8	3.2	3.01-3.49	155-160	31.8%	14.8	70.4%	96.5%	84.1%/OH	80%
59. Arizona State University	51	2.8	2.9	3.15-3.69	154-163	17.4%	13.1	62.0%	88.7%	81.4%/AZ	78%
Brooklyn Law School (NY)	51	2.6	2.7	3.10-3.60	158-162	29.3%	18.1	70.3%	97.9%	81.1%/NY	76%
University of Missouri–Columbia	51	2.7	3.2	3.11-3.67	154-160	35.6%	16.9	59.6%	96.2%	88.7%/MO	80%
University of Oklahoma	51	2.5	2.9	3.25-3.81	153-160	27.8%	15.1	64.8%	94.7%	86.2%/OK	81%
University of San Diego (CA)	51	2.6	2.8	3.09-3.53	158-162	26.8%	16.1	73.1%	93.4%	80.8%/CA	66%
64. Florida State University	50	2.6	2.8	3.16-3.66	153-157	31.8%	20.6	73.2%	99.3%	87.6%/FL	79%
Indiana University–Indianapolis	50	2.5	2.8	3.12-3.63	151-159	33.6%	17.6	N/A	96.2%	81.5%/IN	79%
Temple University (Beasley) (PA)	50	2.6	3.1	3.20-3.62	158-162	31.2%	17.7	63.5%	91.2%	74.3%/PA	76%
University of Kansas	50	2.7	3.1	3.11-3.74	154-160	37.4%	16.0	59.9%	93.4%	94.2%/KS	79%**
University of Nebraska–Lincoln	50	2.5	2.8	3.29-3.88	153-158	47.0%	13.3	65.5%	94.8%	82.4%/NE	81%
69. Illinois Institute of Tech. (Chicago-Kent)	49	2.7	2.6	3.09-3.52	155-159	37.3%	13.2	70.8%	94.9%	78.1%/IL	83%
Lewis and Clark Col. (Northwestern) (OR)	49	2.4	2.9	3.20-3.65	156-163	36.5%	13.3	N/A	93.2%	86.9%/OR	81%
Loyola Law School (CA)	49	2.5	3.0	3.14-3.61	157-162	30.7%	17.1	57.1%	97.1%	79.0%/CA	66%
Loyola University Chicago	49	2.4	3.0	3.04-3.53	157-161	24.5%	21.4	78.7%	97.9%	90.8%/IL	83%
St. John's University (NY)	49	2.2	2.9	3.14-3.58	155-160	27.8%	15.1	79.8%	99.3%	79.7%/NY	76%
University of Houston	49	2.7	2.9	3.29-3.74	154-160	32.8%	16.5	42.6%	88.8%	91.5%/TX	81%
University of Louisville (Brandeis) (KY)	49	2.2	2.8	3.12-3.61	154-159	27.4%	11.4	67.0%	95.0%	75.0%/KY	82%
University of New Mexico	49	2.5	2.7	3.01-3.69	151-160	31.8%	10.4	N/A	90.1%	92.6%/NM	94%
Villanova University (PA)	49	2.5	3.1	3.10-3.56	155-159	37.1%	19.6	68.4%	94.0%	82.0%/PA	76%
78. Rutgers State University–Camden (NJ)	48	2.5	2.9	3.00-3.50	158-163	22.5%	18.6	76.1%	93.9%	69.5%/NJ	73%
Rutgers State University–Newark (NJ)	48	2.7	2.8	3.05-3.55	154-161	21.6%	15.8	N/A	92.0%	74.2%/NJ	73%
University of Denver	48	2.4	2.8	2.85-3.43	152-159	27.5%	14.1	86.5%	99.3%	69.1%/CO	78%
University of Oregon	48	2.8	3.1	3.10-3.60	157-161	37.8%	18.5	52.1%	90.6%	81.8%/OR	81%
University of Richmond (VA)	48	2.3	2.9	3.01-3.53	157-160	30.7%	17.5	75.5%	95.6%	74.4%/VA	73%
University of South Carolina	48	2.3	2.8	3.33-3.65	154-159	29.8%	17.7	71.6%	98.2%	91.5%/SC	85%
84. Catholic University of America (DC)	47	2.5	2.9	3.01-3.50	154-158	35.3%	15.9	74.5%	93.9%	65.3%/MD	72%
University of Miami (FL)	47	2.8	2.9	3.16-3.56	153-158	39.9%	22.2	63.1%	90.5%	83.3%/FL	79%
86. Seton Hall University (NJ)	46	2.4	2.8	2.90-3.44	154-158	39.4%	22.5	86.4%	97.1%	80.1%/NJ	73%
University at Buffalo (NY)	46	2.5	2.4	3.06-3.65	152-158	36.4%	14.1	82.9%	92.5%	67.2%/NY	76%
University of Hawaii	46	2.3	2.6	3.00-3.66	153-159	32.6%	14.4	60.3%	96.2%	81.0%/HI	80%
89. Northeastern University (MA)	45	2.3	2.7	3.09-3.58	155-161	28.6%	18.4	N/A	91.9%	84.8%/MA	81%
University of Mississippi	45	2.3	2.9	3.27-3.72	150-156	35.6%	21.1	71.4%	97.7%	88.9%/MS	87%
91. Georgia State University	44	2.2	2.8	3.10-3.52	154-164	21.6%	16.9	N/A	92.5%	91.4%/GA	85%
Marquette University (WI)	44	2.2	2.9	3.03-3.54	153-158	42.2%	18.2	66.3%	92.5%	100.0%/WI	75%
Mercer University (GA)	44	2.1	2.9	2.94-3.58	151-156	35.7%	14.6	57.5%	95.7%	92.7%/GA	85%
Santa Clara University (CA)	44	2.4	2.9	3.12-3.54	153-159	37.6%	19.3	55.9%	90.0%	82.0%/CA	66%
Seattle University	44	2.1	2.8	3.08-3.55	151-158	44.0%	17.8	63.2%	99.3%	76.9%/WA	76%
University of Arkansas–Fayetteville	44	2.2	2.6	3.04-3.63	149-156	43.2%	14.8	N/A	97.0%	84.6%/AR	82%
97. Louisiana State Univ.–Baton Rouge	43	2.2	2.9	3.15-3.67	150-156	37.1%	17.5	N/A	89.7%	83.3%/LA	71%
Syracuse University (NY)	43	2.4	2.9	3.02-3.55	148-154	41.8%	18.2	73.7%	93.4%	71.3%/NY	76%
University of San Francisco	43	2.2	2.7	3.01-3.45	154-159	32.9%	17.5	N/A	91.8%	72.0%/CA	66%
Wayne State University (MI)	43	2.4	2.6	3.10-3.58	151-157	44.2%	21.0	69.6%	97.3%	81.6%/MI	76%

[1]School did not return its *U.S. News* statistical survey. Sources: *U.S. News* and the schools. Note: Numbers with * are from the fall 2001 entering class or school year and the 2000 graduating class as reported to the American Bar Association. N/A means that the data were not provided by the school. Western State University in California, the University of the District of Columbia, Ave Maria School of Law in Michigan, Barry University in Florida, the University of Nevada–Las Vegas, Appalachian School of Law in Virginia, and three law schools in Puerto Rico—Catholic University, Inter-America University, and the University of Puerto Rico—are not ranked. **The state bar passage rate for Kansas is based on all test takers, not just those taking the test for the first time.

Other schools to consider

The next two quartiles of schools are listed in two groups, the Third Tier and Fourth Tier. Law schools within each of these tiers should be considered broadly similar in quality and therefore are listed alphabetically. To be listed, a law school must be accredited and fully approved by the American Bar Association and must draw most of its students from the United States. Remember that in considering a law school you should look not only at its ranking or tier but also at other characteristics—its location, price, course offerings, and faculty expertise, to name a few—as well as how well a school meets your own needs. More information on all the schools is available in the directory, which begins on Page 93.

More at **www.usnews.com**

School	Peer assessment score (5.0 highest)	Assessment score by lawyers/judges (5.0 highest)	'02 undergrad GPA 25th-75th percentile	'02 LSAT score 25th-75th percentile	'02 acceptance rate	'02 student/faculty ratio	'01 grads employed at graduation	Employed 9 months after graduation	School's bar passage rate in jurisdiction	Jurisdiction's overall bar passage rate
THIRD TIER (ranking begins at 101; schools are listed alphabetically)										
Albany Law School–Union University (NY)	2.2	2.3	2.98-3.50	148-154	51.5%	20.5	76.7%	96.0%	76.8%/NY	76%
Campbell University (NC)	1.5	2.2	2.99-3.51	151-156	27.2%	17.5	55.7%	95.5%	91.6%/NC	95%
Chapman University (CA)	1.5	1.4	2.93-3.47	151-157	36.1%	15.5	65.6%	93.8%	63.6%/CA	66%
Creighton University (NE)	2.0	2.7	3.03-3.53	149-157	51.9%	16.6	53.1%	95.3%	79.7%/NE	81%
DePaul University (IL)	2.3	2.7	3.21-3.65	153-158	31.7%	22.8	74.8%	83.2%	73.6%/IL	83%
Drake University (IA)	2.0	2.7	3.06-3.63	151-156	46.8%	16.8	61.7%	94.8%	84.2%/IA	86%
Duquesne University (PA)	1.9	2.5	3.08-3.63	152-155	46.8%	19.4	63.3%	89.2%	78.4%/PA	76%
Franklin Pierce Law Center (NH)	1.9	2.2	2.89-3.43	148-156	39.4%	13.0	67.0%	88.2%	63.6%/NH	64%
Hofstra University (NY)	2.3	2.7	2.83-3.50	151-157	36.0%	18.9	N/A	94.2%	76.4%/NY	76%
Howard University (DC)	2.1	2.3	2.90-3.34	148-154	32.7%	18.0*	69.5%	88.3%	68.8%/NY	76%
Loyola University–New Orleans	2.0	2.7	2.96-3.47	150-155	42.0%	21.3	97.3%	97.9%	65.7%/LA	71%
New York Law School	2.1	2.6	3.00-3.40	150-154	41.2%	24.2	N/A	91.3%	69.5%/NY	76%
Pace University (NY)	2.0	2.2	3.01-3.52	151-156	35.4%	16.2	61.0%	91.5%	64.8%/NY	76%
Penn State University (Dickinson School of Law)	2.2	3.0	3.05-3.53	151-157	43.0%	19.8	51.5%	87.9%	80.3%/PA	76%
Pepperdine University (CA)	2.2	2.9	3.15-3.65	155-160	35.2%	18.8	53.9%	85.8%	71.4%/CA	66%
Samford University (Cumberland) (AL)	1.8	2.6	2.89-3.43	151-155	43.1%	19.2	58.2%	89.8%	80.4%/AL	69%
Southern Illinois University–Carbondale	2.0	2.3	3.04-3.60	149-154	51.8%	13.1	N/A	94.7%	84.3%/IL	83%
Southwestern University School of Law (CA)	1.9	2.1	3.00-3.50	152-158	39.9%	16.6	84.4%	95.6%	68.0%/CA	66%
Stetson University (FL)	2.1	2.3	2.98-3.55	149-155	34.4%	17.3	N/A	97.8%	82.7%/FL	79%
St. Louis University	2.3	2.9	3.13-3.65	151-158	53.7%	17.8	62.0%	86.2%	80.4%/MO	80%
Suffolk University (MA)	1.9	2.3	3.20-3.50	151-157	48.3%	18.7	61.4%	93.9%	77.3%/MA	81%
University of Akron (OH)	1.8	2.1	2.84-3.60	153-157	30.4%	18.5	52.1%	92.0%	85.6%/OH	80%
University of Arkansas–Little Rock (Bowen)	2.0	2.3	2.92-3.58	149-156	52.7%	16.1	N/A	88.1%	81.7%/AR	82%
University of Idaho	2.0	2.6	3.18-3.68	149-156	47.4%	16.5	50.0%	96.2%	70.6%/ID	77%
University of Maine	2.3	2.8	3.03-3.53	151-157	43.2%	14.9	N/A	78.3%	64.8%/ME	69%
University of Memphis	1.8	2.3	2.95-3.61	151-155	35.5%	21.7	70.1%	96.6%	92.0%/TN	80%
University of Montana	2.1	2.7	3.10-3.65	151-157	42.9%	19.1	66.3%	92.5%	92.5%/MT	92%
University of North Dakota	1.9	2.5	3.13-3.69	148-155	55.0%	17.6	N/A	93.1%	87.9%/MN	90%
University of South Dakota	1.9	2.7	2.79-3.48	146-154	50.1%	17.5	91.2%	91.2%	100.0%/SD	94%
University of the Pacific (McGeorge) (CA)	2.1	2.7	2.86-3.35	150-156	48.8%	23.9	N/A	96.1%	70.4%/CA	66%
University of Toledo (OH)	2.0	2.0	2.84-3.53	153-158	32.6%	12.4	85.0%	96.6%	78.0%/OH	80%
University of Wyoming	2.1	2.5	3.06-3.60	149-156	29.9%	16.2	N/A	89.3%	86.0%/WY	80%
Valparaiso University (IN)	2.0	2.6	3.02-3.59	150-156	56.7%	19.6	61.5%	95.4%	72.9%/IN	79%
Vermont Law School	2.3	2.6	2.83-3.37	149-156	60.9%	19.3	54.7%	86.5%	73.7%/NY	76%
Washburn University (KS)	1.9	2.5	2.89-3.54	145-153	59.0%	16.3	75.4%	94.8%	70.7%/KS	79%**
West Virginia University	2.1	2.5	3.10-3.68	148-154	45.9%	20.9	79.7%	92.3%	71.7%/WV	68%
William Mitchell College of Law (MN)	2.0	2.3	3.03-3.59	152-158	63.7%	22.8	91.7%	93.3%	86.7%/MN	90%
FOURTH TIER (ranking begins at 138; schools are listed alphabetically)										
California Western School of Law	1.7	1.9	2.88-3.44	147-154	63.9%	28.6	N/A	68.7%	63.5%/CA	66%
Capital University (OH)	1.8	2.1	2.96-3.44	148-154	49.5%	21.6	N/A	97.7%	71.0%/OH	80%
Cleveland State University (Marshall)	2.0	2.2	2.62-3.46	147-154	44.8%	20.2	64.0%	91.5%	70.3%/OH	80%
CUNY–Queens College	1.8	2.3	2.82-3.38	145-153	26.0%	14.3	40.4%	74.5%	65.8%/NY	76%
Florida Coastal School of Law	1.2	1.2	2.57-3.17	149-154	36.4%	17.5	N/A	84.0%	56.0%/FL	79%
Golden Gate University (CA)	1.7	1.9	2.77-3.37	147-153	56.0%	17.4	N/A	78.1%	54.0%/CA	66%
Gonzaga University (WA)	2.1	3.0	2.93-3.49	149-155	49.4%	24.8	50.3%	86.7%	63.6%/WA	76%
Hamline University (MN)	1.9	2.0	3.08-3.60	148-156	57.6%	20.6	61.4%	90.7%	85.8%/MN	90%
John Marshall Law School (IL)	1.8	2.2	2.65-3.23	150-154	36.5%	17.9	50.5%	85.7%	69.1%/IL	83%
Michigan State Univ.–DCL Col. of Law	1.9	2.4	2.91-3.51	150-158	53.4%	20.4	N/A	86.4%	77.3%/MI	76%
Mississippi College	1.6	2.4	2.80-3.40	146-151	50.9%	23.8	63.2%	97.4%	80.7%/MS	87%
New England School of Law (MA)	1.8	2.1	2.87-3.37	147-152	58.0%	23.0	43.8%	83.3%	71.5%/MA	81%
North Carolina Central University[1]	1.5	1.8	2.72-3.28*	143-151*	24.6%*	23.7*	N/A	89.7%*	N/A	N/A
Northern Illinois University	1.7	1.9	2.90-3.49	151-157	33.6%	17.0	N/A	91.7%	74.7%/IL	83%
Northern Kentucky University (Chase)	1.6	2.1	2.97-3.56	150-155	46.5%	18.1	63.8%	93.1%	83.3%/OH	80%
Nova Southeastern University[1] (FL)	1.8	1.9	2.68-3.35*	147-152*	49.0%*	16.1*	N/A	82.3%*	N/A	N/A
Ohio Northern University	1.6	1.9	2.76-3.45	145-153	43.0%	15.1	39.8%	90.8%	75.9%/OH	80%
Oklahoma City University	1.5	1.7	2.77-3.40	144-150	56.3%	17.5	N/A	85.7%	75.6%/OK	81%
Quinnipiac University (CT)	1.9	2.1	2.66-3.32	148-153	35.6%	14.9	59.8%	97.6%	76.0%/CT	80%
Regent University (VA)	1.4	1.8	2.86-3.60	148-155	52.9%	17.5	30.4%	86.2%	48.4%/VA	73%
Roger Williams University (RI)	1.6	2.2	2.83-3.36	146-154	57.8%	20.1	N/A	73.7%	68.5%/MA	81%
Southern University[1] (LA)	1.3	1.7	2.45-3.01*	142-148*	34.7%*	13.9*	N/A	98.9%*	N/A	N/A
South Texas College of Law	1.6	2.1	2.80-3.29	148-154	49.3%	19.7	N/A	80.8%	79.0%/TX	81%
St. Mary's University (TX)	1.7	2.3	2.72-3.20	148-153	48.8%	22.4	N/A	65.1%	66.5%/TX	81%
St. Thomas University (FL)	1.4	1.4	2.64-3.22	146-151	50.5%	22.5	N/A	90.0%	73.3%/FL	79%
Texas Southern University[1] (Thurgood Marshall)	1.5	1.7	2.46-3.15*	138-144*	49.5%*	23.2*	N/A	46.0%*	N/A	N/A
Texas Tech University	1.9	2.4	3.17-3.67	150-157	38.4%	19.4	26.9%	89.3%	88.2%/TX	81%
Texas Wesleyan University	1.6	1.7	2.80-3.40	148-154	44.8%	23.0	86.4%	91.3%	76.7%/TX	81%
Thomas Jefferson School of Law (CA)	1.3	1.9	2.60-3.25	148-156	53.9%	21.5	N/A	80.1%*	54.1%/CA	66%
Thomas M. Cooley Law School (MI)	1.4	1.7	2.66-3.22	141-149	68.6%	19.3	N/A	79.7%	62.4%/MI	76%
Touro College (Jacob D. Fuchsberg) (NY)	1.7	1.9	2.62-3.29	145-151	45.0%	17.2	N/A	84.1%	58.2%/NY	76%
University of Baltimore	2.0	2.3	2.87-3.45	150-155	32.7%	19.1	N/A	74.0%	72.9%/MD	72%
University of Dayton (OH)	1.9	2.3	2.84-3.43	147-154	56.9%	18.3	56.3%	90.4%	77.6%/OH	80%
University of Detroit Mercy	1.5	2.1	2.96-3.40	146-153	41.1%	18.6	N/A	90.9%	81.3%/MI	76%
University of Missouri–Kansas City	2.2	2.6	3.03-3.62	150-156	45.8%	17.6	45.3%	74.1%	67.6%/MO	80%
University of Tulsa (OK)	2.0	2.4	2.83-3.46	145-153	52.4%	16.5	36.4%	84.9%	77.8%/OK	81%
Western New England College (MA)	1.6	1.6	2.68-3.42	148-154	48.5%	15.1	62.1%	82.7%	66.7%/MA	81%
Whittier Law School (CA)	1.6	2.1	2.74-3.35	146-152	56.0%	23.0	69.7%	92.5%	46.8%/CA	66%
Widener University (DE)	1.7	2.1	2.72-3.36	147-151	57.2%	21.9	60.5%	82.6%	66.7%/PA	76%
Willamette University (OR)	2.1	2.7	2.94-3.49	151-157	63.3%	16.8	43.0%	80.3%	72.6%/OR	81%

Law School Diversity

Law schools rich in racial and ethnic diversity are thought to offer their students a chance to encounter ideas and experiences different from their own, which can be good practice for the life of a lawyer.

To identify institutions where students are most likely to encounter classmates from different racial or ethnic groups, *U.S. News* has created a diversity index based on the total proportion of minority students—not including international students—and the mix of racial and ethnic groups on campus. The data are drawn from each law school's 2002–2003 student body, including both full- and part-time students. The groups forming the basis for our calculations are African-Americans, Asian-Americans, Hispanics, American Indians, and whites. Our formula produces a diversity index that ranges from 0.0 to 1.0. The closer a school's number is to 1.0, the more diverse is the student population. Schools that have a large proportion of one ethnic group, even if it is a minority group, don't score high in this index.

To be included in the table, a law school must be accredited by the American Bar Association. Because student-body ethnic diversity data are not consistently compiled and reported as yet for other types of graduate schools, *U.S. News* has prepared a diversity table for law schools only.

THE MOST DIVERSE SCHOOLS

School	Diversity index (1.0 highest)	Largest minority and its %
Western State University (CA)	0.61	Asian-American, 19%
University of Southern California	0.60	Asian-American, 20%
Whittier Law School (CA)	0.60	Asian-American, 21%
St. Thomas University (FL)	0.59	Hispanic, 35%
CUNY–Queens College	0.58	African-American, 15%
Loyola Law School (CA)	0.56	Asian-American, 22%
Rutgers State University–Newark (NJ)	0.55	African-American, 15%
Santa Clara University (CA)	0.55	Asian-American, 26%
Southwestern Univ. School of Law (CA)	0.55	Asian-American, 19%
Thomas M. Cooley Law School (MI)	0.53	African-American, 23%
Columbia University (NY)	0.52	Asian-American, 14%
University of California–Berkeley	0.52	Asian-American, 22%
University of Hawaii	0.52	Asian-American, 62%
University of New Mexico	0.52	Hispanic, 23%
University of California–Davis	0.51	Asian-American, 21%
Stanford University (CA)	0.50	Hispanic, 14%
St. Mary's University (TX)	0.50	Hispanic, 31%
George Washington University (DC)	0.49	African-American, 12%
University of California (Hastings)	0.49	Asian-American, 22%
Arizona State University	0.48	Hispanic, 14%
Northwestern University (IL)	0.48	Asian-American, 14%
Yale University (CT)	0.48	Asian-American, 13%
Golden Gate University (CA)	0.46	Asian-American, 13%
University of Chicago	0.46	Asian-American, 14%
University of Miami (FL)	0.46	Hispanic, 16%
University of San Francisco	0.46	Asian-American, 17%
American Univ. (Wash. Col. of Law) (DC)	0.45	Asian-American, 14%
University of California–Los Angeles	0.45	Asian-American, 17%
University of Arizona (Rogers)	0.44	Hispanic, 11%
University of Florida (Levin)	0.44	Hispanic, 11%
University of Illinois–Urbana-Champaign	0.44	Asian-American, 10%
University of Pennsylvania	0.44	Asian-American, 9%
Chapman University (CA)	0.43	Asian-American, 14%
Cornell University (NY)	0.43	Asian-American, 14%
Touro College (Jacob D. Fuchsberg) (NY)	0.43	African-American, 11%
University of San Diego	0.43	Asian-American, 15%

School	Diversity index (1.0 highest)	Largest minority and its %
Fordham University (NY)	0.42	Asian-American, 9%
Georgetown University (DC)	0.41	African-American, 10%
Hofstra University (NY)	0.41	African-American, 8%
Boston University	0.40	Asian-American, 12%
DePaul University (IL)	0.40	Asian-American, 9%
Northeastern University (MA)	0.40	Asian-American, 8%
South Texas College of Law	0.40	Hispanic, 11%
University of Washington	0.40	Asian-American, 16%
University of Wisconsin–Madison	0.40	Asian-American, 8%
California Western School of Law	0.39	Asian-American, 10%
Harvard University (MA)	0.39	Asian-American, 11%
New York University	0.39	Asian-American, 10%
Vanderbilt University (TN)	0.39	African-American, 13%
Florida State University	0.38	Hispanic, 10%
Northern Illinois University	0.38	Hispanic, 9%
St. John's University (NY)	0.38	Asian-American, 9%
University of Maryland	0.38	African-American, 11%
University of Michigan–Ann Arbor	0.38	Asian-American, 10%
Barry University (FL)	0.37	Hispanic, 13%
Boston College	0.37	Asian-American, 9%
Catholic University of America (DC)	0.37	African-American, 9%
Duke University (NC)	0.37	African-American, 9%
Texas Wesleyan University	0.37	Hispanic, 8%
University of the Pacific (McGeorge) (CA)	0.37	Asian-American, 11%
Brooklyn Law School (NY)	0.36	Asian-American, 11%
Seattle University	0.36	Asian-American, 11%
Loyola University–New Orleans	0.35	African-American, 11%
New York Law School	0.35	Asian-American, 7%
Oklahoma City University	0.35	African-American, 7%
Syracuse University (NY)	0.35	Asian-American, 8%
Tulane University (LA)	0.35	African-American, 10%
University of Baltimore	0.35	African-American, 14%
University of Texas–Austin	0.35	Hispanic, 10%
Cardozo-Yeshiva University (NY)	0.34	Asian-American, 9%
Seton Hall University (NJ)	0.34	Hispanic, 7%
Univ. of Nev.–Las Vegas (William S. Boyd)	0.34	Hispanic, 9%

Note: The diversity index is based on data collected by *U.S. News*. The methodology used to compute the index was published in a 1992 article by Philip Meyer and Shawn McIntosh in the *International Journal of Public Opinion Research*. For the purposes of this index, students classified as ethnicity unknown/unreported were counted as white. A more detailed explanation of the methodology is available at www.usnews.com.

MEDICINE

Health of a nation

BY NANCY SHUTE

A few years earlier, Jonathan Links would have ended his December lecture on the health effects of radiation by talking about the 1986 explosion of the Chernobyl nuclear power plant. But in 2002, students in his environmental health class were learning a lesson much closer to home: what to do if a dirty bomb spewed radioactive particles around the shops of Baltimore's Inner Harbor, a few miles south of their lecture hall at Johns Hopkins University's Bloomberg School of Public Health. "Treat and stabilize nonradiation injuries, such as burns, then treat and minimize internal contamination," Links said. He explained that radioactive particles that lodge in lungs or wounds can cause cancer decades later, which is what happened at Chernobyl. "You want to remove the person from the area as quickly as possible and clean wounds as quickly as possible."

Most of Links's students will never find themselves toting a pager, as their professor now does so that he can be reached to help the Baltimore fire department if a dirty bomb is discovered. But the war on terrorism has given new visibility to a profession best known for battling infectious diseases like tuberculosis—yet rarely appreciated for its vital role in keeping the country healthy. "For the first time in generations, people finally understand what public health is all about," says Alfred Sommer, dean of Hopkins's school of public health. "Our trustees now come up to me and say, 'Al, we're counting on you to protect us.'"

Indeed, the terrorist attacks of 2001 made citizens, politicians, and bureaucrats painfully aware of how vulnerable the nation is and how ill-prepared to deal with these new threats. Yet it quickly became apparent that the kinds of skills needed to deal with terror threats—risk assessment, prevention, risk communication, disaster response, and recovery—are just the sorts of things that schools of public health know all about. The federal government has boosted funding for schools of public health by $20 million to work with state and local health departments on terrorism preparedness.

It's the latest twist in a field always remarkable for its variety. Public health differs from medicine in that it focuses on preventing and treating health problems in whole populations, rather than in a single patient—eradicating smallpox worldwide, say, or reducing asthma among inner-

city children, or running campaigns to discourage teenage smoking. It's no small task. Indeed, the remarkable improvements in Americans' health in the past 100 years have been due not to technological feats like heart bypass surgery but to public health campaigns like those to provide clean water, vaccinate children, improve food safety, and discourage smoking.

Public health has always drawn a broad range of students, because it can put just about anybody to good use—liberal arts majors, computer wonks, lawyers, doctors, or returned Peace Corps volunteers. The cornerstone of public health study is epidemiology, the population-based study of disease. It, and biostatistics, which analyzes biological data gained from research such as clinical trials, draw students with strong math and science backgrounds. People who majored in psychology or anthropology might end up in health education or global health. Students with backgrounds in chemistry or biology might be drawn to environmental health, which studies how pollution, chemicals, radiation, and such affect health. And people who majored in business may find that health services administration, another public health discipline, is a good fit. These varied interests are met by a broad range of degrees—the master's in public health, which is designed for M.D.'s and others with relevant experience; Ph.D.'s for the more research oriented; and joint degrees with schools of medicine, law, social work, and public policy. "Our medical problems are more and more social, cultural, and political," says Deborah Prothrow-Stith, an M.D. who teaches public health leadership at Harvard.

Mirette Habib never imagined that she'd put her public health degree to use fighting bioterrorism. After receiving a master's in public health from Hopkins in 2000, she worked for an Irvine, Calif., firm, analyzing the dangers posed by toxic chemicals in the environment. But last year found her in Washington, D.C., helping to plan the deconta-

A POSTDOCTORAL FELLOW AT JOHNS HOPKINS'S BLOOMBERG SCHOOL OF PUBLIC HEALTH WORKS IN THE MALARIA RESEARCH INSTITUTE LAB.

JEFFREY MACMILLAN FOR *USN&WR*

mination of the anthrax-laden Brentwood postal facility. (Two workers died from being exposed to anthrax spores there.) "I learned everything I could about anthrax and applied my risk background, focusing on the human effects," says Habib, 27, who had considered going to medical school but realized she loved science more than doctoring.

Biostatistics and epidemiology, the branch of medicine that investigates the causes of infectious diseases, are key tools in many aspects of public health. Indeed, John Snow, the British physician who is considered the father of modern public health, used exacting data gathering, mapping, and analysis to prove that a 1854 cholera outbreak in London's Soho was caused not by miasma (the 19th-century term for the bad air, caused by decaying organic matter, that some believed spread the disease) but by a contaminated well. Once Snow had the well's pump handle removed, so people could no longer draw water from it, the epidemic ceased.

Snow's investigation is a classic example of public health in action. But many public health students have no intention of ever chasing a microbe. Instead, they plan to apply the skills they acquire to solving broad social problems. "A lot of people don't know that public health exists," says Chad Lipton, a 28-year-old graduate student at Hopkins. He was clued in only because his dad, a physician, suggested that public health might offer practical applications for his son's interest in the environment. He's taking epidemiology and other traditional public health courses as part of a master's of health science, a degree that, unlike an M.P.H., doesn't require applicants to have some previous relevant experience. He's also pursuing a second master's from Hopkins's School of Advanced International Studies, which emphasizes economics and policy. Lipton served as an election observer at the Kenyan polls last December. After he graduates in May, he plans to return to Africa to work on international aid projects to build safer water supplies. "If I can get hands-on experience in any kind of environmental or public health project, I'll be happy," he says.

Sommer and other veteran public health educators are already predicting that the federal government's newfound fascination with public health will wane. "It will be the usual story of public health," Sommer says. "Everybody gets appropriately concerned. As soon as the threat has passed, we go back to paying for coronary bypass surgery." Others hope that the changes wrought by the public's new awareness of the value of public health will resonate, even if today's public health students find themselves dealing with Medicare and clean water supplies, not anthrax. ●

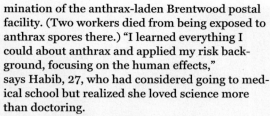

85% OF MED SCHOOL GRADS LAST YEAR SAID THEY HAD BEEN PUBLICLY BELITTLED OR HUMILIATED DURING THEIR TIME IN SCHOOL.

JEFFREY MACMILLAN FOR *USN&WR* (2)

GRAD STUDENTS IN AN ENVIRONMENTAL HEALTH SCIENCES LAB CLASS AT THE JOHNS HOPKINS PUBLIC HEALTH SCHOOL CALIBRATE EQUIPMENT THAT MEASURES ATMOSPHERIC POLLUTION AND CHEMICALS.

Rx for future M.D.'s

For seven years running, admissions deans at the nation's medical schools watched anxiously as the number of applications dropped 2 to 10 percent annually, from 47,000 in 1996 to 33,501 in 2002. Observers attributed the slump largely to bad news about managed care and malpractice costs; the seven to 10 years required by med school and residency; and the massive debt borne by graduates. But that tide appears to be turning. Applications for the fall 2003 class are expected to increase by 4 to 6 percent. "Our studies indicate that the demand for physicians, and the demand for specialists in particular, is very strong," says Ed Salsberg, director of the Center for Health Workforce Studies at the University at Albany, State University of New York. "And most studies show that doctors are still very satisfied professionally." (Officials add that the incoming class of 2003 will be historic: the first ever to be divided fifty-fifty between women and men.)

The bump in applications doesn't mean it's going to suddenly become much harder to win a slot. Admissions officers say that while the number of applications declined, grade-point averages and MCAT scores of applicants for the 16,500 slots in the nation's medical schools actually rose over the same period. In other words, the competition has always been tough. So if you're serious about med school, be prepared to show it not only with good grades (3.5 or above) and board scores (27 and up) but also with solid evidence that you understand what medicine is all about.

"We're looking for people who are altruistic," says Robert Sabalis, associate vice president for student affairs and programs at the Association of American Medical Colleges, "people who are interested in assisting others, as well as evidence that one knows what one is getting into." The best way to show that, Sabalis says, is to have hands-on experience working or volunteering in a medical clinic or as an EMT—"something that leads you to know that it's not *Scrubs*." The idea is to demonstrate that you've got the physical and emotional stamina to succeed not only in medical school but also in the often hectic—and at times tedious—world of healthcare.

Another way to prove that you've done your homework is to have thought through the money question. The average debt load for medical school graduates in 2002 was $103,855. Payments start after graduation, meaning that medical residents have to write loan checks out of salaries that top out at $40,000 or so. Admissions officers say you should expect to be asked during the interview process how you'll manage that financial burden.

You'll also increase your odds of acceptance by choosing a medical school that fits your notion of what kind of doctor you're going to be. Many applicants mistakenly presume they've got to go to a brand-name school. But the Harvards and Stanfords are more geared to students who will end up teaching or doing research at big academic medical centers—like Harvard and Stanford. Someone who's aiming at family practice or pediatrics might find a better

match at schools that specialize in training primary-care docs, like the Brody School of Medicine at East Carolina University. Since 1972, the University of Minnesota's Duluth School of Medicine has consistently led the nation in the numer of graduates who choose family practice—53 percent by last count, compared with 13 percent nationwide. The school also specializes in training rural physicians; students live with and shadow a rural family doctor several times a year. Starting with the class of 2004, the university is opening the program, which has been restricted to residents of Minnesota and parts of Wisconsin, to include people who live in Iowa, all of Wisconsin, and the Dakotas. Third-year students have the option of working for nine months in a rural community. "They actually become one of the community physicians," says Lillian Repesh, associate dean of student affairs and admissions at Duluth. "They could meet a pregnant patient their first week and actually be there to deliver the baby." ●

PUBLIC HEALTH GRAD STUDENTS DAVID HOWARD AND KARA BLACK STUDY IN A HOPKINS STUDENT LOUNGE.

A FAST TRACK TO NURSING

If demand for physicians is strong, it's nothing compared with the need for registered nurses—1 million by 2010, according to the Bureau of Labor Statistics. Nursing schools are responding with "acclerated career-entry" programs designed for people who already have a bachelor's. The notion has been around since the 1970s, but the nursing shortage has sparked an explosion of new graduate programs. Currently, 90 nursing schools offer turbocharged B.S.N.'s for students who already have a bachelor's or master's in another field. At Philadelphia's Drexel College of Nursing and Health Professions, for instance, students can pick up a B.S.N. in 11 months.

Acclerated or "generic" master's degrees, which generally take three years, let students spend the first year earning a B.S.N., with the remainder for a master's of science in nursing."Why would a bachelor's-prepared applicant . . . want to get [only] a second bachelor's in nursing when they can get a professional master's or doctorate in every other healthcare field?" asks Melanie Dreher, dean of the University of Iowa College of Nursing. Iowa's professional master's takes just four semesters, including a semester-long clinical internship. There are 33 accelerated master's programs at nursing schools; 18 more are in the works. Admissions deans say successful applicants to the accelerated programs are bright, organized, and highly motivated. The intensive classroom and clinical schedule is made bearable by the ample financial aid available. Many hospitals now offer scholarships in exchange for a commitment to work at the hospital upon graduation. ●

THE BUREAU OF LABOR STATISTICS PREDICTS THE NEED FOR 1 MILLION NEW NURSES BY 2010.

Schools of Medicine

THE TOP SCHOOLS : RESEARCH

Rank/School	Overall score	Peer assessment score (5.0 highest)	Assessment score by residency directors (5.0 highest)	Selectivity rank	'02 average undergrad GPA	'02 average MCAT score	'02 acceptance rate	'02 NIH research grants (in millions)	'02 faculty/ student ratio	'02 out-of-state tuition and fees	'02 total medical school enrollment
1. Harvard University (MA)	100	4.9	4.7	9	3.78	11.1	4.6%	$957.8	8.1	$32,708	735
2. Johns Hopkins University (MD)	97	4.9	4.7	6	3.83	11.0	5.6%	$372.6	4.1	$32,083	478
Washington University in St. Louis	97	4.6	4.5	1	3.83	12.2	10.8%	$320.4	2.4	$35,780	566
4. Duke University (NC)	93	4.6	4.5	3	3.80	11.6	3.8%	$225.0	3.2	$32,906	454
University of Pennsylvania	93	4.6	4.3	4	3.77	11.5	6.4%	$431.4	3.3	$35,234	597
6. University of California–San Francisco	92	4.6	4.4	9	3.75	11.2	5.8%	$368.7	2.3	$21,577	623
7. Columbia U. College of Physicians and Surgeons (NY)	90	4.3	4.2	2	3.79	11.8	12.1%	$260.5	3.6	$35,954	624
8. Stanford University (CA)	89	4.6	4.4	13	3.74	11.0	3.7%	$198.4 *	1.8	$33,919	465
University of Michigan–Ann Arbor	89	4.4	4.4	9	3.70	11.4	8.1%	$255.7	2.5	$30,595	670
10. Yale University (CT)	87	4.4	4.1	6	3.72	11.4	6.6%	$245.4	2.8	$32,675	507
11. University of Washington	86	4.4	4.2	32	3.67	10.2	8.2%	$431.5	2.3	$27,947	773
12. Baylor College of Medicine (TX)	85	4.0	3.8	5	3.80	11.2	7.8%	$382.8	2.7	$21,143	669
Cornell University (Weill) (NY)	85	4.2	4.1	13	3.68	11.2	4.3%	$227.0	4.3	$30,045	410
14. University of California–Los Angeles (Geffen)	83	4.2	3.9	22	3.68	10.6	4.6%	$340.5	3.1	$21,305	693
Vanderbilt University (TN)	83	4.0	4.0	6	3.78	11.2	8.3%	$180.2	3.2	$30,466	408
16. University of California–San Diego	81	4.0	3.8	13	3.78	10.9	7.1%	$195.7	1.4	$21,774	513
U. of Texas Southwestern Medical Center–Dallas	81	4.2	3.9	19	3.76	10.7	18.0%	$148.8 *	1.5	$21,292	843
18. University of Pittsburgh	79	3.8	3.8	23	3.66	10.7	9.7%	$247.8	3.0	$34,728	569
19. Emory University (GA)	78	3.8	3.9	16	3.75	10.7	8.6%	$134.5	3.3	$31,497	450
Mayo Medical School (MN)	78	3.6	4.0	12	3.80	10.9	3.7%	$126.4	11.3	$21,500	176
21. Northwestern University (Feinberg) (IL)	77	3.7	3.9	16	3.67	11.0	8.1%	$141.1	2.1	$35,616	701
University of Chicago	77	4.1	4.0	35	3.62	10.3	4.4%	$126.4	2.1	$31,238	403
University of North Carolina–Chapel Hill	77	3.9	4.0	37	3.61	10.3	7.8%	$162.1	1.7	$33,536	653
24. Case Western Reserve University (OH)	75	3.8	3.7	32	3.58	10.6	9.5%	$177.5	2.8	$36,379	566
University of Alabama–Birmingham	75	3.9	3.8	46	3.67	10.0	16.5%	$195.7	1.6	$27,339	694
University of Iowa (Roy J. and Lucille A. Carver)	75	3.7	3.8	23	3.75	10.3	11.7%	$136.5	1.3	$36,976	589
27. University of Virginia	74	3.7	3.9	26	3.66	10.6	9.6%	$108.6 *	1.6	$30,567	547
28. New York University	73	3.4	3.5	16	3.70	11.0	16.2%	$128.0	2.3	$31,250	703
29. Mount Sinai School of Medicine (NY)	72	3.6	3.5	27	3.63	10.6	7.0%	$132.3	4.3	$30,700	450
University of Wisconsin–Madison	72	3.6	3.6	28	3.68	10.4	10.8%	$133.3	1.6	$32,849	592
31. University of Rochester (NY)	71	3.6	3.5	30	3.67	10.3	8.6%	$118.4	2.8	$33,057	411
32. Oregon Health and Science University	70	3.4	3.3	28	3.73	10.1	6.7%	$146.3	3.2	$33,517	396
University of Colorado Health Sciences Center	70	3.6	3.4	37	3.69	10.0	10.0%	$143.0 *	2.1	$66,073	534
Yeshiva University (Albert Einstein) (NY)	70	3.5	3.3	37	3.61	10.3	9.2%	$157.7	3.2	$34,675	722
35. Dartmouth Medical School (NH)	69	3.4	3.5	20	3.70	10.6	5.2%	$80.2 *	3.4	$32,050	289
University of Southern California	69	3.2	3.3	23	3.61	10.8	6.7%	$148.9	1.8	$36,184	655
37. Ohio State University	67	3.2	3.3	35	3.65	10.3	13.6%	$133.3	1.7	$23,231	831
University of Minnesota–Twin Cities	67	3.2	3.3	32	3.67	10.3	18.1%	$124.9	2.0	$32,651	806
39. Indiana University–Indianapolis	66	3.3	3.5	51	3.72	9.7	21.9%	$90.6 *	1.0	$35,741	1,116
40. Boston University	65	3.3	3.4	73	3.50	9.6	3.7%	$155.9	1.7	$36,980	621
University of Maryland	65	3.2	3.3	43	3.67	10.0	11.1%	$108.5 *	1.7	$28,764	582
Wake Forest University (NC)	65	3.2	3.4	51	3.60	10.0	5.0%	$95.9 *	1.8	$30,529	431
43. Brown University (RI)	64	3.1	3.4	51	3.60	10.0	8.2%	$86.4	1.9	$32,524	323
Tufts University (MA)	64	3.3	3.5	68	3.48	9.9	9.3%	$83.3	1.8	$40,104	706
University of Florida	64	3.1	3.2	30	3.68	10.3	8.8%	$71.8 *	2.2	$36,524	450
University of Utah	64	3.2	3.5	48	3.66	9.9	12.6%	$72.1	2.1	$23,158	416
47. Georgetown University (DC)	63	3.0	3.4	37	3.63	10.2	5.4%	$64.2	1.0	$31,817	709
University of Cincinnati	63	3.0	3.1	54	3.61	10.0	18.5%	$145.8	1.8	$30,792	623
49. Jefferson Medical College (PA)	61	2.9	3.1	48	3.51	10.4	6.6%	$76.3	2.4	$31,958	908
Medical College of Wisconsin	61	2.9	3.1	43	3.70	9.9	12.0%	$69.4	1.2	$30,288	805
University of Massachusetts–Worcester	61	2.8	3.0	37	3.60	10.6	28.2%	$88.1 *	1.7	N/A	416

N/A: The school does not accept out-of-state students. *means that for fiscal 2002 the school reported only grants NIH made to the medical school. No grants to affiliated hospitals were reported.

Sources: *U.S. News* and the schools. Assessment data collected by Synova

More at **www.usnews.com**

Rank/School	Overall score	Peer assessment score (5.0 highest)	Assessment score by residency directors (5.0 highest)	Selectivity rank	'02 average undergrad GPA	'02 average MCAT score	'02 acceptance rate	% '00-'02 graduates entering primary care	'02 faculty/ student ratio	'02 out-of-state tuition and fees	'02 total medical school enrollment
1. University of Washington	100	4.2	4.4	32	3.67	10.2	8.2%	50.0%	2.3	$27,947	773
2. Oregon Health and Science University	86	3.6	4.0	28	3.73	10.1	6.7%	54.0%	3.2	$33,517	396
3. University of California–San Francisco	82	3.5	4.0	9	3.75	11.2	5.8%	47.3%	2.3	$21,577	623
4. Mich. State U. Coll. of Osteopathic Medicine	78	3.0	3.5	108	3.46	8.2	12.0%	84.0%	0.3	$40,550	529
5. University of Minnesota–Duluth	76	3.1	3.6	73	3.55	9.5	13.8%	70.0%	0.4	$48,150	109
6. University of California–San Diego	75	2.9	3.4	13	3.78	10.9	7.1%	66.0%	1.4	$21,774	513
University of New Mexico	75	3.5	3.6	93	3.50	9.0	12.4%	57.0%	2.0	$28,844	303
University of Wisconsin–Madison	75	3.4	3.7	28	3.68	10.4	10.8%	51.0%	1.6	$32,849	592
9. University of Iowa (Roy J. and Lucille A. Carver)	73	3.5	3.7	23	3.75	10.3	11.7%	45.1%	1.3	$36,976	589
University of Minnesota–Twin Cities	73	3.2	3.6	32	3.67	10.3	18.1%	55.1%	2.0	$32,651	806
University of Rochester (NY)	73	3.4	3.7	30	3.67	10.3	8.6%	48.3%	2.8	$33,057	411
2. University of Colorado Health Sciences Center	72	3.4	3.8	37	3.69	10.0	10.0%	46.0%	2.1	$66,073	534
University of Massachusetts–Worcester	72	3.1	3.3	37	3.60	10.6	28.2%	62.0%	1.7	N/A	416
University of Missouri–Columbia	72	3.2	3.4	54	3.71	9.7	21.0%	60.6%	0.9	$34,754	374
5. University of North Carolina–Chapel Hill	71	3.5	3.7	37	3.61	10.3	7.8%	44.0%	1.7	$33,536	653
6. University of California–Los Angeles (Geffen)	69	3.1	3.5	22	3.68	10.6	4.6%	53.2%	3.1	$21,305	693
7. East Tennessee State Univ. (J.H. Quillen)	68	3.0	3.1	64	3.65	9.3	8.9%	66.7%	1.0	$29,933	234
Harvard University (MA)	68	3.3	3.2	9	3.78	11.1	4.6%	47.0%	8.1	$32,708	735
University of California–Davis	68	3.1	3.6	48	3.52	10.4	6.0%	53.9%	1.4	$21,641	401
0. Michigan State University	67	3.4	3.6	90	3.51	9.2	8.7%	50.0%	0.7	$40,550	447
U. of N. Tex. Hlth. Sci. Ctr. (Tex. Col. of Osteo. Med.)	67	2.7	2.9	93	3.54	8.8	14.0%	83.2%	0.4	$20,902	479
2. University of Alabama–Birmingham	66	3.3	3.6	46	3.67	10.0	16.5%	45.0%	1.6	$27,339	694
University of Maryland	66	3.0	3.5	43	3.67	10.0	11.1%	55.0%	1.7	$28,764	582
University of Michigan–Ann Arbor	66	3.2	3.6	9	3.70	11.4	8.1%	41.9%	2.5	$30,595	670
University of Nebraska College of Medicine	66	2.9	3.4	57	3.70	9.6	19.6%	60.6%	1.0	$35,602	483
6. Baylor College of Medicine (TX)	65	3.0	3.6	5	3.80	11.2	7.8%	44.5%	2.7	$21,143	669
Dartmouth Medical School (NH)	65	3.4	3.4	20	3.70	10.6	5.2%	40.0%	3.4	$32,050	289
University of Virginia	65	3.2	3.5	26	3.66	10.6	9.6%	46.0%	1.4	$30,567	547
9. Wake Forest University (NC)	64	3.0	3.4	51	3.60	10.0	5.0%	54.0%	1.8	$30,529	431
0. Brown University (RI)	62	3.0	3.4	51	3.60	10.0	8.2%	52.3%	1.9	$32,524	323
Okla. State U. Coll. of Osteopathic Medicine	62	2.5	2.6	91	3.58	8.8	13.4%	90.0%	0.2	$30,920	348
Stony Brook University	62	2.8	3.0	43	3.60	10.3	10.5%	63.8%	1.1	$28,525	434
University of Pittsburgh	62	3.1	3.3	23	3.66	10.7	9.7%	47.0%	3.0	$34,728	569
U. of Texas Southwestern Medical Center–Dallas	62	3.1	3.6	19	3.76	10.7	18.0%	42.0%	1.5	$21,292	843
5. Duke University (NC)	61	3.1	3.5	3	3.80	11.6	3.8%	36.2%	3.2	$32,906	454
Emory University (GA)	61	3.0	3.2	16	3.75	10.7	8.6%	48.3%	3.3	$31,497	450
Johns Hopkins University (MD)	61	3.0	3.2	6	3.83	11.0	5.6%	45.7%	4.1	$32,083	478
University of Connecticut	61	3.0	3.2	57	3.60	9.9	9.4%	54.0%	1.3	$28,180	311
Washington University in St. Louis	61	3.1	3.1	1	3.83	12.2	10.8%	40.6%	2.4	$35,780	566
0. Indiana University–Indianapolis	60	3.2	3.5	51	3.72	9.7	21.9%	42.9%	1.0	$35,741	1,116
University of Utah	60	3.1	3.6	48	3.66	9.9	12.6%	42.7%	2.1	$23,158	416
2. Case Western Reserve University (OH)	59	3.1	3.4	32	3.58	10.6	9.5%	43.0%	2.8	$36,379	566
Southern Illinois University–Springfield	59	3.2	3.2	97	3.47	9.0	17.1%	52.5%	1.1	$45,403	287
University of Vermont	59	3.1	3.5	78	3.50	9.5	4.2%	47.3%	1.0	$37,801	396
Yeshiva University (Albert Einstein) (NY)	59	2.8	3.2	37	3.61	10.3	9.2%	55.0%	3.2	$34,675	722
6. East Carolina University (Brody) (NC)	58	3.1	3.4	104	3.40	8.7	9.8%	52.7%	1.1	$28,985	303
Medical College of Wisconsin	58	3.0	3.5	43	3.70	9.9	12.0%	44.0%	1.2	$30,288	805
8. Medical College of Georgia	57	2.8	3.2	64	3.61	9.6	19.2%	57.0%	0.6	$34,630	731
University of Pennsylvania	57	3.1	3.4	4	3.77	11.5	6.4%	34.0%	3.3	$35,234	597
University of Southern California	57	2.7	3.2	23	3.61	10.8	6.7%	53.0%	1.8	$36,184	655

'A: The school does not accept out-of-state students.

Sources: *U.S. News* and the schools. Peer assessment data collected by Synovate

Specialties

MEDICAL SCHOOL DEANS AND SENIOR FACULTY SELECT THE BEST PROGRAMS

WOMEN'S HEALTH

1. Harvard University (MA)
2. University of Pennsylvania
3. Univ. of Calif.–San Francisco
4. Johns Hopkins Univ. (MD)
5. Duke University (NC)
   University of Washington
7. University of Pittsburgh
8. University of N.C.–Chapel Hill
9. Univ. of Michigan–Ann Arbor
   U. of Texas Southwestern
   Medical Center–Dallas
   Washington Univ. in St. Louis

GERIATRICS

1. Johns Hopkins Univ. (MD)
2. U. of Calif.–Los Angeles (Geffen)
3. Mount Sinai School
   of Medicine (NY)
4. Duke University (NC)
5. Harvard University (MA)
6. University of Washington
7. Univ. of Michigan–Ann Arbor
   Yale University (CT)
9. University of Arkansas
   for Medical Sciences
10. UMDNJ–School of
    Osteopathic Medicine

INTERNAL MEDICINE

1. Harvard University (MA)
2. Johns Hopkins Univ. (MD)
3. Univ. of Calif.–San Francisco
4. Washington Univ. in St. Louis
5. University of Pennsylvania
6. University of Washington
7. Duke University (NC)
8. Univ. of Michigan–Ann Arbor
9. U. of Texas Southwestern
   Medical Center–Dallas
10. Yale University (CT)

AIDS

1. Univ. of Calif.–San Francisco
2. Johns Hopkins Univ. (MD)
3. Harvard University (MA)
4. University of Alabama–
   Birmingham
5. University of Washington
6. Columbia U. College of
   Physicians and Surgeons (NY)
7. Duke University (NC)
8. University of California–
   Los Angeles (Geffen)
   Univ. of Calif.–San Diego
10. University of Pennsylvania

DRUG/ALCOHOL ABUSE

1. Johns Hopkins Univ. (MD)
2. Harvard University (MA)
3. Columbia U. College of
   Physicians and Surgeons (NY)
4. University of Pennsylvania
   Yale University (CT)
6. Univ. of Calif.–San Francisco
7. New York University
   Univ. of Calif.–San Diego
9. Washington Univ. in St. Louis
10. Duke University (NC)
    U. of Calif.–Los Angeles (Geffen)
    U. of Colo. Hlth. Sci. Center
    University of Connecticut

RURAL MEDICINE

1. University of Washington
2. University of New Mexico
3. East Tenn. State U. (J.H. Quillen)
4. University of
   Iowa (Roy J. & Lucille A. Carver)
5. East Carolina U. (Brody) (NC)
   Univ. of Minnesota–Duluth
   U. of N.C.–Chapel Hill
8. University of North Dakota
9. University of Kentucky
10. Kirksville College of
    Osteopathic Medicine (MO)
    University of Nebraska
    College of Medicine
    West Virginia School
    of Osteopathic Medicine

PEDIATRICS

1. Harvard University (MA)
   University of Pennsylvania
3. Johns Hopkins Univ. (MD)
4. University of Cincinnati
5. U. of Calif.–San Francisco
6. University of Washington
   Washington Univ. in St. Louis
8. U. of Calif.–Los Angeles (Geffen)
9. Baylor Coll. of Medicine (TX)
10. U. of Colo. Hlth. Sci. Center

FAMILY MEDICINE

1. University of Washington
2. Univ. of Missouri–Columbia
3. Oregon Hlth. & Sci. Univ.
4. Univ. of Michigan–Ann Arbor
5. University of New Mexico
6. Case Western Reserve U. (OH)
   U. of N.C.–Chapel Hill
8. Duke University (NC)
   U. of Colo. Hlth. Sci. Center
   Univ. of Wisconsin–Madison

METHODOLOGY

The 125 medical schools fully accredited by the Liaison Committee on Medical Education plus the 19 schools of osteopathic medicine fully accredited by the American Osteopathic Association were surveyed for the ranking of research medical schools; 117 schools provided the data needed to calculate the research rankings based on the indicators used in the research model. The same medical and osteopathic schools were surveyed for the primary-care ranking; 117 schools provided the data needed to calculate the primary-care ranking. Both rankings are based on a weighted average of seven indicators, six of them common to both models. The research model factors in research activity; the primary-care model adds a measure of the proportion of graduates entering primary-care specialties.

Quality assessment (weighted by .40): Peer assessment surveys were conducted in the fall of 2002, asking medical and osteopathic school deans, deans of academic affairs, and heads of internal medicine or the directors of admissions to rate program quality on a scale of "marginal" (1) to "outstanding" (5). Survey populations were asked to separately rate program quality for both research and primary-care programs on a single survey instrument. The response rate was 53 percent. A research school's average score is weighted .20; the average score in the primary-care model is weighted .25. Residency program directors were also asked to rate programs using the same 5-point scale. The residency program directors surveyed were a geographically balanced selection from the American Medical Association's *Graduate Medical Education Library 2002–2003* and a list of primary-care residency program directors from the American Osteopathic Association. The response rate for those sent the research survey was 32 percent. The response rate for

those sent the primary-care survey was 25 percent. Residency directors' opinions are weighted .20 in the research model and .15 in primary care.

Research activity (.30 in research model only): measured as the total dollar amount of National Institutes of Health research grants awarded to the medical school and its affiliated hospitals, averaged for 2001 and 2002. An asterisk indicates schools that reported grants only to their medical school.

Primary-care rate (.30 in primary-care model only): the percentage of M.D.'s entering primary-care residencies in the fields of family practice, pediatrics, and internal medicine, averaged over 2000, 2001, and 2002.

Student selectivity (.20 in research model, .15 in primary-care model): three components, which describe the class entering in fall 2002: mean composite Medical College Admission Test score (65 percent), mean undergraduate grade-point average (30 percent), and proportion of applicants accepted (5 percent).

Faculty resources (.10 in research model, .15 in primary-care model): The ratio of full-time science and clinical faculty to full-time students in 2002.

Overall rank: The research-activity indicator had significant outliers; to avoid distortion, it was transformed using a logarithmic function. Indicators were standardized about their means, and standardized scores were weighted, totaled, and rescaled so that the top school received 100; other schools received their percentage of the top score.

Specialty rankings: The rankings are based solely on ratings by deans and senior faculty at peer schools.

Medical school deans and senior faculty identified up to 10 schools offering the best programs in each specialty area. The 10 receiving the highest number of nominations appear here.

More at **www.usnews.com**

Health Disciplines

THESE SCHOOLS GET HIGH MARKS FROM PROGRAM DIRECTORS AND FACULTY

AUDIOLOGY

MASTER'S/DOCTORATE Ranked in 2000

Rank/School	Average assessment score (5=highest)
1. University of Iowa	4.5
2. Northwestern University (IL)	4.4
Vanderbilt University (TN)	4.4
4. University of Washington	4.2
5. University of Wisconsin–Madison	4.0
6. University of Arizona	3.9
Washington Univ. in St. Louis (Central Inst. for the Deaf)	3.9
8. University of Minnesota–Twin Cities	3.8
9. Indiana University	3.7
University of Kansas	3.7
University of Memphis	3.7
12. University of Texas–Dallas	3.6
13. Louisiana State Univ. Med. Center–New Orleans	3.5
Ohio State University	3.5
Purdue University–West Lafayette (IN)	3.5
University at Buffalo	3.5
University of Texas–Austin	3.5
18. Arizona State University–Main Campus	3.4
Gallaudet University (DC)	3.4
University of Florida	3.4
University of Illinois–Urbana-Champaign	3.4
University of North Carolina–Chapel Hill	3.4
23. Central Michigan University	3.3
University of Pittsburgh	3.3
25. University of Connecticut	3.2
University of Oklahoma Health Sciences Center	3.2
University of Tennessee	3.2

Note: All schools listed have master's programs; some may not have doctoral programs.

CLINICAL PSYCHOLOGY

DOCTORATE Ranked in 2001

Rank/School	Average assessment score (5=highest)
1. University of California–Los Angeles	4.5
2. Indiana University–Bloomington	4.3
University of Washington	4.3
University of Wisconsin–Madison	4.3
5. University of California–Berkeley	4.1
University of Minnesota–Twin Cities	4.1
University of North Carolina–Chapel Hill	4.1
Yale University (CT)	4.1
9. SUNY–Stony Brook	4.0
University of Illinois–Urbana-Champaign	4.0
University of Virginia (Dept. of Psychology)	4.0
12. Duke University (NC)	3.9
University of Iowa	3.9
14. Penn State University–University Park	3.8
University of Oregon	3.8
University of Pennsylvania	3.8
University of Southern California	3.8
Vanderbilt University (Dept. of Psychology) (TN)	3.8
19. Northwestern University (IL)	3.7

Rank/School	Average assessment score (5=highest)
University of Florida	3.7
University of Kansas	3.7
University of Michigan–Ann Arbor	3.7
University of Pittsburgh	3.7
Washington University in St. Louis	3.7
25. Emory University (GA)	3.6
University of Miami (FL)	3.6
University of Missouri–Columbia	3.6
28. Rutgers State U.–New Brunswick (Dept. of Psych.) (NJ)	3.5
University of Colorado–Boulder	3.5
University of Georgia	3.5
University of Massachusetts–Amherst	3.5
University of Texas–Austin	3.5
Vanderbilt University (Peabody) (TN)	3.5
34. Purdue University–West Lafayette (IN)	3.4
University of Arizona	3.4
36. Arizona State University	3.3
Boston University	3.3
Florida State University	3.3
Ohio State University	3.3
Rutgers State U.–New Brunswick (Dept. of Clinical Psych.) (NJ)	3.3
SUNY–Albany	3.3
Temple University (PA)	3.3
University of Illinois–Chicago	3.3
University of Maryland–College Park	3.3
University of Rochester (NY)	3.3
University of South Florida	3.3
University of Vermont	3.3
Virginia Tech	3.3
West Virginia University	3.3

COMMUNITY HEALTH

MASTER'S/DOCTORATE Ranked in 2003

Rank/School	Average assessment score (5=highest)
1. Tufts University School of Medicine (MA)	3.8
2. Medical College of Wisconsin	3.7
Northwestern University (IL)	3.7
Oregon St. U./Portland St. U./Ore. Health and Sci. U.	3.7
University of Rochester (NY)	3.7
6. Brown University (RI)	3.6
Uniformed Services Univ. of the Health Sciences (MD)	3.6
University of Colorado	3.6
University of Kansas	3.6
University of Utah	3.6
University of Wisconsin–La Crosse	3.6

Note: All schools listed have master's programs; some may not have doctoral programs.

HEALTH SERVICES ADMINISTRATION

MASTER'S Ranked in 2003

Rank/School	Average assessment score (5=highest)
1. University of Michigan–Ann Arbor	4.4
2. University of North Carolina–Chapel Hill	4.3
3. University of Pennsylvania (Wharton)	4.2

Rank/School	Average assessment score (5=highest)
4. Northwestern University (Kellogg) (IL)	4.1
5. University of Minnesota–Twin Cities (Carlson)	3.9
University of Washington	3.9
7. University of California–Berkeley (Haas)	3.7
U. of California–Berkeley (School of Public Health)	3.7
9. University of Alabama–Birmingham	3.6
10. Johns Hopkins University (MD)	3.4
University of California–Los Angeles	3.4
University of Iowa	3.4
13. Duke University (Fuqua) (NC)	3.2
Ohio State University	3.2

NURSING

MASTER'S Ranked in 2003

Rank/School	Average assessment score (5=highest)
1. University of Washington	4.7
2. University of California–San Francisco	4.6
3. University of Michigan–Ann Arbor	4.5
University of Pennsylvania	4.5
5. U. of North Carolina–Chapel Hill (Sch. of Nursing)	4.4
6. Johns Hopkins University (MD)	4.3
Oregon Health Sciences University	4.3
8. University of Illinois–Chicago	4.2
University of Iowa	4.2
10. University of California–Los Angeles	4.1
University of Maryland–Baltimore	4.1
University of Pittsburgh–Main Campus	4.1
U. of North Carolina–Chapel Hill (Sch. of Public Health)	4.1
Yale University (CT)	4.1
15. Case Western Reserve University (OH)	4.0
Indiana Univ.–Purdue Univ.–Indianapolis	4.0
University of Arizona	4.0
University of Colorado Health Sciences Center	4.0
19. Boston College	3.9
Columbia University (NY)	3.9
Ohio State University	3.9
Rush University (IL)	3.9
University of Alabama–Birmingham	3.9
University of Texas–Austin	3.9
University of Wisconsin–Madison	3.9
26. Emory University (GA)	3.8
New York University	3.8
University of Virginia	3.8
29. Duke University (NC)	3.7
Georgetown University (DC)	3.7
University of Kansas	3.7
University of Kentucky	3.7
University of Minnesota–Twin Cities	3.7
University of Rochester (NY)	3.7
University of Wisconsin–Milwaukee	3.7
Univ. of Texas Health Science Center–Houston	3.7
Vanderbilt University (TN)	3.7
Wayne State University (MI)	3.7
39. Arizona State University	3.6
Catholic University of America (DC)	3.6
Loyola University Chicago	3.6
University of Arkansas for Medical Sciences	3.6
University of Florida	3.6
University of Nebraska Medical Center	3.6
University of San Diego	3.6
University of Utah	3.6

Rank/School	Average assessment score (5=highest)
Univ. of Texas Health Science Center–San Antonio	3.6
48. George Mason University (VA)	3.5
Michigan State University	3.5
University of Cincinnati	3.5
University of San Francisco	3.5
Virginia Commonwealth University	3.5
53. Marquette University (WI)	3.4
Medical University of South Carolina	3.4
St. Louis University	3.4
Texas Woman's University	3.4
University of Missouri–Columbia	3.4
58. Baylor University (TX)	3.3
Brigham Young University (UT)	3.3
California State University–Los Angeles	3.3
Clemson University (SC)	3.3
CUNY–Hunter College	3.3
Georgia Southern University	3.3
Medical College of Georgia	3.3
Penn State Univ.–University Park	3.3
University of Connecticut	3.3
University of Louisville (KY)	3.3
University of Massachusetts–Amherst	3.3
University of Massachusetts–Boston	3.3
University of North Carolina–Greensboro	3.3
University of Southern California	3.3
Univ. of South Carolina–Columbia	3.3
Univ. of Texas Medical Branch–Galveston	3.3
Villanova University (PA)	3.3
75. Howard University (DC)	3.2
Indiana State University	3.2
Loma Linda University (CA)	3.2
Loyola University New Orleans	3.2
Medical College of Ohio	3.2
Northeastern University (MA)	3.2
Rutgers State University–Newark (NJ)	3.2
San Diego State University	3.2
San Francisco State University	3.2
Texas Tech University Health Science Center	3.2
University of Colorado–Colorado Springs	3.2
University of Indianapolis	3.2
University of Massachusetts–Worcester	3.2
University of North Carolina–Charlotte	3.2
University of Oklahoma Health Science Center	3.2
University of Portland (OR)	3.2
University of Tennessee–Knoxville	3.2
University of Tennessee–Memphis	3.2
West Virginia University	3.2

NURSING SPECIALTIES

NURSE PRACTITIONER:
FAMILY
1. U. of Calif.–San Francisco
2. University of Washington
3. University of Pennsylvania
4. Yale University (CT)
5. Oregon Health Sciences U.
6. University of Colorado Health Sciences Center
7. Univ. of North Carolina–Chapel Hill (Sch. of Nursing)
8. Columbia University (NY)

9. Univ. of Illinois–Chicago
   U. of Michigan–Ann Arbor

ADULT
1. University of Pennsylvania
2. University of Washington
3. U. of Calif.–San Francisco
4. Oregon Health Sciences U.
5. Columbia University (NY)
   University of Maryland–Baltimore
   Yale University (CT)

More at **www.usnews.com**

8. U. of Michigan–Ann Arbor
9. Univ. of North Carolina–Chapel Hill (Sch. of Nursing)
10. University of Pittsburgh–Main Campus

PEDIATRIC

1. University of Colorado Health Sciences Center
2. University of Pennsylvania
3. University of Washington
4. U. of Calif.–San Francisco
   Yale University (CT)
6. Oregon Health Sciences U.
7. University of Rochester (NY)
8. Rush University (IL)
9. University of Virginia
10. Catholic U. of America (DC)

GERONTOLOGICAL/GERIATRIC

1. University of Pennsylvania
2. University of Iowa
3. New York University
   Oregon Health Sciences U.
5. U. of Calif.–San Francisco
6. University of Washington
7. Case Western Reserve University (OH)
8. Duke University (NC)
   U. of Michigan–Ann Arbor
10. Rush University (IL)
    University of Colorado Health Sciences Center

CLINICAL NURSE SPECIALIST: ADULT/MEDICAL-SURGICAL

1. University of Washington
2. U. of Calif.–San Francisco
3. University of Pennsylvania
4. Indiana Univ.–Purdue Univ.–Indianapolis
5. Rush University (IL)
6. Univ. of Illinois–Chicago
   University of Virginia
8. University of Maryland–Baltimore
   U. of Michigan–Ann Arbor
10. Case Western Reserve University (OH)
    Oregon Health Sciences U.

COMMUNITY/PUBLIC HEALTH

1. University of Washington
2. Johns Hopkins Univ. (MD)
3. U. of North Carolina–Chapel Hill (Sch. of Public Health)
4. U. of Michigan–Ann Arbor
5. Univ. of Illinois–Chicago
6. U. of Minnesota–Twin Cities
7. University of Colorado Health Sciences Center
8. University of Maryland–Baltimore
9. University of California–San Francisco
10. Oregon Health Sciences U.

PSYCHIATRIC/ MENTAL HEALTH

1. University of Washington
2. University of Pennsylvania
3. U. of Calif.–San Francisco
4. Yale University (CT)
5. Indiana Univ.–Purdue Univ.–Indianapolis
   University of Virginia
7. U. of Michigan–Ann Arbor
   Univ. of North Carolina–Chapel Hill (Sch. of Nursing)
9. Oregon Health Sciences U.
   Rutgers State U.–Newark (NJ)
   Univ. of Illinois–Chicago
   University of Pittsburgh–Main Campus

NURSING SERVICE ADMINISTRATION:

1. University of Iowa
2. University of Pennsylvania
3. University of Washington
   Univ. of North Carolina–Chapel Hill (Sch. of Nursing)
5. U. of Michigan–Ann Arbor
6. University of Colorado Health Sciences Center
7. Indiana Univ.–Purdue Univ.–Indianapolis
   Univ. of Illinois–Chicago
   University of Maryland–Baltimore
10. Johns Hopkins Univ. (MD)
    U. of California–Los Angeles

Rank/School	Average assessment score (5=highest)
6. Duke University (NC)	3.5
Oakland University–Beaumont (MI)	3.5
University of Pittsburgh	3.5
University of Texas Health Science Center–Houston	3.5
10. Baylor College of Medicine (TX)	3.4
Cleveland Clinic Foundation/Case Western Reserve Univ.	3.4
Georgetown University (DC)	3.4
Kaiser Permanente Sch. of Anesthesia/Cal. St. U.–Fullerton	3.4
Samuel Merritt College (CA)	3.4
University at Buffalo	3.4
University of Cincinnati	3.4
Wake Forest Univ./Univ. of North Carolina–Greensboro	3.4

NURSING-MIDWIFERY

MASTER'S/DOCTORATE Ranked in 2003

Rank/School	Average assessment score (5=highest)
1. Oregon Health and Science University	4.3
University of Pennsylvania	4.3
3. University of Illinois–Chicago	4.2
University of Michigan–Ann Arbor	4.2
University of Minnesota–Twin Cities	4.2
University of New Mexico	4.2
7. Emory University (GA)	4.0
University of Washington	4.0
U. of Calif.–San Francisco/San Fran. General Hospital	4.0
10. Boston University	3.9
University of Colorado–Denver	3.9
Yale University (CT)	3.9

Note: All schools listed have master's programs; some may not have doctoral programs.

OCCUPATIONAL THERAPY

MASTER'S/DOCTORATE Ranked in 2001

Rank/School	Average assessment score (5=highest)
1. University of Southern California	4.7
2. Boston U., Sargent College/Rehab. Sci.	4.6
3. University of Illinois–Chicago	4.3
Washington University in St. Louis	4.3
5. Tufts U.–Boston School/Occupational Therapy	4.0
University of North Carolina–Chapel Hill	4.0
7. New York University	3.9
8. Texas Woman's University	3.8
University of Kansas Medical Center	3.8
10. Colorado State University	3.7
Columbia University (NY)	3.7
Medical College of Ohio	3.7
University of Washington	3.7
14. Thomas Jefferson University (PA)	3.6
15. University of Puget Sound (WA)	3.5
University of Wisconsin–Milwaukee	3.5

Note: All schools listed have master's programs; some may not have doctoral programs.

NURSING-ANESTHESIA

MASTER'S Ranked in 2003

Rank/School	Average assessment score (5=highest)
1. Virginia Commonwealth University	4.0
2. U.S. Army Graduate Program in Anesthesia Nursing (TX)	3.8
3. Navy Nurse Corps (MD)	3.7
Rush University (IL)	3.7
5. Albany Medical College (NY)	3.6

PHYSICAL THERAPY

MASTER'S/DOCTORATE Ranked in 2000

Rank/School	Average assessment score (5=highest)
1. Washington University in St. Louis	4.3
2. University of Southern California	3.9
3. Duke University (NC)	3.8
Emory University (GA)	3.8
University of Iowa	3.8

Rank/School	Average assessment score (5=highest)
University of Miami (FL)	3.8
University of North Carolina–Chapel Hill	3.8
University of Pittsburgh	3.8
9. Arcadia College (PA)	3.7
MGH Institute of Health Professions (MA)	3.7
Northwestern University (IL)	3.7
University of Delaware	3.7
13. Texas Woman's University	3.6
U.S. Army-Baylor University (TX)	3.6
15. Boston University	3.5
Temple University (PA)	3.5
U. of California–San Francisco/San Francisco State U.	3.5
Virginia Commonwealth University	3.5
19. New York University	3.4
University of Alabama–Birmingham	3.4
21. Columbia University (NY)	3.3
Creighton University (NE)	3.3
23. Marquette University (WI)	3.2
Northern Arizona University	3.2
Simmons College (MA)	3.2
University of Indianapolis (IN)	3.2
University of Wisconsin–La Crosse	3.2
28. Drexel University (PA)	3.1
Old Dominion University (VA)	3.1
Thomas Jefferson University (PA)	3.1
University of Kansas Medical Center	3.1
University of Minnesota–Twin Cities	3.1

Note: All schools listed have master's programs; some may not have doctoral programs.

PHYSICIAN ASSISTANT

MASTER'S Ranked in 2003

Rank/School	Average assessment score (5=highest)
1. Duke University (NC)	4.4
2. University of Iowa	4.1
3. Emory University (GA)	4.0
George Washington University (DC)	4.0
5. University of Utah	3.9
6. University of Colorado Health Sciences Center	3.8
7. Baylor College of Medicine (TX)	3.7
University of Texas Medical Branch–Galveston	3.7
University of Texas Southwestern Medical Center–Dallas	3.7
10. Oregon Health Sciences University	3.6
St. Francis University (PA)	3.6
Yale University (CT)	3.6
13. Wake Forest University (NC)	3.5
14. Quinnipiac University (CT)	3.4
University of Nebraska Medical Center	3.4
University of Texas Health Science Center–San Antonio	3.4
17. Finch U. of Health Sci.-Chicago Medical School	3.3
Northeastern University (MA)	3.3
St. Louis University	3.3
University of Florida	3.3
University of Oklahoma	3.3

REHABILITATION COUNSELING

MASTER'S/DOCTORATE Ranked in 2003

Rank/School	Average assessment score (5=highest)
1. Michigan State University	4.3
2. University of Wisconsin–Madison	4.2
3. Southern Illinois University–Carbondale	4.0

Rank/School	Average assessment score (5=highest)
University of Iowa	4.0
5. Boston University	3.8
George Washington University (DC)	3.8
Illinois Institute of Technology	3.8
Penn State University–University Park	3.8
9. University of Florida	3.6
University of Maryland–College Park	3.6
University of Wisconsin–Stout	3.6
12. San Diego State University	3.5
University of Arizona	3.5
14. Louisiana State Univ. Health Sci. Center–New Orleans	3.4
15. East Carolina University (NC)	3.3
Syracuse University (NY)	3.3
University of Arkansas–Fayetteville	3.3
University of Texas–Austin	3.3
Utah State University	3.3

Note: All schools listed have master's programs; some may not have doctoral programs.

PUBLIC HEALTH

MASTER'S/DOCTORATE Ranked in 2003

Rank/School	Average assessment score (5=highest)
1. Johns Hopkins University (MD)	4.9
2. Harvard University (MA)	4.7
University of North Carolina–Chapel Hill	4.7
4. University of Washington	4.5
5. University of Michigan–Ann Arbor	4.2
6. Columbia University (NY)	3.9
7. University of California–Berkeley	3.7
University of California–Los Angeles	3.7
9. Emory University (GA)	3.6
10. University of Minnesota–Twin Cities	3.5

Note: All schools listed have master's programs; some may not have doctoral programs.

SOCIAL WORK

MASTER'S Ranked in 2000

Rank/School	Average assessment score (5=highest)
1. University of Michigan	4.4
2. Washington University in St. Louis	4.3
3. Columbia University (NY)	4.2
University of California–Berkeley	4.2
University of Washington	4.2
6. University of Chicago	4.1
7. University of North Carolina–Chapel Hill	4.0
8. Case Western Reserve University (OH)	3.8
University of Southern California	3.8
10. University of Texas–Austin	3.7
11. University of Pennsylvania	3.6
University of Wisconsin–Madison	3.6
13. Fordham University (NY)	3.5
University of California–Los Angeles	3.5
University of Pittsburgh	3.5
Virginia Commonwealth University	3.5
17. CUNY-Hunter College	3.4
Smith College (MA)	3.4
19. Boston College	3.3
Boston University	3.3
Bryn Mawr College (PA)	3.3
SUNY-Albany	3.3
University of Kansas	3.3

Rank/School	Average assessment score (5=highest)
University of Minnesota–Twin Cities	3.3
25. Florida State University	3.2
New York University	3.2
University of Illinois–Urbana-Champaign	3.2
University of Maryland–Baltimore	3.2
29. University of Hawaii–Manoa	3.1
University of Illinois–Chicago	3.1
University of South Carolina	3.1
University of Tennessee–Knoxville	3.1

SPEECH-LANGUAGE PATHOLOGY

MASTER'S Ranked in 2000

Rank/School	Average assessment score (5=highest)
1. University of Iowa	4.7
2. University of Washington	4.6
University of Wisconsin–Madison	4.6
4. Northwestern University (IL)	4.5
Purdue University–West Lafayette (IN)	4.5
6. University of Arizona	4.4
7. University of Kansas	4.2
8. Indiana University	4.1
Vanderbilt University (TN)	4.1
10. University of Illinois–Urbana-Champaign	4.0
University of Memphis	4.0
12. University of North Carolina–Chapel Hill	3.9
University of Texas–Austin	3.9
14. University of Minnesota–Twin Cities	3.8
15. Arizona State University–Main Campus	3.7
Ohio State University	3.7
University of Florida	3.7
18. Syracuse University (NY)	3.6
University of Nebraska–Lincoln	3.6
University of Pittsburgh–Main Campus	3.6
21. Boston University	3.5
Emerson College (MA)	3.5
Penn State University–University Park	3.5
University of Colorado–Boulder	3.5
University of Connecticut	3.5
26. Gallaudet University (DC)	3.4
Teachers College, Columbia University (NY)	3.4
University at Buffalo	3.4
University of Texas–Dallas	3.4
30. George Washington University (DC)	3.3
James Madison University (VA)	3.3
Louisiana State University Medical Center	3.3
Rush U. of Rush-Presby.-St. Luke's Med. Ctr. (IL)	3.3
San Diego State University	3.3
Temple University (PA)	3.3
University of Cincinnati	3.3
University of Maryland–College Park	3.3
University of Massachusetts–Amherst	3.3
University of Oklahoma Health Sci. Center	3.3
Western Michigan University	3.3
41. Case Western Reserve University (OH)	3.2
Michigan State University	3.2
Northern Illinois University	3.2
University of Georgia	3.2
Wichita State University (KS)	3.2
46. Baylor University (TX)	3.1
Florida State University	3.1
Kent State University (OH)	3.1
Ohio University	3.1
University of Virginia	3.1

VETERINARY

DOCTOR OF VETERINARY MEDICINE Ranked in 2003

Rank/School	Average assessment score (5=highest)
1. Cornell University (NY)	4.4
2. Colorado State University	4.2
3. University of Pennsylvania	4.1
4. North Carolina State University	3.9
5. Texas A&M University–College Station	3.8
6. Michigan State University	3.7
Ohio State University	3.7
8. University of Wisconsin–Madison	3.6
9. University of Florida	3.3
University of Georgia	3.3
11. University of Minnesota–Twin Cities	3.2

METHODOLOGY

The health rankings are based solely on the results of peer assessment surveys sent to deans, other administrators, and/or faculty at accredited degree programs or schools in each discipline. All schools surveyed in a discipline were sent the same number of surveys. Respondents rated the academic quality of programs on a 5-point scale: outstanding (5 points); strong (4); good (3); adequate (2); or marginal (1), based on their assessment of the curriculum, faculty, and graduates. They were instructed to select "don't know" if they did not have enough knowledge to rate a program. Scores for each school were determined by computing a trimmed mean of the ratings of all respondents who rated that school; scores were then sorted in descending order. Only fully accredited programs in good standing during the survey period are ranked.

In the fall of 2002, surveys were conducted for 2003 rankings of community health programs and schools of public health accredited by the Council on Education for Public Health (response rates: 67 percent and 68 percent, respectively); health services administration programs accredited by the Accrediting Commission on Education for Health Services Administration (61 percent); master's programs in nursing accredited by either the Commission on Collegiate Nursing or the National League for Nursing Accrediting Commission (48 percent); graduate nurse anesthesia programs accredited by the Council of Accreditation of Nurse Anesthesia Educational Programs of the American Association of Nurse

Anesthetists (54 percent); graduate nurse-midwifery programs accredited by the American College of Nurse-Midwives Division of Accreditation (71 percent); physician assistant programs accredited by the American Academy of Physician Assistants (70 percent); rehabilitation counselor education programs accredited by the Council on Rehabilitation Education (59 percent); and veterinary schools accredited by the American Veterinary Medical Association (67 percent). Nursing specialty rankings are based solely on ratings by educators at peer schools. From the list of nursing schools surveyed, nursing educators nominated up to 10 schools for excellence in each area. Those with the most votes appear here.

In the fall of 2000, surveys were conducted for 2001 rankings of doctoral programs in clinical psychology accredited by the American Psychological Association (response rate: 20 percent) and graduate programs in occupational therapy accredited by the American Occupational Therapy Association (57 percent). In fall 1999, surveys were conducted for 2000 rankings of audiology programs and speech-language-pathology programs accredited by the American Speech-Language-Hearing Association (response rates: 57 percent and 45 percent, respectively); physical therapy programs accredited by the American Physical Therapy Association (52 percent); and master of social work programs accredited by the Council on Social Work Education (53 percent). Peer assessment surveys were conducted by Synovate.

EDUCATION

Learning on the job

BY MARGARET LOFTUS

When they weren't launching spitballs or laughing at her, most of the students in Katharine Kilbourn's 10th-grade history class at South Boston High School were making a beeline for the bathroom or "bouncing off the walls," she says. In short, the rookie's first six weeks of teaching were a nightmare. Were it not for her previous experience in a year-long internship at the urban Boston Arts Academy, she says, "I never, never would have lasted."

Kilbourn called on skills she had learned as a student at Tufts University's master's of education program. In the past decade, Tufts and several other innovative schools, like Boston College's Lynch School of Education and the University of Connecticut's Neag School of Education in Hartford, have been grooming their grads for the long haul by requiring lengthy in-classroom internships. "The more they know about what they are facing that first year," says Mary Brabeck, Lynch's dean, "the more they are likely to stay."

The problem is that many of today's teachers aren't staying. Nearly half of all teachers quit within their first five years. In high-poverty schools, 20 percent of teachers leave each year. And while more and more alternative certification programs are churning out teachers to fill the much-publicized shortage—the United States needs an estimated 2.2 million teachers by 2010—a recent report by the National Commission on Teaching and America's Future says the real crisis is not a lack of newcomers but the staggering turnover rate. According to the commission, the number of teachers leaving the field in 1999–2000 exceeded the number of incoming teachers by 24 percent. In low-income areas, some students are encountering new teachers several times a year, says Tom Carroll, NCTAF's executive director. "High turnover undermines teacher quality, just as it would in any business."

The reasons behind the mass exodus are no mystery. Poor working conditions and low pay top the list. But lack of preparation is a close third, argues Richard Ingersoll, a professor of education at the University of Pennsylvania who studies teacher supply and demand. In a 2000–2001 survey, he found that first-year teachers who hadn't had practice teaching were twice as likely to quit as those who had 10 or more weeks of student teaching. What's more, research has shown that teachers don't hit their peak performance until their seventh year on the job. "Rather than trying to constantly refill positions, we need to have a system in place to encourage and keep good people," says Richard Schwab, dean of the Neag School.

While 10 to 12 weeks of student-teaching is

BRIDGET BESAW GORMAN—AURORA FOR *USN&WR*

standard—and it's not uncommon for teachers to hit the ground running with none at all—more graduate-level education programs now require a full academic year in a professional development school, or PDS. Not unlike the medical school model, where a university partners with a hospital to give its students in-the-trenches training, a PDS is a partnership between an ed school and a local public school. And like in a big-city teaching hospital, students learn in an environment that is not only diverse but where'll they encounter veterans modeling best practices.

At Tufts, for example, interns spend the school year co-teaching, observing classes, participating in group discussions, and taking courses designed to complement the PDS curriculum. While teaching, say, math, an intern will study children's development in math. Although Claremont Graduate University in Claremont, Calif., does not work with a PDS, the model is similar: Each student teaches in a public urban school for one school year and has a full-time mentor. Dur-

BECKY GOLANSKI, A UNIVERSITY OF CONNECTICUT EDUCATION STUDENT, INTERNS IN A SCHOOL.

ing the year, they are asked to identify the five students in their class who they feel are the least successful and make a case study of each by collecting data and discussing their findings in Saturday group sessions. These discussions set an important example for the future, says Linda Beardsley, director of teacher education and school partnerships at Tufts. By giving student teachers ample opportunity to forge relationships and problem-solve with colleagues and faculty, she hopes the discussions will establish a pattern of reaching out that will continually refuel a teacher's sense of commitment.

At Neag's integrated five-year combined bachelor's and master's program, master's students work with one of 22 PDSs to develop their own internships, whether ongoing school projects like upgrading the computer lab or independent initiatives. At Batchelder Elementary in Hartford, Conn., for example, intern Becky Golanski developed a workshop for teachers on how to create a Web site for their classroom. She also taught a six-week minicourse on anthropology to seventh graders and began an after-school "adventure club" for fourth graders. Her wide range of experiences, including a semester of student teaching in her senior year, has prepared her well, she says. "I'm ready to jump into the classroom."

And chances are she'll stay there. More than 90 percent of Claremont and Neag grads are still teaching after five years. "Our students have had another year to learn the system," says Schwab. "So when they start, they have a huge repertoire and they are ready to go." But educators don't want the nurturing to end there. "It's very scary being a teacher," says Ellen Condliffe Lagemann, dean of Harvard Graduate School of Education. "It helps if you know you have a buddy down the hall when you have a problem." Harvard tries to place graduates together or with other alumni. Other schools are working on more-formal support programs. As part of its Teachers for a New Era initiative, Carnegie Corp. of New York is funding reform efforts at four universities. To ease the student-to-teacher transition, graduates will be mentored by master teachers in a two-year residency.

And currently in the works is the Penn Beginning Teachers Network, a collaboration among IBM, the Pennsylvania Department of Education, and area ed schools. "What we're hoping to do is to grow and share with new teachers so they don't feel like they are so much on their own," says Nancy Streim, the program's director and associate dean of the ed school at Penn. She envisions a future where the training and employment of a teacher may involve multiple steps—again similar to the medical model, where upon graduation "you don't just throw your interns out there to the world." ●

THE AVERAGE SALARY FOR BEGINNING TEACHERS IS JUST UNDER $29,000.

Classrooms with room

igning bonuses, relocation assistance, and loan forgiveness are just some of the perks being offered to teachers certified in critical shortage areas. Incentives are also being used to lure teachers to high-poverty districts, where on average 1 in 5 quits annually. At the same time, there is an urgent need for teachers who mirror the student population. According to a 2002 survey conducted by Recruiting New Teachers, a nonprofit clearinghouse, 36 percent of school-age children are of African, Latino, Asian, or Native American descent, compared with only 13 percent of K-12 teachers. Men, too, are sought after in this predominantly female field.

One caveat: There seem to be about enough teachers of arts and humanities (like drama and social studies), according to a 2002 survey by the American Association for Employment in Education. In such fields, says Leslie Getzinger, a senior associate at the American Federation for Teachers, "it could be very difficult to get a position in some districts."

Overall, teacher salaries, as well as those of librarians and principals, are determined by school district rather than subject area. On average, the highest paid public school teachers are in Connecticut ($53,507), the lowest in South Dakota ($30,265). But rest assured, districts will be snapping up teachers in the following fields well into this decade.

Special education. The number of children with special needs has increased by 30 percent in the last 10 years. Of the seven areas deemed in considerable shortage by the AAEE survey, five are special ed concentrations. What's more, the burnout rate for special ed teachers is as high as 20 percent in some school systems.

Math and sciences. "We've had a shortage of math and science teachers for 75 years," says David Imig, president and CEO of the American Association of Colleges for Teacher Education. Nearly 1 in 5 science teachers, and 28 percent of math teachers, are not certified in their field.

HOW TO LEARN TO TEACH

The country may need millions of teachers and administrators, but that doesn't mean getting into a good ed school will be a cinch. Thanks to calls for higher teacher quality and an influx of applications from recession refugees, competition for a spot in a top-tier master's program has gotten a lot tougher over the past few years.

Besides solid grades—Harvard, for one, likes to see a minimum 3.5 undergraduate GPA in a subject specialty—experience is strongly encouraged. "That could be someone who has been involved with Boy Scouts, summer camp, Sunday school, or a person who has raised children," says Mary Poplin, dean of Claremont Graduate University's education school in Claremont, Calif. Admissions deans are also on the lookout for anyone who has been involved in some sort of social work. And naturally, spending a year teaching can't be beat. Some programs require that entering students have at least one year of teaching experience. If you haven't spent time with children in a classroom, says Joanne McNergney, assistant dean of admissions at the Curry School at the University of Virginia, "it can be a real shock to your system."

There is hope, however, if your GPA is less than stellar. Some schools weigh experience and goals more heavily than academics. At Curry, for example, a definitive "goal statement" could redeem an unimpressive undergraduate career. "It's your opportunity to talk about who you are and if you were immature as an undergrad," says McNergney, and,

UNIVERSITY OF CONNECTICUT EDUCATION STUDENTS ENJOY A DINNER PARTY AT THE HOME OF FELLOW STUDENT LISA BOK.

doubled in the past decade.

School librarians. More than a quarter of librarians with master's degrees will reach age 65 by 2011. "School libraries expanded a great deal in the late 1960s and early 1970s," says Larry Nesbit, director of information resources at Mansfield University in Mansfield, Pa. "Now, that group of librarians is ready to retire." The Bureau of Labor Statistics predicts 25,000 school librarians will be needed by 2010—more than the number of graduates from all ALA-accredited programs in the past six years.

Principals. A recent study by the Educational Research Service estimates that more than 40 percent of public school principals will retire over the next decade. Although the average salary for a principal is double that of a teacher, school systems all across the board are having trouble finding candidates willing to step up to the plate. Because of the high level of stress, says Bobby Malone, an education professor at Ball State University, "Many veteran teachers who would make good principals have little interest in moving into administration." ●

MORE THAN 12% OF TEACHERS ENTER THE WORKFORCE WITH NO TRAINING. AN ADDITIONAL 15% HAVE NOT MET STATE STANDARDS.

Bilingual education. Nearly 10 percent of public school students are "English language learners"—meaning English is not their first language—an increase of 32 percent since the 1997–98 school year, according to the National Clearinghouse for English Language Acquisition. Demand is high for teachers who can instruct in Spanish and English, as well as those qualified to teach English as a second language, especially in urban districts. While there continues to be a shortage in historically Latino areas— last year Texas was unable to fill a quarter of bilingual and ESL jobs—the most severe need is in states that have not traditionally had large immigrant populations, such as Indiana, where the Latino population

most important, what you want to do beyond "help people." If you're unsure, take education classes without formally enrolling in a program. For instance, in its professional development status program, Curry allows anyone with a bachelor's degree to take up to 12 credits upon enrollment that may be applicable toward a degree.

Ph.D. and Ed.D. candidates should have significant experience and a strong interest in a specific line of research. "They need to have a passion about what they want to do," says Richard Schwab, dean of the University of Connecticut's Neag School of Education. For example, Ed.D. applicants should usually have at least two to three years of successful teaching on their résumés.

Master's programs vary widely. Some target mid-career professionals or experienced teachers looking for a leg up. If your teaching experience is limited, "find programs that are going to put you in the classroom," advises David Imig, president of the American Association of Colleges for Teacher Education. Look for a graduate program that has a strong relationship with a good public school or professional development school. "Ask how much support you are really going to get," urges Linda Beardsley, director of student teaching and school partnerships at Tufts University's ed program in Boston. "Unless you have an opportunity to combine your learning about classroom practice and the theories that underlie it, you really miss out." And if you're not sure in which environment you'd like to teach—urban, suburban, rural—you might want to choose a school, like the University of Connecticut, that exposes students to teaching in all three. ●

Schools of Education

THE TOP SCHOOLS

Rank/School	Overall score	Peer assessment score (5.0 highest)	Superintendent assessment score (5.0 highest)	'02 mean GRE scores verbal/quantitative[1]	'02 Ph.D. & Ed.D. acceptance rate	'02 student/faculty ratio[2]	Ph.D.'s & Ed.D.'s granted 2001-02	'02 % Ph.D. & Ed.D. students	'02 funded research (millions)	'02 funded research/faculty member (thousands)
1. Harvard University (MA)	100	4.4	4.7	596/613	13.3%	20.8	72	41.0%	$18.8	$586.8
2. Stanford University (CA)	95	4.7	4.6	554/646	10.8%	8.6	29	53.2%	$14.4	$495.1
3. University of California–Los Angeles	93	4.1	4.1	538/608	26.7%	13.5	82	45.6%	$30.4	$895.5
4. Teachers College, Columbia University (NY)	90	4.4	4.6	545/621	25.0%	9.7	178	37.3%	$25.0	$430.9
Vanderbilt University (Peabody) (TN)	90	4.3	4.6	587/658	41.0%	5.8	34	50.6%	$20.5	$621.2
6. University of Pennsylvania	88	3.7	4.3	595/637	21.3%	11.2	48	51.5%	$22.1	$818.6
7. University of Oregon	85	3.3	3.9	621/643	18.8%	8.5	32	28.0%	$22.8	$1,428.0
8. University of Michigan–Ann Arbor	83	4.3	4.4	568/652	37.1%	7.0	22	61.5%	$15.3	$294.7
9. Northwestern University (IL)	82	3.7	4.4	632/694	16.3%	5.9	11	27.2%	$10.5	$478.3
University of Wisconsin–Madison	82	4.4	4.4	479/591 *	41.7%	4.1	121	57.4%	$18.1	$518.3
11. University of California–Berkeley	80	4.3	4.3	583/615	19.8%	12.9	38	54.7%	$9.0	$390.9
12. University of Minnesota–Twin Cities	78	4.0	4.1	540/623	34.0%	10.3	232	38.0%	$21.8	$279.3
13. University of Texas–Austin	77	4.0	4.4	541/582	41.7%	6.5	120	63.1%	$16.4	$468.6
14. New York University	76	3.5	4.2	592/624	12.4%	10.5	131	18.2%	$30.2	$331.5
15. Michigan State University	74	4.2	4.3	536/614	35.8%	3.8	58	33.0%	$15.0	$356.3
16. Arizona State University–Main Campus	71	3.7	4.0	588/620	20.9%	5.3	94	44.2%	$11.2	$508.9
17. Indiana University–Bloomington	69	3.9	4.2	496/595	24.2%	5.3	71	57.9%	$18.0	$345.9
Ohio State University–Columbus	69	4.0	4.1	482/604	43.9%	5.5	87	28.8%	$20.7	$344.5
19. George Washington University (DC)	68	3.4	4.1	507/559	67.2%	9.4	45	38.6%	$19.3	$714.8
Temple University (PA)	68	3.3	4.1	553/552	36.4%	2.7	75	34.6%	$16.8	$578.4
21. University of Maryland–College Park	67	3.9	4.1	552/615	41.7%	5.4	61	52.6%	$12.9	$257.7
University of Virginia (Curry)	67	4.0	4.3	540/570	56.2%	7.4	92	49.6%	$9.2	$174.2
23. Boston College (Lynch)	66	3.4	4.1	541/587	33.3%	7.3	40	28.2%	$12.4	$294.2
24. Cornell University (NY)	65	3.4	4.5	650/630	15.8%	6.0	13	40.5%	$1.2	$197.8
Penn State University–University Park	65	4.0	4.3	484/593	48.4%	4.6	94	67.3%	$6.8	$122.8
University of Illinois–Urbana-Champaign	65	4.2	4.1	490/575	46.2%	4.7	63	46.5%	$8.6	$127.6
27. University of Florida	64	3.5	4.2	530/612	37.6%	11.2	48	39.1%	$16.8	$373.2
University of Georgia	64	3.9	4.0	517/588	41.0%	4.9	122	36.9%	$17.1	$151.2
University of Washington	64	3.9	4.0	542/602	35.7%	8.7	26	35.9%	$9.0	$257.1
30. University of Iowa	63	3.6	4.1	551/656	46.1%	6.1	43	47.4%	$11.6	$173.4
31. University of North Carolina–Chapel Hill	61	3.8	4.4	523/575	41.3%	5.8	24	38.1%	$6.2	$328.6
32. University of Missouri–Columbia	60	3.4	4.0	498/616	34.7%	8.2	69	30.1%	$12.8	$336.9
33. University of Colorado–Boulder	59	3.6	3.9	586/617	40.6%	8.1	12	17.1%	$4.1	$185.0
University of North Carolina–Greensboro	59	3.1	3.9	521/534	38.7%	5.1	37	29.3%	$16.9	$602.9
35. Rutgers State University–New Brunswick (NJ)	58	3.3	4.0	584/632	26.7%	4.5	36	32.7%	$6.4	$227.5
University of Kansas	58	3.6	4.0	497/546	59.8%	15.5	56	32.4%	$15.9	$293.7
University of Miami (FL)	58	2.8	3.6	559/669	17.2%	5.9	16	19.3%	$11.1	$444.3
University of Southern California (Rossier)	58	3.4	4.2	495/548	37.9%	21.4	102	64.4%	$4.7	$263.3
39. Virginia Commonwealth University	56	2.8	3.9	562/578	55.0%	5.7	18	12.4%	$12.7	$976.9
40. Texas A&M University–College Station	55	3.4	4.2	477/535	59.3%	4.4	100	60.0%	$9.3	$252.5
41. Lehigh University (PA)	54	2.8	3.8	559/599	27.3%	6.8	10	29.9%	$9.6	$507.6
Syracuse University (NY)	54	3.4	4.1	559/645	42.3%	5.5	26	31.7%	$4.4	$221.7
University of Pittsburgh	54	3.5	4.2	503/525	71.0%	7.4	76	43.0%	$8.3	$175.6
44. College of William and Mary (VA)	52	3.3	4.3	524/530	48.9%	4.9	22	33.3%	$4.5	$223.8
Purdue University–West Lafayette (IN)	52	3.3	4.2	498/591	31.4%	2.3	71	55.4%	$2.9	$86.7
46. SUNY–Albany	51	3.2	3.8	535/641	30.1%	6.5	33	23.5%	$6.9	$265.3
47. University of Delaware	49	3.1	3.6	536/623	36.4%	2.9	19	39.1%	$7.5	$339.5
University of Tennessee–Knoxville	49	3.1	4.0	489/571	56.2%	6.0	59	31.4%	$10.4	$471.5
49. Fordham University (NY)	48	3.0	4.2	525/587	43.0%	5.2	51	22.2%	$3.0	$137.5
University of Massachusetts–Amherst	48	3.4	4.1	512/543 *	44.8%	6.8	42	41.7%	$3.3	$94.1
University of Oklahoma	48	3.0	3.5	510/540	19.0%	7.1	24	48.6%	$10.4	$324.6
Utah State University	48	2.9	3.5	525/550	43.6%	3.5	20	22.8%	$17.0	$460.8
Washington University in St. Louis	48	3.1	3.9	568/674 *	28.6%	1.8	3	17.9%	$0.0 [3]	$14.2

[1]GRE scores are for doctoral students only; * means that the school could not break out GRE scores for doctoral students; average scores for all entering students are shown. [2]Student/faculty ratio is for all full-time students and faculty. [3]The school had less than $50,000 in externally funded research.

Sources: *U.S. News* and the schools. Assessment data collected by Synova

More at **www.usnews.com**

Specialties

PROGRAMS IN 10 AREAS RANKED BEST BY EDUCATION SCHOOL DEANS

ADMINISTRATION/SUPERVISION
1. Univ. of Wisconsin–Madison
2. Ohio State Univ.–Columbus
3. Stanford University (CA)
4. Harvard University (MA)
5. Vanderbilt Univ. (Peabody) (TN)
6. Penn State University–University Park
7. Teachers College, Columbia University (NY)
8. University of Texas–Austin
9. Indiana Univ.–Bloomington
   Michigan State University
   University of Michigan–Ann Arbor

EDUCATION POLICY
1. Stanford University (CA)
2. Harvard University (MA)
3. Univ. of Wisconsin–Madison
4. Teachers College, Columbia University (NY)
   University of Michigan–Ann Arbor
6. Univ. of California–Berkeley
7. Univ. of Calif.–Los Angeles
8. Michigan State University
9. Vanderbilt Univ. (Peabody) (TN)
10. University of Illinois–Urbana-Champaign

EDUCATIONAL PSYCHOLOGY
1. Stanford University (CA)
   Univ. of Wisconsin–Madison
3. University of Michigan–Ann Arbor
4. University of Illinois–Urbana-Champaign
5. Michigan State University
6. University of Minnesota–Twin Cities
7. Univ. of California–Berkeley
8. Teachers College, Columbia University (NY)
9. Univ. of Calif.–Los Angeles
10. Harvard University (MA)
    University of Georgia
    University of Maryland–College Park

ELEMENTARY EDUCATION
1. Michigan State University
2. Univ. of Wisconsin–Madison
3. Ohio State University–Columbus
4. Teachers College,

Columbia University (NY)
5. University of Georgia
6. University of Illinois–Urbana-Champaign
   Vanderbilt Univ. (Peabody) (TN)
8. Indiana Univ.–Bloomington
   University of Virginia (Curry)
10. U. of Michigan–Ann Arbor

SECONDARY EDUCATION
1. Michigan State University
2. University of Wisconsin–Madison
3. Ohio State University–Columbus
4. Stanford University (CA)
5. Teachers College, Columbia University (NY)
   University of Illinois–Urbana-Champaign
7. University of Georgia
8. University of Virginia (Curry)
9. Indiana University–Bloomington
   University of Washington

HIGHER EDUCATION ADMINISTRATION
1. University of Michigan–Ann Arbor
2. Penn State University–University Park
3. University of California–Los Angeles
4. Indiana University–Bloomington
5. Michigan State University
6. Harvard University (MA)
7. Stanford University (CA)
   University of Southern California (Rossier)
9. Teachers College, Columbia University (NY)
10. University of Maryland–College Park

SPECIAL EDUCATION
1. Vanderbilt Univ. (Peabody) (TN)
2. University of Kansas
3. University of Oregon
4. University of Minnesota–Twin Cities
5. University of Illinois–Urbana-Champaign
   University of Maryland–College Park
   University of Virginia (Curry)

8. University of Texas–Austin
9. University of Wisconsin–Madison
10. University of Florida
    University of Washington

VOCATIONAL/TECHNICAL
1. Ohio State University–Columbus
2. University of Minnesota–Twin Cities
3. Penn State University–University Park
   University of Georgia
   Virginia Tech
6. University of Illinois–Urbana-Champaign
7. Oklahoma State University
   University of Missouri–Columbia
9. Colorado State University
10. University of Wisconsin–Madison

COUNSELING/PERSONNEL SERVICES
1. University of Maryland–College Park
2. Ohio State University–Columbus
3. University of Florida
4. University of Georgia
5. University of North Carolina–Greensboro
6. University of Minnesota–Twin Cities
   Univ. of Wisconsin–Madison
8. Indiana Univ.–Bloomington
9. Univ. of Missouri–Columbia
10. Penn State University–University Park

CURRICULUM/INSTRUCTION
1. Univ. of Wisconsin–Madison
2. Michigan State University
3. Teachers College, Columbia University (NY)
4. Ohio State University–Columbus
   University of Illinois–Urbana-Champaign
6. University of Georgia
7. Stanford University (CA)
   U. of Michigan–Ann Arbor
9. Indiana University–Bloomington
   Vanderbilt Univ. (Peabody) (TN)

Teacher preparation at top education schools

Below, you'll find key information about teacher-prep programs at the top 50 *U.S. News* education schools, listed alphabetically. This table is not a ranking of these programs. Key attributes to consider when choosing a program include whether it is accredited, whether students intern in a professional development school that is closely tied to the university, and whether they meet regularly to share insights with a group of their peers.

School	NCATE accredited[1]	Type of education school undergrad/grad	'02 grads licensed to teach[2]	'02 enrollment in master's teaching programs	Alternative route to licensure program	Students trained in professional development school	Students assigned to peer working groups	'02 students preparing for national certification
Arizona State University–Main Campus	No	U and G	667	406	No	All	All	90
Boston College (Lynch)	Yes	U and G	267	401	Yes	All	All	0
College of William and Mary (VA)	Yes	Grad	124	87	No	Some	All	0
Cornell University (NY)	Applying	U and G	30	38	No	All	All	21
Fordham University (NY)	Yes	Grad	228	601	Yes	Some	All	N/A
George Washington University (DC)	Yes	Grad	115	404	Yes	Some	All	536
Harvard University (MA)	No	Grad	58	61	No	All	All	60
Indiana University–Bloomington	Yes	U and G	681	203	Yes	Some	Some	N/A
Lehigh University (PA)	No	Grad	20	82	No	Some	All	0
Michigan State University	No	U and G	568	538	Yes	All	All	0
New York University	No	U and G	457	685	Yes	Some	All	0
Northwestern University (IL)	No	U and G	41	103	Yes	All	All	4
Ohio State University–Columbus	Yes	U and G	N/A	640	No	All	All	206
Penn State University–University Park	Yes	U and G	882	141	No	Some	All	N/A
Purdue University–West Lafayette (IN)	Yes	U and G	474	N/A	Yes	Some	Some	N/A
Rutgers State University–New Brunswick (NJ)	No	Grad	191	373	No	Some	All	N/A
Stanford University (CA)	Yes	Grad	55	63	No	All	All	N/A
SUNY–Albany	No	Grad	159	634	No	Some	All	0
Syracuse University (NY)	Applying	U and G	201	252	No	All	All	N/A
Teachers College, Columbia University (NY)	Applying	Grad	425	423	No	Some	All	N/A
Temple University (PA)	Yes	U and G	N/A	752	No	Some	Some	12
Texas A&M University–College Station	Yes	U and G	N/A	79	Yes	Some	All	N/A
University of California–Berkeley	No	Grad	46	108	No	All	All	0
University of California–Los Angeles	No	Grad	111	327	Yes	All	All	0
University of Colorado–Boulder	Yes	U and G	154	336	No	All	All	N/A
University of Delaware	Yes	U and G	386	209	Yes	All	Some	25
University of Florida	Yes	U and G	341	365	No	Some	Some	N/A
University of Georgia	Yes	U and G	651	661	Yes	Some	All	97
University of Illinois–Urbana-Champaign	Applying	U and G	499	49	No	No	All	0
University of Iowa	No	U and G	373	332	No	No	All	0
University of Kansas	Yes	U and G	129	318	No	Some	Some	0
University of Maryland–College Park	Yes	U and G	415	N/A	Yes	Some	All	20
University of Massachusetts–Amherst	Yes	U and G	N/A	338	Yes	Some	Some	N/A
University of Miami (FL)	Yes	U and G	127	217	No	All	All	0
University of Michigan–Ann Arbor	No	U and G	305	105	No	Some	All	N/A
University of Minnesota–Twin Cities	Yes	U and G	389	977	No	Some	All	N/A
University of Missouri–Columbia	Applying	U and G	197	N/A	Yes	All	Some	N/A
University of North Carolina–Chapel Hill	Yes	U and G	132	181	No	Some	All	0
University of North Carolina–Greensboro	Yes	U and G	334	N/A	Yes	Some	Some	3
University of Oklahoma	Yes	U and G	141	121	No	All	All	N/A
University of Oregon	No	U and G	224	120	No	All	All	N/A
University of Pennsylvania	No	Grad	114	221	Yes	Some	Some	0
University of Pittsburgh	No	U and G	168	450	Yes	All	All	0
University of Southern California (Rossier)	No	U and G	109	162	No	No	All	N/A
University of Tennessee–Knoxville	Yes	Grad	298	457	Yes	Some	All	0
University of Texas–Austin	No	U and G	659	187	No	Some	All	0
University of Virginia (Curry)	Yes	U and G	124	328	No	No	All	0
University of Washington	Yes	Grad	N/A	176	No	All	All	N/A
University of Wisconsin–Madison	No	U and G	N/A	N/A	No	Some	Some	N/A
Utah State University	Yes	U and G	750	506	Yes	No	All	0
Vanderbilt University (Peabody) (TN)	Yes	Grad	102	145	No	Some	All	N/A
Virginia Commonwealth University	Yes	U and G	138	369	Yes	Some	Some	22
Washington University in St. Louis	Yes	U and G	37	23	No	Some	All	N/A

[1]Status as of February 2003. [2]Includes those licensed with baccalaureate degrees where applicable.
N/A means not available. Sources: *U.S. News* and the schools

More at **www.usnews.com**

ENGINEERING

Outside the box

BY ALICIA ABELL

Kenny Yarmosh, 22, is getting a master's degree in telecommunications and networking from the University of Pennsylvania's School of Engineering and Applied Science. But he hasn't been taught by a single telecommunications or networking professor. Instead, his master's program is made up of electrical engineering courses, systems engineering classes, and even business courses at Penn's Wharton School.

Fifteen years ago, the typical engineering student wouldn't have taken classes outside his home department, much less outside the engineering school altogether. Today's engineers in training are much more like Yarmosh, who takes courses in numerous engineering subspecialties and sometimes roams into other departments. Rather than conducting research with just one professor, grad students are increasingly likely to work with faculty-student teams from all over the university, often trying to develop marketable products—"smart wraps" that could monitor food products for spoilage, for instance, or military uniforms that could automatically dispense medicines to soldiers. "We're currently witnessing the most significant structural changes in schools of engineering in 30 years," says Thomas Magnanti, dean of engineering at the Massachusetts Institute of Technology.

The trend toward interdisciplinary research is being driven first and foremost by money. For years, federal agencies such as the National Science Foundation, the National Institutes of Health, and the Department of Defense funded curiosity-driven projects run by a single researcher; the idea was to solve a scientific puzzle, not necessarily to develop a commercial application. Over the past five to 10 years, however, these same government agencies have been allocating more and more of their resources to attacking big-picture problems: developing, say, environmentally friendly energy sources, or lifesaving medical devices. Such projects by their nature require a large number of researchers from a variety of disciplines. As a result, engineering students often

find themselves working alongside colleagues from the medical school, business school, law school—or from another university entirely.

The more potential for commercialization a project has, the more likely it is to get funding not only from the government but also from the private sector. By developing marketable products, schools also bring in revenue to their home institution. In the past six years, 17 start-up companies have emerged from Columbia University's Fu Foundation School of Engineering and Applied Science. One firm alone produced $10 million in revenues for the university. That's one reason for the natural symbiosis between engineering and business schools. In one of Yarmosh's classes at Penn, he's been assigned to work with a team of fellow engineers and M.B.A. students to develop a complete business plan for a hypothetical company, which they may present to a real venture capital firm when the course is over.

The nature of engineering education is also changing because of plain old scientific progress. There has always been discipline-crossing work in this field, says Jim Plummer, dean of engineering at Stanford University, but advances in technology—and human knowledge—are enabling connections between fields that have never before been related. At Stanford, a new Global Climate and Energy Project, which aims to find clean, sustainable energy sources, includes researchers from the earth sciences department, the law school, and the public-policy school as well as the mechanical, chemical, and civil engineering departments.

Collaborations between engineering and medical schools are especially common. Within the past five years, says Joseph Walsh, professor of biomedical engineering and associate dean for graduate studies and research at Northwestern University, almost every major research university in the country has formed—or is forming—a biomedical engineering department. In Atlanta, for example, the Georgia Institute of Technology and the Emory Medical Center operate a joint department that is working on tissue engineering, which involves growing tissues for implants,

FOREIGN STUDENTS EARNED 43% OF MASTER'S DEGREES AND 54% OF DOCTORATES IN ENGINEERING IN 2001.

UNIVERSITY OF CALIFORNIA–SAN DIEGO ENGINEERING STUDENTS TEST SEISMIC EQUIPMENT.

transplants, and artificial organs. These scholarly joint ventures have translated into new research opportunities for students like Elizabeth Viriya. Between classes in Columbia's biomedical engineering department, Viriya, 22, pops into the lab and works alongside peers who are studying engineering, biology, or dentistry. Her role: experimenting with different arrangements of cell types and nutrient doses to find the right conditions for cells to develop into cartilage that could be used for arthritis patients.

Almost everyone agrees that the intersection of traditional disciplines—and the creation of new ones—are a good thing. "Technology and the job market are changing so rapidly that we need to prepare students for flexibility," says Frieder Seible, interim dean of the Jacobs School of Engineering at the University of California–San Diego. "It's no longer the model of learn one thing and stick with it for the rest of your life."

However, some deans say the interdisciplinary shift can put stresses and strains on traditional engineering curricula. "Should we tamper with core courses that have served us well all along?" asks Geoffrey Orsak, executive director of the Institute for Engineering Education at Southern Methodist University in Dallas. Critics say some schools are no longer placing enough emphasis on basics such as physics and math. Instead, they're focusing too much on trends, Seible says—"nano-this and nano-that." (Nanotechnology, which combines electrical engineering, physics, and chemistry to create what MIT's Magnanti calls "tiny technologies"—robots smaller than a pin tip, for example—barely existed 10 years ago. Now it's an introductory course at most schools.) The effect of not mastering the basics, Seible adds, becomes clear when an engineer faces a new problem. "You can't just teach them cookbooks and recipes," he explains, "because what will happen when the recipes run out?"

For his part, Penn's Yarmosh is happy to be in a program that gives him flexibility. The interdisciplinary approach works well for him because his goal is to consult on engineering issues in the business world, a job that will require him to understand technologies but not create them. Students in his program who want to do more "hardcore engineering," he says, can choose to take more physics and math than he has. And they don't have to take classes outside the engineering school if they don't want to. "It's a choice, and I think that's the benefit of the program," he says. "There are required courses, but [beyond that] you can choose which route you want to go." That, after all, is the beauty of interdisciplinary work: finding solutions to new problems and taking new paths to get there. ●

Choose your tools

The numbers can be overwhelming: hundreds of graduate programs to choose from and thousands of applicants to compete with. But following a few basic principles can make the process of applying to engineering schools much easier—and more successful. Here are a few guidelines for choosing, and being chosen by, engineering programs:

Focus on your specialty. Often, the strength of an individual program or department is more important than the quality or reputation of the school as a whole, says Penn State engineering dean David Wormley. If you want to go into a particular industry, look at master's programs that have a track record of placing people with your career goals in good jobs. If you plan to do independent research or end up in academia, aim for a Ph.D. at a school where faculty members are working in a subfield that interests you. Despite the increasingly interdisciplinary nature of engineering research, a doctoral candidate is still very much tied to a single faculty adviser when writing the all-important thesis.

Consider your colleagues. Faculty aren't the only people you should investigate; take a look at who will be your fellow students as well. Visit the campus, go into its laboratories, and talk to as many people as possible, says the University of California–San Diego's Frieder Seible. How excited are the students about their work? Do they both play and work together, or do they scatter like mice once outside the lab? Anybody hoping for racially and ethnically diverse classmates should bear in mind that blacks and Hispanics are sparsely represented at most schools. And women make up only 20 percent of all engineering students, according to the American Society for Engineering Education. Prospective students may want to look carefully not only at enrollment numbers but also at dropout rates and support services for women and minorities.

Show a passion for research. Almost all applicants who are accepted to graduate engineering programs have undergrad degrees in the subject as well. That's because they usually have research experience. Undergraduate research is a must for Ph.D. students, but master's applicants have some wiggle room. If you switched majors in the middle of college or somehow man-

REVENGE OF THE NERDS

Despite the current economic downturn, a shortage of engineering grads is keeping job prospects good. The 63,000 engineers who received bachelor's degrees from U.S. universities in 2000 weren't nearly enough; the United States had to import 21,000 foreign engineers on special visas to fill jobs, estimates William Wulf, president of the National Academy of Engineering. Here's a guide to some of the most promising specialties.

Computer/electrical. Computer and electrical engineers, whose training gives them enormous flexibility, are in greater demand than any other type of engineer. Knowledge of electrical engineering, for instance, is essential for anyone who wants to pursue the popular fields of telecommunications and wireless technology. The Bureau of Labor Statistics projects that computer software engineering will be the fastest growing of all occupations between 2000 and 2010. Computer and electrical engineers "can go into almost any industry," says MIT's dean of engineering, Thomas Magnanti. Starting salaries are higher than for most other master's grads in engineering—around $63,000.

Bioengineering/biomedical. Many of today's great medical advances—CT scans, MRIs, artificial hearts and limbs—are engineering breakthroughs, and the demand for such technologies should continue. Opportunities in genetic engineering are increasing as well, as are jobs related to antiterrorism efforts. Since the September 11 attacks, the government has initiated many engineering-based programs aimed at the detection of biological weapons. Biomedical engineers also make some of the highest salaries in the business: an average of $62,600 to start for those with master's degrees.

BIOENGINEERING STUDENTS AT UC–SAN DIEGO MIX AND MINGLE IN THE GRAD LOUNGE AT THE JACOBS SCHOOL OF ENGINEERING.

Seible. The key is to give a compelling reason for why you want to switch fields.

Come highly recommended. Grades, GRE scores, and letters of recommendation have always been the Big Three in engineering admissions, but in recent years the last category has become increasingly important. Why? According to engineering deans, grade inflation is so rampant that perfect GPAs aren't always helpful in distinguishing between candidates. What catches the eye of Zvi Galil, dean of Columbia University's engineering school, is an outstanding letter of recommendation from a faculty member who knew the student well as an undergraduate. "Not just the standard kind of letter," he explains, "but one that says, 'This is the strongest student I've seen in the past five years.'" If you don't think your references will stand out, try visiting the campus and meeting with a professor or two. "Students should not be afraid to call up faculty and make appointments," says Seible. "Personal visits really help." ●

aged to get a B.S. in engineering without doing research, getting an engineering-related job could help, says Northwestern University biomedical engineering professor Joseph Walsh. Or you could point to undergraduate coursework that included lab experience, he says. "The idea is to show some basis by which you're deriving this inspiration for doing research."

If your undergraduate degree is in something other than engineering, building a case for admission is even harder, although the occasional biology or architecture student switches to biomedical or structural engineering, says

SINCE 1980, NONACADEMIC ENGINEERING JOBS HAVE INCREASED AT MORE THAN FOUR TIMES THE RATE OF THE U.S. LABOR FORCE AS A WHOLE.

Aerospace/defense. Stepped-up national security efforts mean engineers are in high demand at places like Los Alamos National Laboratory in New Mexico. Why? Mechanical engineers with information-technology backgrounds are able to analyze massive amounts of data and pick out what's important, while electrical engineers are naturals at "electronic eavesdropping" and code breaking. Rising defense spending—and an aging workforce—also mean opportunities for aerospace engineers. According to NASA Administrator Sean O'Keefe, scientists and engineers 60 years and older outnumber those under 30 by a 3-to-1 margin at the space agency.

Environmental. The BLS predicts faster-than-average growth for environmental engineers through 2010. Building design is increasingly taking environmental concerns into account; the private sector now consults engineers on how to clean up hazardous materials and meet environmental regulations. But because politics often determines the number and stringency of environmental regulations, the volume of job openings in this area is likely to vary with Republican and Democratic administrations.

Financial. Jobs in finance might be rarer these days, but financial engineering—which involves developing instruments to predict investment outcomes—is hot. That's because almost all of the financial analysis on Wall Street involves complex technological and mathematical skills. "Wall Street is a big hirer of [grads with] advanced degrees in engineering," says Geoffrey Orsak, executive director of the Institute for Engineering Education at Southern Methodist University.

Nanotechnology. Nanotechnology—engineering at the submicroscopic level—is a still-developing field that intersects with many other areas of engineering. The most common paths for those interested in nanotech are mechanical and electrical engineering. ●

Schools of Engineering

THE TOP SCHOOLS

Rank/School	Overall score	Peer assessment score (5.0 highest)	Recruiter assessment score (5.0 highest)	'02 average quantitative GRE score	'02 average analytical GRE score	'02 acceptance rate	'02 Ph.D. students/ faculty	'02 faculty membership in National Academy of Engineering	'02 engineering school research expenditures (in millions)	'02 research expenditures per faculty member (in thousands)	Ph.D.'s granted 2001-02
1. Massachusetts Institute of Technology	100	5.0	4.8	774	716	23.6%	3.7	13.4%	$219.0	$623.9	229
2. Stanford University (CA)	93	4.9	4.7	781	725	28.7%	5.0	17.1%	$113.6	$732.8	191
3. University of California–Berkeley	90	4.8	4.5	785	744	16.1%	5.3	20.6%	$114.9	$510.8	170
4. University of Illinois–Urbana-Champaign	81	4.6	4.4	773	722	13.3%	3.9	3.7%	$176.8	$491.0	194
5. Georgia Institute of Technology	80	4.5	4.2	755	683	32.0%	4.0	4.7%	$183.5	$408.7	188
6. University of Michigan–Ann Arbor	77	4.5	4.2	772	714	32.5%	3.7	3.6%	$130.2	$455.1	195
7. California Institute of Technology	74	4.8	4.6	762	722	8.6%	5.0	13.8%	$48.3	$514.3	52
8. University of Southern California	71	3.5	3.4	761	673	36.5%	5.2	11.7%	$120.6	$988.4	67
9. Purdue University–West Lafayette (IN)	70	4.2	4.1	756	688	22.5%	3.7	2.7%	$156.0	$709.2	132
University of Texas–Austin	70	4.3	4.1	761	696	25.6%	3.3	9.4%	$98.7	$495.8	136
11. Carnegie Mellon University (PA)	69	4.3	4.1	766	718	19.5%	3.6	8.4%	$101.4	$545.1	109
Cornell University (NY)	69	4.3	4.1	765	700	26.9%	3.5	7.9%	$88.9	$728.8	73
University of California–San Diego	69	3.7	3.6	767	707	16.7%	3.9	10.7%	$129.6	$925.5	54
14. Texas A&M University–College Station	67	3.7	3.8	754	661	29.1%	2.6	3.9%	$164.1	$792.9	125
15. University of Wisconsin–Madison	64	4.0	3.9	780	741	26.8%	2.8	4.4%	$106.3	$492.0	95
16. University of Maryland–College Park	62	3.6	3.7	770	720	18.4%	4.0	4.0%	$114.5	$590.4	118
17. Harvard University (MA)	61	3.6	4.0	787	734	12.9%	3.9	16.7%	$27.6	$746.2	14
18. Princeton University (NJ)	60	4.2	4.2	710	674	14.8%	3.8	13.7%	$48.7	$416.3	49
19. Northwestern University (IL)	58	4.0	4.0	762	721	19.6%	4.2	5.8%	$51.1	$373.2	72
University of California–Los Angeles	58	3.8	3.7	760	680	25.2%	5.2	7.3%	$58.0	$426.2	90
21. Penn State University–University Park	56	3.9	3.7	755	687	25.3%	2.2	2.0%	$97.9	$280.6	130
22. Johns Hopkins University (MD)	53	3.9	3.9	766	715	14.2%	3.6	2.4%	$51.6	$415.8	50
University of Minnesota–Twin Cities	53	3.8	3.8	762	703	26.8%	3.0	5.4%	$55.4	$256.6	93
24. Ohio State University	51	3.5	3.6	769	715	29.7%	2.8	2.0%	$85.1	$371.6	101
University of California–Santa Barbara	51	3.4	3.5	769	726	18.9%	4.2	13.1%	$38.5	$326.3	53
26. Columbia University (Fu Foundation) (NY)	50	3.5	3.5	762	694	26.2%	2.9	7.5%	$57.6	$600.0	45
University of Florida	50	3.5	3.5	750	664	11.2%	3.6	1.5%	$75.9	$416.9	100
Virginia Tech	50	3.7	3.7	746	672	24.7%	1.5	2.5%	$58.1	$225.2	98
29. University of Pennsylvania	49	3.5	3.6	753	696	31.1%	3.7	6.7%	$41.8	$480.4	31
University of Washington	49	3.7	3.5	733	675	33.9%	3.8	3.7%	$73.0	$384.1	91
31. Rice University (TX)	48	3.7	3.8	755	698	11.0%	4.1	7.2%	$24.0	$285.7	34
32. North Carolina State University	47	3.4	3.5	736	672	17.3%	2.5	3.5%	$75.3	$390.4	84
33. Duke University (NC)	46	3.6	3.7	762	719	21.0%	3.5	2.1%	$32.2	$423.7	27
Rensselaer Polytechnic Institute (NY)	46	3.7	3.9	738	670	23.3%	2.8	4.2%	$25.9	$231.2	83
35. Washington University in St. Louis	45	3.3	3.6	770	710	28.4%	2.8	3.6%	$41.5	$584.3	27
36. University of California–Davis	44	3.5	3.7	753	670	33.9%	2.8	4.2%	$41.9	$243.6	65
37. University of Colorado–Boulder	43	3.5	3.3	753	691	55.0%	2.1	3.5%	$58.1	$409.4	61
38. Case Western Reserve University (OH)	42	3.4	3.5	771	712	22.2%	2.2	4.3%	$34.8	$362.3	51
Iowa State University	42	3.3	3.7	767	703	16.8%	1.9	0.0%	$42.8	$299.6	55
University of Virginia	42	3.4	3.2	755	702	12.8%	2.9	4.6%	$38.5	$343.5	40
41. Lehigh University (PA)	41	3.2	3.6	764	701	19.6%	2.4	5.9%	$24.1	$471.9	29
Yale University (CT)	41	3.3	3.5	782	727	14.0%	2.5	7.8%	$18.6	$314.9	20
43. Rutgers State University–New Brunswick (NJ)	40	3.1	3.4	756	676	18.4%	1.4	3.2%	$71.7	$369.7	50
44. Dartmouth College (Thayer) (NH)	39	3.0	3.4	767	709	18.4%	2.8	2.6%	$22.3	$636.2	9
University of Delaware	39	3.1	3.5	751	683	14.6%	4.1	2.2%	$30.8	$335.0	41
University of Rochester (NY)	39	2.8	3.0	770	741	9.7%	3.5	1.4%	$58.5	$790.2	21
47. Brown University (RI)	36	3.3	3.5	N/A	N/A	17.7%	2.4	10.5%	$13.4	$247.3	22
University of California–Irvine	36	3.0	3.2	760	678	25.4%	4.2	3.1%	$28.2	$266.1	38
University of Massachusetts–Amherst	36	3.0	3.4	742	676	11.7%	3.4	0.7%	$33.5	$288.7	64
50. Boston University	35	2.8	3.1	746	697	27.2%	2.6	3.6%	$34.8	$490.7	24
University of Arizona	35	3.2	3.1	731	650	36.0%	2.5	6.3%	$24.9	$228.4	46

Sources: *U.S. News*, the schools. Assessment data collected by Synova.

More at **www.usnews.com**

Specialties

GRADUATE PROGRAMS RATED BEST BY ENGINEERING SCHOOL DEANS

AEROSPACE
1. Massachusetts Inst. of Tech.
2. Stanford University (CA)
3. California Inst. of Technology
4. Georgia Inst. of Technology
5. U. of Michigan–Ann Arbor
6. Purdue University–
   West Lafayette (IN)
7. University of Illinois–
   Urbana-Champaign
8. University of Texas–Austin
9. Princeton University (NJ)
10. U. of Maryland–College Park

BIOMEDICAL
1. Johns Hopkins Univ. (MD)
2. Duke University (NC)
3. Mass. Inst. of Technology
4. University of California–
   San Diego
5. University of Washington
6. Georgia Inst. of Technology
7. Case Western Reserve
   University (OH)
8. University of Pennsylvania
9. U. of California–Berkeley/U.
   of California–San Francisco
10. U. of Michigan–Ann Arbor

CHEMICAL
1. Massachusetts Inst. of Tech.
2. Univ. of California–Berkeley
3. U. of Minnesota–Twin Cities
4. Univ. of Wisconsin–Madison
5. California Inst. of Technology
6. University of Texas–Austin
7. Stanford University (CA)
8. University of Illinois–
   Urbana-Champaign
9. University of Delaware
10. Princeton University (NJ)

CIVIL
1. Univ. of California–Berkeley
2. University of Illinois–
   Urbana-Champaign
3. Massachusetts Inst. of Tech.
   University of Texas–Austin
5. Georgia Inst. of Technology
6. Stanford University (CA)
7. Purdue University–
   West Lafayette (IN)
8. U. of Michigan–Ann Arbor
9. Cornell University (NY)
10. Texas A&M University–
    College Station

COMPUTER ENGINEERING
1. Massachusetts Inst. of Tech.
2. Carnegie Mellon Univ. (PA)
   Stanford University (CA)
4. Univ. of California–Berkeley
5. University of Illinois–
   Urbana-Champaign
6. U. of Michigan–Ann Arbor
7. Princeton University (NJ)
8. University of Texas–Austin
9. University of Washington
10. Cornell University (NY)

ELECTRICAL/ELECTRONIC
1. Massachusetts Inst. of Tech.
2. Univ. of California–Berkeley
3. Stanford University (CA)
4. University of Illinois–
   Urbana-Champaign
5. U. of Michigan–Ann Arbor
6. Georgia Inst. of Technology
7. California Inst. of Technology
   Cornell University (NY)
9. University of Texas–Austin
10. Carnegie Mellon Univ. (PA)
    Purdue University–
    West Lafayette (IN)

ENVIRONMENTAL
1. Stanford University (CA)
2. U. of Michigan–Ann Arbor
3. Univ. of California–Berkeley
4. Johns Hopkins Univ. (MD)
5. University of Illinois–
   Urbana-Champaign
6. University of Texas–Austin
7. Massachusetts Inst. of Tech.
8. California Inst. of Technology
9. Georgia Inst. of Technology
10. University of North
    Carolina–Chapel Hill

INDUSTRIAL/
MANUFACTURING
1. Georgia Inst. of Technology
2. U. of Michigan–Ann Arbor
3. Purdue University–
   West Lafayette (IN)
4. Penn State U.–Univ. Park
5. Univ. of California–Berkeley
6. Texas A&M University–
   College Station
7. Northwestern University (IL)
   Stanford University (CA)
9. Virginia Tech
10. Univ. of Wisconsin–Madison

MATERIALS
1. Massachusetts Inst. of Tech.
2. University of Illinois–
   Urbana-Champaign
3. Stanford University (CA)
4. Northwestern University (IL)
5. Univ. of California–Berkeley
6. University of California–
   Santa Barbara
7. U. of Michigan–Ann Arbor
8. Cornell University (NY)
   Penn State U.–Univ. Park
10. University of Florida

MECHANICAL
1. Massachusetts Inst. of Tech.
2. Univ. of California–Berkeley
3. Stanford University (CA)
4. U. of Michigan–Ann Arbor
5. University of Illinois–
   Urbana-Champaign
6. Georgia Inst. of Technology
7. Purdue University–
   West Lafayette (IN)
8. California Inst. of Technology
9. Cornell University (NY)
10. University of Texas–Austin

NUCLEAR
1. Massachusetts Inst. of Tech.
2. Univ. of California–Berkeley
3. Texas A&M University–
   College Station
   University of Illinois–
   Urbana-Champaign
   U. of Michigan–Ann Arbor
   Univ. of Wisconsin–Madison
7. Purdue University–
   West Lafayette (IN)
8. North Carolina State Univ.
9. Penn State U.–Univ. Park
10. University of Florida

AGRICULTURAL
1. Texas A&M University–
   College Station
2. Purdue University–
   West Lafayette (IN)
   Univ. of California–Davis
4. Cornell University (NY)
5. University of Illinois–
   Urbana-Champaign
6. North Carolina State Univ.
   Penn State U.–Univ. Park
8. Michigan State University
   Univ. of Nebraska–Lincoln
10. Iowa State University

METHODOLOGY

Programs at 185 engineering schools that granted doctoral degrees were surveyed; 169 responded; 168 provided the data needed to calculate rankings based on a weighted average of the 11 indicators described below. (All schools are listed in the directory, beginning on Page 93.)

Quality assessment (weighted by .40): Two surveys were conducted in the fall of 2002. Engineering school deans and deans of graduate studies were asked to rate program quality from marginal (1) to outstanding (5); 54 percent responded. The resulting score is weighted by .25. Corporate recruiters who hire from previously ranked programs were also asked to rate programs; 29 percent responded. Their opinions are weighted by .15.

Student selectivity (.10): The strength of students entering in fall 2002 was measured by mean GRE quantitative and analytical scores (45 percent each) and the acceptance rate (10 percent).

Faculty resources (.25): Based on the 2002 ratios of full-time doctoral students to full-time faculty (30 percent) and full-time master's students to full-time faculty (15 percent); the proportions of full-time faculty in the National Academy of Engineering in 2002 (30 percent); and number of doctoral degrees granted in last school year (25 percent).

Research activity (.25): Based on total research expenditures (60 percent) and research dollars per faculty member engaged in research (40 percent). Expenditures refer to separately funded research, public and private, conducted by the school, averaged over fiscal years 2001 and 2002.

Overall rank: Data were standardized about their means, and standardized scores were weighted, totaled, and rescaled so that the top-scoring school received 100; others received their percentage of the top score.

Specialty rankings: These rankings are based solely on nomination by educators at peer schools. From the list of schools surveyed, deans nominated up to 10 schools for excellence in each area. Those with the most votes appear here.

The public goods

BY RACHEL HARTIGAN SHEA

It may sound unlikely, but working for the federal government is becoming cool. Last fall the General Accounting Office, Congress's investigative arm, received one third more applications than it did the year before, while the number of people taking the Foreign Service Exam more than doubled. Applications to Duke's Terry Sanford Institute of Public Policy are up by 34 percent, while 35 percent more graduates of Harvard's John F. Kennedy School of Government are heading to jobs in the public sector than in the previous year.

Continued bad news about the economy and a sense of purpose left over from the September 11 attacks have made the bureaucratic life more attractive than ever. After all, the feds offer benefits that are hard to come by in the private sector: job security, generous healthcare, and a robust retirement system. A government job also promises the morale boost of serving the public, an important perk in this era of business bankruptcies and corporate corruption.

Interest in government careers could not come at a better time—right in the midst of a federal labor shortage. But anyone who has ever considered a career in the public sector has probably wondered how much truth lies in the old stereotypes about bureaucratic red tape and paltry pay. Certainly, the dreaded red tape does exist—and no one gets rich working for Uncle Sam. Public-sector salaries don't match up with those in the private sector for many professionals, including lawyers, information technology specialists, and medical personnel, although in an attempt to compete, a few agencies, including the Internal Revenue Service and the Patent and Trademark Office, now offer hiring bonuses to hot prospects and repay the student loans of some new employees.

But with 1.8 million people employed in just about every occupational field—from accountants analyzing budgets to the zoologists tending pandas Mei Xiang and Tian Tian at the National Zoo in Washington— many federal workers have found good reasons to stay. For one thing, responsibility comes quickly, even in entry-level jobs. And since 88 percent of the jobs are outside the D.C. metropolitan area, it's relatively easy to relocate.

Because the federal government employs individuals in such a wide array of occupations, educational degree requirements vary enormously. Professional-level positions generally require an advanced degree, but a master's in public administration, public affairs, or public policy is the best preparation for the widest variety of jobs.

Public-affairs graduates also get a leg up on federal employment through the prestigious presidential management internship. After two years rotating through federal agencies, most interns are hired at a midlevel job. Twenty-nine-year-old Matthew Payne's experience as an emergency medical technician and his master's in public administration from Syracuse University helped him get an internship with the Department of Health and Human Services. Now employed there in a permanent position, he helps the agency predict which medical supplies, equipment, and staff would be needed during a bioterrorist attack. He spent the week after 9/11 at the World Trade Center site, organizing medical teams. A few weeks later, he was back in Washington, trying to contain the anthrax outbreak. That morale boost that comes from serving the public? He gets it. ●

SCOTT GOLDSMITH

A SENSE OF NATIONAL PURPOSE HAS LED TO INCREASED INTEREST IN THE PUBLIC SECTOR.

Public Affairs

Our ranking, completed in 2001, is based on a survey of deans, directors, and department chairs representing 259 master's programs.

Rank/School	Average assessment score (5=highest)
1. Harvard University (MA)	4.5
Syracuse University (NY)	4.5
3. Indiana University–Bloomington	4.3
4. Princeton University (NJ)	4.2
University of California–Berkeley	4.2
6. University of Georgia	4.0
7. Carnegie Mellon University (PA)	3.9
University of Michigan–Ann Arbor	3.9
University of Southern California	3.9
University of Texas–Austin	3.9
11. University of Wisconsin–Madison	3.8
12. American University (DC)	3.7
Columbia University (NY)	3.7
SUNY–Albany	3.7
University of Chicago	3.7
University of Kansas	3.7
University of Minnesota–Twin Cities	3.7
University of North Carolina–Chapel Hill	3.7
19. Duke University (NC)	3.6
George Washington University (DC)	3.6
New York University	3.6
University of Maryland–College Park	3.6
University of Pittsburgh	3.6
24. Arizona State University	3.5
Florida State University	3.5
University of California–Los Angeles	3.5
University of Washington	3.5
Virginia Tech	3.5
29. Georgetown University (DC)	3.4
Johns Hopkins University (MD)	3.4
31. Georgia State University	3.3
University of Arizona	3.3
University of Kentucky	3.3
University of Nebraska–Omaha	3.3
35. Cleveland State University	3.2
Cornell University (NY)	3.2
Ohio State University	3.2
University of Colorado–Denver	3.2
University of Missouri–Columbia	3.2
University of Pennsylvania	3.2
41. North Carolina State University	3.1
Northern Illinois University	3.1
Rutgers State University–Newark (NJ)	3.1
University of Delaware	3.1
University of Utah	3.1
46. CUNY–Baruch College	3.0
George Mason University (VA)	3.0
Naval Postgraduate School (CA)	3.0
Rutgers State University–New Brunswick (NJ)	3.0
Texas A&M University–College Station	3.0

Note: Lists of schools and persons surveyed were provided by the National Association of Schools of Public Affairs and Administration and the Association for Public Policy Analysis and Management. Respondents were asked to rate the academic quality of programs on a scale of 1 (marginal) to 5 (distinguished). The response rate was 46 percent. Surveys were conducted by Synovate.

The institutions below received the greatest number of nominations from survey respondents for their excellence in a given specialty. Keep in mind that nominees were drawn only from the schools surveyed. So, for example, a university like Yale—which offers a degree in environmental management through its School of Forestry and Environmental Management but not a degree in public affairs—would not show up here.

PUBLIC-POLICY ANALYSIS
1. Harvard University (MA)
2. Univ. of California–Berkeley
3. Univ. of Michigan–Ann Arbor
4. Carnegie Mellon Univ. (PA)
5. University of Chicago
6. Princeton University (NJ)
7. Duke University (NC)
8. Syracuse University (NY)
9. Indiana Univ.–Bloomington
10. Univ. of Wisconsin–Madison

PUBLIC MANAGEMENT/ADMIN.
1. Syracuse University (NY)
2. Harvard University (MA)
3. University of Georgia
4. Indiana Univ.–Bloomington
5. Univ. of Southern California
6. American University (DC)
7. University of Kansas
8. SUNY–Albany
9. Univ. of California–Berkeley
10. Arizona State University
    Virginia Tech

PUBLIC FINANCE & BUDGETING
1. Syracuse University (NY)
2. Indiana Univ.–Bloomington
3. University of Georgia
4. Harvard University (MA)
5. University of Kentucky
6. Carnegie Mellon Univ. (PA)
   Georgia State University
8. New York University
9. Univ. of California–Berkeley
10. University of Maryland–College Park

SOCIAL POLICY
1. Harvard University (MA)
2. University of Chicago
3. University of California–Berkeley
   Univ. of Michigan–Ann Arbor
5. Univ. of Wisconsin–Madison
6. Syracuse University (NY)
7. Duke University (NC)
   Princeton University (NJ)
9. Brandeis University (MA)
10. University of Maryland–College Park

CRIMINAL JUSTICE POLICY & MANAGEMENT
1. CUNY–John Jay College
2. Harvard University (MA)
3. Carnegie Mellon Univ. (PA)
4. SUNY–Albany
5. American University (DC)
6. University of Maryland–College Park

HEALTH POLICY & MGT.
1. New York University
2. Harvard University (MA)
3. Univ. of Michigan–Ann Arbor
4. Johns Hopkins University (MD)
5. Duke University (NC)
6. University of North Carolina–Chapel Hill
7. Univ. of Minn.–Twin Cities
8. Columbia University (NY)
   Georgetown University (DC)
   Princeton University (NJ)
   Univ. of California–Berkeley

ENVIRONMENTAL POLICY & MANAGEMENT
1. Indiana Univ.–Bloomington
2. Duke University (NC)
3. Harvard University (MA)
   Univ. of California–Berkeley
5. University of Washington
6. Syracuse University (NY)
   Univ. of Michigan–Ann Arbor
   University of North Carolina–Chapel Hill
9. University of Maryland–College Park
10. Carnegie Mellon Univ. (PA)

INFORMATION & TECHNOLOGY MANAGEMENT
1. Carnegie Mellon Univ. (PA)
2. Syracuse University (NY)
3. Harvard University (MA)
4. Georgia Inst. of Technology
5. Indiana Univ.–Bloomington
6. SUNY–Albany
7. Univ. of Nebraska–Omaha
8. Ohio State University
9. Univ. of California–Berkeley
   Univ. of Michigan–Ann Arbor

J-school confidential

BY DAN GILGOFF

ANDREW LICHTENSTEIN—AURORA FOR *USN&WR*

ANDREW BUTTERS IS STUDYING MAGAZINE JOURNALISM AT COLUMBIA. BUT MANY EDITORS PREFER REAL-WORLD EXPERIENCE.

Reid Epstein was a senior at Emory University and editor of its student newspaper, the *Emory Wheel,* when he received two tempting offers on the same spring day in 2001. The first was a reporting job with the *Chattanooga Times Free Press,* a Tennessee daily with a circulation of 74,000; the second, an acceptance from Columbia University's prestigious Graduate School of Journalism.

Epstein's subsequent career path might look like an advertisement for J-school. Upon graduating from Columbia in spring 2002, he landed an internship with the *Wall Street Journal,* and he is now a reporter for the *Milwaukee Journal Sentinel,* with more than half a million readers. But Epstein says those successes owe less to his master's than to his reporting credentials. While at Columbia, he spent his free time freelancing for U.S. and Canadian papers, often writing about New York in the wake of the September 11 attacks. It was those clips, he says, that impressed the *Journal Sentinel.* "I don't think anyone cares about my degree," says Epstein, 23.

He's probably right. Most editors and news directors still favor the police-beat school of journalism over even the best J-schools. "Learning about journalism without having experience," says Peter Landis, news director for NY1 News, a Manhattan television station, "is like knowing how to play the notes on the saxophone without knowing any songs." While J-schools send students into the field to report stories, most

managers put little stock in assignments produced outside actual newsrooms, complete with real-world pressure to get facts right and meet deadlines. Programs offering job experience, like the University of Missouri (which runs a commercial TV and a public radio station) and Northwestern's Medill School of Journalism (which operates news services in Chicago and Washington, D.C.), have strong reputations in newsrooms.

For fledgling journalists who need help jump-starting their careers, connections to leading media organizations may be J-schools' strongest selling point. "If a journalism professor from Columbia calls and says, 'I've got a student you should take a look at here,' that carries weight with me," says Mark Seibel, managing editor of the *Miami Herald.* Many J-school alums say that simply securing job interviews with midsize media organizations was all but

impossible without getting help from a university's career placement office. Before enrolling at Medill in 1994, Joanne Gerstner edited publications for sports leagues like the NBA. As her program wound down, she interviewed with nearly a dozen news outlets that Medill had invited to campus. She took an internship with the *Cincinnati Enquirer* that led to a string of other reporting jobs—and to her current "dream job" as a sportswriter for the *Detroit News.*

Success stories notwithstanding, many news execs say they prefer job candidates with master's degrees in other fields. (Columbia's J-school has even suspended its search for a new dean as it considers whether to give students more-scholarly training.) Jane Fritsch, assistant bureau chief for the Associated Press in Chicago, recommends a master's in "history, literature—almost anything *other* than journalism." ●

MEDILL STUDENTS RACK UP 1,000 BYLINES A YEAR IN CHICAGO NEWSPAPERS THROUGH THE MEDILL NEWS SERVICE.

The Arts & Sciences Programs

Before you start the long, hard slog toward a master's or Ph.D., you'll want to investigate what it will *really* take for you to snag that degree—and where the jobs are afterward. How do you pick a school? How do you persuade a school to pick you? This chapter will tell you all that and more, with sections on the sciences, social sciences, humanities, arts, and creative writing—plus the exclusive *U.S. News* rankings.

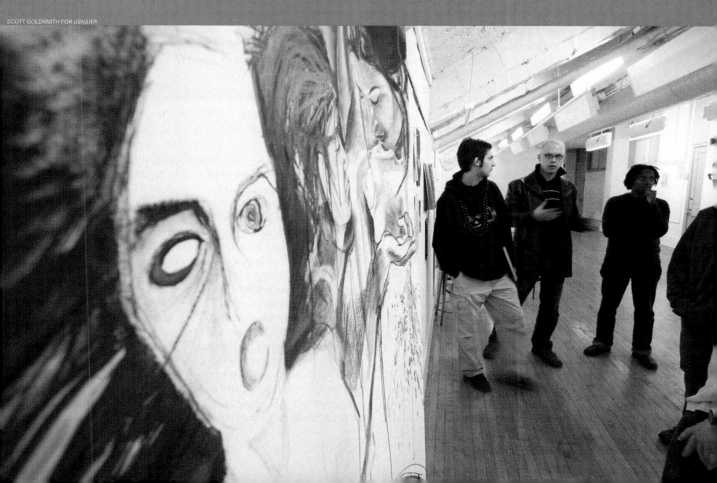

A long day at the MLA

BY ANDREW CURRY

It was 4:30 on a Saturday afternoon in New York, and Sam Cohen was amazingly calm, all things considered. The newly minted Ph.D. and father of a 3-day-old son had just been through five job interviews in 24 hours. Five more were scheduled for Sunday. Pausing over a cup of coffee in a packed hotel bar, he decided things had gone well so far—nothing like the year before, when nine heavyweights from a top English department sat him in an overstuffed wingback chair and grilled him for 50 minutes. "It can be really nice and intimate, or it can get really ugly," Cohen says. "So far, they've all been pleasant people who realize the artificiality of the whole thing."

At the Modern Language Association meetings, where Cohen was job hunting, interviews were held in hotel rooms scattered across midtown Manhattan or in "the pit": a football-field-size conference room neatly lined with 154 tables, sometimes with 154 conversations going on at once. Elsewhere, nervous graduate students in ill-fitting suits sat staring hard at nothing in particular, tapping fingers and compulsively checking watches.

It's a scene repeated at academic conventions around the country where thousands compete for a shrinking pool of jobs. Officials at this year's MLA announced a 20 percent decline in job openings—the steepest drop in more than a decade. "It's really hard to take people into the community, train them, and then wash your hands of them when

34.5% OF 2001 HUMANITIES PH.D.'S GRADUATED WITHOUT JOBS OF ANY KIND.

they enter a difficult job market," says MLA president and Harvard English professor Stephen Greenblatt. Increasingly, doctoral students are having second thoughts. "People leave the field because there isn't a future for them," says Stanford University comparative literature professor Haun Saussy. In 2000–2001, the number of doctorates earned in English or American literature declined almost 10 percent.

Still, departments receive hundreds of applications in popular fields like American literature or Spanish. They whittle that down to 10 or 20 candidates who are interviewed at the convention, and maybe invite three or four to a final-round visit on campus. But the scale of the convention and the rush of interviews turn it into a uniquely pressured environment. Candidates must sum up years of research and writing —the average Ph.D. student at the MLA has been in grad school

CATRINA GENOVESE FOR *USN&WR*

COLUMBIA UNIVERSITY PH.D. SAM COHEN HAD 10 JOB INTERVIEWS AT THIS YEAR'S MLA—JUST DAYS AFTER THE BIRTH OF HIS SON.

more than eight years—in 20 minutes. A first impression may determine an entire career. Interviewers are well aware they may be spending the next several decades with the grad student now wedged into their hotel room. And having to act as a personnel officer makes lots of profs uncomfortable, resulting in an interview process that is painful for those on both sides of the table.

With jobs so tight, there's always the temptation to specialize in a field that looks hot. But given the time commitment a doctorate represents, it's a bad idea. "You can't predict at all who's going to be retiring, how long it's going to take you to finish, or how good the market is going to be when you get out," says Stephanie O'Hara, a Duke University Romance Studies Ph.D. specializing in 17th-century French literature. "You have to go with what you feel most passionate about." ●

U.S.News will fund three scholarships totaling $10,000

to be used for graduate study during the 2004-2005 academic year.

Eligibility: Applicants must be college seniors or graduates who will enter graduate programs of study at accredited colleges or universities during the 2004-2005 academic year. Students already enrolled in graduate programs are ineligible to participate.

Scholarship recipients will be selected on the basis of academic record, participation in college and community activities, and essay. Recipients are selected solely by Citizen's Scholarship Foundation of America Inc. (CSFA). Decisions are final.

Awards: Three (3) scholarships will be awarded -- $5,000, $3,000 and $2,000. The awards are for one year only. The scholarships may be used to pay for graduate tuition only.

How to Apply: The application process is simple. **Go to www.usnews.com/gradscholarship/** and print out the application. Complete and submit the application form, along with a transcript of school grades and an essay to the scholarship administrator, CSFA. If you are unable to print this application, please send a self-addressed stamped envelope with your name, mailing address and e-mail address to:

U.S.News & World Report
Graduate Scholarship Program 2004
Attn: Emily Sopha
1050 Thomas Jefferson Street, NW
Washington, DC 20007

An application will be mailed to you.

For more information, go to www.usnews.com/gradscholarship/

State of the unions

BY VICKY HALLETT

Last summer, Cornell made a historic announcement, unique among private universities: If its teaching assistants chose to unionize, the administration would honor the vote. But although many of her fellow graduate students seemed sold on the idea, Amanda Holland-Minkley, a 29-year-old computer-science Ph.D. candidate, was wary of the plan. She helped found a group dedicated to discussing the downside of unionization. "People weren't aware of basic things—like you have to pay union dues," she says. On election day, with 90 percent turnout, the union was soundly defeated.

As the economy has forced educational institutions to cut budgets, graduate students have increasingly shouldered a greater workload as teaching and research assistants, often without substantial pay or healthcare benefits. Elizabeth Williamson, a graduate student in English at the University of Pennsylvania who is organizing her school's union drive, says some of her friends have had to take incompletes in their courses in order to keep up with their grading workloads. And even with a recent stipend increase, she says, the amount of money TAs earn (about $15,000 annually) is not nearly enough to live on in Philadelphia. The solution, say unionization fans, is for grad students to organize and bargain collectively over everything from wages to workloads. For groups like the United Auto Workers and the AFL-CIO, campuses are untapped

UNIONS NOW REPRESENT NEARLY 40,000 TEACHING ASSISTANTS NATIONWIDE. MORE THAN A THIRD ARE MEMBERS OF THE UNITED AUTO WORKERS.

GRADUATE TEACHING ASSISTANTS WENT ON STRIKE AT THE UNIVERSITY OF WASHINGTON.

sources of membership as the number of unionized industries drops. And a growing number of grad students are signing up.

The University of Wisconsin–Madison unionized back in 1969, and a few other public institutions have organized since then, but it is only in the past few years that private schools have joined in. When the National Labor Relations Board ruled in 2000 that graduate students at New York University could unionize, it created a domino effect: Unionizing campaigns sprouted up all over at places like Brown, Columbia, and Pennsylvania State University.

Union foes say grad students shouldn't be viewed as workers but as apprentices, whose teaching and research duties prepare them to become academics. Introducing union negotiations and work rules into the halls of academe, they fear, will turn what should be collegial relationships between professors and students into difficult, even adversarial ones. "Before, a student could sit down with a faculty member and talk about his problems," says NYU humanities Prof. Herb London. "All of that is gone now." But to students like Williamson, unionizing is a crucial symbol of recognition. Otherwise, student demands have no teeth, she explains: "We can say, 'Gosh, we really need a better healthcare plan.' But there's no power behind that voice."

Union detractors at Cornell had success with their arguments about the professional ramifications of striking when employed by an adviser, the bureaucracy of the grievance process, and the possibility that the UAW could eventually put professional organizers in charge, rather than students. But plenty of students elsewhere remain convinced that unions are a necessity. Even the prospect of unionization, some say, is enough to improve conditions. Anita Seth, head of Yale's decade-long organizing effort, says that although the university has yet to recognize the union, the fight has fattened grad students' stipends and secured free healthcare coverage. "It has made Yale a more amazing place," she says. ●

THE SCIENCES

Campus insecurity

BY RACHEL HARTIGAN SHEA

tephen St. Jeor, a professor of microbiology at the University of Nevada–Reno, is all for fighting terrorism, but he doesn't want the battle to completely disrupt his lab. St. Jeor studies viruses like South American hemorrhagic fever, which is among 82 potential biological weapons to which the Centers for Disease Control and Prevention and the Department of Agriculture have limited access for research purposes. Since the university installed an expensive security system last year, St. Jeor needs a key card to enter his lab, and he must account for every one of the hundreds of vials of virus in his freezer. Those security measures don't bother him, though. What he worries about are new restrictions on his graduate students, most of whom come from foreign nations. "These people came here because I am working on viruses present in their countries," he says. "Now I'm supposed to run background checks on them."

The homeland security debate promises to have far-reaching consequences for scientists and universities. "The war on terrorism will be won in the laboratory just as much as on the battlefield," said Sherwood Boehlert, a Republican representative from New York, at a congressional hearing last fall. But the drive for innovation coexists uneasily with the need to keep the country safe. Scientists and policymakers are struggling to come up with ways to maintain the openness that allows scientists to build on one another's work, while preventing terrorists from obtaining information and materials that could be used to launch deadly attacks.

This discussion is not new. In the late 1930s, for example, the National Research Council, the policy arm of the National Academy of Sciences, set up a group to review, and censor, papers of military import. At other times, government officials have stepped in: In 1985, the Pentagon prevented some American scientists from presenting unclassified papers at an international conference on optical engineering because it didn't want the Soviets to find out about U.S. laser research. With bioterrorism

JIM LO SCALZO FOR *USN&WR*

CINDY SHIH BAITS A MAZE TO TEST THE MEMORY OF GENETICALLY MODIFIED MICE. SHE IS A PH.D. CANDIDATE IN BRAIN AND COGNITIVE SCIENCES AT MIT.

now a major threat to national security—and the main focus of federally funded research, with $2.9 billion requested for 2003—there's already been loud criticism of scientists who have published "weaponizable" research. "Before September 11," says Ariella Rosengard, an immunobiology researcher at the University of Pennsylvania, "most people yawned when I told them that I worked on a smallpox protein." But last spring, her article in the *Proceedings of the National Academy of Sciences* describing how that protein blocks one part of the human immune response to the disease was accompanied by an editorial defending its publication. And last summer, Eckard Wimmer, a molecular biologist at the State University of New York–Stony Brook, found his work on poliovirus denounced on the floor of the House of Representatives.

Neither Rosengard nor Wimmer broke any laws by publishing their research. But in February 2003 the editors of more than 20 scientific journals agreed to carefully monitor articles containing potentially dangerous information. Since 9/11 there has also been a flurry of new regulations for laboratories. All researchers studying "select agents"—the lethal viruses, toxins, bacteria, and fungi restricted by the government—must undergo background checks through the Department of Justice, which wants to ferret out any terrorist ties. People from countries that have been determined to support terrorism may not work with select agents. Labs must tighten security as well, locking up the select agents when they will be out of direct view of authorized staff and closely watching workers without security clearances, such as janitors.

The most contentious issue in university labs, however, is whether federally funded research

45% OF PHYSICAL SCIENCE DOCTORATES ARE EARNED BY FOREIGN STUDENTS.

will be subject to review before it can be published. After scientists protested the optical engineering censorship, the Reagan administration resolved the matter by declaring that the government can control the release of potentially sensitive information only by declaring it classified up front—before a grant is awarded and the work begun. Last spring, however, the Pentagon announced that all research financed by the Department of Defense, classified or not, would be assessed before scientists could publish. After a storm of protest, the requirement was shelved.

Lately, though, the term "sensitive but unclassified" has been popping up in research contracts from the Defense Department to the Federal Aviation Administration. "It's not a category with an honest-to-God definition," says Gail Habicht, vice president for research at SUNY–Stony Brook, who fears that the vague wording implies that research may be examined for sensitive content at any time and access to its results restricted. Critics of the policy argue that public health is undermined when major developments are hidden from other scientists. And researchers could be stuck with years of

Finding a lab for you

Choosing and getting into science Ph.D. programs seems a lot simpler than applying to college: You pick departments strong in your area of interest, and the admitting professors select you based on your academic record and test scores. They don't care about your skills with the bassoon or whether your football team had a winning season. But there's more to picking a graduate school program than academics. Check out the other factors that can make or break your doctoral experience, along with some hints on what schools want to see on your application:

A high graduation rate. Some programs accept a relatively large number of students and then use the first few years to weed out those who are less promising, by denying them either adequate funding or the attention they need to progress

toward a thesis. Be prepared to ask questions faculty don't always like to answer: What percentage of students are fully funded? What fraction leave before earning a Ph.D.?

A short time to degree. Washington University in St. Louis dramatically shortened the time its grad students spent on campus by accepting only Ph.D. candidates it could support financially for the time it would take to finish their dissertations. Student morale has shot up, says dean Robert Thach, and degree completion now averages just six years—shorter than the national average by more than one year.

A flexible advising system. Many schools are making it easier for students to pick a compatible adviser. Instead of arriving on campus with an adviser already selected, first-year Har-

vard molecular biology students rotate through four labs so they can get a feel for the professors running them. This opportunity to choose has served Adam Fagen, 32, in good stead. When he realized he preferred teaching to research, his adviser helped him negotiate university bureaucracy to set up a degree in both microbiology and education.

Job help. More than 25 percent of science Ph.D.'s go on to jobs outside academia. "All schools need to do a better job of being more creative about finding alternatives to academic careers," says Kristin Williams, dean of graduate student enrollment at George Washington University. Schools like Yale and the University of Pennsylvania have opened career services offices separate from those serving undergraduates.

Writing skills. It's no surprise that admissions committees ex-work that is unpublishable—a career killer in these days of publish or perish. Replying to those concerns, John Marburger, director of the White House's Office of Science and Technology Policy, said recently that only in "rare and exceptional circumstances" will the government restrict nonclassified research on national security grounds.

Even so, academics worry especially about how graduate students will be affected. "A grad student at the beginning of his career is in a vulnerable position if the world doesn't know what he did," says Habicht. She and other university officials also wonder whether graduate students, and their thesis advisers, will be able to access their own data once research has been declared sensitive. The Massachusetts Institute of Technology has decided to avoid the issue altogether: The school announced last summer that it would not accept contracts that allow the funding agency to declare the research sensitive. Says President Charles Vest, "Areas such as biology progress and change so rapidly that it is going to be impossible to bureaucratically establish lists of what kind of work is off limits for whom." But the school still supports off-campus classified research at federally funded centers such as the MIT-affiliated Lincoln Laboratory in Lexington, Mass.

So far, Stephen St. Jeor's graduate students have faced relatively few problems. Argentine Mariana Bego has had trouble sending hantavirus cultures to her country's National Institute for Biological Research, and Russian Albert Rizvanov's visa renewal has been delayed. Varough Mohamed Deyde was thoroughly searched last time he traveled home to Mauritania, but he shrugs off the inconvenience. These students understand the dangers of letting biological agents into the wrong hands. But, along with their professors, they worry about security measures so sweeping that they may discourage legitimate research by the foreign students who flock to America's vaunted graduate programs. That could mean fewer scientists will be doing the very work that could combat bioterrorism. ●

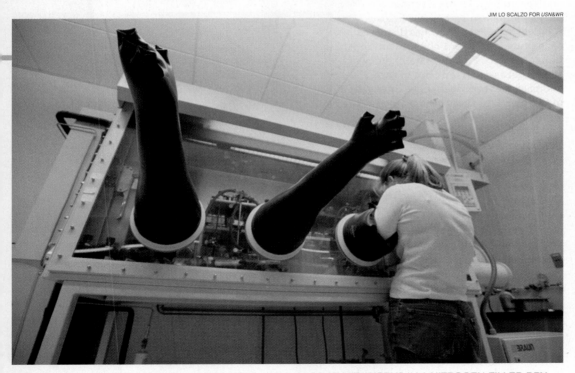

EMILY CARSON, A THIRD-YEAR CHEMISTRY PH.D. CANDIDATE AT MIT, WORKS IN A NITROGEN-FILLED DRY GLOVE BOX BECAUSE THE COMPOUNDS SHE IS SYNTHESIZING ARE OXYGEN-SENSITIVE.

pect to see impressive performances in upper division courses in the sciences, but they also want to confirm that you can write and speak clearly. A grade of D in English composition "spells doom for the future thesis adviser," says Calvin Barnes, a professor in the geosciences department at Texas Tech University in Lubbock.

Undergraduate research. With more colleges encouraging undergraduate research, it has almost become a requirement for admittance to science programs. "Graduate schools know that the success rate of students who have done undergraduate research is very high," says James Gentile, dean of the natural sciences at Hope College in Holland, Mich. A further advantage to engaging in research: You're likely to get to know a professor well, which can come in handy when it's time to ask for recommendations. At Harvard's physics department, a recommendation from a professorial research partner is very important, followed by grades and test scores, says Gary Feldman, the department's graduate admissions committee chair. And some faculty have pipelines straight to good programs. University of Washington physicist John Rehr says he relies on a few professors at Reed College, among other schools, to direct their strongest students his way. ●

MAD FOR SCIENTISTS

Scientists haven't completely escaped the economic downturn. Pharmaceutical and biotech companies aren't recruiting as aggressively as they had been, industry labs have shut down, and some cash-strapped universities aren't hiring at all. But despite the slowdown, science Ph.D.'s "have too many skills not to find a position," says Eleanor Babco, the executive director of the nonprofit Commission on Professionals in Science and Technology. Here's a rundown on the job outlook in several key fields:

IN 1966, WOMEN EARNED 8% OF SCIENCE AND ENGINEERING PH.D.'S; BY 1997, THE PROPORTION HAD RISEN TO 33%.

Patent law. "Patent law has displaced consulting as the No. 1 nonacademic option for science Ph.D.'s," says Malaina Brown, an assistant director of career and placement services at the University of Chicago. Law firms need science advisers to translate scientific language into layperson-friendly patent applications. Bioinformatics and genomics are particularly hot right now, but people with doctorates in other fields who can write clearly and have some work experience outside academia are also getting snapped up by recruiters. On the patent-granting end, the U.S. Patent and Trademark Office plans to hire 750 examiners in the next two years.

Academia. Despite hopes that a wave of retirements would lead to the mass hiring of new Ph.D.'s, the professorial market is not encouraging. While 40 percent of new math graduates landed campus jobs in 2001, only 9 percent of graduating biologists got hired in academia. Even teaching-intensive jobs at liberal arts colleges are highly competitive. The people getting hired tend to do cross-disciplinary work—computational biology, for example—and have at least two postdocs under their belt. Indeed, over a quarter of all new Ph.D.'s head directly to postdoctoral study after finishing their dissertation.

Forensic science. With law enforcement agencies eager to use DNA evidence to solve everything from murders to petty larceny, experts predict that as many as 10,000 forensic scientists will be hired in the next decade. Private labs like Bode Technology Group in Springfield, Va., are expanding by recruiting Ph.D. chemists, biochemists, geneticists, molecular biologists, and statisticians. Salaries start around $55,000 and rise quickly once new hires have been trained in forensic work. In 2000, while finishing up his dissertation on green algae, botanist Matthew Cimino was hired by Bode to develop new ways to analyze plant DNA in dust from crime scenes. His tests help police determine if a suspect has been near

JIM LO SCALZO FOR *USN&WR*

A PH.D. STUDENT IN EARTH ATMOSPHERIC AND PLANETARY SCIENCES SLICES BEDROCK SAMPLES FOR ANALYSIS.

the crime scene. Last summer, he joined a new forensic biotechnology company as a principal investigator, where he writes his own grant proposals, works on his own projects, and makes far more than he could as an academic.

Government intelligence. The continuing war on terrorism requires more than soldiers: Federal agencies like the CIA, the National Security Agency, and the Department of Defense need scientists to assess biological and chemical warfare threats, computer specialists to develop communications systems, and mathematicians to analyze data and crack codes. Salaries for scientists and analysts start around $35,000 but can go much higher. ●

The Sciences

PH.D. PROGRAMS RANKED BEST BY DEANS AND DEPARTMENT CHAIRS

BIOLOGICAL SCIENCES

Ranked in 2002

Programs surveyed are drawn from the National Science Foundation's "Science and Engineering Doctorate Awards: 1999." Listed schools may have multiple programs. Methodology is on Page 75.

Rank/School	Average assessment score (5=highest)
1. Stanford University (CA)	4.9
2. Harvard University (MA)	4.8
Massachusetts Institute of Technology	4.8
University of California–Berkeley	4.8
5. California Institute of Technology	4.7
Johns Hopkins University (MD)	4.7
University of California–San Francisco	4.7
8. Rockefeller University (NY)	4.6
9. Princeton University (NJ)	4.5
Scripps Research Institute (CA)	4.5
Yale University (CT)	4.5
12. Duke University (NC)	4.4
University of Wisconsin–Madison	4.4
14. Columbia University (NY)	4.3
Cornell University (NY)	4.3
University of California–San Diego	4.3
University of Michigan–Ann Arbor	4.3
Univ. of Texas Southwestern Medical Center–Dallas	4.3
Washington University in St. Louis	4.3
20. University of California–Los Angeles	4.2
University of Chicago	4.2
University of Washington	4.2
23. University of Pennsylvania	4.1
24. Baylor College of Medicine (TX)	4.0
University of California–Davis	4.0
University of Illinois–Urbana-Champaign	4.0
27. University of Colorado–Boulder	3.9
University of North Carolina–Chapel Hill	3.9
29. Cornell University (Weill) (NY)	3.7
Emory University (GA)	3.7
Mayo Medical School (MN)	3.7
University of Minnesota–Twin Cities	3.7
University of Texas–Austin	3.7
Vanderbilt University (TN)	3.7
Yeshiva University (Albert Einstein) (NY)	3.7
36. Brandeis University (MA)	3.6
Northwestern University (IL)	3.6
Purdue University–West Lafayette (IN)	3.6
University of California–Irvine	3.6
University of Virginia	3.6
41. Case Western Reserve University (OH)	3.5
Indiana University–Bloomington	3.5
University of Arizona	3.5
University of Colorado Health Sciences Center	3.5
45. Brown University (RI)	3.4
Dartmouth College (NH)	3.4
Michigan State University	3.4
Pennsylvania State University–University Park	3.4
Rice University (TX)	3.4
SUNY–Stony Brook	3.4

Rank/School	Average assessment score (5=highest)
University of Alabama–Birmingham	3.4
University of Iowa	3.4
University of Maryland–College Park	3.4
54. Carnegie Mellon University (PA)	3.3
Ohio State University	3.3
Rutgers State University–New Brunswick (NJ)	3.3
University of Florida	3.3
University of Georgia	3.3
University of Oregon	3.3
60. Texas A&M University–College Station	3.2
Tufts University (MA)	3.2
University of California–Santa Barbara	3.2
University of Massachusetts–Amherst	3.2
University of Pittsburgh	3.2
University of Rochester (NY)	3.2
University of Texas Health Science Center–Houston	3.2
University of Utah	3.2

BIOLOGICAL SCIENCES SPECIALTIES

BIOCHEMISTRY
1. Harvard University (MA)
2. Stanford University (CA)
3. Univ. of Calif.–San Francisco
4. Johns Hopkins Univ. (MD)
   Univ. of California–Berkeley
6. Univ. of Wisconsin–Madison
7. Massachusetts Inst. of Tech.
8. California Inst. of Tech.
9. Univ. of Texas Southwestern Medical Center–Dallas
10. Rockefeller University (NY)
    Yale University (CT)

CELL BIOLOGY
1. Harvard University (MA)
   Stanford University (CA)
3. Massachusetts Inst. of Tech.
   Univ. of Calif.–San Francisco
   Yale University (CT)
6. Johns Hopkins Univ. (MD)
7. Rockefeller University (NY)
8. Univ. of California–Berkeley
9. California Inst. of Tech.
10. Washington University in St. Louis

MICROBIOLOGY
1. Harvard University (MA)
2. Stanford University (CA)
3. Univ. of Wisconsin–Madison
4. Johns Hopkins Univ. (MD)
   University of Illinois–Urbana-Champaign
6. Wash. Univ. in St. Louis

7. Univ. of Calif.–Los Angeles
   University of Michigan–Ann Arbor
9. Univ. of Calif.–San Francisco
   University of Washington

NEUROSCIENCE
1. Univ. of Calif.–San Francisco
2. Harvard University (MA)
3. Stanford University (CA)
4. Columbia University (NY)
   Johns Hopkins Univ. (MD)
6. Washington University in St. Louis
7. Univ. of Calif.–San Diego
8. Yale University (CT)
9. Univ. of Calif.–Los Angeles
10. Duke University (NC)
    University of Pennsylvania
    University of Washington

MOLECULAR BIOLOGY
1. Harvard University (MA)
2. Stanford University (CA)
3. Massachusetts Inst. of Tech.
4. Univ. of California–Berkeley
5. Johns Hopkins Univ. (MD)
6. Princeton University (NJ)
   Univ. of Calif.–San Francisco
8. California Inst. of Technology
9. Yale University (CT)
10. Univ. of Texas Southwestern Medical Center–Dallas
    Univ. of Wis.–Madison
    Wash. Univ. in St. Louis

CHEMISTRY

Ranked in 2002

Rank/School	Average assessment score (5=highest)
1. University of California–Berkeley	5.0
2. California Institute of Technology	4.9
Harvard University (MA)	4.9
Massachusetts Institute of Technology	4.9
5. Stanford University (CA)	4.8
6. Scripps Research Institute (CA)	4.5
University of Illinois–Urbana-Champaign	4.5
8. Columbia University (NY)	4.4
Cornell University (NY)	4.4
University of Wisconsin–Madison	4.4
11. University of California–Los Angeles	4.3
12. Northwestern University (IL)	4.2
University of Texas–Austin	4.2
14. Princeton University (NJ)	4.1
University of Chicago	4.1
University of North Carolina–Chapel Hill	4.1
Yale University (CT)	4.1
18. Pennsylvania State Univ.–University Park	4.0
Purdue University–West Lafayette (IN)	4.0
University of Pennsylvania	4.0
21. University of Michigan–Ann Arbor	3.9
22. Ohio State University	3.8
Texas A&M University–College Station	3.8
University of California–San Diego	3.8
University of Colorado–Boulder	3.8
University of Minnesota–Twin Cities	3.8
27. Indiana University–Bloomington	3.7
Johns Hopkins University (MD)	3.7
University of Washington	3.7
30. University of California–Irvine	3.6
University of California–Santa Barbara	3.6
32. Georgia Institute of Technology	3.5
Iowa State University	3.5
Michigan State University	3.5
Rice University (TX)	3.5
University of Florida	3.5
37. Colorado State University	3.4
University of Arizona	3.4
University of California–Davis	3.4
University of California–San Francisco	3.4
University of Pittsburgh	3.4
University of Utah	3.4
43. Duke University (NC)	3.3
Emory University (GA)	3.3
University of Maryland–College Park	3.3
Washington University in St. Louis	3.3
47. SUNY–Stony Brook	3.2
University of Rochester (NY)	3.2
University of Southern California	3.2
University of Virginia	3.2

CHEMISTRY SPECIALTIES

ANALYTIC
1. Univ. of North Carolina–Chapel Hill
2. Purdue University–West Lafayette (IN)
3. University of Illinois–Urbana-Champaign
4. Indiana Univ.–Bloomington
5. Iowa State University
6. University of Arizona

7. University of Florida
8. Pennsylvania State University–University Park
9. University of Texas–Austin
10. Univ. of Wisconsin–Madison

INORGANIC
1. Massachusetts Inst. of Tech.
2. California Inst. of Technology
3. Northwestern University (IL)
4. Univ. of California–Berkeley
5. University of Illinois–Urbana-Champaign
6. Texas A&M University–College Station
7. Stanford University (CA)
8. Univ. of Wisconsin–Madison
9. Univ. of North Carolina–Chapel Hill
10. Univ. of Minn.–Twin Cities

ORGANIC
1. Harvard University (MA)
2. Scripps Research Inst. (CA)
3. Univ. of California–Berkeley
4. Massachusetts Inst. of Tech.
5. California Inst. of Technology
6. Stanford University (CA)
7. Columbia University (NY)
8. University of Illinois–Urbana-Champaign
9. Univ. of Wisconsin–Madison
10. University of Pennsylvania

PHYSICAL
1. Univ. of California–Berkeley
2. California Inst. of Technology
3. Massachusetts Inst. of Tech.
4. Stanford University (CA)
5. Harvard University (MA)
6. University of Chicago
7. University of Colorado–Boulder
   Univ. of Wisconsin–Madison
9. University of Illinois–Urbana-Champaign
10. Columbia University (NY)
    Cornell University (NY)

COMPUTER SCIENCE

Ranked in 2002

Rank/School	Average assessment score (5=highest)
1. Carnegie Mellon University (PA)	4.9
Massachusetts Institute of Technology	4.9
Stanford University (CA)	4.9
University of California–Berkeley	4.9
5. University of Illinois–Urbana-Champaign	4.6
6. Cornell University (NY)	4.5
7. University of Texas–Austin	4.4
University of Washington	4.4
9. Princeton University (NJ)	4.3
10. California Institute of Technology	4.1
University of Wisconsin–Madison	4.1
12. Georgia Institute of Technology	4.0
University of Maryland–College Park	4.0
14. Brown University (RI)	3.9
University of California–Los Angeles	3.9
University of Michigan–Ann Arbor	3.9
17. Rice University (TX)	3.8
University of North Carolina–Chapel Hill	3.8
University of Pennsylvania	3.8
20. Columbia University (NY)	3.7
Duke University (NC)	3.7
Harvard University (MA)	3.7
Purdue University–West Lafayette (IN)	3.7
University of California–San Diego	3.7
25. University of Massachusetts–Amherst	3.6
Yale University (CT)	3.6
27. University of Southern California	3.5
University of Virginia	3.5
29. Johns Hopkins University (MD)	3.3
New York University	3.3
Rutgers State University–New Brunswick (NJ)	3.3
SUNY–Stony Brook	3.3
University of California–Irvine	3.3
University of Utah	3.3

Rank/School	Average assessment score (5=highest)
35. Ohio State University	3.2
Pennsylvania State University–University Park	3.2
University of Arizona	3.2
University of Chicago	3.2
University of Colorado–Boulder	3.2
University of Minnesota–Twin Cities	3.2
Washington University in St. Louis	3.2

COMPUTER SCIENCE SPECIALTIES

SYSTEMS

1. Univ. of California–Berkeley
2. Carnegie Mellon Univ. (PA)
   Massachusetts Inst. of Tech.
4. Stanford University (CA)
5. University of Washington
6. University of Illinois–Urbana-Champaign
7. Univ. of Wisconsin–Madison
8. Georgia Inst. of Technology
9. University of Texas–Austin
10. Rice University (TX)

6. Carnegie Mellon Univ. (PA)
7. Harvard University (MA)
   University of Washington
9. Yale University (CT)
10. Brown University (RI)

ARTIFICIAL INTELLIGENCE

1. Massachusetts Inst. of Tech.
2. Carnegie Mellon Univ. (PA)
3. Stanford University (CA)
4. Univ. of California–Berkeley
5. University of Texas–Austin
6. Univ. of Massachusetts–Amherst
7. University of Pennsylvania
   University of Washington
9. University of Illinois–Urbana-Champaign
10. Univ. of Mich.–Ann Arbor

THEORY

1. Massachusetts Inst. of Tech.
2. Univ. of California–Berkeley
3. Cornell University (NY)
4. Princeton University (NJ)
5. Stanford University (CA)

GEOLOGY

Ranked in 1999

Rank/School	Average assessment score (5=highest)
1. California Institute of Technology	4.9
2. Massachusetts Institute of Technology	4.8
3. Stanford University (CA)	4.5
University of California–Berkeley	4.5
5. Columbia University (NY)	4.3
University of Michigan–Ann Arbor	4.3
7. Harvard University (MA)	4.1
Pennsylvania State University–University Park	4.1
University of Arizona	4.1
10. University of Chicago	4.0
11. Cornell University (NY)	3.9
Johns Hopkins University (MD)	3.9
Princeton University (NJ)	3.9
University of California–Los Angeles	3.9
University of California–San Diego	3.9
University of Texas–Austin	3.9
17. University of Wisconsin–Madison	3.8
18. Brown University (RI)	3.7
University of Washington	3.7
20. Yale University (CT)	3.6
21. University of California–Santa Barbara	3.5
University of Minnesota–Twin Cities	3.5
23. University of California–Santa Cruz	3.4
Washington University in St. Louis	3.4
25. Arizona State University	3.3
SUNY–Stony Brook	3.3
University of California–Davis	3.3

GEOLOGY SPECIALTIES

GEOPHYSICS

1. California Inst. of Technology
2. Massachusetts Inst. of Tech.
3. Stanford University (CA)
4. Columbia University (NY)
5. Univ. of California–Berkeley
6. Univ. of California–San Diego
7. Harvard University (MA)
8. Princeton University (NJ)
9. University of Washington
10. University of California–Los Angeles

GEOCHEMISTRY

1. California Inst. of Technology
2. Univ. of Michigan–Ann Arbor
3. Univ. of California–Berkeley
4. Massachusetts Inst. of Tech.
5. Penn State University–University Park
6. Columbia University (NY)
7. Yale University (CT)
8. University of Chicago
9. Harvard University (MA)
10. Washington Univ. in St. Louis

TECTONICS/STRUCTURE

1. Massachusetts Inst. of Tech.
2. Stanford University (CA)
3. California Inst. of Technology
4. Cornell University (NY)
   University of Arizona
6. University of Texas–Austin
7. Princeton University (NJ)
8. University of California–Santa Barbara
9. Columbia University (NY)
10. University of California–Los Angeles

HYDROGEOLOGY

1. University of Arizona
2. Stanford University (CA)

3. University of Wisconsin–Madison
4. New Mexico Institute of Mining and Technology
5. Penn State University–University Park
6. University of Texas–Austin
7. University of Minnesota–Twin Cities
8. Massachusetts Institute of Tech.
   University of Illinois–Urbana-Champaign
   University of Nevada–Reno

PALEONTOLOGY

1. Univ. of California–Berkeley
2. University of Chicago
3. Harvard University (MA)
4. University of Michigan–Ann Arbor
5. University of Kansas
6. Yale University (CT)
7. University of Iowa
8. Ohio State University
9. University of Cincinnati
   University of Texas–Austin

SEDIMENTOLOGY/STRATIGRAPHY

1. University of Texas–Austin
2. University of Michigan–Ann Arbor
3. Penn State University–University Park
4. University of Arizona
5. Stanford University (CA)
6. Massachusetts Inst. of Tech.
   University of Wisconsin–Madison
8. Columbia University (NY)
9. Virginia Tech
10. University of Kansas

APPLIED MATHEMATICS

Ranked in 2002

Rank/School	Average assessment score (5=highest)
1. Massachusetts Institute of Technology	4.7
New York University	4.7
3. California Institute of Technology	4.6
4. Stanford University (CA)	4.5
5. Brown University (RI)	4.4
Princeton University (NJ)	4.4
University of California–Berkeley	4.4
University of California–Los Angeles	4.4
9. University of Minnesota–Twin Cities	4.3
10. Cornell University (NY)	4.2
11. Carnegie Mellon University (PA)	4.0
University of Maryland–College Park	4.0

Rank/School	Average assessment score (5=highest)
University of Texas–Austin	4.0
14. Northwestern University (IL)	3.9
Rice University (TX)	3.9
University of Washington	3.9
University of Wisconsin–Madison	3.9
18. Georgia Institute of Technology	3.8
University of Chicago	3.8
University of Michigan–Ann Arbor	3.8
21. Harvard University (MA)	3.7
Rensselaer Polytechnic Institute (NY)	3.7
Rutgers State University–New Brunswick (NJ)	3.7
SUNY–Stony Brook	3.7
University of Arizona	3.7
University of Colorado–Boulder	3.7
27. Duke University (NC)	3.6
Purdue University–West Lafayette	3.6
University of Illinois–Urbana-Champaign	3.6
Yale University (CT)	3.6
31. North Carolina State University	3.5
University of California–San Diego	3.5
33. Columbia University (NY)	3.4
Indiana University–Bloomington	3.4
Johns Hopkins University (MD)	3.4
Pennsylvania State University–University Park	3.4
University of California–Davis	3.4

JIM LO SCALZO FOR *USN&WR*

BIOLOGY AND CHEMISTRY GRAD STUDENTS AT AN MIT LAB

Rank/School	Average assessment score (5=highest)
Virginia Tech	3.4
39. Ohio State University	3.3
Texas A&M University–College Station	3.3
University of North Carolina–Chapel Hill	3.3
University of Utah	3.3

MATHEMATICS

Ranked in 2002

Rank/School	Average assessment score (5=highest)
1. Massachusetts Institute of Technology	5.0
2. Harvard University (MA)	4.9
Princeton University (NJ)	4.9
Stanford University (CA)	4.9
University of California–Berkeley	4.9
6. University of Chicago	4.8
7. Yale University (CT)	4.7
8. California Institute of Technology	4.6
University of Michigan–Ann Arbor	4.6
10. Cornell University (NY)	4.4
New York University (NY)	4.4
University of California–Los Angeles	4.4
13. Columbia University (NY)	4.3
University of Wisconsin–Madison	4.3
15. University of Texas–Austin	4.2
16. Rutgers State Univ.–New Brunswick (NJ)	4.1
University of Illinois–Urbana-Champaign	4.1
University of Maryland–College Park	4.1
University of Minnesota–Twin Cities	4.1
University of Pennsylvania	4.1
21. Brown University (RI)	4.0
Northwestern University (IL)	4.0
SUNY–Stony Brook	4.0
University of California–San Diego	4.0
25. Duke University (NC)	3.9
26. Indiana University–Bloomington	3.8
Johns Hopkins University (MD)	3.8
Pennsylvania State University–University Park	3.8
Purdue University–West Lafayette (IN)	3.8
Rice University (TX)	3.8
University of Washington	3.8
32. Ohio State University	3.7
University of North Carolina–Chapel Hill	3.7
34. Brandeis University (MA)	3.6
Carnegie Mellon University (PA)	3.6
CUNY Graduate School and University Center	3.6
37. Georgia Institute of Technology	3.5
Michigan State University	3.5
University of Illinois–Chicago	3.5
University of Utah	3.5
Washington University in St. Louis	3.5

PHYSICS

Ranked in 2002

Rank/School	Average assessment score (5=highest)
1. California Institute of Technology	5.0
Massachusetts Institute of Technology	5.0
3. Harvard University (MA)	4.9
Princeton University (NJ)	4.9
Stanford University (CA)	4.9

More at **www.usnews.com**

Rank/School	Average assessment score (5=highest)
University of California–Berkeley	4.9
7. Cornell University (NY)	4.6
University of Chicago	4.6
9. University of Illinois–Urbana-Champaign	4.5
10. Columbia University (NY)	4.3
University of California–Santa Barbara	4.3
12. Yale University (CT)	4.2
13. University of Maryland–College Park	4.1
University of Michigan–Ann Arbor	4.1
University of Texas–Austin	4.1
16. University of California–Los Angeles	4.0
University of California–San Diego	4.0
University of Washington	4.0
University of Wisconsin–Madison	4.0
20. Johns Hopkins University (MD)	3.9
University of Colorado–Boulder	3.9
University of Pennsylvania	3.9
23. SUNY–Stony Brook	3.8
24. Ohio State University	3.7
Rutgers State University–New Brunswick (NJ)	3.7
University of Minnesota–Twin Cities	3.7
27. Pennsylvania State University–University Park	3.6
28. Brown University (RI)	3.5
Carnegie Mellon University (PA)	3.5
Michigan State University	3.5
Northwestern University (IL)	3.5
32. Duke University (NC)	3.4
Georgia Institute of Technology	3.4
Indiana University–Bloomington	3.4
Purdue University–West Lafayette (IN)	3.4
Rice University (TX)	3.4
University of Rochester (NY)	3.4
38. Florida State University	3.3
University of Arizona	3.3
University of California–Irvine	3.3
University of Florida	3.3
University of North Carolina–Chapel Hill	3.3
University of Virginia	3.3

PHYSICS SPECIALTIES

ATOMIC/MOLECULAR/ OPTICAL/PLASMA

1. Massachusetts Institute of Technology
2. University of Colorado–Boulder
3. Stanford University (CA)
4. Harvard University (MA)
5. University of Michigan–Ann Arbor
6. University of Rochester (NY)
7. University of California–Berkeley
8. University of Texas–Austin
9. California Institute of Technology
10. Princeton University (NJ)

CONDENSED MATTER/ LOW TEMPERATURE

1. University of Illinois–Urbana-Champaign
2. Massachusetts Institute of Technology
3. Cornell University (NY)
4. Univ. of California–Berkeley
5. University of California–Santa Barbara
6. Harvard University (MA)
   Stanford University (CA)
8. Princeton University (NJ)
9. University of Chicago
10. University of Maryland–College Park

PHYSICS SPECIALTIES

ELEMENTARY PARTICLE/ NUCLEAR

1. Stanford University (CA)
2. Massachusetts Institute of Technology
3. California Institute of Technology

Univ. of California–Berkeley
5. Princeton University (NJ)
6. Harvard University (MA)
7. University of Chicago
8. SUNY–Stony Brook
   University of Washington
10. Cornell University (NY)

METHODOLOGY

Rankings of doctoral programs in the sciences are based on the results of surveys sent to academics in each discipline during the fall of 2001 (or, in the case of geology, during the fall of 1998). Rankings were published the following spring. The questionnaires asked individuals to rate the quality of the program at each institution on a 5-point scale: outstanding (5); strong (4); good (3); adequate (2); or marginal (1). Individuals who were unfamiliar with a particular school's programs were asked to select "don't know." Scores for each institution were totaled and divided by the number of respondents who rated that school.

Surveys in the biological sciences, chemistry, computer science, mathematics, applied mathematics, and physics were conducted by T. E. Systems Inc. The National Science Foundation report "Science and Engineering Doctorate Awards: 1999" was the source for the lists of programs surveyed in each of these disciplines. In the biological sciences, graduate programs may be offered in a university's medical school as well as its college of arts and sciences. In those cases where the NSF report showed two separate program listings at a university, the U.S. News survey did also. Otherwise, schools were listed only once on the survey, even though they may have programs in the biological sciences that are housed in separate institutional units.

Questionnaires were sent to the department heads and deans or directors of graduate studies at each program in each discipline. Response rates were as follows: for the biological sciences, 31 percent of those surveyed responded; for chemistry, 46 percent; for computer science, 57 percent; for mathematics, 43 percent; for applied mathematics, 40 percent; and for physics, 50 percent.

The survey of graduate programs in geology was conducted by Synovate. For geology, the survey covered all schools that had granted a total of five or more doctorates in the field during the five-year period from 1992 through 1996. Fifty-two percent of those surveyed responded.

SOCIAL SCIENCES
& HUMANITIES

A god in ruins?

BY RACHEL HARTIGAN SHEA

Is it worth the trouble? That's the question Jane Barnette kept asking herself last year. A Ph.D. candidate in theater history and criticism at the University of Texas–Austin, Barnette was hip deep in her dissertation on the effects of the burgeoning railroad system on Chicago-area theater when she started wondering why she was working so hard in a field with so few job prospects. "I was thinking that graduate school hadn't given me what I'd paid for," she says, "and that it was somebody else's fault besides my own."

If humanities scholars feel beleaguered, they've got good cause. The job market has been discouraging for years; their own university administrators seem to prefer economic development over literary theory; and the national media take pleasure in mocking their scholarly work as irrelevant and incomprehensible. But it turns out that malaise can be invigorating, as academics across the country realize that it is up to them to articulate why the humanities matter.

"I see them as a god in ruins stirring to take a proper place again," says Robert Weisbuch, the president of the Woodrow Wilson National Fellowship Foundation, an educational organization that seeks to reinvigorate the liberal arts. A tally of students who graduated in the 1999–2000 school year with bachelor's degrees in all of the humanities disciplines combined comes to less than half of those who majored in business. University donors are more likely to funnel their money toward scientific endeavors, which are already eating up a growing share of university budgets, sparking speculation that humanities and social science graduate students are losing out on assistantships, fellowships, and stipends.

Meanwhile, the race for tenure keeps getting more extreme. "Higher education stands to lose, or at least severely to damage, a generation of

young scholars," wrote Stephen Greenblatt, a noted Shakespeare scholar and the president of the Modern Language Association of America, in an open letter to the organization's members last spring. Most departments now require junior faculty to have published at least one book before they will be considered for tenure. (Some elite departments even require two.) Yet financially strapped university presses have had to scale back their lists in disciplines like philosophy, English, and foreign languages, heightening scholarly competition and anxiety.

But despite the dire anecdotes, no one can really say for sure how the humanities are faring. Unlike science education, which is tracked by the government-funded National Science Board as a matter of national importance, the humanities have never been thoroughly examined. "The humanities community itself, including its funders, knows deplorably little about what is taught to whom and by whom, how long it takes, where graduates and postgraduates go, what they do when they get there, and how many of them there are," says the Nobel Prize-winning economist Robert Solow, who is working with the American Academy of Arts and Sciences, an organization of prominent scholars, businesspeople, artists, and public servants, to come up with a system of collecting and analyzing data about the humanities. Members of the academy hope that they'll be able to track not only the humanists who stay in their field but the humanities majors who go on to other areas such as law or business, thereby measuring to some degree the contribution of humanists to society.

After all, there's as much evidence that the humanities are thriving as there is that they're doomed. For one thing, ordinary people still read history, biographies, and fiction. "Borders and Barnes & Noble are crowded from early morning to late night," says Weisbuch. And recent state

ONLY 44% OF HUMANITIES INSTRUCTORS TODAY ARE FULL TIME AND TENURE TRACK.

LESLIE HOLLAND, A FIRST-YEAR PH.D. STUDENT IN FRENCH AT THE UNIVERSITY OF TEXAS–AUSTIN

budget crises have not targeted the humanities more than any other disciplines. "The budget crisis shows that the core is liberal arts," says Edward Ayers, dean of the college and graduate school of arts and sciences at the University of Virginia. His school had to cut $3.9 million from its total budget of roughly $74 million, but "the stature of humanities was not diminished," he says. In fact, graduate-level funding actually increased. Brown University plans to open a new humanities center in about a year, a move that was unanimously supported by campus leaders. Dartmouth College successfully opened one three years ago that focuses on putting science and technology into context. "Most students still want something to help them generate a meaningful narrative for how they live their lives," says Eric Gould, chair of the English department at the University of Denver.

Meanwhile, scholars, employers, and students are thinking about the humanities in a different way. In his forthcoming book, *The University in a Corporate Culture*, Gould proposes that general undergraduate education should be organized around interdisciplinary topics such as the nature of capitalism, rather than divided by disciplinary lines. "It's taken humanities a little longer [than sciences] to move in the direction of interdisciplinary studies," says Linda Brady, dean of the humanities and social sciences college at North Car-

olina State University, but she reports that faculty at her school are getting grants from the National Science Foundation to develop programs with campus scientists in bioethics.

Some are drawing direct links between skills learned as, say, a philosopher to skills required to work for an arts organization or even a corporation. The Woodrow Wilson Foundation funds humanities graduate students who set up internships with nonacademic organizations such as broadcasting companies, for example, or museums, while the University of California–Davis may create a new "applied humanities" master's program to train students how to work in organizations that require both managerial and intellectual skills.

Jane Barnette herself is caught up in the revival. In the midst of her academic funk, she signed up for a course in UT's "intellectual entrepreneurship" program, which teaches grad students to think of ways their work can be applied to the world outside the ivory tower. "It busted my scholarship wide open," she says. Despite theater studies' traditional division between performer and scholar, she has returned to the university stage while finishing her Ph.D. And on the side, she's been teaching in the graduate school writing program. "I'm a writing consultant and an artist-scholar," she says. All of a sudden, the job market has opened wide. ●

Oh, the places to go

There are two rules for picking a program in the humanities or social sciences. One, choose a department with a strong faculty presence in your area of study. Two, if you want to be a professor, get yourself into the best school possible. Given the job market, says Edward Ayers, a historian and dean at the University of Virginia, "fine students with good dissertations [from middle-of-the-road programs] are precluded from getting jobs." At minimum, that means you had better have impressive undergraduate grades and top scores on the GRE subject test if your field is one of the eight that have one, or on the general GRE test if it isn't. More tips on what to look for in a department and what they're looking for in you:

The right size. Worried about a glut in Ph.D.'s, some graduate schools have reduced their class size. That's good news for the students who do make it in, since they're much more likely to receive the academic and financial support they need to succeed.

Academic support. Universities are beginning to offer their Ph.D. and master's candidates the kind of services, like writing tutorials, they've long offered to undergraduates. The philosophy department at the University of Michigan, for example, requires students to work on two pre-dissertation papers: one that reviews the available literature on the proposed topic and another that outlines the scope of their subject. By the time students finish both papers, they have a jump-start on the dissertation, as well as a trial run with a potential dissertation adviser.

Professor prep. While grad students often get more experience with teaching than they'd prefer, the other aspects of a professor's job—advising, grant writing, and committee work, for example—all remain a little mysterious, even after several years in graduate school. Fortunately, many universities have instituted Preparing Future Faculty programs, which teach students how to be faculty members. Through partnerships among neighboring institutions, the programs also show students what it's like to work at different types of schools, from small community colleges to research behemoths.

Job help. Ask professors where their graduated Ph.D.'s have been hired. The answers—and any evasions—will tell you how seriously the department takes doctoral job hunts. At Brown's English department, professors prep students on job talks, put them through excruciating practice interviews, and read over all their application materials. "I have to whip graduate students into shape," says Nancy Armstrong, the chair of

IN 1976, ONLY 26% OF DOCTORATE RECIPIENTS IN THE SOCIAL SCIENCES WERE WOMEN. TODAY, THAT NUMBER IS 54%.

WILL THERE BE JOBS?

People have long predicted that the dismal job market for Ph.D.'s would rebound once the scholars who grabbed all the academic positions in the 1960s began to retire and the baby boomlet started pouring onto campus, pushing up the number of instructors. Well, the demographic boom is here, and the profs are starting to retire, but cash-strapped universities are filling those promised slots with underpaid adjuncts, not new tenure-track professors. Still, not all is bleak. Employers outside of academia are increasingly looking for individuals with sophisticated analytic skills, opening up a much wider range of job options than ever before for Ph.D.'s.

Government. Nobody's recruiting grad students on a large scale, but "in a world of lots of littles," says Louma Ghandour, an assistant director of career services at Rice, "the federal government is the biggest." Political scientists, especially those who specialize in the Middle East, are being recruited by the Department of State, while the National Security Agency is looking for linguists adept in languages like Urdu, Arabic, and Pashto.

Geographic information systems. The need by businesses, governments, and researchers to map information to understand, for example, the best location for a new store, or where an oil spill is likely to spread, has led to a boom for geographers. Demand is highest in aerospace and defense-related industries, says Richard Beck, a professor of geography at the University of Cincinnati, with salaries for Ph.D.'s starting at a generous $80,000. The

HOLLAND ALSO FINDS TIME FOR DANCE CLASSES WHEN SHE ISN'T STUDYING FRENCH LITERATURE.

the department. "That's my job."

Research. "It's the brightest, most enterprising, most intuitive, risk-taking students who do research as an undergraduate," says Chris Barker, a linguistics professor at the University of California–San Diego. In other words, those applicants prove that they have what it takes to be

successful Ph.D. candidates. And they know what they are getting into as graduate students. "People who are serious about becoming historians will have done research papers and will have signed up for independent studies," says Karen Ordahl Kupperman, a professor in New York University's history department.

Your application. The statement of purpose should prove your grasp of the field and your understanding of the department. "It is essential that prospective students know about the research and published work of a potential adviser," says Daniel Weiss, dean of Johns Hopkins's Krieger School of Arts and Sciences. ●

---

academic job market is also strong, but salaries are in the more modest $40,000-to-$60,000 range.

Psychology. With the growing recognition of the link between behavior and health, psychologists will increasingly be called upon to help patients heal their minds while medical doctors heal their bodies. Often, these practitioners will be crucial members of treatment teams in hospitals, counseling patients on how to cope with invasive surgery or life-altering drugs. Jessica Kohout of the Washington, D.C.-based American Psychological Association also sees growth for psychologists working in preventive care, guiding patients who aren't ill but whose behavior puts them at risk for lung cancer or AIDS, for example. Salaries start in the low $40,000s for clinicians at HMOs and in the low $50,000s at hospitals.

Writing. Complaints about the sorry state of un-

dergraduate writing are good news for Ph.D.'s in rhetoric and composition. With an increasing number of universities requiring students to take a writing course, there is a growing market for writing instructors. "Ph.D. graduates in composition and rhetoric are expected to do very well in the academic job market over the next five years," says Carol Lipson, a professor of writing at Syracuse University. Tech-savvy scholars are also strong candidates for jobs in corporate communications departments, as technical writers, or as researchers at think tanks.

Teaching. Some presidents of community colleges predict that as much as half of their faculty will retire in the next three years. Starting salaries range from $30,000 to $40,000 a year, a little lower than those at four-year schools, but Ph.D.'s typically can command the higher end of this pay range. ●

Social Sciences & Humanities

PH.D. PROGRAMS TOP RATED BY DEPARTMENT CHAIRS AND SENIOR FACULTY

ECONOMICS

Ranked in 2001

Rank/School	Average assessment score (5=highest)
1. Massachusetts Institute of Technology	5.0
2. Harvard University (MA)	4.9
Princeton University (NJ)	4.9
Stanford University (CA)	4.9
University of Chicago	4.9
6. University of California–Berkeley	4.8
7. Yale University (CT)	4.7
8. Northwestern University (IL)	4.6
9. University of Pennsylvania	4.4
10. University of Wisconsin–Madison	4.2
11. University of California–Los Angeles	4.1
University of Michigan–Ann Arbor	4.1
University of Minnesota–Twin Cities	4.1
14. California Institute of Technology	4.0
Columbia University (NY)	4.0
University of Rochester (NY)	4.0
17. Cornell University (NY)	3.9
University of California–San Diego	3.9
19. Carnegie Mellon University (PA)	3.7
New York University	3.7
21. Brown University (RI)	3.6
Duke University (NC)	3.6
University of Texas–Austin	3.6
24. Johns Hopkins University (MD)	3.5
University of Maryland–College Park	3.5

ECONOMICS SPECIALTIES

MICROECONOMICS
1. Massachusetts Institute of Technology
2. Harvard University (MA)
3. Stanford University (CA)
4. Princeton University (NJ)
5. University of Chicago
6. Yale University (CT)
7. Northwestern University (IL)
8. Univ. of Calif.–Berkeley
9. University of Pennsylvania
10. California Institute of Technology

MACROECONOMICS
1. University of Chicago
2. Harvard University (MA)
3. Mass. Inst. of Tech.
4. Stanford University (CA)
5. Princeton University (NJ)
6. University of Minnesota–Twin Cities
7. Univ. of Calif.–Berkeley
8. University of Rochester (NY)
9. Northwestern University (IL)
   Yale University (CT)

INDUSTRIAL ORGANIZATION
1. Massachusetts Institute of Technology
2. Northwestern University (IL)
3. Stanford University (CA)
4. Harvard University (MA)
5. Univ. of Calif.–Berkeley
6. University of Chicago
7. Princeton University (NJ)
8. Yale University (CT)
9. Univ. of Wisconsin–Madison
10. University of Pennsylvania

INTERNATIONAL ECONOMICS
1. Princeton University (NJ)
2. Harvard University (MA)
3. Mass. Inst. of Tech.
4. Columbia University (NY)
   Univ. of Calif.–Berkeley

6. Stanford University (CA)
7. Univ. of Calif.–Los Angeles
   Univ. of Michigan–Ann Arbor
   Yale University (CT)
10. University of Pennsylvania

PUBLIC FINANCE
1. Harvard University (MA)
2. Massachusetts Institute of Technology

3. Stanford University (CA)
4. Princeton University (NJ)
5. University of Chicago
6. University of California–Berkeley
7. Univ. of Michigan–Ann Arbor
8. University of Wisconsin–Madison
9. University of Pennsylvania
10. Northwestern University (IL)

ENGLISH

Ranked in 2001

Rank/School	Average assessment score (5=highest)
1. Harvard University (MA)	4.8
Stanford University (CA)	4.8
University of California–Berkeley	4.8
Yale University (CT)	4.8
5. University of Chicago	4.7
6. Cornell University (NY)	4.6
Princeton University (NJ)	4.6
8. Columbia University (NY)	4.5
Johns Hopkins University (MD)	4.5
10. University of Pennsylvania	4.4
11. University of California–Los Angeles	4.3
University of Michigan–Ann Arbor	4.3
University of Virginia	4.3
14. Brown University (RI)	4.2
15. Duke University (NC)	4.1
University of California–Irvine	4.1
17. University of Wisconsin–Madison	4.0
18. Northwestern University (IL)	3.9
Rutgers State University–New Brunswick (NJ)	3.9
University of Illinois–Urbana-Champaign	3.9
University of North Carolina–Chapel Hill	3.9
University of Texas–Austin	3.9
23. Indiana University–Bloomington	3.8
University of Washington	3.8
25. New York University	3.7

ENGLISH SPECIALTIES

MEDIEVAL/RENAISSANCE LITERATURE
1. Univ. of California–Berkeley
2. Yale University (CT)
3. Harvard University (MA)
4. University of Pennsylvania
5. Columbia University (NY)
6. University of California–Los Angeles
7. Stanford University (CA)
8. University of Chicago
9. University of Virginia

10. University of Notre Dame (IN)

COLONIAL AMERICAN LITERATURE
1. Harvard University (MA)
2. Univ. of California–Berkeley
3. Yale University (CT)
4. University of Virginia
5. Columbia University (NY)
   Stanford University (CA)
7. Univ. of N.C.–Chapel Hill
   University of Pennsylvania

More at **www.usnews.com**

9. Rutgers State University–
   New Brunswick (NJ)
10. Duke University (NC)

18TH-TO-20TH-CENTURY BRITISH LITERATURE
1. Yale University (CT)
2. Univ. of Calif.–Berkeley
3. Stanford University (CA)
4. University of Pennsylvania
5. Harvard University (MA)
6. University of Virginia
7. Cornell University (NY)
8. Princeton University (NJ)
9. Indiana Univ.–Bloomington
   University of Chicago

AMERICAN LITERATURE AFTER 1865
1. Univ. of California–Berkeley
2. Harvard University (MA)
3. Univ. of Calif.–Los Angeles
4. Johns Hopkins Univ. (MD)
5. Yale University (CT)
6. University of Virginia
7. University of Chicago
8. Duke University (NC)
   Rutgers State University–
   New Brunswick (NJ)
10. Columbia University (NY)

AFRICAN-AMERICAN LITERATURE
1. Harvard University (MA)
2. Duke University (NC)
3. Yale University (CT)
4. University of Pennsylvania

5. Univ. of California–Berkeley
6. Univ. of Calif.–Los Angeles
   University of North Carolina–
   Chapel Hill
8. Cornell University (NY)
9. Rutgers State University–
   New Brunswick (NJ)
   Stanford University (CA)
   Univ. of Michigan–Ann Arbor
   University of Virginia

GENDER & LITERATURE
1. Univ. of California–Berkeley
2. Duke University (NC)
3. Rutgers State University–
   New Brunswick (NJ)
4. New York University
5. Princeton University (NJ)
   Univ. of Michigan–Ann Arbor
7. Cornell University (NY)
   Stanford University (CA)
9. Columbia University (NY)
   CUNY Graduate School and
   University Center

LITERARY CRITICISM & THEORY
1. Univ. of California–Irvine
2. Duke University (NC)
3. Univ. of California–Berkeley
4. Yale University (CT)
5. Cornell University (NY)
6. Johns Hopkins Univ. (MD)
7. University of Chicago
8. Harvard University (MA)
9. Columbia University (NY)
10. Stanford University (CA)

HISTORY

Ranked in 2001

Rank/School	Average assessment score (5=highest)
1. Princeton University (NJ)	4.9
Yale University (CT)	4.9
3. Stanford University (CA)	4.8
University of California–Berkeley	4.8
5. Columbia University (NY)	4.7
University of Chicago	4.7
University of Michigan–Ann Arbor	4.7
8. Harvard University (MA)	4.6
9. University of California–Los Angeles	4.5
10. Cornell University (NY)	4.4
Johns Hopkins University (MD)	4.4
University of Wisconsin–Madison	4.4
13. University of North Carolina–Chapel Hill	4.3
University of Pennsylvania	4.3
15. Brown University (RI)	4.1
Duke University (NC)	4.1
Northwestern University (IL)	4.1
University of Virginia	4.1

Rank/School	Average assessment score (5=highest)
19. Indiana University–Bloomington	4.0
Rutgers State University–New Brunswick (NJ)	4.0
University of Minnesota–Twin Cities	4.0
22. University of Illinois–Urbana-Champaign	3.9
University of Texas–Austin	3.9
24. New York University	3.8
25. Emory University (GA)	3.7
Ohio State University–Columbus	3.7

HISTORY SPECIALTIES

MODERN U.S. HISTORY
1. Yale University (CT)
2. Columbia University (NY)
   Univ. of California–Berkeley
4. Stanford University (CA)
5. Princeton University (NJ)
6. Harvard University (MA)
7. Univ. of Wisconsin–Madison
8. University of Chicago
9. Univ. of N.C.–Chapel Hill
10. Univ. of Michigan–Ann Arbor

U.S. COLONIAL HISTORY
1. Yale University (CT)
2. College of William
   and Mary (VA)
3. Harvard University (MA)
4. Johns Hopkins
   University (MD)
5. Princeton University (NJ)
6. University of Pennsylvania
7. Univ. of Calif.–Los Angeles
8. Columbia University (NY)
   University of Virginia
10. Brown University (RI)

EUROPEAN HISTORY
1. Princeton University (NJ)
2. Univ. of California–Berkeley
3. Yale University (CT)
4. University of Chicago
5. Harvard University (MA)
   Univ. of Michigan–Ann Arbor
7. Univ. of Calif.–Los Angeles
8. Stanford University (CA)
9. Columbia University (NY)
10. Johns Hopkins
    University (MD)

WOMEN'S HISTORY
1. Rutgers State University–
   New Brunswick (NJ)
2. Univ. of Michigan–Ann Arbor
   Univ. of Wisconsin–Madison
   Yale University (CT)
5. Univ. of Calif.–Los Angeles
   Univ. of N.C.–Chapel Hill

7. Univ. of California–Berkeley
   Univ. of Minn.–Twin Cities
9. Stanford University (CA)
10. New York University

AFRICAN-AMERICAN HISTORY
1. Univ. of Michigan–Ann Arbor
2. Harvard University (MA)
   New York University
4. Columbia University (NY)
   Princeton University (NJ)
   Rutgers State University–
   New Brunswick (NJ)
   Yale University (CT)
8. Duke University (NC)
9. University of Chicago
10. Stanford University (CA)
    Univ. of California–Berkeley
    Univ. of Wisconsin–Madison

CULTURAL HISTORY
1. Univ. of California–Berkeley
2. University of Chicago
3. Princeton University (NJ)
4. Univ. of California–
   Los Angeles
   Yale University (CT)
6. Columbia University (NY)
7. Harvard University (MA)
8. New York University
   University of Michigan–
   Ann Arbor
10. Cornell University (NY)
    Stanford University (CA)

LATIN AMERICAN HISTORY
1. University of Texas–Austin
2. Yale University (CT)
3. Univ. of California–Berkeley
4. Univ. of Calif.–Los Angeles
5. University of Chicago
   Univ. of Wisconsin–Madison
7. Harvard University (MA)
8. Indiana Univ.–Bloomington
   Univ. of Calif.–San Diego
10. Duke University (NC)
    University of Arizona

HISTORY SPECIALTIES

ASIAN HISTORY
1. Univ. of California–Berkeley
2. Harvard University (MA)
3. Univ. of Calif.–Los Angeles
4. Stanford University (CA)
5. Yale University (CT)
6. University of Chicago
7. Columbia University (NY)
8. Princeton University (NJ)
9. Univ. of Michigan–Ann Arbor
10. Cornell University (NY)
    University of Washington

POLITICAL SCIENCE

Ranked in 2001

Rank/School	Average assessment score (5=highest)
1. Harvard University (MA)	4.9
2. Stanford University (CA)	4.7
University of California–Berkeley	4.7
University of Michigan–Ann Arbor	4.7
5. Yale University (CT)	4.6
6. Princeton University (NJ)	4.5
7. University of California–San Diego	4.3
8. Duke University (NC)	4.2
University of California–Los Angeles	4.2
University of Chicago	4.2
11. Columbia University (NY)	4.0
Massachusetts Institute of Technology	4.0
University of Rochester (NY)	4.0
University of Wisconsin–Madison	4.0
15. Ohio State University–Columbus	3.9
University of Minnesota–Twin Cities	3.9
University of North Carolina–Chapel Hill	3.9
18. Indiana University–Bloomington	3.7
Washington University in St. Louis	3.7
20. Cornell University (NY)	3.6
Northwestern University (IL)	3.6
22. Michigan State University	3.5
23. SUNY–Stony Brook	3.4
University of Illinois–Urbana-Champaign	3.4
University of Texas–Austin	3.4
University of Washington	3.4

POLITICAL SCIENCE SPECIALTIES

AMERICAN POLITICS
1. University of Michigan–Ann Arbor
2. Harvard University (MA)
3. Stanford University (CA)
4. Univ. of California–Berkeley
5. Yale University (CT)
6. Univ. of California–San Diego
7. Ohio State Univ.–Columbus
8. Princeton University (NJ)
9. University of Minnesota–Twin Cities
10. University of California–Los Angeles

INTERNATIONAL POLITICS
1. Harvard University (MA)
2. Stanford University (CA)
3. Columbia University (NY)
4. Yale University (CT)
5. Univ. of Michigan–Ann Arbor
6. Princeton University (NJ)
   University of California–Berkeley
8. Duke University (NC)
9. Univ. of California–San Diego
10. University of Chicago

COMPARATIVE POLITICS
1. Harvard University (MA)
2. University of California–San Diego
3. University of California–Berkeley
4. Stanford University (CA)
5. University of California–Los Angeles
6. Yale University (CT)
7. Princeton University (NJ)
8. Columbia University (NY)
   Duke University (NC)
10. University of Michigan–Ann Arbor

POLITICAL THEORY
1. Harvard University (MA)
2. Princeton University (NJ)
   University of Chicago
4. Yale University (CT)
5. Johns Hopkins Univ. (MD)
6. University of California–Berkeley
7. University of Minnesota–Twin Cities
8. Duke University (NC)
9. Columbia University (NY)
   University of Michigan–Ann Arbor

PSYCHOLOGY

Ranked in 2001
Unless otherwise designated in parentheses, the program is in the department of psychology.

Rank/School	Average assessment score (5=highest)
1. Stanford University (CA)	4.7
2. University of Michigan–Ann Arbor	4.6
3. Univ. of Minnesota–Twin Cities (Inst. of Child Development)	4.4
University of Illinois–Urbana-Champaign	4.4
Yale University (CT)	4.4
6. Harvard University (MA)	4.3
University of California–Berkeley	4.3
University of California–Los Angeles	4.3
9. Carnegie Mellon University (PA)	4.2
University of Wisconsin–Madison	4.2
11. Columbia University (NY)	4.1
Mass. Inst. of Tech. (Dept. of Brain and Cognitive Sciences)	4.1
Princeton University (NJ)	4.1
University of Minnesota–Twin Cities	4.1
15. Cornell University (NY)	4.0
University of Pennsylvania	4.0
17. Indiana University–Bloomington	3.9
Northwestern University (IL)	3.9
University of California–San Diego	3.9
University of North Carolina–Chapel Hill	3.9
University of Texas–Austin	3.9
University of Virginia	3.9
University of Washington	3.9
24. Duke University (NC)	3.8
Harvard Univ. (Programs in Human Develop. and Psych.) (MA)	3.8
Johns Hopkins University (MD)	3.8
Ohio State University–Columbus	3.8
Univ. of California–Irvine (Dept. of Neurobiology & Behavior)	3.8
Univ. of Mich.–Ann Arbor (Combined Prog. in Ed. and Psych.)	3.8
30. Brown University (RI)	3.7
Cornell University (Dept. of Human Development) (NY)	3.7
Indiana Univ.–Bloomington (Cognitive Science Program)	3.7
New York University	3.7
Penn St. U.–Univ. Park (Prog. in Human Dev. & Fam. Studies)	3.7
Stanford University (Psych. Studies in Education) (CA)	3.7
University of California–Irvine (Cognitive Sci. Dept.)	3.7
University of Chicago	3.7
University of Colorado–Boulder	3.7
39. Carnegie Mellon Univ. (Grad. School of Industrial Admin.) (PA)	3.6
Penn State University–University Park	3.6
U. of Illinois–Urbana-Champaign (Dept. of Ed. Psych.)	3.6
Vanderbilt University (Peabody) (TN)	3.6
Vanderbilt University (TN)	3.6
Washington University in St. Louis	3.6

Rank/School	Average assessment score (5=highest)
45. Arizona State University	3.5
Duke University (Dept. of Experimental Psych.) (NC)	3.5
University of Arizona	3.5
University of California–Berkeley (School of Education)	3.5
University of Iowa	3.5
University of Massachusetts–Amherst	3.5
Univ. of Mich.–Ann Arbor (Org. Behavior & Human Resources)	3.5
University of Oregon	3.5
University of Pittsburgh–Main Campus	3.5
54. Purdue University–West Lafayette (IN)	3.4
Rutgers State University–New Brunswick (NJ)	3.4
Univ. of California–Irvine (Psych. & Social Behavior Dept.)	3.4
University of California–Santa Barbara	3.4
University of Chicago (Educational and Developmental Psych.)	3.4
U. of Ill.–Urbana-Champaign (Human and Community Dev.)	3.4
University of Maryland–College Park	3.4
61. Dartmouth College (NH)	3.3
Emory University (GA)	3.3
Michigan State University	3.3
Northwestern University (Dept. of Organization Behavior) (IL)	3.3
SUNY–Stony Brook	3.3
Univ. of Texas–Austin (Child Dev. and Family Relations)	3.3
University of California–Davis	3.3
University of Florida	3.3
University of Iowa (Psychological and Quantitative Foundations)	3.3
University of Kansas	3.3
University of Missouri–Columbia	3.3
University of Southern California	3.3
73. Teachers Coll., Columbia Univ. (Dept. of Human Dev.) (NY)	3.2
U. of Md.–College Park (Dept. of Human Dev./Inst. for Child Study)	3.2
University of Connecticut	3.2
University of Georgia	3.2
University of Pennsylvania (Psychology in Education Division)	3.2
University of Rochester (NY)	3.2
University of Texas–Austin (Dept. of Educational Psych.)	3.2
80. Cornell University (Dept. of Education) (NY)	3.1
Georgia Institute of Technology	3.1
Purdue Univ.–West Lafayette (Dept. of Child Development) (IN)	3.1
Rice University (TX)	3.1
SUNY–Albany	3.1
Univ. of Kansas (Dept. of Human Development & Family Life)	3.1

PSYCHOLOGY SPECIALTIES

COGNITIVE PSYCHOLOGY
1. Stanford University (CA)
2. Carnegie Mellon University (PA)
3. University of Illinois–Urbana-Champaign
   University of Michigan–Ann Arbor
5. University of California–Berkeley
6. Harvard University (MA)
7. University of California–Los Angeles
   University of California–San Diego
9. Massachusetts Institute of Technology
   Princeton University (NJ)

EXPERIMENTAL PSYCHOLOGY
1. Stanford University (CA)
2. University of Michigan–Ann Arbor
3. University of California–Berkeley
4. University of Illinois–Urbana-Champaign
5. University of California–Los Angeles
   Yale University (CT)

7. Harvard University (MA)
   University of Wisconsin–Madison
9. Indiana University–Bloomington
10. Princeton University (NJ)

INDUSTRIAL/ORGANIZATIONAL PSYCHOLOGY
1. Michigan State University
2. University of Minnesota–Twin Cities
3. Penn State University–University Park
4. Bowling Green State University (OH)
   University of Maryland–College Park
6. University of Illinois–Urbana-Champaign
7. University of South Florida
8. George Mason Univ. (VA)
   Univ. of Akron (OH)
10. Georgia Institute of Technology

DEVELOPMENTAL PSYCHOLOGY
1. Univ. of Minnesota–Twin Cities (Inst. of Child Development)
2. University of Michigan–Ann Arbor
3. Stanford University (CA)
4. University of California–Berkeley
5. University of Virginia
6. University of California–Los Angeles
7. Penn State University–Univ. Park (Program in Human Development & Family Studies)
   University of Illinois–Urbana-Champaign
9. University of North Carolina–Chapel Hill
   Yale University (CT)

SOCIOLOGY

Ranked in 2001

Rank/School	Average assessment score (5=highest)
1. University of California–Berkeley	4.8
University of Wisconsin–Madison	4.8
3. University of Chicago	4.7
University of Michigan–Ann Arbor	4.7
5. Stanford University (CA)	4.6
University of North Carolina–Chapel Hill	4.6
7. Harvard University (MA)	4.4
University of California–Los Angeles	4.4
9. Northwestern University (IL)	4.2
Princeton University (NJ)	4.2
11. Indiana University–Bloomington	4.1
University of Arizona	4.1
University of Pennsylvania	4.1
14. Columbia University (NY)	3.9
Cornell University (NY)	3.9
16. Duke University (NC)	3.8
University of Texas–Austin	3.8
University of Washington	3.8
19. Johns Hopkins University (MD)	3.7
Pennsylvania State University–University Park	3.7
21. Ohio State University–Columbus	3.6
22. New York University	3.5
University of Minnesota–Twin Cities	3.5
24. SUNY–Albany	3.4
University of California–Santa Barbara	3.4
University of Maryland–College Park	3.4
Yale University (CT)	3.4

SOCIOLOGY SPECIALTIES

SOCIOLOGY OF CULTURE
1. Northwestern University (IL)
2. Princeton University (NJ)
3. Univ. of California–Berkeley
4. University of California–San Diego

SOCIOLOGY SPECIALTIES

5. University of California–Santa Barbara
6. University of California–Los Angeles
   University of Chicago
8. New School for Social Research (NY)
   Rutgers State University–New Brunswick (NJ)
10. University of Arizona
    University of California–Davis

SOCIAL STRATIFICATION

1. University of Wisconsin–Madison
2. Univ. of California–Berkeley
3. University of Chicago
   Univ. of Michigan–Ann Arbor
5. Harvard University (MA)
   University of California–Los Angeles
7. University of Pennsylvania
8. Univ. of N.C.–Chapel Hill

9. Indiana University–Bloomington
10. Ohio State Univ.–Columbus

HISTORICAL SOCIOLOGY

1. Univ. of Michigan–Ann Arbor
2. Univ. of California–Berkeley
3. Harvard University (MA)
4. University of California–Los Angeles
5. Columbia University (NY)
6. New York University
   Northwestern University (IL)
   Princeton University (NJ)
   University of Chicago
   University of Minnesota–Twin Cities

SOCIAL PSYCHOLOGY

1. Stanford University (CA)
2. Indiana University–Bloomington
3. Univ. of Michigan–Ann Arbor

4. University of Iowa
5. University of Arizona
6. University of California–Los Angeles
7. University of Washington
   University of Wisconsin–Madison
9. Cornell University (NY)
   Washington State University

ECONOMIC SOCIOLOGY

1. Stanford University (CA)
2. University of California–Berkeley
3. Princeton University (NJ)
4. Cornell University (NY)
   University of Wisconsin–Madison
6. Columbia University (NY)
   Northwestern University (IL)
8. University of California–Los Angeles
   University of Pennsylvania
10. Univ. of Michigan–Ann Arbor

Rankings of doctoral programs in the social sciences and humanities are based on the results of surveys sent to academics in each discipline. Each school (or, in the case of psychology, each institutional unit) offering a doctoral program was sent two surveys. The questionnaires asked respondents to rate the quality of the program at each institution as distinguished (5); strong (4); good (3); adequate (2); or marginal (1). Individuals who were unfamiliar with a particular school's programs were asked to select "don't know." Scores for each school were totaled and divided by the number of respondents who rated that school.

Surveys were conducted in the fall of 2000 by Synovate. Questionnaires were sent to department heads and directors of graduate studies (or alternatively, a senior faculty member who teaches graduate students) at schools that had granted a total of five or more doctorates in each discipline during the five-year period from 1991 through 1995, supplemented by programs that appeared on the 1998 Survey of Earned Doctorates. The surveys asked about Ph.D. programs in economics (response rate: 38 percent); English (43 percent); history (36 percent); political science (43 percent); psychology (20 percent); and sociology (45 percent).

As noted in the psychology table, some schools are listed more than once because separate doctoral programs are offered in different university units. Surveys were sent to the department chair or dean of the school of psychology and the director of graduate studies in each institutional unit that offered a doctoral program. Unless otherwise noted in parentheses, the psychology program ranked is located in the department of psychology. Accredited doctoral programs in clinical psychology are ranked separately in the health professions section on starting on Page 41. Expanded rankings can be found at www.usnews.com.

WILLIAM MERCER MCLEOD FOR USN&WR

GRAD STUDENT TRANSPORTATION OUTSIDE STANFORD UNIVERSITY'S MEYER LIBRARY

THE ARTS

Out and about

SCOTT GOLDSMITH FOR *USN&WR*

COSTUME DESIGNER AND PERFORMANCE ARTIST SHANA MOULTON IN HER STUDIO AT CARNEGIE MELLON. A SECOND-YEAR M.F.A. STUDENT, SHE IS EXPLORING NONLINGUISTIC COMMUNICATION AND FANTASY.

BY CAROLYN KLEINER

rtistic inspiration struck Julie Anand in a flash. Standing atop Cedar Mesa in southwestern Utah and staring down at two, symmetrical tinajas—dry, shallow depressions filled with microorganisms that come alive when it rains—she realized they resembled a dividing cell. "It just hit me all of a sudden that things change," says Anand, 28, now in her second year of the three-year M.F.A.–Photography program at the University of New Mexico in Albuquerque. "Entropy sets in and undoes whatever we do, unless we undo it first. It's something I never would have realized if I was holed up in my studio as usual." She dug a circle and filled it with mud from a third tinaja. Then she walked away,

leaving nature, in the form of the next passing shower, to finish this particular work of art.

What brought Anand out to this patch of desert is Land Arts of the American West, an innovative new program offered jointly by UNM and the University of Texas–Austin. Land Arts takes M.F.A. students on a semester-long adventure to sites across the Southwest, from the Grand Canyon and Piro ruins along the Rio Grande to *Double Negative,* Michael Heizer's earthwork sculpture near Lake Mead, Nev. Along the way, students explore anthropology, archaeology, architecture, and geography—not to mention art and their own art making. Ultimately, they are responsible for creating eight works, including one site-specific sculpture and one site-specific shelter made of indigenous materials like mud and plants. "Art is less and less about creating objects and putting them in galleries," says program founder Bill Gilbert, a ceramics professor at UNM. Carol Becker, dean of the faculty at the School of the Art Institute of Chicago, agrees. "If we look at art making in the 21st century, there are people working in so many different ways: You can show in a gallery, do an installation in a public space, do interventions into the world and collaborate with ecologists or engineers working on inner-city projects, do performances," she says. "There are many ways to push the limits of the art world and say, 'This, too, is art,' and students need to get out and see all of these."

Traveling locally or even to far-flung countries is now de rigueur at many schools, as is the interdisciplinary seminar. At the Art Institute of Chicago, for instance, groups of students and professors from different departments meet regularly to critique each other's work. "People begin to understand that, really, the ideas are what matter," says Becker. And as the intersection of the arts and technology becomes increasingly relevant in

our Internet-based society, many institutions have created entirely new departments to keep artists on the cutting edge. San Francisco State University, for example, offers an innovative M.F.A. with a focus on "conceptual information" that encourages students to push the boundaries of art by delving into robotics, computer-generated conceptual work, sound art, and the union of art and science.

A few schools have taken a more radical approach. Take Carnegie Mellon University in Pittsburgh, which redesigned its entire M.F.A. program to incorporate cross-disciplinary ideals and community interaction throughout. With four semesters of mandatory one-course electives, Takahiro Noguchi, a third-year student, has taken classes in Marxism, the philosophy of aesthetics, and electronics, among other topics. "I think the more educated I can be as an artist, in terms of understanding my tools or understanding the nature or development of particular kinds of ideas . . . the more I can fashion them and interpret them and incorporate them into my work, and the more in-

Working for a living

"Thank God, I have my work, but instead of earning money by it, I need money to be able to work; that is the difficulty," wrote Vincent van Gogh to his brother, Theo, in 1882.

Unfortunately, making a living making art is still a struggle, especially with the flailing economy taking a toll on arts organizations everywhere. But there are still opportunities, whether in academia, animation, computer gaming, curating, or any number of related fields; grants and residencies; old day-job standbys like waitressing; or any combination thereof. In fact, a would-be artist's most inspired design may well be figuring out how to cobble together a living while pursuing a passion for painting or potting. According to the most recent Information on Artists survey from the Research Center for Arts and

Culture at Columbia University's Teachers College, the median annual income for an artist is $25,000. And only $5,000 of that comes from making art.

"You definitely have to be very creative, not only with your craft but with finding job opportunities and situations where you can make some money," says Sanford Biggers, a New York-based visual artist whose work appeared in the most recent Whitney Biennial. A support network of fellow creative types is essential, he says, noting that peers are the best source of information on which galleries are looking to show what kind of work at any given time, as well as job and grant openings. Biggers got his start while still in graduate school at the Art Institute of Chicago, after volunteering to help an established artist with a performance in New York

City. One day, before going onstage, Biggers met the director of the SculptureCenter, now in Queens, and struck up a conversation that continued via E-mail. After he graduated a year and a half later, in 1999, his new mentor recommended him for a job at an outreach program at Cooper Union, where he trained undergraduates to teach design and painting to local children, all while working on his own art. Today, Biggers continues to consult for the program, in between jetting off to residencies at museums and foundations in Budapest, Hungary, and California and overseeing current exhibitions of his work in New York, New Jersey, and Houston.

Staying plugged into any and all opportunities is key. That's where resources like the New York Foundation for the Arts Source, at *www.nyfa.org*, come

IN A RECENT STUDY, 68% OF ARTISTS SAID THEY EARNED UNDER $20,000 FOR THEIR ART PER YEAR. BUT 73% WERE SATISFIED WITH THEIR CAREERS.

teresting it will be," says the 28-year-old, whose thesis involves university janitors and FM radio.

Meanwhile, second-year student Ruth Stanford is working with local cemeteries for her "community affiliation" project, a required two-semester venture that has students interacting with a range of local organizations, from environmental nonprofits to nearby jails. Stanford's output thus far includes a headstone that juts out from a wall with no visible means of support; a patch of vibrant, verdant grass grows where the inscription should be. Being out of the studio so much has inspired Stanford, 38, and several peers to focus on alternative exhibition spaces: This spring, she and five fellow M.F.A. candidates will install their paintings, sculptures, and prints all along the bus route that runs through Pittsburgh's major nightlife and cultural district. "If you're only working within the gallery context, it's sort of like preaching to the converted," she says.

The value of such outside-the-box experiences is inestimable, say students like Anand. She returned from Land Arts bursting with fresh inspiration, with works like "Nomadic Germination," a number of gourds that she planted, replanted, and nourished over the course of the semester—watering them daily and lying over them in her sleeping bag at night to keep them warm—and then potted in the graduate student gallery at the University of New Mexico. The artist is waiting for vines to sprout on an attached trellis so she can sleep underneath the plants, bringing the project full circle. "The idea is that nature works in cycles, and not in lines that have a beginning and middle and end," says Anand. "I see things as going on and constantly changing in nature as well as in my work. After all, art is all about growth, too." ●

SCOTT GOLDSMITH FOR *USN&WR*

FERESHTEH TOOSI CALCULATES LAYOUT DIMENSIONS DURING THE INSTALLATION OF HER FABRIC AND TEXTILE PROJECT. SHE IS A SECOND-YEAR STUDENT IN THE M.F.A. PROGRAM AT CARNEGIE MELLON.

in. It's a searchable, nationwide database of over 2,800 grants, residencies, and apprenticeships, 3,100 arts organizations, and more, including listings of emerging-artist grants of up to $7,000 from the American Craft Council and the Honickman First Book prize from the

Center for Documentary Studies at Duke University, which provides a $3,000 monetary award, publication of a book of photographs, and inclusion in a traveling exhibit.

Above all, today's artist must be a driven, dedicated entrepreneur. Many grad schools now offer business-skills classes, and Web sites like *thepauper.com* ("Helping artists with the art of survival") provide advice on issues like financial planning and health insurance, not to mention a community. In addition, it's important for modern artists to look beyond the traditional gallery to sell their work, say experts like Daniel Grant, author of *The Business of Being an Artist,* who suggests opening private studios to the public, working with consultants who buy art for corporate offices, and participating in artist-curated shows at nonprofit art centers, art competitions, and craft fairs, among other tactics.

And no matter what, keep at it—even if success remains elusive in this lifetime. "I am absorbed in my work," van Gogh wrote to his brother. "I have confidence . . . I will succeed in earning enough to keep myself, not in luxury, but as one who eats his bread in the sweat of his brow." ●

GETTING THERE

Why spend tens of thousands of dollars on further study when you can simply head out into the world and start creating? If you want to teach at the college level or above, an M.F.A. degree is mandatory. Otherwise, "it's essentially just time and space," says Stuart Hyatt, who designed interactive exhibits for science and technology museums before

EVERY WEEK, CARNEGIE MELLON M.F.A. STUDENTS MEET FOR A THREE-HOUR SEMINAR TO DISCUSS ISSUES RELATING TO THEIR WORK.

returning to school full time. Don't underestimate the value of the two: "At this moment . . . I have a modest but steady income, an enormous studio space, access to all sorts of fabrication tools, and digital media tools at the ready," says Hyatt, 28, now in his last year of the M.F.A.–Sculpture program at Indiana University–Bloomington. "If I can't realize ambitious projects under these ideal conditions, then I shouldn't be making art."

That said, the competition to get into M.F.A. programs can be fierce. The University of California–Los Angeles School of the Arts and Architecture, for one, saw a 44 percent jump in applications last year, to 530, and ended up admitting fewer than 3 percent of candidates—compare that with a 12.6 percent acceptance rate at Harvard Law. "So many people think the M.F.A. is not a real advanced degree," says Kavin Buck, director of recruitment and outreach and an M.F.A. grad himself, as well as a practicing artist, teacher, and curator. "But our ranks are growing, and we are now looking at the same level of competitiveness as top law schools or business schools."

As a result, only those with a demonstrated commitment—in the form of focused undergraduate study, say, or a long history of inking complex comic books on the sly—need apply to leading schools. While the GRE is usually not required, candidates almost always have to submit official academic transcripts, a statement of purpose, and up to three letters of recommendation. Still, your grade-point average is far less important than an accomplished, varied portfolio that is carefully cultivated and meticulously presented, says Katharine Willman, dean of admissions at the Cranbrook Academy of Art in Bloomfield Hills, Mich. Schools often require between 10 and 20 slides of artwork, with submission requirements that can verge on the byzantine. Some, like Yale's prestigious program, require applicants who make the first cut to send or bring in their actual work.

You also need to make sure this is the right M.F.A. program for you, says Willman. "The most important factor is the critique base," she says. "That is, in what ways will the program and the individuals support your work?" Other administrators note the importance of school facilities, breadth of offerings, and a faculty filled with professional artists who are readily accessible, who continue to practice while they teach, and who have shown their work broadly and been recognized for it.

Despite the significant financial investment and any number of bureaucratic frustrations that may arise during the course of an M.F.A. program, students like Hyatt insist that close interaction with successful artist-professors and a group of talented, motivated peers makes the experience worthwhile. "The challenge is to maintain that web of support when we graduate," he says, "because when you remove the time and the space, all you have left are people." ●

Master of Fine Arts

THE TOP SCHOOLS

Our ranking is based on a 2003 survey of deans and department chairs, one per school, at 213 master of fine arts programs in art and design.

Rank/School	Average reputation score (5=highest)
1. Rhode Island School of Design	4.4
School of the Art Institute of Chicago	4.4
Yale University (CT)	4.4
4. California Institute of the Arts	4.1
5. Cranbrook Academy of Art (MI)	4.0
6. Alfred U.–New York State Col. of Ceramics	3.9
Art Center College of Design (CA)	3.9
University of California–Los Angeles	3.9
Virginia Commonwealth University	3.9
10. Carnegie Mellon University (PA)	3.7
School of Visual Arts (NY)	3.7
University of Iowa	3.7
13. Arizona State University	3.6
California College of Arts and Crafts	3.6
Indiana University–Bloomington	3.6
Maryland Institute College of Art	3.6
Pratt Institute (NY)	3.6
Rochester Institute of Technology (NY)	3.6
San Francisco Art Institute	3.6
University of Wisconsin–Madison	3.6
21. Columbia University (NY)	3.5
Massachusetts College of Art	3.5
Temple University (PA)	3.5
University of Georgia	3.5
University of Illinois–Urbana-Champaign	3.5
University of Texas–Austin	3.5
Washington University in St. Louis	3.5
28. Bard College (NY)	3.4
New School Univ.–Parsons School of Design (NY)	3.4
Ohio State University	3.4
University of California–Davis	3.4
University of the Arts (PA)	3.4
University of Washington	3.4
34. American Film Institute Conservatory (CA)	3.3
Claremont Graduate University (CA)	3.3
Cleveland Institute of Art	3.3
Otis College of Art and Design (CA)	3.3
Rutgers State University–New Brunswick (NJ)	3.3
Syracuse University (NY)	3.3
University of Arizona	3.3
University of California–Irvine	3.3
University of California–San Diego	3.3
University of Michigan	3.3
University of Pennsylvania	3.3
45. Cornell University (NY)	3.2
Minneapolis College of Art and Design	3.2
New York University	3.2
Southern Illinois University–Carbondale	3.2
Tufts U./School of the Museum of Fine Arts–Boston	3.2
University of California–Berkeley	3.2
University of New Mexico	3.2
University of North Texas	3.2
University of Tennessee–Knoxville	3.2

SPECIALTIES

The institutions below received the most nominations from survey respondents at peer institutions for their excellence in a given specialty.

CERAMICS

1. Alfred University–New York State College of Ceramics
2. Cranbrook Academy of Art (MI)
3. University of Washington
4. Cal. College of Arts and Crafts
5. Louisiana State University
   Ohio University
   Rhode Island School of Design
8. Ohio State University
9. Univ. of Colorado–Boulder
10. Cal. State Univ.–Long Beach
    Penn. State U.–Univ. Park
    University of California–Davis
    U. of Minnesota–Twin Cities

GRAPHIC DESIGN

1. Rhode Island School of Design
2. Yale University (CT)
3. Cranbrook Academy of Art (MI)
4. Art Center Col. of Design (CA)
   Virginia Commonwealth Univ.
6. Carnegie Mellon Univ. (PA)
7. North Carolina State Univ.
   U. of Ill.–Urbana-Champaign
9. Pratt Institute (NY)
   School of Visual Arts (NY)

INDUSTRIAL DESIGN

1. Art Center Col. of Design (CA)
2. Rhode Island School of Design
3. Carnegie Mellon Univ. (PA)
   Cranbrook Academy of Art (MI)
5. Pratt Institute (NY)

MULTIMEDIA/VISUAL COMMUNICATIONS

1. California Institute of the Arts
2. Carnegie Mellon Univ. (PA)
   Sch. of the Art Inst. of Chicago
4. U. of California–Los Angeles
5. School of Visual Arts (NY)
6. New York University
   Univ. of California–San Diego
8. Art Center Col. of Design (CA)
   Rensselaer Polytechnic Institute (NY)
10. Rhode Island School of Design

PAINTING/DRAWING

1. Yale University (CT)
2. Sch. of the Art Inst. of Chicago
3. U. of California–Los Angeles
4. Rhode Island School of Design
5. Maryland Institute Col. of Art
   Temple University (PA)
7. San Francisco Art Institute
   University of Texas–Austin
9. Indiana Univ.–Bloomington
10. Cranbrook Academy of Art (MI)
    Virginia Commonwealth Univ.

PHOTOGRAPHY

1. Sch. of the Art Inst. of Chicago
2. Rhode Island School of Design
   University of New Mexico
4. Rochester Inst. of Tech. (NY)
5. Arizona State University
   San Francisco Art Institute
7. Yale University (CT)
8. California Institute of the Arts
9. University of Arizona
   U. of California–Los Angeles

PRINTMAKING

1. Univ. of Wisconsin–Madison
2. University of Iowa
3. Arizona State University
   University of Georgia
   U. of Tennessee–Knoxville
6. Sch. of the Art Inst. of Chicago
   University of Texas–Austin
8. Cranbrook Academy of Art (MI)
   Rutgers St. U.–New Brunswick
10. Rhode Island School of Design

SCULPTURE

1. Virginia Commonwealth Univ.
2. Yale University (CT)
3. Sch. of the Art Inst. of Chicago
4. U. of California–Los Angeles
5. Cranbrook Academy of Art (MI)
6. Rhode Island School of Design
7. Maryland Institute Col. of Art
   Ohio State University
   Temple University (PA)
10. California Institute of the Arts
    Syracuse University (NY)

Methodology: The master of fine arts program rankings are based solely on the results of a peer assessment survey. Respondents were asked to rate the academic quality of programs on a scale of 1 (marginal) to 5 (outstanding). Scores for each school were totaled and divided by the number of respondents who rated that school. The response rate was 48 percent. Surveys were conducted by Synovate. Note: Lists of schools, persons surveyed at each school, and specialty concentrations were developed in cooperation with the Slane College of Communications and Fine Arts at Bradley University in Illinois.

Writers in residence

BY ULRICH BOSER

DANUTA OTFINOWSKI FOR *USN&WR*

JETT MCALISTER AT MILLER'S BAR NEAR THE UNIVERSITY OF VIRGINIA

L et me swim / in the ink-swelled undarked darkness of language," writes Jett McAlister in his poem tentatively called "Proem." Penned during the first semester of a creative-writing graduate program at the University of Virginia, it's a line that McAlister says describes the experience of writing. "I spend a long time every day just playing with words and seeing what comes of it."

Is this how you see spending your days, too? There are over 100 universities that now offer a master of fine arts degree in creative writing, up from 15 in 1975, according to the nonprofit Associated Writing Programs. Perhaps best known is the program at the University of Iowa Writers' Workshop, which dates back to the 1930s. Iowa receives more than 700 applications each year for the school's 25 fiction spots; seven of the 2001 fiction graduates have already published books.

STUDENTS AT ONE IOWA WORKSHOP INCLUDED ANDRE DUBUS, GAIL GODWIN, AND JOHN IRVING.

"A creative writing program allows you to stay out of the labor pool and spend time reading and writing," says the author Frank Conroy, who directs the Iowa workshop. "Writing is hard, and often students need to go someplace where people are serious about it." Not only do students spend time with other young writers discussing literature and its creation, he says, but they also learn about technical aspects like voice and narration. "You can do it alone," he says. "But this saves you time."

It also can give you contact with famous writers, which not only will help your writing but boost your contacts in the publishing world. A number of well-known writers are creative-writing teachers, including Alice McDermott at Johns Hopkins and Tobias Wolff at Stanford.

But writing programs don't guarantee artistic or even career success. "An M.F.A. is not an M.B.A.," says David Bosworth, director of the Creative Writing Program at the University of Washington. "It's not a job-producing degree." (And at $27,000 for an Iowa M.F.A., for example, it's no bargain, although many students receive some kind of aid.) While many graduates publish stories or poems in small literary magazines, and some go on to teach creative writing, only a small minority actually produce a novel or a book of poems.

"Writing programs can hurt writers who really need to get out and get their hands dirty," says Kate Moses, a literary editor turned novelist. "They can give a false sense of your skill level. You may have a bag of technical skills, but you might not have something to write about." Writing programs also get criticized for encouraging homogeneity. "If you spend too much time taking creative-writing classes, your writing can get a little ingrown and lose its individuality," says David Radavich, a professor of English at Eastern Illinois University, who teaches poetry. "You don't want to McDonaldize your writing."

For some writers, however, the time and support a school can provide is just what they need. "I have never been happier," says Chris Wiberg, 26, who left a job in computer technical support to enroll in the new two-year graduate writing program at the University of Illinois–Urbana-Champaign. "I just want to pursue my writing," he says. ●

Directory Best Graduate Schools

On the following pages you'll find a directory of useful information and statistics about graduate schools and programs in business, education, engineering, law, and medicine. The schools are listed alphabetically by state within each discipline; their data are accurate as of February 2003. An index to the directory begins on Page 191. A key to terminology used in the directory will be found at the beginning of each area of study.

www.usnews.com

BUSINESS

The business school directory lists all 363 U.S. schools offering master's programs in business accredited by AACSB International, the Association to Advance Collegiate Schools of Business, as of August 2002. Most offer the M.B.A. degree; a few offer the master of business. Two hundred eighty-four schools responded to the *U.S. News* survey conducted in fall 2002, and their data are reported below. Schools that did not respond to the survey have abbreviated entries.

TERMINOLOGY

1 A school whose name is footnoted with the numeral 1 did not return the *U.S. News* statistical survey; limited data appear in its entry.

N/A. Not available from the school or not applicable.

E-mail. The electronic address of the admissions office. If, instead of an E-mail address, a Web site address is given in this field, the Web site will automatically present an E-mail screen programmed to reach the admissions office.

Internet application. The electronic address for online applications.

Application deadline. For fall 2004 enrollment. "Rolling" means there is no application deadline; the school acts on applications as they are received. "Varies" means deadlines vary according to department or whether applicants are U.S. citizens or foreign nationals.

Tuition. For the 2002–2003 academic year. Includes fees.

Room/board/expenses. For the 2002–2003 academic year.

Credit hour. The cost per credit hour for the 2002–2003 academic year.

Enrollment. Full and part time for fall 2002.

Minorities. For fall 2002, percent of students who are Asian-American, African-American, Hispanic, or American Indian. (When the U.S. Department of Education calculates minority enrollment percentages, these are the demographic groupings it uses.)

Acceptance rate. Percent of applicants who were accepted for fall 2002.

Average undergraduate grade-point average (1.0 to 4.0). For students who entered in fall 2002.

TOEFL requirement. A "yes" means that students from non-English-speaking countries must submit scores for the Test of English as a Foreign Language.

Minimum TOEFL score. The lowest score on the paper TOEFL accepted for admission. (The computer-administered TOEFL is graded on a different scale.)

College-funded aid and international-student aid. A "yes" means the school provides its own financial aid to students.

Total fellowships, teaching assistantships, and research assistantships. For the 2002–2003 academic year.

Average indebtedness. Computed for 2002 graduates who incurred business school debt.

Average Graduate Management Admission Test (GMAT) score. Calculated separately for full- and part-time students who entered in fall 2002.

Average undergraduate grade-point average. Calculated for full-time students who entered in fall 2002.

Average age of the entering class. Calculated for full-time students who entered in fall 2002.

Average months of prior work experience. Calculated for full-time students who entered in fall 2002. Refers to postbaccalaureate work experience only.

Most popular departments. Based on student demand in the 2002–2003 academic year.

Mean starting base salary for 2002 graduates. Calculated only for graduates who were full-time students, had accepted full-time job offers, and reported salary data. Excludes employer-sponsored students, signing bonuses, and other forms of compensation such as stock options.

Employment locations. For the 2002 graduating class. Abbreviations: **Intl.** International; **N.E.** Northeast (Conn., Maine, Mass., N.H., N.J., N.Y., R.I., Vt.); **M.A.** Middle Atlantic (Del., D.C., Md., Pa., Va., W.Va.); **S.** South (Ala., Ark., Fla., Ga., Ky., La., Miss., N.C., S.C., Tenn.); **M.W.** Midwest (Ill., Ind., Iowa, Kan., Mich., Minn., Mo., Neb., N.D., Ohio, S.D., Wis.); **S.W.** Southwest (Ariz., Colo., N.M., Okla., Texas); **W.** West (Alaska, Calif., Hawaii, Idaho, Mont., Nev., Ore., Utah, Wash., Wyo.).

ALABAMA

Auburn University–Main Campus
415 W. Magnolia, Suite 503
Auburn University, AL 36849-5240
Public
Admissions: (334) 844-4060
E-mail: mbadmis@business.auburn.edu
Web site: http://www.mba.business.auburn.edu
Internet application: http://www.grad.auburn.edu/admissions.htm
Financial aid: (334) 844-4367
Application deadline: 03/01
In-state tuition: full time: $6,075; part time: $487/credit hour
Out-of-state tuition: full time: $17,025
Room/board/expenses: $15,500
College-funded aid: YES
International student aid: YES
Fellowships: 0
Research assistantships: 40
Teaching assistantships: 8
Full-time enrollment: 83
men: 64%; women: 36%; minorities: 4%; international: 14%
Part-time enrollment: 294
men: 71%; women: 29%; minorities: 2%; international: 1%
Acceptance rate (full time): 52%
Average GMAT (full time): 572
Average GMAT (part time): 587
Average GPA (full time): 3.25
Average age of entrants to full-time program: 25
Average months of prior work experience (full time): 24
TOEFL requirement: YES
Minimum TOEFL score: 550
Most popular departments: finance, marketing, management information systems, operations management, sports business

Auburn University–Montgomery
7300 University Drive
Montgomery, AL 36117
Public
Admissions: (334) 244-3611
E-mail: sjeffcoa@mickey.aum.edu
Web site: http://www.aum.edu
Financial aid: (334) 244-3571
Application deadline: rolling
In-state tuition: full time: $136/credit hour; part time: N/A
Out-of-state tuition: full time: $408/credit hour
Room/board/expenses: N/A
College-funded aid: YES
International student aid: NO
Research assistantships: 5
Full-time enrollment: 257
men: 55%; women: 45%; minorities: 12%; international: 4%
Part-time enrollment: N/A
men: N/A; women: N/A; minorities: N/A; international: N/A
Acceptance rate (full time): 87%
Average GMAT (full time): 510
Average GPA (full time): 3.00
Average age of entrants to full-time program: 28
Average months of prior work experience (full time): 62
TOEFL requirement: YES
Minimum TOEFL score: 500

Most popular departments: accounting, finance, general management, marketing, management information systems

Birmingham-Southern College[1]
900 Arkadelphia Road
Birmingham, AL 35254
Private
Admissions: (205) 226-4803
E-mail: graduate@bsc.edu
Web site: http://www.bsc.edu/
Internet application: http://bsc.edu/admission/online.htm
Financial aid: (205) 226-4688
Tuition: N/A
Room/board/expenses: N/A
Enrollment: N/A

Jacksonville State University
700 Pelham Road, N
Jacksonville, AL 36265
Public
Admissions: (256) 782-5329
E-mail: graduate@jsucc.jsu.edu
Web site: http://www.jsu.edu
Financial aid: (256) 782-5006
Application deadline: N/A
In-state tuition: full time: $3,240; part time: $162/credit hour
Out-of-state tuition: full time: $6,480
Room/board/expenses: $10,000
College-funded aid: YES
International student aid: YES
Average student indebtedness at graduation: $12,000
Full-time enrollment: N/A
men: N/A; women: N/A; minorities: N/A; international: N/A
Part-time enrollment: 89
men: 51%; women: 49%; minorities: 20%; international: 2%
TOEFL requirement: YES
Minimum TOEFL score: 500
Most popular departments: accounting, general management

Samford University
800 Lakeshore Drive
Birmingham, AL 35229
Private
Admissions: (205) 726-2931
E-mail: business.graduate.studies@samford.edu
Web site: http://www.samford.edu
Financial aid: (205) 726-2860
Application deadline: 06/15
Tuition: full time: $410/credit hour; part time: $410/credit hour
Room/board/expenses: N/A
College-funded aid: NO
International student aid: NO
Full-time enrollment: N/A
men: N/A; women: N/A; minorities: N/A; international: N/A
Part-time enrollment: 188
men: 59%; women: 41%; minorities: 11%; international: N/A
Average GMAT (part time): 520
TOEFL requirement: YES
Minimum TOEFL score: N/A

University of Alabama–Birmingham

1530 Third Avenue S, BEC 219
Birmingham, AL 35294-4460
Public
Admissions: (205) 934-8817
E-mail: mlake@uab.edu
Web site:
http://www.business.uab.edu
Internet application:
http://www.uab.edu/
graduate/apply/bus-apply.htm
Financial aid: (205) 934-8223
Application deadline: 07/01
In-state tuition: full time:
$123/credit hour; part time:
$123/credit hour
Out-of-state tuition: full time:
$277/credit hour
Room/board/expenses: N/A
College-funded aid: YES
International student aid: YES
Fellowships: 0
Research assistantships: 0
Teaching assistantships: 0
Full-time enrollment: N/A
men: N/A; women: N/A; minorities:
N/A; international: N/A
Part-time enrollment: 403
men: 63%; women: 37%; minori-
ties: 9%; international: 4%
Average GMAT (part time): 543
TOEFL requirement: YES
Minimum TOEFL score: 550
Most popular departments: entre-
preneurship, finance, general
management, manufacturing
and technology management,
marketing

University of Alabama–Huntsville[1]

ASB Room 102
Huntsville, AL 35899
Public
Admissions: (256) 824-6002
E-mail: msmprog@email.uah.edu
Web site: http://www.uah.edu/
colleges/adminsci
Financial aid: (256) 824-6024
Tuition: N/A
Room/board/expenses: N/A
Enrollment: N/A

University of Alabama–Tuscaloosa (Manderson)

Box 870223
Tuscaloosa, AL 35487
Public
Admissions: (888) 863-2622
E-mail: mba@cba.ua.edu
Web site:
http://www.cba.ua.edu/~mba
Financial aid: (205) 348-6517
Application deadline: 04/15
In-state tuition: full time: $5,156;
part time: N/A
Out-of-state tuition: full time:
$11,224
Room/board/expenses: $9,006
College-funded aid: YES
International student aid: YES
Fellowships: 4
Research assistantships: 46
Teaching assistantships: 1
**Average student indebtedness at
graduation:** $11,913
Full-time enrollment: 116
men: 66%; women: 34%; minori-
ties: 7%; international: 12%
Part-time enrollment: N/A
men: N/A; women: N/A; minorities:
N/A; international: N/A
Acceptance rate (full time): 44%
Average GMAT (full time): 603
Average GPA (full time): 3.40
**Average age of entrants to full-time
program:** 25

**Average months of prior work expe-
rience (full time):** 15
TOEFL requirement: YES
Minimum TOEFL score: 575
Most popular departments: consult-
ing, finance, marketing, manage-
ment information systems, real
estate
**Mean starting base salary for 2002
full-time graduates:** $52,390
**Employment location for 2002
class:** Intl. N/A; N.E. N/A; M.A.
N/A; S. 91%; M.W. 9%; S.W. N/A;
W. N/A

University of South Alabama[1]

Mitchell College of Business
Mobile, AL 36688
Public
Admissions: (251) 460-6141
E-mail:
rflynn@usamail.usouthal.edu
Web site: http://www.usaonline.
southalabama.edu
Financial aid: (251) 460-6231
Tuition: N/A
Room/board/expenses: N/A
Enrollment: N/A

University of Alaska–Anchorage[1]

3211 Providence Drive
Anchorage, AK 99508
Public
Admissions: (907) 786-1480
E-mail: agenrol@uaa.alaska.edu
Web site:
http://www.scob.alaska.edu
Financial aid: (907) 786-1586
Tuition: N/A
Room/board/expenses: N/A
Enrollment: N/A

University of Alaska–Fairbanks

PO Box 756080
Fairbanks, AK 99775-6080
Public
Admissions: (800) 478-1823
E-mail: fyapply@uaf.edu
Web site:
http://www.uaf.edu/som/bad.html
Internet application:
http://www.uaf.edu/admissions/
apply/index.html
Financial aid: (907) 474-7256
Application deadline: 08/01
In-state tuition: full time:
$184/credit hour; part time:
$184/credit hour
Out-of-state tuition: full time:
$358/credit hour
Room/board/expenses: $6,010
College-funded aid: YES
International student aid: YES
Teaching assistantships: 4
Full-time enrollment: 15
men: 73%; women: 27%; minori-
ties: 27%; international: 20%
Part-time enrollment: 23
men: 43%; women: 57%; minori-
ties: 13%; international: 0%
Acceptance rate (full time): 67%
Average GMAT (full time): 434
Average GMAT (part time): 490
Average GPA (full time): 3.45
**Average age of entrants to full-time
program:** 28
TOEFL requirement: YES
Minimum TOEFL score: 550
Most popular departments: general
management, other

Arizona State University–Main Campus

ASU MBA Program Office
Tempe, AZ 85287-4906
Public
Admissions: (480) 965-3332
E-mail: asu.mba@asu.edu
Web site:
http://www.cob.asu.edu/mba/
Internet application:
http://www.asu.edu/gradapp
Financial aid: (480) 965-3521
Application deadline: 05/01
In-state tuition: full time: $11,585;
part time: $12,585
Out-of-state tuition: full time:
$20,105
Room/board/expenses: $13,484
College-funded aid: YES
International student aid: YES
Fellowships: 45
Research assistantships: 34
Teaching assistantships: 42
**Average student indebtedness at
graduation:** $23,982
Full-time enrollment: 296
men: 79%; women: 21%; minori-
ties: 12%; international: 22%
Part-time enrollment: 591
men: 74%; women: 26%; minori-
ties: 14%; international: 6%
Acceptance rate (full time): 29%
Average GMAT (full time): 654
Average GMAT (part time): 592
Average GPA (full time): 3.42
**Average age of entrants to full-time
program:** 28
**Average months of prior work expe-
rience (full time):** 52.8
TOEFL requirement: YES
Minimum TOEFL score: 580
Most popular departments: finance,
marketing, management informa-
tion systems, sports business,
supply chain management
**Mean starting base salary for 2002
full-time graduates:** $74,518
**Employment location for 2002
class:** Intl. 10%; N.E. 7%; M.A. 2%;
S. 5%; M.W. 10%; S.W. 43%; W.
23%

Arizona State University West

4701 W. Thunderbird Road
PO Box 37100
Phoenix, AZ 85069-7100
Public
Admissions: (602) 543-6201
E-mail: mba_info@
asuwest-online.west.asu.edu
Web site:
http://www.west.asu.edu/
som/mba
Financial aid: (602) 543-8178
Application deadline: 06/01
In-state tuition: full time: N/A; part
time: $131/credit hour
Out-of-state tuition: full time: N/A
Room/board/expenses: N/A
College-funded aid: YES
International student aid: YES
Teaching assistantships: 0
Full-time enrollment: N/A
men: N/A; women: N/A; minorities:
N/A; international: N/A
Part-time enrollment: 429
men: 67%; women: 33%; minori-
ties: 13%; international: 1%
Average GMAT (part time): 585
TOEFL requirement: YES
Minimum TOEFL score: 600

Northern Arizona University

PO Box 15066
Flagstaff, AZ 86011-5066
Public
Admissions: (928) 523-7342
E-mail: joseph.anderson@nau.edu
Web site: http://www.cba.nau.edu/
mbaprogram
Internet application:
http://www.cba.nau.edu/
degreeprograms/grad/
mba/admit.asp
Financial aid: (928) 523-4951
Application deadline: 03/01
In-state tuition: full time: $5,565;
part time: $126/credit hour
Out-of-state tuition: full time:
$13,258
Room/board/expenses: $8,359
College-funded aid: YES
International student aid: YES
Fellowships: 0
Research assistantships: 10
Teaching assistantships: 6
Full-time enrollment: 42
men: 67%; women: 33%; minori-
ties: 5%; international: 26%
Part-time enrollment: N/A
men: N/A; women: N/A; minorities:
N/A; international: N/A
Acceptance rate (full time): 54%
Average GMAT (full time): 538
Average GPA (full time): 3.35
**Average age of entrants to full-time
program:** 25
**Average months of prior work expe-
rience (full time):** 51
TOEFL requirement: YES
Minimum TOEFL score: 600
Most popular departments: ac-
counting, entrepreneurship, fi-
nance, general management,
management information systems

Thunderbird, The American Graduate School of International Management

15249 N. 59th Avenue
Glendale, AZ 85306-6000
Private
Admissions: (602) 978-7100
E-mail: tbird@thunderbird.edu
Web site:
http://www.thunderbird.edu
Financial aid: (602) 978-7130
Application deadline: 07/15
Tuition: full time: $27,760; part
time: N/A
Room/board/expenses: $12,285
College-funded aid: YES
International student aid: YES
Fellowships: 0
Research assistantships: 0
Teaching assistantships: 0
**Average student indebtedness at
graduation:** $51,804
Full-time enrollment: 1,052
men: 73%; women: 27%; minori-
ties: 7%; international: 59%
Part-time enrollment: N/A
men: N/A; women: N/A; minorities:
N/A; international: N/A
Acceptance rate (full time): 80%
Average GMAT (full time): 600
Average GPA (full time): 3.20
**Average age of entrants to full-time
program:** 29
**Average months of prior work expe-
rience (full time):** 64
TOEFL requirement: YES
Minimum TOEFL score: 600
Most popular departments: finance,
general management, internation-
al business, marketing, other

**Mean starting base salary for 2002
full-time graduates:** $63,079
**Employment location for 2002
class:** Intl. 40%; N.E. 20%; M.A.
5%; S. 6%; M.W. 9%; S.W. 11%;
W. 9%

University of Arizona (Eller)

McClelland Hall, Room 210
Tucson, AZ 85721-0108
Public
Admissions: (520) 621-4008
E-mail: mba_admissions@
eller.arizona.edu
Web site:
http://ellermba.arizona.edu
Financial aid: (520) 621-4008
Application deadline: 04/15
In-state tuition: full time: $11,594;
part time: N/A
Out-of-state tuition: full time:
$20,114
Room/board/expenses: $10,670
College-funded aid: YES
International student aid: YES
Fellowships: 0
Research assistantships: 0
Teaching assistantships: 21
**Average student indebtedness at
graduation:** $28,000
Full-time enrollment: 67
men: 75%; women: 25%; minori-
ties: 10%; international: 25%
Part-time enrollment: 69
men: 74%; women: 26%; minori-
ties: 26%; international: 1%
Acceptance rate (full time): 59%
Average GMAT (full time): 636
Average GMAT (part time): 580
Average GPA (full time): 3.34
**Average age of entrants to full-time
program:** 28
**Average months of prior work expe-
rience (full time):** 53
TOEFL requirement: YES
Minimum TOEFL score: 600
Most popular departments: entre-
preneurship, finance, marketing,
management information systems,
other
**Mean starting base salary for 2002
full-time graduates:** $64,476
**Employment location for 2002
class:** Intl. 16%; N.E. 7%; M.A. 0%;
S. 0%; M.W. 5%; S.W. 50%; W.
23%

Arkansas State University[1]

PO Box 2220
State University, AR 72467
Public
Admissions: (870) 972-3029
E-mail:
colbus@chickasaw.astate.edu
Web site: http://business.astate.
edu/mba/mba1.htm
Financial aid: (870) 972-2310
Tuition: N/A
Room/board/expenses: N/A
Enrollment: N/A

Henderson State University[1]

1100 Henderson Street
Box 7801
Arkadelphia, AR 71999-0001
Public
Admissions: (870) 230-5126
E-mail: grad@hsu.edu
Web site: http://www.hsu.edu/
dept/bus/mba.html
Financial aid: (870) 230-5148
Tuition: N/A
Room/board/expenses: N/A
Enrollment: N/A

University of Arkansas–Fayetteville (Walton)

475 Business Building
Fayetteville, AR 72701
Public
Admissions: (479) 575-2851
E-mail: gsb@walton.uark.edu
Web site: http://gsb.uark.edu
Internet application:
https://www2.uark.edu/
servlet/edu.uark.emgt.
admissions.Application
Financial aid: (479) 575-3806
Application deadline: 02/15
In-state tuition: total program:
$11,802 (full time); part time:
$275/credit hour
Out-of-state tuition: total program:
$22,776 (full time)
Room/board/expenses: $10,979
College-funded aid: YES
International student aid: YES
Fellowships: 8
Research assistantships: 30
Teaching assistantships: 0
Average student indebtedness at graduation: $11,380
Full-time enrollment: 61
men: 61%; women: 39%; minorities: 8%; international: 23%
Part-time enrollment: 86
men: 71%; women: 29%; minorities: 7%; international: 10%
Acceptance rate (full time): 69%
Average GMAT (full time): 593
Average GMAT (part time): 540
Average GPA (full time): 3.31
Average age of entrants to full-time program: 25
Average months of prior work experience (full time): 32
TOEFL requirement: YES
Minimum TOEFL score: 550
Most popular departments: entrepreneurship, finance, international business, marketing, other
Mean starting base salary for 2002 full-time graduates: $55,400
Employment location for 2002 class: Intl. 6%; N.E. 6%; M.A. 6%; S. 81%; M.W. 0%; S.W. 0%; W. 0%

University of Arkansas–Little Rock[1]

2801 S. University Avenue
Little Rock, AR 72204
Public
Admissions: (501) 569-3356
E-mail: rmmoore@ualr.edu
Web site: http://cba.ualr.edu
Financial aid: (501) 569-3035
Tuition: N/A
Room/board/expenses: N/A
Enrollment: N/A

University of Central Arkansas[1]

201 Donaghey
Conway, AR 72035
Public
Admissions: (501) 450-5316
E-mail: rebeccag@mail.uca.edu
Web site: http://www.business.uca.edu/~mba/home.htm
Internet application:
http://www.business.uca.edu/~mba/online_manuals_applications.htm
Financial aid: (501) 450-3140
Tuition: N/A
Room/board/expenses: N/A
Enrollment: N/A

CALIFORNIA

California State Polytechnic University–Pomona[1]

3801 W. Temple Avenue
Pomona, CA 91768
Public
Admissions: (909) 869-2363
E-mail:
directorgba@csupomona.edu
Web site: http://www.csupomona.edu/~mba
Internet application:
http://www.csumentor.edu/AdmissionApp/
Financial aid: (909) 869-3700
Tuition: N/A
Room/board/expenses: N/A
Enrollment: N/A

California State University–Bakersfield[1]

9001 Stockdale Highway
Bakersfield, CA 93311-1099
Public
Admissions: (661) 664-3036
E-mail: hmontalvo@csubak.edu
Web site:
http://www.csub.edu/BPA
Financial aid: (661) 664-3016
Tuition: N/A
Room/board/expenses: N/A
Enrollment: N/A

California State University–Chico[1]

College of Business
Graduate Programs
Chico, CA 95929-0041
Public
Admissions: (530) 898-4428
E-mail: info@csuchico.edu
Web site: http://www.csuchico.edu
Internet application:
http://www.csuchico.edu/gisp/ip/Apply.html
Financial aid: (530) 898-6451
Tuition: N/A
Room/board/expenses: N/A
Enrollment: N/A

California State University–Fresno (Craig)[1]

5245 N. Backer Avenue
Fresno, CA 93740-8001
Public
Admissions: (559) 278-2107
E-mail: mkeppler@csufresno.edu
Web site: http://www.craig.csufresno.edu/mba
Internet application:
http://www.csumentor.edu/admissionapp/grad_apply.asp
Financial aid: (559) 278-2183
Tuition: N/A
Room/board/expenses: N/A
Enrollment: N/A

California State University–Fullerton[1]

PO Box 6900
Fullerton, CA 92834-6900
Public
Admissions: (714) 278-2300
E-mail: mba@fullerton.edu
Web site:
http://business.fullerton.edu
Internet application:
http://www.csumentor.edu/AdmissionApp/grad_apply.asp
Financial aid: (714) 278-3125
Tuition: N/A

Room/board/expenses: N/A
Enrollment: N/A

California State University–Hayward

25800 Carlos Bee Boulevard
Hayward, CA 94542
Public
Admissions: (510) 885-2784
E-mail: adminfo@csuhayward.edu
Web site:
http://sbegrad.csuhayward.edu
Internet application:
http://www.csumentor.edu/AdmissionApp/
Financial aid: (510) 885-3616
Application deadline: 06/01
In-state tuition: full time: $2,504;
part time: $1,664
Out-of-state tuition: full time:
$11,528
Room/board/expenses: $11,908
College-funded aid: YES
International student aid: NO
Fellowships: 4
Research assistantships: 0
Teaching assistantships: 0
Average student indebtedness at graduation: $23,828
Full-time enrollment: N/A
men: N/A; women: N/A; minorities: N/A; international: N/A
Part-time enrollment: 524
men: 53%; women: 47%; minorities: 67%; international: 41%
Average GMAT (part time): 539
Average age of entrants to full-time program: N/A
Average months of prior work experience (full time): N/A
TOEFL requirement: YES
Minimum TOEFL score: 550
Most popular departments: accounting, e-commerce, economics, entrepreneurship, finance, general management, human resources management, international business, marketing, management information systems, operations management, supply chain management, statistics and operations research, tax, other

California State University–Long Beach

1250 Bellflower Boulevard
Long Beach, CA 90840-8501
Public
Admissions: (562) 985-7988
E-mail: mba@csulb.edu
Web site: http://www.csulb.edu/colleges/cba
Financial aid: (562) 985-4141
Application deadline: 04/30
In-state tuition: full time: N/A; part time: N/A
Out-of-state tuition: full time: N/A
Room/board/expenses: N/A
College-funded aid: YES
International student aid: NO
Full-time enrollment: 95
men: N/A; women: N/A; minorities: N/A; international: N/A
Part-time enrollment: 238
men: N/A; women: N/A; minorities: N/A; international: N/A
TOEFL requirement: YES
Minimum TOEFL score: 550
Most popular departments: finance, general management, human resources management, marketing, management information systems

California State University–Sacramento

6000 J Street
Sacramento, CA 95819-6088
Public
Admissions: (916) 278-6772
E-mail: cbagrad@csus.edu
Web site:
http://www.csus.edu/cbagrad
Internet application:
http://www.csumentor.edu/admissionapp
Financial aid: (916) 278-6554
Application deadline: 04/01
In-state tuition: full time: $3,930;
part time: $3,300
Out-of-state tuition: full time:
$9,015
Room/board/expenses: $9,500
College-funded aid: YES
International student aid: YES
Fellowships: 0

California State University–Los Angeles

5151 State University Drive
Los Angeles, CA 90032-8120
Public
Admissions: (323) 343-5156
E-mail:
bcarter@cslanet.calstatela.edu
Web site: http://cbe.calstatela.edu/mba/index.htm
Financial aid: (323) 343-1784
Application deadline: 06/01
In-state tuition: full time: N/A; part time: N/A
Out-of-state tuition: full time: N/A
Room/board/expenses: N/A
College-funded aid: NO
International student aid: NO
Fellowships: 0
Research assistantships: 0
Teaching assistantships: 0
Full-time enrollment: N/A
men: N/A; women: N/A; minorities: N/A; international: N/A
Part-time enrollment: 250
men: 47%; women: 53%; minorities: 53%; international: 27%
Average GMAT (part time): 550
TOEFL requirement: YES
Minimum TOEFL score: 550
Most popular departments: accounting, finance, general management, marketing, management information systems

California State University–Northridge

18111 Nordhoff Street
Northridge, CA 91330-8380
Public
Admissions: (818) 677-3700
E-mail: mba@csun.edu
Web site:
http://www.csun.edu/mba
Internet application:
http://www.csumentor.edu/admissionapp
Financial aid: (818) 677-3000
Application deadline: 05/01
In-state tuition: full time: N/A; part time: $1,262
Out-of-state tuition: full time: N/A
Room/board/expenses: N/A
College-funded aid: YES
International student aid: YES
Full-time enrollment: N/A
men: N/A; women: N/A; minorities: N/A; international: N/A
Part-time enrollment: 202
men: 59%; women: 41%; minorities: 21%; international: 11%
TOEFL requirement: YES
Minimum TOEFL score: 550

Research assistantships: 0
Teaching assistantships: 7
Full-time enrollment: N/A
men: N/A; women: N/A; minorities: N/A; international: N/A
Part-time enrollment: 689
men: 53%; women: 47%; minorities: 26%; international: 14%
Average GMAT (part time): 579
TOEFL requirement: YES
Minimum TOEFL score: 550
Most popular departments: finance, general management, human resources management, marketing, management information systems

California State University–San Bernardino

5500 University Parkway
San Bernardino, CA 92407
Public
Admissions: (909) 880-5200
E-mail: tthomas@mail.csusb.edu
Web site: http://www.csusb.edu
Internet application:
http://enrollment.csusb.edu/admiss.html
Financial aid: (909) 880-5222
Application deadline: 08/15
In-state tuition: full time: $2,720;
part time: N/A
Out-of-state tuition: full time:
$181/credit hour
Room/board/expenses: N/A
College-funded aid: YES
International student aid: YES
Research assistantships: 15
Teaching assistantships: 8
Full-time enrollment: 231
men: 55%; women: 45%; minorities: 7%; international: 74%
Part-time enrollment: 104
men: 44%; women: 56%; minorities: 31%; international: 0%
Acceptance rate (full time): 67%
Average GMAT (full time): 522
Average GMAT (part time): 522
Average GPA (full time): 3.17
Average age of entrants to full-time program: 28
Average months of prior work experience (full time): 36
TOEFL requirement: YES
Minimum TOEFL score: 550
Most popular departments: accounting, finance, marketing, management information systems, public administration

Cal Poly–San Luis Obispo

1 Grand Avenue
San Luis Obispo, CA 93407
Public
Admissions: (805) 756-2311
E-mail: admissions@calpoly.edu
Web site: http://www.calpoly.edu/
Internet application:
http://www.csumentor.edu/admissionapp
Financial aid: (805) 756-2927
Application deadline: 07/01
In-state tuition: full time: $2,823;
part time: N/A
Out-of-state tuition: full time:
$9,189
Room/board/expenses: $7,245
College-funded aid: NO
International student aid: NO
Full-time enrollment: 105
men: 71%; women: 29%; minorities: 21%; international: 8%
Part-time enrollment: N/A
men: N/A; women: N/A; minorities: N/A; international: N/A
Acceptance rate (full time): 53%
Average GMAT (full time): 598
Average GPA (full time): 3.27

Average age of entrants to full-time program: 26
Average months of prior work experience (full time): 26
TOEFL requirement: YES
Minimum TOEFL score: 550
Most popular departments: entrepreneurship, finance, general management, marketing, other

Chapman University (Argyros)

1 University Drive
Orange, CA 92866
Private
Admissions: (714) 997-6596
E-mail: mba@chapman.edu
Web site: http://www.chapman.edu/argyros
Internet application: http://www.chapman.edu/argyros
Financial aid: (714) 997-6741
Application deadline: 07/01
Tuition: full time: $15,240; part time: $635/credit hour
Room/board/expenses: $12,000
College-funded aid: YES
International student aid: YES
Average student indebtedness at graduation: $15,885
Full-time enrollment: N/A
men: N/A; women: N/A; minorities: N/A; international: N/A
Part-time enrollment: 131
men: 55%; women: 45%; minorities: 29%; international: 25%
Average GMAT (part time): 535
TOEFL requirement: YES
Minimum TOEFL score: 550
Most popular departments: accounting, entrepreneurship, finance, international business, marketing

Claremont Graduate University (Drucker)

1021 N. Dartmouth Avenue
Claremont, CA 91711-6184
Private
Admissions: (800) 944-4312
E-mail: drucker@cgu.edu
Web site: http://www.drucker.cgu.edu
Internet application: http://administration.cgu.edu/admissions/pdf/app.pdf
Financial aid: (909) 621-8337
Application deadline: 05/01
Tuition: full time: $33,568; part time: $1,044/credit hour
Room/board/expenses: $15,000
College-funded aid: YES
International student aid: YES
Fellowships: 10
Research assistantships: 12
Teaching assistantships: 0
Average student indebtedness at graduation: $42,686
Full-time enrollment: 172
men: 66%; women: 34%; minorities: 27%; international: 47%
Part-time enrollment: 30
men: 73%; women: 27%; minorities: 23%; international: 0%
Acceptance rate (full time): 49%
Average GMAT (full time): 614
Average GMAT (part time): 592
Average GPA (full time): 3.20
Average age of entrants to full-time program: 28
Average months of prior work experience (full time): 60
TOEFL requirement: YES
Minimum TOEFL score: 600
Most popular departments: finance, general management, leadership, marketing, management information systems
Mean starting base salary for 2002 full-time graduates: $64,397

Employment location for 2002 class: Intl. 0%; N.E. 4%; M.A. 0%; S. 0%; M.W. 0%; S.W. 0%; W. 96%

Loyola Marymount University

1 LMU Drive, MS 8387
Los Angeles, CA 90045-2659
Private
Admissions: (310) 338-2848
E-mail: mbapc@lmumail.lmu.edu
Web site: http://mba.lmu.edu
Internet application: http://www.lmu.edu/graduate/home/index.html
Financial aid: (310) 338-2753
Application deadline: rolling
Tuition: full time: $756/credit hour; part time: $756/credit hour
Room/board/expenses: $12,000
College-funded aid: YES
International student aid: YES
Fellowships: 9
Research assistantships: 26
Teaching assistantships: 0
Average student indebtedness at graduation: $34,000
Full-time enrollment: 109
men: 61%; women: 39%; minorities: 29%; international: 30%
Part-time enrollment: 256
men: 62%; women: 38%; minorities: 29%; international: 0%
Acceptance rate (full time): 74%
Average GMAT (full time): 565
Average GMAT (part time): 565
Average GPA (full time): 3.26
Average age of entrants to full-time program: 23
Average months of prior work experience (full time): 36
TOEFL requirement: YES
Minimum TOEFL score: 600
Most popular departments: entrepreneurship, finance, international business, marketing, organizational behavior

Monterey Institute of International Studies (Fisher)

460 Pierce Street
Monterey, CA 93940
Private
Admissions: (831) 647-4123
E-mail: fgsib@miis.edu
Web site: www.miis.edu
Internet application: www.miis.edu/admfi-admi-onapp.html
Financial aid: (831) 647-4119
Application deadline: 08/01
Tuition: full time: $21,150; part time: $940/credit hour
Room/board/expenses: $11,287
College-funded aid: YES
International student aid: YES
Fellowships: 0
Research assistantships: 10
Teaching assistantships: 0
Average student indebtedness at graduation: $19,000
Full-time enrollment: 91
men: 46%; women: 54%; minorities: 16%; international: 36%
Part-time enrollment: N/A
men: N/A; women: N/A; minorities: N/A; international: N/A
Acceptance rate (full time): 88%
Average GMAT (full time): 553
Average GPA (full time): 3.17
Average age of entrants to full-time program: 27
Average months of prior work experience (full time): 39
TOEFL requirement: YES
Minimum TOEFL score: 550
Most popular departments: consulting, entrepreneurship, finance, international business, marketing

Naval Postgraduate School[1]

1 University Circle
Monterey, CA 39343
Public
Admissions: (831) 656-3218
E-mail: dabrook@nps.navy.mil
Web site: http://web.nps.navy.mil/~sm/
Financial aid: (831) 656-3093
Tuition: N/A
Room/board/expenses: N/A
Enrollment: N/A

Pepperdine University (Graziadio)

24255 Pacific Coast Highway
Malibu, CA 90263
Private
Admissions: (310) 568-5535
E-mail: bschool@pepperdine.edu
Web site: http://www.bschool.pepperdine.edu
Internet application: http://www.bschool.pepperdine.edu/programs/apply.html
Financial aid: (310) 568-5530
Application deadline: 05/01
Tuition: full time: $26,505; part time: $890/credit hour
Room/board/expenses: $12,020
College-funded aid: YES
International student aid: YES
Fellowships: 0
Research assistantships: 0
Teaching assistantships: 17
Average student indebtedness at graduation: $51,793
Full-time enrollment: 199
men: 58%; women: 42%; minorities: 39%; international: 37%
Part-time enrollment: 1,465
men: 61%; women: 39%; minorities: 36%; international: 9%
Acceptance rate (full time): 56%
Average GMAT (full time): 640
Average GMAT (part time): 554
Average GPA (full time): 3.10
Average age of entrants to full-time program: 27
Average months of prior work experience (full time): 42
TOEFL requirement: YES
Minimum TOEFL score: 550
Most popular departments: entrepreneurship, finance, general management, international business, leadership
Mean starting base salary for 2002 full-time graduates: $58,740
Employment location for 2002 class: Intl. 12%; N.E. 0%; M.A. 4%; S. 4%; M.W. 0%; S.W. 4%; W. 77%

San Diego State University

5500 Campanile Drive
San Diego, CA 92182-8228
Public
Admissions: (619) 594-1008
E-mail: sdsumba@mail.sdsu.edu
Web site: http://www.sdsu.edu/mba
Internet application: http://www.csumentor.edu/admissionapp
Financial aid: (619) 594-6323
Application deadline: 04/15
In-state tuition: full time: $1,948; part time: $1,318
Out-of-state tuition: full time: $8,716

Mean starting base salary for 2002 full-time graduates: $66,870
Employment location for 2002 class: Intl. 40%; N.E. 0%; M.A. 0%; S. 0%; M.W. 0%; S.W. 0%; W. 60%

Room/board/expenses: N/A
College-funded aid: YES
International student aid: NO
Full-time enrollment: 399
men: 62%; women: 38%; minorities: 15%; international: 22%
Part-time enrollment: 328
men: 61%; women: 39%; minorities: 15%; international: 0%
Acceptance rate (full time): 42%
Average GMAT (full time): 602
Average GMAT (part time): 602
Average GPA (full time): 3.30
Average age of entrants to full-time program: 28
Average months of prior work experience (full time): 60
TOEFL requirement: YES
Minimum TOEFL score: 570
Most popular departments: entrepreneurship, finance, general management, marketing, management information systems

San Francisco State University[1]

1600 Holloway Avenue
San Francisco, CA 94132
Public
Admissions: (415) 338-1279
E-mail: mba@sfsu.edu
Web site: http://www.sfsu.edu/~mba
Internet application: http://www.csumentor.edu
Financial aid: (415) 338-1581
Tuition: N/A
Room/board/expenses: N/A
Enrollment: N/A

San Jose State University

1 Washington Square
San Jose, CA 95192-0162
Public
Admissions: (408) 924-3420
E-mail: mba@cob.sjsu.edu
Web site: http://www.cob.sjsu.edu/graduate
Internet application: http://www.csumentor.edu/admissionapp
Financial aid: (408) 283-7500
Application deadline: 05/01
In-state tuition: full time: $2,221; part time: $1,495
Out-of-state tuition: full time: $7,297
Room/board/expenses: N/A
International student aid: NO
Full-time enrollment: 46
men: 48%; women: 52%; minorities: N/A; international: N/A
Part-time enrollment: 500
men: 60%; women: 40%; minorities: N/A; international: N/A
Acceptance rate (full time): 59%
Average GMAT (full time): 540
Average GMAT (part time): 572
Average GPA (full time): 3.31
Average age of entrants to full-time program: 29
TOEFL requirement: YES
Minimum TOEFL score: 550
Most popular departments: accounting, finance, general management, marketing, management information systems

Santa Clara University (Leavey)

Kenna Hall
Santa Clara, CA 95053
Private
Admissions: (408) 554-4539
E-mail: mbaadmissions@scu.edu
Web site: http://business.scu.edu

Internet application: https://app.applyyourself.com/?id=SCU-MBA
Financial aid: (408) 554-4505
Application deadline: 05/01
Tuition: full time: $594/credit hour; part time: $594/credit hour
Room/board/expenses: $12,670
College-funded aid: YES
International student aid: NO
Fellowships: 25
Research assistantships: 0
Teaching assistantships: 0
Full-time enrollment: 188
men: 55%; women: 45%; minorities: 30%; international: 29%
Part-time enrollment: 800
men: 68%; women: 32%; minorities: 31%; international: 22%
Average GMAT (part time): 615
TOEFL requirement: YES
Minimum TOEFL score: 600
Most popular departments: entrepreneurship, finance, international business, leadership, marketing

Stanford University

518 Memorial Way
Stanford, CA 94305-5015
Private
Admissions: (650) 723-2766
E-mail: mba@gsb.stanford.edu
Web site: http://www.gsb.stanford.edu
Internet application: http://www.gsb.stanford.edu/apply
Financial aid: (650) 723-3282
Application deadline: 03/17
Tuition: full time: $33,300; part time: N/A
Room/board/expenses: $21,102
College-funded aid: YES
International student aid: YES
Fellowships: 383
Average student indebtedness at graduation: $48,127
Full-time enrollment: 749
men: 62%; women: 38%; minorities: 25%; international: 32%
Part-time enrollment: N/A
men: N/A; women: N/A; minorities: N/A; international: N/A
Acceptance rate (full time): 8%
Average GMAT (full time): 716
Average GPA (full time): 3.58
Average months of prior work experience (full time): 56
TOEFL requirement: YES
Minimum TOEFL score: 600
Most popular departments: entrepreneurship, finance, general management, international business, organizational behavior
Mean starting base salary for 2002 full-time graduates: $95,000
Employment location for 2002 class: Intl. 13%; N.E. 16%; M.A. 4%; S. 1%; M.W. 9%; S.W. 3%; W. 54%

University of California–Berkeley (Haas)

545 Student Services Building
Berkeley, CA 94720-1900
Public
Admissions: (510) 642-1405
E-mail: mbaadms@haas.berkeley.edu
Web site: http://www.haas.berkeley.edu
Internet application: https://ssl.haas.berkeley.edu/admissions/
Financial aid: (510) 643-0183
Application deadline: 03/14
In-state tuition: full time: $10,621; part time: $27,136
Out-of-state tuition: full time: $21,753

Room/board/expenses: $18,772
College-funded aid: YES
International student aid: YES
Fellowships: 68
Research assistantships: 7
Teaching assistantships: 73
Average student indebtedness at graduation: $38,648
Full-time enrollment: 496
men: 70%; women: 30%; minorities: 20%; international: 33%
Part-time enrollment: 398
men: 74%; women: 26%; minorities: 41%; international: 17%
Acceptance rate (full time): 11%
Average GMAT (full time): 703
Average GMAT (part time): 680
Average GPA (full time): 3.55
Average age of entrants to full-time program: 28
Average months of prior work experience (full time): 66
TOEFL requirement: YES
Minimum TOEFL score: 570
Most popular departments: entrepreneurship, finance, general management, manufacturing and technology management, marketing
Mean starting base salary for 2002 full-time graduates: $84,504
Employment location for 2002 class: Intl. 21%; N.E. 8%; M.A. 2%; S. 2%; M.W. 1%; S.W. 3%; W. 63%

University of California–Davis

1 Shields Avenue
Davis, CA 95616-8609
Public
Admissions: (530) 752-7399
E-mail: admissions@gsm.ucdavis.edu
Web site: http://www.gsm.ucdavis.edu
Internet application: http://www.gsm.ucdavis.edu/admissions/apply.htm
Financial aid: (530) 752-9246
Application deadline: 04/01
In-state tuition: full time: $11,092; total program: $36,960 (part time)
Out-of-state tuition: full time: $22,224
Room/board/expenses: $13,056
College-funded aid: YES
International student aid: NO
Average student indebtedness at graduation: $30,087
Full-time enrollment: 121
men: 54%; women: 46%; minorities: 16%; international: 19%
Part-time enrollment: 285
men: 79%; women: 21%; minorities: 19%; international: 9%
Acceptance rate (full time): 24%
Average GMAT (full time): 669
Average GMAT (part time): 616
Average GPA (full time): 3.30
Average age of entrants to full-time program: 30
Average months of prior work experience (full time): 60
TOEFL requirement: YES
Minimum TOEFL score: 600
Most popular departments: finance, general management, international business, marketing, technology
Mean starting base salary for 2002 full-time graduates: $68,619
Employment location for 2002 class: Intl. N/A; N.E. 0%; M.A. 3%; S. 0%; M.W. 0%; S.W. 0%; W. 97%

University of California–Irvine

GSM, University of California–Irvine
Irvine, CA 92697-3125
Public
Admissions: (949) 824-4622
E-mail: gsm-mba@uci.edu
Web site: http://www.gsm.uci.edu
Internet application: http://www.gsm.uci.edu/go/application
Financial aid: (949) 824-5728
Application deadline: 05/17
In-state tuition: full time: $11,648; part time: $19,500
Out-of-state tuition: full time: $22,780
Room/board/expenses: $19,240
College-funded aid: YES
International student aid: YES
Fellowships: 45
Research assistantships: 15
Teaching assistantships: 25
Average student indebtedness at graduation: $28,500
Full-time enrollment: 231
men: 71%; women: 29%; minorities: 23%; international: 23%
Part-time enrollment: 398
men: 74%; women: 26%; minorities: 27%; international: 6%
Acceptance rate (full time): 31%
Average GMAT (full time): 682
Average GMAT (part time): 578
Average GPA (full time): 3.34
Average age of entrants to full-time program: 29
Average months of prior work experience (full time): 62
TOEFL requirement: YES
Minimum TOEFL score: 600
Most popular departments: finance, marketing, management information systems, operations management, other
Mean starting base salary for 2002 full-time graduates: $70,000
Employment location for 2002 class: Intl. 6%; N.E. 0%; M.A. 1%; S. 0%; M.W. 0%; S.W. 19%; W. 74%

University of California–Los Angeles (Anderson)

110 Westwood Plaza
Box 951481
Los Angeles, CA 90095-1481
Public
Admissions: (310) 825-6944
E-mail: mba.admissions@anderson.ucla.edu
Web site: http://www.anderson.ucla.edu
Internet application: http://www.anderson.ucla.edu/programs/mba/download.html
Financial aid: (310) 825-2746
Application deadline: 04/04
In-state tuition: full time: $11,820; part time: $21,084
Out-of-state tuition: full time: $22,952
Room/board/expenses: $20,508
College-funded aid: YES
International student aid: YES
Fellowships: 108
Research assistantships: 97
Teaching assistantships: 65
Average student indebtedness at graduation: $45,200
Full-time enrollment: 670
men: 71%; women: 29%; minorities: 19%; international: 22%
Part-time enrollment: 563
men: 75%; women: 25%; minorities: 27%; international: 0%
Acceptance rate (full time): 15%
Average GMAT (full time): 699

Average GMAT (part time): 664
Average GPA (full time): 3.60
Average age of entrants to full-time program: 28
Average months of prior work experience (full time): 56
TOEFL requirement: YES
Minimum TOEFL score: 600
Most popular departments: entrepreneurship, finance, general management, marketing, operations management
Mean starting base salary for 2002 full-time graduates: $82,715
Employment location for 2002 class: Intl. 15%; N.E. 10%; M.A. 2%; S. 1%; M.W. 7%; S.W. 1%; W. 65%

University of San Diego

5998 Alcala Park
San Diego, CA 92110-2492
Private
Admissions: (619) 260-4506
E-mail: grads@sandiego.edu
Web site: http://www.sandiego.edu/gradmiss/
Internet application: http://www.sandiego.edu/gradmiss/application.html
Financial aid: (619) 260-4514
Application deadline: 05/01
Tuition: full time: $775/credit hour; part time: $775/credit hour
Room/board/expenses: $12,152
College-funded aid: YES
International student aid: YES
Fellowships: 123
Research assistantships: 0
Teaching assistantships: 0
Average student indebtedness at graduation: $30,000
Full-time enrollment: N/A
men: N/A; women: N/A; minorities: N/A; international: N/A
Part-time enrollment: 204
men: 64%; women: 36%; minorities: 25%; international: 13%
Average GMAT (part time): 541
TOEFL requirement: YES
Minimum TOEFL score: 580
Most popular departments: finance, general management, international business, supply chain management, other

University of San Francisco (McLaren)

2130 Fulton Street
San Francisco, CA 94117-1080
Private
Admissions: (415) 422-2865
E-mail: mbausf@usfca.edu
Web site: http://www.usfca.edu/usf/sobam
Internet application: http://www.usfca.edu/sobam/MBA/apply-form.htm
Financial aid: (415) 422-6303
Application deadline: 06/01
Tuition: full time: $20,520; part time: $855/credit hour
Room/board/expenses: $18,500
College-funded aid: YES
International student aid: YES
Full-time enrollment: 299
men: 52%; women: 48%; minorities: 34%; international: 57%
Part-time enrollment: 164
men: 52%; women: 48%; minorities: 30%; international: 0%
Acceptance rate (full time): 80%
Average GMAT (full time): 535
Average GMAT (part time): 535
Average GPA (full time): 3.00
Average age of entrants to full-time program: 27
TOEFL requirement: YES
Minimum TOEFL score: 600

Most popular departments: finance, general management, international business, marketing, technology
Mean starting base salary for 2002 full-time graduates: $62,730

University of Southern California (Marshall)

University Park
Los Angeles, CA 90089-1421
Private
Admissions: (213) 740-7846
E-mail: marshallmba@marshall.usc.edu
Web site: http://www.marshall.usc.edu
Internet application: http://apply.embark.com/mbaedge/usc/mba
Financial aid: (213) 740-1111
Application deadline: 04/01
Tuition: full time: $31,680; part time: $916/credit hour
Room/board/expenses: $12,000
College-funded aid: YES
International student aid: YES
Average student indebtedness at graduation: $45,000
Full-time enrollment: 581
men: 69%; women: 31%; minorities: 33%; international: 24%
Part-time enrollment: 749
men: 71%; women: 29%; minorities: 40%; international: 4%
Acceptance rate (full time): 21%
Average GMAT (full time): 684
Average GMAT (part time): 623
Average GPA (full time): 3.35
Average age of entrants to full-time program: 28
Average months of prior work experience (full time): 55
TOEFL requirement: YES
Minimum TOEFL score: 600
Most popular departments: entrepreneurship, finance, general management, manufacturing and technology management, marketing
Mean starting base salary for 2002 full-time graduates: $75,134
Employment location for 2002 class: Intl. 7%; N.E. 12%; M.A. 3%; S. 0%; M.W. 3%; S.W. 5%; W. 70%

University of the Pacific (Eberhardt)

3601 Pacific Avenue
Stockton, CA 95211
Private
Admissions: (209) 946-2261
E-mail: mba@uop.edu
Web site: http://www1.uop.edu/esb/mba/index.html
Internet application: http://nt02.esb.uop.edu/admin/mbaapp/mbaapp.asp
Financial aid: (209) 946-2421
Application deadline: 03/01
Tuition: full time: $21,095; part time: $694/credit hour
Room/board/expenses: $10,000
College-funded aid: YES
International student aid: YES
Fellowships: 15
Research assistantships: 10
Teaching assistantships: 8
Average student indebtedness at graduation: $15,000
Full-time enrollment: 39
men: 67%; women: 33%; minorities: 21%; international: 13%
Part-time enrollment: 27
men: 63%; women: 37%; minorities: 15%; international: 4%
Acceptance rate (full time): 45%
Average GMAT (full time): 574
Average GMAT (part time): 563

Average GPA (full time): 3.49
Average age of entrants to full-time program: 23
Average months of prior work experience (full time): 22
TOEFL requirement: YES
Minimum TOEFL score: 550
Most popular departments: entrepreneurship, finance, general management, marketing, management information systems
Mean starting base salary for 2002 full-time graduates: $54,315
Employment location for 2002 class: Intl. 0%; N.E. 0%; M.A. 0%; S. 17%; M.W. 0%; S.W. 17%; W. 67%

COLORADO

Colorado State University

161 Rockwell Hall
Fort Collins, CO 80523-1270
Public
Admissions: (970) 491-4650
E-mail: grad@mail.biz.colostate.edu
Web site: http://www.biz.colostate.edu
Internet application: http://www.colostate.edu/~cwis177/
Financial aid: (970) 491-6321
Application deadline: 06/01
In-state tuition: full time: N/A; total program: $9,306 (part time)
Out-of-state tuition: full time: N/A
Room/board/expenses: $9,300
College-funded aid: YES
International student aid: YES
Fellowships: 0
Research assistantships: 0
Teaching assistantships: 46
Average student indebtedness at graduation: $2,200
Full-time enrollment: N/A
men: N/A; women: N/A; minorities: N/A; international: N/A
Part-time enrollment: 440
men: 76%; women: 24%; minorities: 13%; international: 6%
Average GMAT (part time): 631
TOEFL requirement: YES
Minimum TOEFL score: 565

University of Colorado–Boulder (Leeds)

Leeds School of Business
Building #4, 419 UCB
Boulder, CO 80309
Public
Admissions: (303) 492-8397
E-mail: LeedsMBA@Colorado.edu
Web site: http://leeds.colorado.edu
Internet application: http://leeds.colorado.edu/mba/application/applyonline.cfm
Financial aid: (303) 492-5091
Application deadline: 04/01
In-state tuition: full time: $5,646; part time: $14,154
Out-of-state tuition: full time: $20,402
Room/board/expenses: $16,000
College-funded aid: YES
International student aid: YES
Fellowships: 50
Research assistantships: 0
Teaching assistantships: 4
Average student indebtedness at graduation: $29,504
Full-time enrollment: 121
men: 70%; women: 30%; minorities: 9%; international: 17%
Part-time enrollment: 60
men: 77%; women: 23%; minorities: 0%; international: 17%

Acceptance rate (full time): 47%
Average GMAT (full time): 636
Average GMAT (part time): 638
Average GPA (full time): 3.19
Average age of entrants to full-time program: 28
Average months of prior work experience (full time): 54
TOEFL requirement: YES
Minimum TOEFL score: 600
Most popular departments: entrepreneurship, finance, marketing, operations management, real estate
Mean starting base salary for 2002 full-time graduates: $70,850
Employment location for 2002 class: Intl. 6%; N.E. 3%; M.A. 6%; S. 3%; M.W. 9%; S.W. 71%; W. 3%

University of Colorado–Colorado Springs
1420 Austin Bluffs Parkway
Colorado Springs, CO 80918
Public
Admissions: (719) 262-3408
E-mail: busadvsr@uccs.edu
Web site: http://web.uccs.edu/business
Financial aid: (719) 262-3460
Application deadline: 06/01
In-state tuition: full time: $227/credit hour; part time: $227/credit hour
Out-of-state tuition: full time: $824/credit hour
Room/board/expenses: $10,000
College-funded aid: YES
International student aid: NO
Fellowships: 5
Teaching assistantships: 0
Full-time enrollment: N/A
men: N/A; women: N/A; minorities: N/A; international: N/A
Part-time enrollment: 273
men: 60%; women: 40%; minorities: 9%; international: 6%
Average GMAT (part time): 534
TOEFL requirement: YES
Minimum TOEFL score: 550
Most popular departments: finance, general management, manufacturing and technology management, marketing, technology

University of Colorado–Denver
Campus Box 165
PO Box 173364
Denver, CO 80217-3364
Public
Admissions: (303) 556-5900
E-mail: grad.business@cudenver.edu
Web site: http://www.business.cudenver.edu
Financial aid: (303) 556-2886
Application deadline: 06/01
In-state tuition: full time: $262/credit hour; part time: $262/credit hour
Out-of-state tuition: full time: $948/credit hour
Room/board/expenses: N/A
College-funded aid: YES
International student aid: YES
Full-time enrollment: 49
men: 69%; women: 31%; minorities: 2%; international: 16%
Part-time enrollment: 811
men: 62%; women: 38%; minorities: 10%; international: 9%
Acceptance rate (full time): 60%
Average GMAT (full time): 592
Average GMAT (part time): 535
Average GPA (full time): 3.20
Average age of entrants to full-time program: 30

Average months of prior work experience (full time): 96
TOEFL requirement: YES
Minimum TOEFL score: 525
Most popular departments: accounting, entrepreneurship, finance, international business, management information systems

University of Denver (Daniels)
2101 S. University Boulevard
Denver, CO 80208
Private
Admissions: (303) 871-3416
E-mail: dcb@du.edu
Web site: http://www.daniels.du.edu/
Internet application: http://www.daniels.du.edu/prospective/graduate/admissionrequirements.asp
Financial aid: (303) 871-3416
Application deadline: 05/15
Tuition: full time: $23,780; part time: $630/credit hour
Room/board/expenses: $14,659
College-funded aid: YES
International student aid: YES
Fellowships: 0
Research assistantships: 6
Teaching assistantships: 6
Full-time enrollment: 291
men: 65%; women: 35%; minorities: 6%; international: 31%
Part-time enrollment: 335
men: 66%; women: 34%; minorities: 11%; international: 9%
Acceptance rate (full time): 82%
Average GMAT (full time): 553
Average GMAT (part time): 566
Average GPA (full time): 3.23
Average age of entrants to full-time program: 28
Average months of prior work experience (full time): 64
TOEFL requirement: YES
Minimum TOEFL score: 550
Most popular departments: finance, general management, international business, marketing, management information systems
Mean starting base salary for 2002 full-time graduates: $58,641
Employment location for 2002 class: Intl. 21%; N.E. 3%; M.A. 0%; S. 2%; M.W. 3%; S.W. 60%; W. 11%

Fairfield University (Dolan)
1073 N. Benson Road
Fairfield, CT 06824
Private
Admissions: (203) 254-4000
E-mail: mba@mail.fairfield.edu
Web site: http://www.fairfield.edu
Internet application: http://www.fairfield.edu/academic/gradbusi/gbdet.htm
Financial aid: (203) 254-4125
Application deadline: rolling
Tuition: full time: $19,350; part time: $510/credit hour
Room/board/expenses: N/A
College-funded aid: NO
International student aid: NO
Fellowships: 0
Research assistantships: 0
Teaching assistantships: 0
Full-time enrollment: 52
men: N/A; women: N/A; minorities: N/A; international: N/A
Part-time enrollment: 348
men: N/A; women: N/A; minorities: N/A; international: N/A
Acceptance rate (full time): 100%
Average GMAT (part time): 540

Average age of entrants to full-time program: 25
Average months of prior work experience (full time): 12
TOEFL requirement: YES
Minimum TOEFL score: 550
Most popular departments: accounting, finance, general management, human resources management, international business, marketing

Quinnipiac University (Lender)
275 Mt. Carmel Avenue
Hamden, CT 06518
Private
Admissions: (800) 462-1944
E-mail: graduate@quinnipiac.edu
Web site: http://www.quinnipiac.edu
Internet application: http://www.quinnipiac.edu/x106.xml
Financial aid: (203) 582-8588
Application deadline: 07/30
Tuition: full time: $475/credit hour; part time: $475/credit hour
Room/board/expenses: $13,704
College-funded aid: YES
International student aid: YES
Fellowships: 1
Research assistantships: 0
Teaching assistantships: 0
Average student indebtedness at graduation: $18,406
Full-time enrollment: 54
men: 56%; women: 44%; minorities: 17%; international: 11%
Part-time enrollment: 149
men: 52%; women: 48%; minorities: 7%; international: 1%
Acceptance rate (full time): 79%
Average GMAT (full time): 505
Average GMAT (part time): 505
Average GPA (full time): 3.14
Average age of entrants to full-time program: 27
Average months of prior work experience (full time): 36
TOEFL requirement: YES
Minimum TOEFL score: 575
Most popular departments: accounting, finance, general management, marketing, operations management

University of Connecticut
2100 Hillside Road
Unit 1041
Storrs, CT 06269-1041
Public
Admissions: (860) 486-2872
E-mail: uconnmba@business.uconn.edu
Web site: http://www.business.uconn.edu
Internet application: http://www.business.uconn.edu
Financial aid: (860) 486-2819
Application deadline: 04/01
In-state tuition: full time: $6,836; part time: $490/credit hour
Out-of-state tuition: full time: $15,928
Room/board/expenses: $13,000
College-funded aid: YES
International student aid: YES
Fellowships: 0
Research assistantships: 25
Teaching assistantships: 0
Full-time enrollment: 97
men: 56%; women: 44%; minorities: 8%; international: 47%
Part-time enrollment: 707
men: 67%; women: 33%; minorities: 14%; international: 4%
Acceptance rate (full time): 63%
Average GMAT (full time): 628

Average GMAT (part time): 578
Average GPA (full time): 3.44
Average age of entrants to full-time program: 28
Average months of prior work experience (full time): 66
TOEFL requirement: YES
Minimum TOEFL score: 575
Most popular departments: consulting, finance, healthcare administration, marketing, technology
Mean starting base salary for 2002 full-time graduates: $69,000
Employment location for 2002 class: Intl. 16%; N.E. 77%; M.A. 3%; S. 0%; M.W. 0%; S.W. 3%; W. 0%

University of Hartford (Barney)
200 Bloomfield Avenue
West Hartford, CT 06117
Private
Admissions: (860) 768-4900
E-mail: csilver@hartford.edu
Web site: http://barney.hartford.edu
Financial aid: (860) 768-4900
Application deadline: rolling
Tuition: full time: $450/credit hour; part time: $450/credit hour
Room/board/expenses: N/A
College-funded aid: YES
International student aid: YES
Fellowships: 0
Research assistantships: 25
Teaching assistantships: 0
Full-time enrollment: N/A
men: N/A; women: N/A; minorities: N/A; international: N/A
Part-time enrollment: 360
men: 63%; women: 37%; minorities: 13%; international: 22%
Average GMAT (part time): 500
TOEFL requirement: YES
Minimum TOEFL score: 550
Most popular departments: finance, healthcare administration, insurance, international business, leadership

Yale University
Box 208200
New Haven, CT 06520-8200
Private
Admissions: (203) 432-5932
E-mail: mba.admissions@yale.edu
Web site: http://mba.yale.edu
Internet application: https://apply.embark.com/MBAEdge/Yale/21/
Financial aid: (203) 432-5173
Application deadline: 03/15
Tuition: full time: $31,650; part time: N/A
Room/board/expenses: $15,290
College-funded aid: YES
International student aid: YES
Fellowships: 30
Teaching assistantships: 80
Average student indebtedness at graduation: $53,517
Full-time enrollment: 481
men: 70%; women: 30%; minorities: 20%; international: 38%
Part-time enrollment: N/A
men: N/A; women: N/A; minorities: N/A; international: N/A
Acceptance rate (full time): 15%
Average GMAT (full time): 698
Average GPA (full time): 3.50
Average age of entrants to full-time program: 28
Average months of prior work experience (full time): 59
TOEFL requirement: YES
Minimum TOEFL score: 600
Most popular departments: consulting, entrepreneurship, finance, general management, marketing

Mean starting base salary for 2002 full-time graduates: $85,368
Employment location for 2002 class: Intl. 13%; N.E. 63%; M.A. 11%; S. 2%; M.W. 3%; S.W. 3%; W. 6%

University of Delaware
103 MBNA America Hall
Newark, DE 19716
Public
Admissions: (302) 831-2221
E-mail: mbaprogram@udel.edu
Web site: http://www.mba.udel.edu
Financial aid: (302) 831-4596
Application deadline: 05/01
In-state tuition: full time: $3,217; part time: $334/credit hour
Out-of-state tuition: full time: $7,137
Room/board/expenses: $9,500
College-funded aid: YES
International student aid: YES
Research assistantships: 40
Full-time enrollment: 113
men: N/A; women: N/A; minorities: N/A; international: 42%
Part-time enrollment: 258
men: N/A; women: N/A; minorities: N/A; international: 7%
Acceptance rate (full time): 56%
Average GMAT (full time): 575
Average GMAT (part time): 544
Average months of prior work experience (full time): 40
TOEFL requirement: YES
Minimum TOEFL score: 587
Most popular departments: entrepreneurship, finance, international business, marketing, management information systems

American University (Kogod)
4400 Massachusetts Avenue NW
Washington, DC 20016
Private
Admissions: (202) 885-1913
E-mail: mbakogod@american.edu
Web site: http://www.kogod.american.edu
Financial aid: (202) 885-1907
Application deadline: 06/01
Tuition: full time: $23,222; part time: $827/credit hour
Room/board/expenses: $11,504
College-funded aid: YES
International student aid: YES
Fellowships: 5
Research assistantships: 45
Teaching assistantships: 0
Average student indebtedness at graduation: $45,000
Full-time enrollment: 229
men: 60%; women: 40%; minorities: 17%; international: 55%
Part-time enrollment: 133
men: 60%; women: 40%; minorities: 35%; international: 10%
Acceptance rate (full time): 60%
Average GMAT (full time): 580
Average GMAT (part time): 580
Average GPA (full time): 3.04
Average age of entrants to full-time program: 28
Average months of prior work experience (full time): 60
TOEFL requirement: YES
Minimum TOEFL score: 600
Most popular departments: finance, international business, marketing, management information systems, real estate
Mean starting base salary for 2002 full-time graduates: $55,544

Employment location for 2002 class: Intl. 31%; N.E. 7%; M.A. 61%; S. 0%; M.W. 0%; S.W. 1%; W. 0%

Georgetown University (McDonough)

206 Old North
Washington, DC 20057-1147
Private
Admissions: (202) 687-4200
E-mail: mba@georgetown.edu
Web site: http://www.msb.edu
Internet application:
http://www.msb.edu/
mba/admissions/procedure.htm
Financial aid: (202) 687-4547
Application deadline: 04/22
Tuition: full time: $29,976; part time: N/A
Room/board/expenses: $15,000
College-funded aid: YES
International student aid: YES
Fellowships: 50
Research assistantships: 50
Teaching assistantships: 30
Average student indebtedness at graduation: $75,000
Full-time enrollment: 528
men: 70%; women: 30%; minorities: 16%; international: 35%
Part-time enrollment: N/A
men: N/A; women: N/A; minorities: N/A; international: N/A
Acceptance rate (full time): 23%
Average GMAT (full time): 663
Average GPA (full time): 3.35
Average age of entrants to full-time program: 28
Average months of prior work experience (full time): 64
TOEFL requirement: YES
Minimum TOEFL score: 600
Most popular departments: consulting, finance, general management, marketing
Mean starting base salary for 2002 full-time graduates: $81,994
Employment location for 2002 class: Intl. 11%; N.E. 33%; M.A. 38%; S. 4%; M.W. 1%; S.W. 7%; W. 5%

George Washington University

710 21st Street NW
Washington, DC 20052
Private
Admissions: (202) 994-5536
E-mail: mbaft@gwu.edu
Web site: http://www.mba.gwu.edu
Internet application:
http://www.mba.gwu.edu/
prospective/apply
Financial aid: (202) 994-6620
Application deadline: 12/01
Tuition: full time: $810/credit hour; part time: $810/credit hour
Room/board/expenses: $16,680
College-funded aid: YES
International student aid: YES
Fellowships: 50
Research assistantships: 10
Teaching assistantships: 10
Average student indebtedness at graduation: $34,439
Full-time enrollment: 271
men: 54%; women: 46%; minorities: 15%; international: 39%
Part-time enrollment: 582
men: 59%; women: 41%; minorities: 26%; international: 4%
Acceptance rate (full time): 31%
Average GMAT (full time): 618
Average GMAT (part time): 550
Average GPA (full time): 3.25
Average age of entrants to full-time program: 27
Average months of prior work experience (full time): 48

TOEFL requirement: YES
Minimum TOEFL score: 620
Most popular departments: entrepreneurship, finance, international business, marketing, management information systems
Mean starting base salary for 2002 full-time graduates: $60,456
Employment location for 2002 class: Intl. 16%; N.E. 4%; M.A. 64%; S. 4%; M.W. 2%; S.W. 0%; W. 9%

Howard University

2600 Sixth Street NW
Suite 236
Washington, DC 20059
Private
Admissions: (202) 806-1725
E-mail:
mba_bschool@howard.edu
Web site: http://www.bschool.howard.edu/mba
Internet application:
http://www.bschool.howard.edu/admissions/graduate.htm
Financial aid: (202) 806-2820
Application deadline: 04/01
Tuition: full time: $12,395; part time: $644/credit hour
Room/board/expenses: $12,395
College-funded aid: YES
International student aid: YES
Fellowships: 2
Research assistantships: 12
Teaching assistantships: 0
Average student indebtedness at graduation: $9,007
Full-time enrollment: 49
men: 51%; women: 49%; minorities: 76%; international: 24%
Part-time enrollment: N/A
men: N/A; women: N/A; minorities: N/A; international: N/A
Acceptance rate (full time): 33%
Average GMAT (full time): 510
Average GPA (full time): 3.08
Average age of entrants to full-time program: 28
Average months of prior work experience (full time): 42
TOEFL requirement: YES
Minimum TOEFL score: 550
Most popular departments: finance, general management, international business, marketing, supply chain management
Mean starting base salary for 2002 full-time graduates: $71,178
Employment location for 2002 class: Intl. 0%; N.E. 33%; M.A. 44%; S. 0%; M.W. 22%; S.W. 0%; W. 0%

FLORIDA

Florida Atlantic University

777 Glades Road
Boca Raton, FL 33431
Public
Admissions: (561) 297-3624
E-mail: gradadm@fau.edu
Web site:
http://newfaucob.accrisoft.com/
Internet application:
http://www.fau.edu/academic/gradstud/online.htm
Financial aid: (561) 297-3131
Application deadline: 07/01
In-state tuition: full time: $187/credit hour; part time: $187/credit hour
Out-of-state tuition: full time: $679/credit hour
Room/board/expenses: $16,000
College-funded aid: YES
International student aid: YES

Full-time enrollment: N/A
men: N/A; women: N/A; minorities: N/A; international: N/A
Part-time enrollment: 435
men: 51%; women: 49%; minorities: 25%; international: 4%
Average GMAT (part time): 532
TOEFL requirement: YES
Minimum TOEFL score: 600
Most popular departments: accounting, e-commerce, finance, marketing, sports business

Florida International University

11200 SW Eighth Street
310 Ryder Business Building
Miami, FL 33199-0001
Public
Admissions: (305) 348-6880
E-mail: imba@fiu.edu
Web site:
http://www.fiu.edu/~mba
Internet application:
http://www.fiu.edu/orgs/admiss/application.html
Financial aid: (305) 348-2489
Application deadline: 03/31
In-state tuition: total program: $26,000 (full time); $11,088 (part time)
Out-of-state tuition: total program: $30,000 (full time)
Room/board/expenses: $10,000
College-funded aid: YES
International student aid: YES
Fellowships: 0
Research assistantships: 6
Teaching assistantships: 0
Average student indebtedness at graduation: $1,717
Full-time enrollment: 81
men: 51%; women: 49%; minorities: 27%; international: 57%
Part-time enrollment: 351
men: 65%; women: 35%; minorities: 66%; international: 12%
Acceptance rate (full time): 74%
Average GMAT (full time): 469
Average GMAT (part time): 550
Average GPA (full time): 3.31
Average age of entrants to full-time program: 26
Average months of prior work experience (full time): 36
TOEFL requirement: YES
Minimum TOEFL score: 550
Most popular departments: finance, human resources management, international business, marketing, management information systems
Mean starting base salary for 2002 full-time graduates: $53,700
Employment location for 2002 class: Intl. 29%; N.E. 6%; M.A. 4%; S. 61%; M.W. 0%; S.W. 0%; W. 0%

Florida State University

Graduate Office
Room 318 RBA
Tallahassee, FL 32306-1110
Public
Admissions: (850) 644-7837
E-mail: brobinso@cob.fsu.edu
Web site: http://www.mba.fsu.edu
Internet application:
http://www.fsu.edu/prospective/admissions
Financial aid: (850) 644-5716
Application deadline: 02/01
In-state tuition: full time: $178/credit hour; part time: $178/credit hour
Out-of-state tuition: full time: $671/credit hour
Room/board/expenses: $15,000
College-funded aid: YES
International student aid: YES
Fellowships: 3

Research assistantships: 5
Teaching assistantships: 0
Full-time enrollment: 30
men: 67%; women: 33%; minorities: 30%; international: 0%
Part-time enrollment: 136
men: 54%; women: 46%; minorities: 13%; international: 0%
Acceptance rate (full time): 67%
Average GMAT (full time): 600
Average GMAT (part time): 521
Average GPA (full time): 3.36
Average age of entrants to full-time program: 27
Average months of prior work experience (full time): 44
TOEFL requirement: YES
Minimum TOEFL score: 600
Most popular departments: accounting, entrepreneurship, finance, insurance, supply chain management
Mean starting base salary for 2002 full-time graduates: $44,900
Employment location for 2002 class: Intl. 0%; N.E. 0%; M.A. 0%; S. 100%; M.W. 0%; S.W. 0%; W. 0%

Rollins College (Crummer)

1000 Holt Avenue-2722
Winter Park, FL 32789-4499
Private
Admissions: (800) 866-2405
E-mail: cschram@rollins.edu
Web site:
http://www.crummer.rollins.edu
Internet application:
https://apply.embark.com/mbaedge/rollins/mba/19/
Financial aid: (407) 646-2395
Application deadline: rolling
Tuition: full time: $22,430; part time: $700/credit hour
Room/board/expenses: $12,000
College-funded aid: YES
International student aid: YES
Average student indebtedness at graduation: $25,616
Full-time enrollment: 176
men: 65%; women: 35%; minorities: 12%; international: 26%
Part-time enrollment: 251
men: 65%; women: 35%; minorities: 22%; international: 1%
Acceptance rate (full time): 61%
Average GMAT (full time): 599
Average GMAT (part time): 543
Average GPA (full time): 3.30
Average age of entrants to full-time program: 25
Average months of prior work experience (full time): 47
TOEFL requirement: YES
Minimum TOEFL score: 560
Most popular departments: finance, general management, international business, marketing, operations management
Mean starting base salary for 2002 full-time graduates: $50,379
Employment location for 2002 class: Intl. 6%; N.E. 6%; M.A. 6%; S. 79%; M.W. 2%; S.W. 0%; W. 2%

Stetson University

421 N. Woodland Boulevard
Unit 8398
DeLand, FL 32720
Private
Admissions: (386) 822-7410
E-mail: frank.dezoort@stetson.edu
Web site: http://www.stetson.edu
Financial aid: (386) 822-7120
Application deadline: rolling
Tuition: full time: N/A; part time: N/A
Room/board/expenses: N/A
College-funded aid: YES

International student aid: NO
Fellowships: 2
Research assistantships: 0
Teaching assistantships: 0
Full-time enrollment: 15
men: 60%; women: 40%; minorities: 73%; international: 27%
Part-time enrollment: N/A
men: N/A; women: N/A; minorities: N/A; international: N/A
Acceptance rate (full time): 73%
Average age of entrants to full-time program: 24
TOEFL requirement: YES
Minimum TOEFL score: 550
Most popular departments: e-commerce, entrepreneurship, general management, marketing, management information systems

University of Central Florida

PO Box 161400
Orlando, FL 32816-1400
Public
Admissions: (407) 823-2766
E-mail: graduate@mail.ucf.edu
Web site:
http://www.ucfmba.ucf.edu
Internet application:
http://www.graduate.ucf.edu/gradonlineapp/
Financial aid: (407) 823-2827
Application deadline: 06/15
In-state tuition: full time: $181/credit hour; part time: $181/credit hour
Out-of-state tuition: full time: $667/credit hour
Room/board/expenses: $10,000
College-funded aid: YES
International student aid: YES
Fellowships: 20
Research assistantships: 90
Teaching assistantships: 0
Full-time enrollment: 27
men: 48%; women: 52%; minorities: 22%; international: 0%
Part-time enrollment: 451
men: 57%; women: 43%; minorities: 10%; international: 9%
Acceptance rate (full time): 81%
Average GMAT (full time): 551
Average GMAT (part time): 536
Average GPA (full time): 3.50
Average age of entrants to full-time program: 25
Average months of prior work experience (full time): 11
TOEFL requirement: YES
Minimum TOEFL score: 575
Most popular departments: accounting, finance, international business, marketing, management information systems

University of Florida (Warrington)

134 Bryan Hall
PO Box 117152
Gainesville, FL 32611-7152
Public
Admissions: (352) 392-7992
E-mail: floridamba@cba.ufl.edu
Web site:
http://www.floridamba.ufl.edu
Internet application:
http://www.floridamba.ufl.edu/prosp_stu/admiss/apply.asp
Financial aid: (352) 392-1275
Application deadline: 04/15
In-state tuition: full time: $179/credit hour; part time: N/A
Out-of-state tuition: full time: $668/credit hour
Room/board/expenses: $22,040
College-funded aid: YES
International student aid: YES
Fellowships: 31
Research assistantships: 17

Teaching assistantships: 0
Average student indebtedness at graduation: $13,168
Full-time enrollment: 114
men: 75%; women: 25%; minorities: 13%; international: 26%
Part-time enrollment: N/A
men: N/A; women: N/A; minorities: N/A; international: N/A
Acceptance rate (full time): 23%
Average GMAT (full time): 658
Average GPA (full time): 3.30
Average age of entrants to full-time program: 27
Average months of prior work experience (full time): 51
TOEFL requirement: YES
Minimum TOEFL score: 600
Most popular departments: finance, marketing, management information systems, portfolio management, real estate
Mean starting base salary for 2002 full-time graduates: $61,900
Employment location for 2002 class: Intl. N/A; N.E. 10%; M.A. 14%; S. 52%; M.W. 10%; S.W. N/A; W. 14%

University of Miami
PO Box 248027
Coral Gables, FL 33124-6520
Private
Admissions: (305) 284-4607
E-mail: mba@miami.edu
Web site:
http://www.bus.miami.edu/grad
Financial aid: (305) 284-5212
Application deadline: 07/31
Tuition: full time: $1,010/credit hour; part time: $1,010/credit hour
Room/board/expenses: $12,202
College-funded aid: YES
International student aid: YES
Fellowships: 25
Research assistantships: 40
Teaching assistantships: 0
Average student indebtedness at graduation: $40,295
Full-time enrollment: 378
men: 64%; women: 36%; minorities: 23%; international: 37%
Part-time enrollment: 122
men: 55%; women: 45%; minorities: 40%; international: 19%
Acceptance rate (full time): 61%
Average GMAT (full time): 652
Average GPA (full time): 3.24
Average age of entrants to full-time program: 26
Average months of prior work experience (full time): 36
TOEFL requirement: YES
Minimum TOEFL score: 550
Most popular departments: finance, general management, international business, marketing, management information systems
Mean starting base salary for 2002 full-time graduates: $50,495
Employment location for 2002 class: Intl. 13%; N.E. N/A; M.A. 5%; S. 75%; M.W. 5%; S.W. N/A; W. 2%

University of North Florida
4567 St. John's Bluff Road S
Jacksonville, FL 32224-2645
Public
Admissions: (904) 620-2624
E-mail: osprey@unf.edu
Web site: http://www.unf.edu/coba
Financial aid: (904) 620-2604
Application deadline: rolling
In-state tuition: full time: $4,446; part time: $185/credit hour
Out-of-state tuition: full time: $15,390
Room/board/expenses: $6,933

College-funded aid: YES
International student aid: YES
Average student indebtedness at graduation: $12,859
Full-time enrollment: 131
men: 55%; women: 45%; minorities: 15%; international: 14%
Part-time enrollment: 307
men: 55%; women: 45%; minorities: 15%; international: 2%
Acceptance rate (full time): 53%
Average GMAT (full time): 525
Average GPA (full time): 3.17
Average age of entrants to full-time program: 28
Average months of prior work experience (full time): 0
TOEFL requirement: YES
Minimum TOEFL score: 550

University of South Florida
4202 Fowler Avenue
Tampa, FL 33620
Public
Admissions: (813) 974-3335
E-mail: mba@coba.usf.edu
Web site: http://www.coba.usf.edu
Internet application:
http://www.grad.usf.edu
Financial aid: (813) 974-4700
Application deadline: 05/15
In-state tuition: full time: $184/credit hour; part time: $184/credit hour
Out-of-state tuition: full time: $676/credit hour
Room/board/expenses: $13,300
College-funded aid: YES
International student aid: YES
Full-time enrollment: 202
men: 58%; women: 42%; minorities: 18%; international: 11%
Part-time enrollment: 296
men: 61%; women: 39%; minorities: 19%; international: 0%
Acceptance rate (full time): 63%
Average GMAT (full time): 560
Average GMAT (part time): 550
Average GPA (full time): 3.23
Average age of entrants to full-time program: 26
Average months of prior work experience (full time): 20
TOEFL requirement: YES
Minimum TOEFL score: 550
Most popular departments: finance, general management, international business, marketing, management information systems

University of Tampa (Sykes)
401 W. Kennedy
Tampa, FL 33606-1490
Public
Admissions: (813) 258-7409
E-mail: mba@ut.edu
Web site: http://mba.ut.edu
Internet application:
http://mba.ut.edu
Financial aid: (813) 253-6219
Application deadline: rolling
In-state tuition: full time: $352/credit hour; part time: $352/credit hour
Out-of-state tuition: full time: $352/credit hour
Room/board/expenses: $7,095
College-funded aid: YES
International student aid: YES
Average student indebtedness at graduation: $19,300
Full-time enrollment: 162
men: 48%; women: 52%; minorities: 14%; international: 48%
Part-time enrollment: 256
men: 64%; women: 36%; minorities: 17%; international: 9%
Acceptance rate (full time): 58%

Average GMAT (full time): 515
Average GMAT (part time): 530
Average GPA (full time): 3.33
Average age of entrants to full-time program: 26
Average months of prior work experience (full time): 32
TOEFL requirement: YES
Minimum TOEFL score: 577
Most popular departments: finance, general management, international business, marketing, management information systems

University of West Florida
11000 University Parkway
Pensacola, FL 32514
Public
Admissions: (850) 474-3125
E-mail: mba@uwf.edu
Web site: http://uwf.edu
Internet application:
http://uwf.edu/admissions/happsus.htm
Financial aid: (850) 474-2400
Application deadline: 06/01
In-state tuition: full time: $174/credit hour; part time: $174/credit hour
Out-of-state tuition: full time: $620/credit hour
Room/board/expenses: $6,538
College-funded aid: YES
International student aid: YES
Research assistantships: 0
Teaching assistantships: 0
Full-time enrollment: 44
men: 59%; women: 41%; minorities: 23%; international: 14%
Part-time enrollment: 105
men: 62%; women: 38%; minorities: 21%; international: 1%
Acceptance rate (full time): 78%
Average GMAT (full time): 520
Average GMAT (part time): 548
Average GPA (full time): 3.08
Average age of entrants to full-time program: 29
TOEFL requirement: YES
Minimum TOEFL score: 550

GEORGIA

Augusta State University[1]
2500 Walton Way
Augusta, GA 30904-2200
Public
Admissions: (706) 737-1565
E-mail: mbainfo@aug.edu
Web site:
http://www.aug.edu/coba
Financial aid: (706) 737-1431
Tuition: N/A
Room/board/expenses: N/A
Enrollment: N/A

Clark Atlanta University[1]
223 James P. Brawley Drive SW
Atlanta, GA 30314
Private
Admissions: (404) 880-8447
E-mail: sbus@sbus.cau.edu
Web site: http://www.cau.edu
Financial aid: (404) 880-8992
Tuition: N/A
Room/board/expenses: N/A
Enrollment: N/A

Emory University (Goizueta)
1300 Clifton Road NE
Atlanta, GA 30322
Private
Admissions: (404) 727-6311
E-mail:
admissions@bus.emory.edu

Web site:
http://www.goizueta.emory.edu
Internet application:
http://www.goizueta.emory.edu/degree/apply.html
Financial aid: (404) 727-6039
Application deadline: 03/15
Tuition: full time: $29,408; part time: $19,517
Room/board/expenses: $18,354
College-funded aid: YES
International student aid: YES
Fellowships: 266
Research assistantships: 50
Teaching assistantships: 50
Average student indebtedness at graduation: $56,010
Full-time enrollment: 388
men: 76%; women: 24%; minorities: 12%; international: 31%
Part-time enrollment: 167
men: 82%; women: 18%; minorities: 22%; international: 8%
Acceptance rate (full time): 24%
Average GMAT (full time): 675
Average GMAT (part time): 644
Average GPA (full time): 3.40
Average age of entrants to full-time program: 28
Average months of prior work experience (full time): 77
TOEFL requirement: YES
Minimum TOEFL score: 600
Most popular departments: consulting, entrepreneurship, finance, general management, marketing
Mean starting base salary for 2002 full-time graduates: $74,175
Employment location for 2002 class: Intl. 14%; N.E. 16%; M.A. 4%; S. 55%; M.W. 7%; S.W. 3%; W. 1%

Georgia College and State University (Whitney)
Campus Box 019
Milledgeville, GA 31061
Public
Admissions: (478) 445-6289
E-mail: lwolfgan@gcsu.edu
Web site: http://www.gcsu.edu
Internet application: http://www.applyweb.com/aw?gcsu
Financial aid: (478) 445-5149
Application deadline: 07/15
In-state tuition: full time: N/A; total program: $5,250 (part time)
Out-of-state tuition: full time: N/A
Room/board/expenses: $4,843
College-funded aid: YES
International student aid: YES
Fellowships: 0
Research assistantships: 0
Teaching assistantships: 0
Full-time enrollment: N/A
men: N/A; women: N/A; minorities: N/A; international: N/A
Part-time enrollment: 144
men: 54%; women: 46%; minorities: 17%; international: 14%
Average GMAT (part time): 476
TOEFL requirement: YES
Minimum TOEFL score: 500

Georgia Institute of Technology (DuPree)
755 Ferst Drive
Room 212
Atlanta, GA 30332-0520
Public
Admissions: (404) 894-8722
E-mail: mba@mgt.gatech.edu
Web site:
http://www.dupree.gatech.edu
Internet application: http://www.dupree.gatech.edu/mba
Financial aid: (404) 894-4160
Application deadline: 03/20

In-state tuition: full time: $6,140; part time: N/A
Out-of-state tuition: full time: $19,574
Room/board/expenses: $11,400
College-funded aid: YES
International student aid: YES
Fellowships: 0
Research assistantships: 50
Teaching assistantships: 0
Average student indebtedness at graduation: $20,845
Full-time enrollment: 221
men: 72%; women: 28%; minorities: 14%; international: 28%
Part-time enrollment: N/A
men: N/A; women: N/A; minorities: N/A; international: N/A
Acceptance rate (full time): 39%
Average GMAT (full time): 645
Average GPA (full time): 3.20
Average age of entrants to full-time program: 27
Average months of prior work experience (full time): 54
TOEFL requirement: YES
Minimum TOEFL score: 600
Most popular departments: entrepreneurship, finance, general management, management information systems, operations management
Mean starting base salary for 2002 full-time graduates: $65,500
Employment location for 2002 class: Intl. 19%; N.E. 2%; M.A. 8%; S. 60%; M.W. 8%; S.W. 0%; W. 2%

Georgia Southern University
PO Box 8050
Statesboro, GA 30460-8002
Public
Admissions: (912) 681-5767
E-mail: mba@gasou.edu
Web site: http://www2.gasou.edu/mba/main.htm
Internet application:
http://www2.gasou.edu/gradcoll/application.html
Financial aid: (912) 681-5413
Application deadline: 07/01
In-state tuition: full time: $101/credit hour; part time: $101/credit hour
Out-of-state tuition: full time: $402/credit hour
Room/board/expenses: $10,404
College-funded aid: YES
International student aid: YES
Fellowships: 0
Research assistantships: 18
Teaching assistantships: 0
Average student indebtedness at graduation: $19,197
Full-time enrollment: 74
men: 58%; women: 42%; minorities: 14%; international: 34%
Part-time enrollment: 124
men: 62%; women: 38%; minorities: 13%; international: 4%
Average GMAT (full time): 466
Average GMAT (part time): 484
Average age of entrants to full-time program: 25
Average months of prior work experience (full time): 24
TOEFL requirement: YES
Minimum TOEFL score: 550
Most popular departments: accounting, general management, healthcare administration, international business

Georgia State University (Robinson)

MSC 4A0725
33 Gilmer Street SE, Unit 4
Atlanta, GA 30303-3084
Public
Admissions: (404) 651-1913
E-mail: rcb-oaa@gsu.edu
Web site: http://www.gsu.edu
Internet application: http://robinson.gsu.edu/apply/index.html
Financial aid: (404) 651-2227
Application deadline: 04/01
In-state tuition: full time: $3,472; part time: $155/credit hour
Out-of-state tuition: full time: $11,842
Room/board/expenses: $12,000
College-funded aid: YES
International student aid: YES
Fellowships: 0
Research assistantships: 205
Teaching assistantships: 0
Full-time enrollment: 917
men: 65%; women: 35%; minorities: 13%; international: 28%
Part-time enrollment: 1,532
men: 66%; women: 34%; minorities: 14%; international: 6%
Acceptance rate (full time): 45%
Average GMAT (full time): 600
Average GMAT (part time): 600
Average GPA (full time): 3.21
Average age of entrants to full-time program: 28
Average months of prior work experience (full time): 61
TOEFL requirement: YES
Minimum TOEFL score: 600
Most popular departments: accounting, finance, general management, marketing, management information systems
Mean starting base salary for 2002 full-time graduates: $51,015
Employment location for 2002 class: Intl. N/A; N.E. 5%; M.A. N/A; S. 86%; M.W. 9%; S.W. N/A; W. N/A

Kennesaw State University (Coles)[1]

1000 Chastain Road
Kennesaw, GA 30144-5591
Public
Admissions: (770) 420-4377
E-mail: ksugrad@kennesaw.edu
Web site: http://coles.kennesaw.edu
Financial aid: (770) 423-6525
Tuition: N/A
Room/board/expenses: N/A
Enrollment: N/A

State University of West Georgia (Richards)[1]

1600 Maple Street
Carrollton, GA 30118-3000
Public
Admissions: (770) 836-6467
E-mail: mba@westga.edu
Web site: http://www.westga.edu/~busn/mba.html
Internet application: http://chicken-hawk.westga.edu:9001/grad
Financial aid: (770) 836-6421
Tuition: N/A
Room/board/expenses: N/A
Enrollment: N/A

University of Georgia (Terry)

346 Brooks Hall
Athens, GA 30602-6264
Public
Admissions: (706) 542-5671
E-mail: terrymba@terry.uga.edu
Web site: http://www.terry.uga.edu/mba
Financial aid: (706) 542-6147
Application deadline: 05/01
In-state tuition: full time: $4,574; part time: $390/credit hour
Out-of-state tuition: full time: $15,618
Room/board/expenses: $15,160
College-funded aid: YES
International student aid: YES
Fellowships: 99
Research assistantships: 99
Full-time enrollment: 169
men: 74%; women: 26%; minorities: 7%; international: 30%
Part-time enrollment: 162
men: 75%; women: 25%; minorities: 13%; international: 7%
Acceptance rate (full time): 27%
Average GMAT (full time): 658
Average GMAT (part time): 572
Average GPA (full time): 3.29
Average age of entrants to full-time program: 27
Average months of prior work experience (full time): 57
TOEFL requirement: YES
Minimum TOEFL score: 577
Most popular departments: entrepreneurship, finance, insurance, marketing, real estate
Mean starting base salary for 2002 full-time graduates: $67,781
Employment location for 2002 class: Intl. 3%; N.E. 4%; M.A. 9%; S. 72%; M.W. 9%; S.W. 0%; W. 3%

Valdosta State University[1]

1500 N. Patterson Street
Business School
Valdosta, GA 31698
Public
Admissions: (229) 245-2236
E-mail: joliver@valdosta.edu
Web site: http://teach.valdosta.edu/cobagrad
Financial aid: (229) 333-5935
Tuition: N/A
Room/board/expenses: N/A
Enrollment: N/A

HAWAII

University of Hawaii–Manoa

2404 Maile Way
Business Administration B201
Honolulu, HI 96822
Public
Admissions: (808) 956-8266
E-mail: osasgrad@cba.hawaii.edu
Web site: http://www.cba.hawaii.edu
Internet application: http://www.hawaii.edu/graduate/download/forms/admission/app2003_4.pdf
Financial aid: (808) 956-7251
Application deadline: 05/01
In-state tuition: full time: $6,132; part time: $250/credit hour
Out-of-state tuition: full time: $12,180
Room/board/expenses: $14,690
College-funded aid: YES
International student aid: YES
Average student indebtedness at graduation: $12,281

Full-time enrollment: 217
men: 62%; women: 38%; minorities: 33%; international: 38%
Part-time enrollment: 117
men: 61%; women: 39%; minorities: 66%; international: 6%
Acceptance rate (full time): 55%
Average GMAT (full time): 548
Average GMAT (part time): 586
Average GPA (full time): 3.32
Average age of entrants to full-time program: 29
Average months of prior work experience (full time): 60
TOEFL requirement: YES
Minimum TOEFL score: 550
Most popular departments: accounting, entrepreneurship, finance, international business, technology
Mean starting base salary for 2002 full-time graduates: $52,000
Employment location for 2002 class: Intl. 42%; N.E. 6%; M.A. 0%; S. 0%; M.W. 0%; S.W. 16%; W. 35%

IDAHO

Boise State University

1910 University Drive, B318
Boise, ID 83725-1600
Public
Admissions: (208) 426-1126
E-mail: ranchust@boisestate.edu
Web site: http://cobe.boisestate.edu/graduate
Internet application: http://cobe.boisestate.edu/mba/admissn.htm
Financial aid: (208) 426-1664
Application deadline: 02/01
In-state tuition: full time: $4,117; part time: $184/credit hour
Out-of-state tuition: full time: $10,517
Room/board/expenses: $8,000
College-funded aid: YES
International student aid: YES
Fellowships: 0
Research assistantships: 9
Teaching assistantships: 2
Full-time enrollment: 37
men: 59%; women: 41%; minorities: 16%; international: 22%
Part-time enrollment: 91
men: 62%; women: 38%; minorities: 7%; international: 7%
TOEFL requirement: YES
Minimum TOEFL score: 587

Idaho State University

PO Box 8020
Pocatello, ID 83209
Public
Admissions: (208) 282-2504
E-mail: mba@cob.isu.edu
Web site: http://cob.isu.edu
Financial aid: (208) 282-2756
Application deadline: 07/01
In-state tuition: full time: $4,316; part time: $189/credit hour
Out-of-state tuition: full time: $10,558
Room/board/expenses: N/A
College-funded aid: YES
International student aid: YES
Fellowships: 0
Research assistantships: 2
Teaching assistantships: 7
Full-time enrollment: 78
men: 69%; women: 31%; minorities: 12%; international: 14%
Part-time enrollment: 73
men: 70%; women: 30%; minorities: 3%; international: 0%
Acceptance rate (full time): 84%
Average GMAT (part time): 543
Average age of entrants to full-time program: 27

Average months of prior work experience (full time): 44
TOEFL requirement: YES
Minimum TOEFL score: 550
Most popular departments: accounting, finance, general management, healthcare administration, management information systems

ILLINOIS

Bradley University (Foster)

1501 W. Bradley Avenue
Peoria, IL 61625
Private
Admissions: (309) 677-2253
E-mail: mba@bradley.edu
Web site: http://www.bradley.edu/fcba/mba
Financial aid: (309) 677-2375
Application deadline: rolling
Tuition: full time: N/A; part time: $435/credit hour
Room/board/expenses: N/A
College-funded aid: YES
International student aid: YES
Fellowships: 2
Research assistantships: 19
Teaching assistantships: 0
Average student indebtedness at graduation: $16,842
Full-time enrollment: N/A
men: N/A; women: N/A; minorities: N/A; international: N/A
Part-time enrollment: 167
men: 63%; women: 37%; minorities: 3%; international: 11%
TOEFL requirement: YES
Minimum TOEFL score: 550
Most popular departments: finance, general management, management information systems

DePaul University (Kellstadt)

1 E. Jackson Boulevard
Chicago, IL 60604-2287
Private
Admissions: (312) 362-8810
E-mail: mbainfo@depaul.edu
Web site: http://www.depaul.edu/kellstadt
Financial aid: (312) 362-8091
Application deadline: 07/01
Tuition: full time: N/A; part time: N/A
Room/board/expenses: N/A
College-funded aid: YES
International student aid: YES
Research assistantships: 14
Average student indebtedness at graduation: $18,870
Full-time enrollment: 62
men: 45%; women: 55%; minorities: 8%; international: 40%
Part-time enrollment: 2,300
men: 60%; women: 40%; minorities: N/A; international: N/A
Acceptance rate (full time): 52%
Average GMAT (full time): 620
Average GMAT (part time): 553
Average GPA (full time): 3.19
Average age of entrants to full-time program: 27
Average months of prior work experience (full time): 48
TOEFL requirement: YES
Minimum TOEFL score: 550
Most popular departments: accounting, finance, international business, marketing, operations management
Mean starting base salary for 2002 full-time graduates: $72,700
Employment location for 2002 class: Intl. 14%; N.E. 3%; M.A. 3%; S. N/A; M.W. 66%; S.W. 7%; W. 7%

Eastern Illinois University (Lumpkin)

600 Lincoln Avenue
Charleston, IL 61920-3099
Public
Admissions: (217) 581-3028
E-mail: mba@eiu.edu
Web site: http://www.eiu.edu/~mba
Financial aid: (217) 581-3714
Application deadline: 08/01
In-state tuition: full time: $114/credit hour; part time: $114/credit hour
Out-of-state tuition: full time: $343/credit hour
Room/board/expenses: $6,800
College-funded aid: YES
International student aid: YES
Research assistantships: 6
Teaching assistantships: 6
Full-time enrollment: 77
men: 53%; women: 47%; minorities: 3%; international: 30%
Part-time enrollment: 86
men: 56%; women: 44%; minorities: 3%; international: 3%
Acceptance rate (full time): 95%
Average GMAT (full time): 535
Average GMAT (part time): 510
Average GPA (full time): 3.30
Average age of entrants to full-time program: 25
Average months of prior work experience (full time): 42
TOEFL requirement: YES
Minimum TOEFL score: 550
Most popular departments: accounting, general management

Illinois Institute of Technology (Stuart)

565 W. Adams Street
Chicago, IL 60661
Private
Admissions: (312) 906-6571
E-mail: admissions@stuart.iit.edu
Web site: http://www.stuart.iit.edu
Internet application: http://www.stuart.iit.edu/apply1.html
Financial aid: (312) 906-5180
Application deadline: rolling
Tuition: full time: $610/credit hour; part time: $610/credit hour
Room/board/expenses: $19,700
College-funded aid: YES
International student aid: YES
Fellowships: 6
Research assistantships: 0
Teaching assistantships: 0
Full-time enrollment: 122
men: 72%; women: 28%; minorities: 11%; international: 77%
Part-time enrollment: 146
men: 75%; women: 25%; minorities: 25%; international: 27%
Acceptance rate (full time): 78%
Average GMAT (full time): 542
Average GMAT (part time): 548
Average age of entrants to full-time program: 25
TOEFL requirement: YES
Minimum TOEFL score: 550
Most popular departments: entrepreneurship, finance, general management, marketing, other

Illinois State University

327 Williams Hall
Normal, IL 61790-5500
Public
Admissions: (309) 438-8388
E-mail: isumba@exchange.cob.ilstu.edu
Web site: http://www.mba.ilstu.edu/

Internet application: http://www.mba.ilstu.edu/pros_stu/mba_application.htm
Financial aid: (309) 438-2231
Application deadline: 03/01
In-state tuition: full time: $2,205; part time: $122/credit hour
Out-of-state tuition: full time: $4,770
Room/board/expenses: $8,034
College-funded aid: YES
International student aid: YES
Fellowships: 2
Research assistantships: 34
Teaching assistantships: 1
Full-time enrollment: 51
men: 69%; women: 31%; minorities: 6%; international: 43%
Part-time enrollment: 126
men: 62%; women: 38%; minorities: 8%; international: 6%
Acceptance rate (full time): 75%
Average GMAT (full time): 535
Average GMAT (part time): 550
Average GPA (full time): 3.66
Average age of entrants to full-time program: 24
TOEFL requirement: YES
Minimum TOEFL score: 600

Loyola University Chicago

820 N. Michigan Avenue
Chicago, IL 60611
Private
Admissions: (312) 915-6120
E-mail: mba-loyola@luc.edu
Web site: http://www.gsb.luc.edu
Internet application: http://www.embark.com
Financial aid: (312) 915-6659
Application deadline: rolling
Tuition: full time: $775/credit hour; part time: $775/credit hour
Room/board/expenses: $13,000
College-funded aid: YES
International student aid: YES
Average student indebtedness at graduation: $37,000
Full-time enrollment: N/A
men: N/A; women: N/A; minorities: N/A; international: N/A
Part-time enrollment: 730
men: 58%; women: 42%; minorities: 14%; international: 23%
Average GMAT (part time): 540
TOEFL requirement: YES
Minimum TOEFL score: 550
Most popular departments: accounting, finance, general management, marketing, management information systems

Northern Illinois University

Office of MBA Programs
Barsema Hall 203
De Kalb, IL 60115-2897
Public
Admissions: (800) 323-8714
E-mail: cobgrads@niu.edu
Web site: http://www.cob.niu.edu/grad/grad.html
Financial aid: (815) 753-1395
Application deadline: 06/01
In-state tuition: full time: N/A; part time: $413/credit hour
Out-of-state tuition: full time: N/A
Room/board/expenses: N/A
College-funded aid: YES
International student aid: YES
Full-time enrollment: N/A
men: N/A; women: N/A; minorities: N/A; international: N/A
Part-time enrollment: 542
men: 56%; women: 44%; minorities: 14%; international: 5%
Average GMAT (part time): 519
TOEFL requirement: YES
Minimum TOEFL score: 550
Most popular departments: finance, general management, international business, marketing, management information systems

Northwestern University (Kellogg)

2001 Sheridan Road
Evanston, IL 60208-2001
Private
Admissions: (847) 491-3308
E-mail: MBAadmissions@kellogg.northwestern.edu
Web site: http://www.kellogg.northwestern.edu
Financial aid: (847) 491-3308
Application deadline: 03/14
Tuition: full time: $32,040; part time: $3,204/credit hour
Room/board/expenses: $12,726
College-funded aid: YES
International student aid: YES
Average student indebtedness at graduation: $55,000
Full-time enrollment: 1,058
men: 70%; women: 30%; minorities: 19%; international: 34%
Part-time enrollment: 1,262
men: 66%; women: 34%; minorities: 12%; international: 18%
Acceptance rate (full time): 13%
Average GMAT (full time): 700
Average GMAT (part time): 690
Average GPA (full time): 3.45
Average age of entrants to full-time program: 28
Average months of prior work experience (full time): 54
TOEFL requirement: YES
Minimum TOEFL score: N/A
Most popular departments: accounting, finance, marketing, organizational behavior, other
Mean starting base salary for 2002 full-time graduates: $87,910
Employment location for 2002 class: Intl. 16%; N.E. 16%; M.A. 6%; S. 4%; M.W. 36%; S.W. 5%; W. 16%

Southern Illinois University–Carbondale

Rehn Hall
Carbondale, IL 62901
Public
Admissions: (618) 453-3030
E-mail: mbagp@cba.siu.edu
Web site: http://www.cba.siu.edu/mba
Financial aid: (618) 453-4334
Application deadline: 06/01
In-state tuition: full time: N/A; part time: N/A
Out-of-state tuition: full time: N/A
Room/board/expenses: N/A
College-funded aid: YES
International student aid: YES
Research assistantships: 25
Teaching assistantships: 0
Full-time enrollment: 144
men: 61%; women: 39%; minorities: 13%; international: 43%
Part-time enrollment: N/A
men: N/A; women: N/A; minorities: N/A; international: N/A
Acceptance rate (full time): 54%
Average GMAT (full time): 539
Average GPA (full time): 3.19
Average age of entrants to full-time program: 27
Average months of prior work experience (full time): 36
TOEFL requirement: YES
Minimum TOEFL score: 550
Most popular departments: finance, general management, international business, marketing, management information systems

Southern Illinois University–Edwardsville

Box 1051
Edwardsville, IL 62026-1051
Public
Admissions: (618) 650-3840
E-mail: mba@siue.edu
Web site: http://www.siue.edu/BUSINESS
Financial aid: (618) 650-3800
Application deadline: rolling
In-state tuition: full time: $119/credit hour; part time: $119/credit hour
Out-of-state tuition: full time: $238/credit hour
Room/board/expenses: $8,000
College-funded aid: YES
International student aid: YES
Fellowships: 0
Research assistantships: 15
Teaching assistantships: 0
Full-time enrollment: N/A
men: N/A; women: N/A; minorities: N/A; international: N/A
Part-time enrollment: 256
men: 57%; women: 43%; minorities: 9%; international: 16%
Average GMAT (part time): 521
TOEFL requirement: YES
Minimum TOEFL score: 550
Most popular departments: general management, management information systems

University of Chicago

1101 E. 58th Street
Chicago, IL 60637
Private
Admissions: (773) 702-7369
E-mail: admissions@gsb.uchicago.edu
Web site: http://gsb.uchicago.edu
Financial aid: (773) 702-3076
Application deadline: N/A
Tuition: full time: $32,602; part time: $3,250/credit hour
Room/board/expenses: $19,050
College-funded aid: YES
International student aid: YES
Fellowships: 0
Research assistantships: 0
Teaching assistantships: 0
Average student indebtedness at graduation: $75,000
Full-time enrollment: 990
men: 74%; women: 26%; minorities: 19%; international: 29%
Part-time enrollment: 1,399
men: 77%; women: 23%; minorities: 21%; international: 13%
Acceptance rate (full time): 15%
Average GMAT (full time): 687
Average GPA (full time): 3.44
Average age of entrants to full-time program: 28
Average months of prior work experience (full time): 53
TOEFL requirement: YES
Minimum TOEFL score: 600
Most popular departments: accounting, economics, entrepreneurship, finance, general management, marketing
Mean starting base salary for 2002 full-time graduates: $88,019
Employment location for 2002 class: Intl. 17%; N.E. 24%; M.A. 4%; S. 3%; M.W. 37%; S.W. 4%; W. 11%

University of Illinois–Chicago

815 W. Van Buren Street
Suite 220, M/C 077
Chicago, IL 60607
Public
Admissions: (312) 996-4573
E-mail: mba@uic.edu
Web site: http://www.uic.edu/cba/mba
Internet application: http://www.uic.edu/cba/mba
Financial aid: (312) 996-3126
Application deadline: 06/01
In-state tuition: full time: $12,026; part time: $501/credit hour
Out-of-state tuition: full time: $20,008
Room/board/expenses: $11,190
College-funded aid: YES
International student aid: YES
Full-time enrollment: 322
men: 61%; women: 39%; minorities: 14%; international: 30%
Part-time enrollment: 246
men: 59%; women: 41%; minorities: 25%; international: 2%
Acceptance rate (full time): 61%
Average GMAT (full time): 570
Average GMAT (part time): 530
Average GPA (full time): 3.10
Average age of entrants to full-time program: 27
Average months of prior work experience (full time): 46
TOEFL requirement: YES
Minimum TOEFL score: 570
Most popular departments: accounting, entrepreneurship, finance, marketing, management information systems
Mean starting base salary for 2002 full-time graduates: $54,518
Employment location for 2002 class: Intl. 0%; N.E. 0%; M.A. 0%; S. 0%; M.W. 94%; S.W. 0%; W. 6%

University of Illinois–Urbana-Champaign

260 Wohlers Hall
1206 S. Sixth Street
Champaign, IL 61801
Public
Admissions: (217) 244-7602
E-mail: mba@uiuc.edu
Web site: http://www.mba.uiuc.edu
Internet application: http://www.mba.uiuc.edu/prospect/admissions
Financial aid: (217) 244-4275
Application deadline: 03/15
In-state tuition: full time: $15,328; part time: N/A
Out-of-state tuition: full time: $24,254
Room/board/expenses: $11,150
College-funded aid: YES
International student aid: YES
Fellowships: 0
Research assistantships: 0
Teaching assistantships: 0
Average student indebtedness at graduation: $33,000
Full-time enrollment: 365
men: 72%; women: 28%; minorities: 15%; international: 48%
Part-time enrollment: N/A
men: N/A; women: N/A; minorities: N/A; international: N/A
Acceptance rate (full time): 31%
Average GMAT (full time): 640
Average GPA (full time): 3.30
Average age of entrants to full-time program: 26
Average months of prior work experience (full time): 47
TOEFL requirement: YES
Minimum TOEFL score: N/A
Most popular departments: accounting, finance, marketing, management information systems, technology
Mean starting base salary for 2002 full-time graduates: $69,050
Employment location for 2002 class: Intl. 21%; N.E. 7%; M.A. 5%; S. 5%; M.W. 51%; S.W. 2%; W. 9%

Western Illinois University[1]

1 University Circle
Macomb, IL 61455
Public
Admissions: (309) 298-2442
E-mail: dj-bloomberg@wiu.edu
Web site: http://www.wiu.edu/grad/busad.htm
Internet application: http://www.wiu.edu/grad/students/prospect.htm
Financial aid: (309) 298-2446
Tuition: N/A
Room/board/expenses: N/A
Enrollment: N/A

INDIANA

Ball State University

Whitinger Building,147
Muncie, IN 47306
Public
Admissions: (765) 285-1931
E-mail: mba@bsu.edu
Web site: http://www.bsu.edu/mba/
Financial aid: (765) 285-5600
Application deadline: 07/15
In-state tuition: total program: $7,398 (full time); $8,298 (part time)
Out-of-state tuition: total program: $19,008 (full time)
Room/board/expenses: $12,480
College-funded aid: YES
International student aid: YES
Fellowships: 1
Research assistantships: 34
Full-time enrollment: 42
men: 69%; women: 31%; minorities: 24%; international: 29%
Part-time enrollment: 129
men: 66%; women: 34%; minorities: 5%; international: 5%
Acceptance rate (full time): 73%
Average GMAT (full time): 524
Average GMAT (part time): 553
Average age of entrants to full-time program: 24
Average months of prior work experience (full time): 11
TOEFL requirement: YES
Minimum TOEFL score: 550
Most popular departments: entrepreneurship, finance, operations management

Butler University

4600 Sunset Avenue
Indianapolis, IN 46208-3485
Private
Admissions: (317) 940-9221
E-mail: mba@butler.edu
Web site: http://www.butler.edu
Internet application: http://www.butler.edu/admissions/adm_applyonline.asp
Financial aid: (317) 940-8200
Application deadline: rolling
Tuition: full time: $450/credit hour; part time: $450/credit hour
Room/board/expenses: $9,000
College-funded aid: NO
International student aid: NO
Fellowships: 0
Research assistantships: 0
Teaching assistantships: 0
Average student indebtedness at graduation: $0
Full-time enrollment: N/A
men: N/A; women: N/A; minorities: N/A; international: N/A
Part-time enrollment: 327
men: 69%; women: 31%; minorities: 6%; international: 9%
Average GMAT (part time): 556
Average age of entrants to full-time program: N/A

KEY TO TERMINOLOGY ON PAGE 94

Average months of prior work experience (full time): N/A
TOEFL requirement: YES
Minimum TOEFL score: 550
Most popular departments: finance, leadership, marketing

Indiana State University[1]
School of Business
Room 1109
Terre Haute, IN 47809
Public
Admissions: (812) 237-2002
E-mail: mba@indstate.edu
Web site: http://web.indstate.edu/schbus/mba.html
Financial aid: (812) 237-2215
Tuition: N/A
Room/board/expenses: N/A
Enrollment: N/A

Indiana University–Bloomington (Kelley)
1275 East 10th Street
Suite 2010
Bloomington, IN 47405-1703
Public
Admissions: (812) 855-8006
E-mail: mbaoffice@indiana.edu
Web site: http://www.kelley.indiana.edu/mba
Internet application: http://apply.embark.com/mbaedge/indiana/fulltime/
Financial aid: (812) 855-8006
Application deadline: 04/15
In-state tuition: full time: $12,187; part time: $330/credit hour
Out-of-state tuition: full time: $23,391
Room/board/expenses: $16,204
College-funded aid: YES
International student aid: YES
Average student indebtedness at graduation: $33,538
Full-time enrollment: 547
men: 77%; women: 23%; minorities: 14%; international: 31%
Part-time enrollment: 310
men: 81%; women: 19%; minorities: 5%; international: 10%
Acceptance rate (full time): 22%
Average GMAT (full time): 651
Average GMAT (part time): 606
Average GPA (full time): 3.35
Average age of entrants to full-time program: 29
Average months of prior work experience (full time): 64
TOEFL requirement: YES
Minimum TOEFL score: 580
Most popular departments: accounting, entrepreneurship, finance, marketing, statistics and operations research
Mean starting base salary for 2002 full-time graduates: $76,934
Employment location for 2002 class: Intl. 10%; N.E. 10%; M.A. 3%; S. 8%; M.W. 55%; S.W. 4%; W. 10%

Indiana University–Kokomo
2300 S. Washington Street
Kokomo, IN 46904-9003
Public
Admissions: (765) 455-9462
E-mail: kparkiso@iuk.edu
Web site: http://www.iuk.edu/academics/business
Internet application: http://www.iuk.edu/admission/onlineapp.htm
Financial aid: (765) 455-9216
Application deadline: 08/04
In-state tuition: full time: N/A; part time: N/A

Out-of-state tuition: full time: N/A
Room/board/expenses: N/A
College-funded aid: YES
International student aid: YES
Fellowships: 0
Research assistantships: 0
Teaching assistantships: 0
Full-time enrollment: N/A
men: N/A; women: N/A; minorities: N/A; international: N/A
Part-time enrollment: 73
men: 53%; women: 47%; minorities: N/A; international: N/A
TOEFL requirement: YES
Minimum TOEFL score: 550
Most popular departments: general management

Indiana University–Purdue University–Fort Wayne[1]
2101 Coliseum Boulevard E
Fort Wayne, IN 46805-1499
Public
Admissions: (260) 481-6498
E-mail: mba@ipfw.edu
Web site: http://www.ipfw.edu/bms/mba1.htm
Financial aid: (260) 481-6820
Tuition: N/A
Room/board/expenses: N/A
Enrollment: N/A

Indiana University South Bend
1700 Mishawaka Avenue
PO Box 7111
South Bend, IN 46634-7111
Public
Admissions: (574) 237-4138
E-mail: gradbus@iusb.edu
Web site: http://www.iusb.edu/~gradbus
Financial aid: (574) 237-4357
Application deadline: 07/01
In-state tuition: full time: $171/credit hour; part time: $171/credit hour
Out-of-state tuition: full time: $407/credit hour
Room/board/expenses: $7,500
College-funded aid: NO
International student aid: NO
Fellowships: 0
Research assistantships: 0
Teaching assistantships: 0
Full-time enrollment: N/A
men: N/A; women: N/A; minorities: N/A; international: N/A
Part-time enrollment: 185
men: 62%; women: 38%; minorities: 6%; international: 29%
Average GMAT (part time): 516
TOEFL requirement: YES
Minimum TOEFL score: 550

Indiana University–Southeast[1]
4201 Grant Line Road
New Albany, IN 47150
Public
Admissions: (812) 941-2364
E-mail: ebeckman@ius.edu
Web site: http://www.ius.edu/mba
Internet application: http://www2.ius.edu/apply
Financial aid: (812) 941-2246
Tuition: N/A
Room/board/expenses: N/A
Enrollment: N/A

Purdue University–West Lafayette (Krannert)
Krannert Building 160
403 W. State Street
West Lafayette, IN 47907-2056
Public
Admissions: (765) 494-0773
E-mail: krannert_ms@mgmt.purdue.edu
Web site: http://www.mgmt.purdue.edu/programs/masters
Internet application: http://apply.embark.com/mbaedge/purdue
Financial aid: (765) 494-5050
Application deadline: 05/15
In-state tuition: full time: $12,798; part time: N/A
Out-of-state tuition: full time: $23,582
Room/board/expenses: $9,500
College-funded aid: YES
International student aid: YES
Fellowships: 32
Research assistantships: 82
Teaching assistantships: 23
Average student indebtedness at graduation: $25,116
Full-time enrollment: 295
men: 79%; women: 21%; minorities: 19%; international: 36%
Part-time enrollment: N/A
men: N/A; women: N/A; minorities: N/A; international: N/A
Acceptance rate (full time): 27%
Average GMAT (full time): 651
Average GPA (full time): 3.23
Average age of entrants to full-time program: 27
Average months of prior work experience (full time): 50
TOEFL requirement: YES
Minimum TOEFL score: 575
Most popular departments: finance, general management, manufacturing and technology management, marketing, operations management
Mean starting base salary for 2002 full-time graduates: $78,763
Employment location for 2002 class: Intl. 9%; N.E. 15%; M.A. 11%; S. 4%; M.W. 45%; S.W. 4%; W. 12%

University of Notre Dame (Mendoza)
276 Mendoza College of Business
Notre Dame, IN 46556
Private
Admissions: (574) 631-8488
E-mail: mba.1@nd.edu
Web site: http://www.nd.edu/~mba/
Internet application: http://mba.nd.edu/apply
Financial aid: (574) 631-6436
Application deadline: 03/15
Tuition: full time: $26,485; part time: N/A
Room/board/expenses: $11,220
College-funded aid: YES
International student aid: YES
Fellowships: 122
Average student indebtedness at graduation: $42,695
Full-time enrollment: 322
men: 77%; women: 23%; minorities: 13%; international: 27%
Part-time enrollment: N/A
men: N/A; women: N/A; minorities: N/A; international: N/A
Acceptance rate (full time): 23%
Average GMAT (full time): 668
Average GPA (full time): 3.40
Average age of entrants to full-time program: 26
Average months of prior work experience (full time): 49

TOEFL requirement: YES
Minimum TOEFL score: 600
Most popular departments: entrepreneurship, finance, general management, marketing, portfolio management
Mean starting base salary for 2002 full-time graduates: $71,873
Employment location for 2002 class: Intl. 5%; N.E. 16%; M.A. 8%; S. 7%; M.W. 39%; S.W. 9%; W. 16%

University of Southern Indiana
8600 University Boulevard
Evansville, IN 47712
Public
Admissions: (812) 465-7015
E-mail: eotto@usi.edu
Web site: http://www.usi.edu
Internet application: https://www.usi.edu/ADMISSN/ssl/admissions_grad_app.asp
Financial aid: (812) 464-1767
Application deadline: rolling
In-state tuition: full time: $166/credit hour; part time: $166/credit hour
Out-of-state tuition: full time: $333/credit hour
Room/board/expenses: $14,155
College-funded aid: YES
International student aid: YES
Research assistantships: 2
Full-time enrollment: N/A
men: N/A; women: N/A; minorities: N/A; international: N/A
Part-time enrollment: 117
men: 57%; women: 43%; minorities: N/A; international: 3%
Average GMAT (part time): 502
Average age of entrants to full-time program: N/A
Average months of prior work experience (full time): N/A
TOEFL requirement: YES
Minimum TOEFL score: 550
Most popular departments: accounting, finance, healthcare administration, industrial management, marketing

Drake University
2507 University Avenue
Des Moines, IA 50311
Private
Admissions: (515) 271-2188
E-mail: cbpa.gradprograms@drake.edu
Web site: http://www.drake.edu/cbpa/grad
Internet application: http://www.drake.edu/admissions/graduate.html
Financial aid: (515) 271-2905
Application deadline: rolling
Tuition: full time: $360/credit hour; part time: $360/credit hour
Room/board/expenses: $7,000
College-funded aid: YES
International student aid: NO
Fellowships: 0
Research assistantships: 0
Teaching assistantships: 0
Average student indebtedness at graduation: $0
Full-time enrollment: 58
men: 52%; women: 48%; minorities: 5%; international: 33%
Part-time enrollment: 226
men: 65%; women: 35%; minorities: 4%; international: 5%
Acceptance rate (full time): 100%
Average GMAT (full time): 519
Average GMAT (part time): 519
Average GPA (full time): 3.18

Average age of entrants to full-time program: 25
TOEFL requirement: YES
Minimum TOEFL score: 550
Most popular departments: accounting, finance, general management, human resources management, marketing

Iowa State University
218 Carver Hall
Ames, IA 50011
Public
Admissions: (515) 294-8118
E-mail: busgrad@iastate.edu
Web site: http://www.bus.iastate.edu/grad
Financial aid: (515) 294-2223
Application deadline: 05/01
In-state tuition: full time: $4,770; part time: $318/credit hour
Out-of-state tuition: full time: $13,296
Room/board/expenses: $10,840
College-funded aid: YES
International student aid: YES
Full-time enrollment: 72
men: 69%; women: 31%; minorities: 3%; international: 22%
Part-time enrollment: 160
men: 68%; women: 32%; minorities: 0%; international: 1%
Acceptance rate (full time): 48%
Average GMAT (full time): 622
Average GMAT (part time): 543
Average GPA (full time): 3.37
Average age of entrants to full-time program: 26
Average months of prior work experience (full time): 36
TOEFL requirement: YES
Minimum TOEFL score: 570
Most popular departments: finance, human resources management, marketing, management information systems
Mean starting base salary for 2002 full-time graduates: $45,167
Employment location for 2002 class: Intl. 9%; N.E. N/A; M.A. N/A; S. N/A; M.W. 78%; S.W. 9%; W. 4%

University of Iowa (Tippie)
108 John Pappajohn Business Building, Suite C140
Iowa City, IA 52242
Public
Admissions: (319) 335-1039
E-mail: iowamba@uiowa.edu
Web site: http://www.biz.uiowa.edu/mba
Internet application: https://apply.embark.com/MBAEdge/Uoflowa/14/
Financial aid: (319) 335-1039
Application deadline: 07/15
In-state tuition: full time: $9,899; part time: $387/credit hour
Out-of-state tuition: full time: $18,211
Room/board/expenses: $13,476
College-funded aid: YES
International student aid: YES
Fellowships: 55
Research assistantships: 25
Average student indebtedness at graduation: $25,300
Full-time enrollment: 152
men: 81%; women: 19%; minorities: 3%; international: 43%
Part-time enrollment: 704
men: 69%; women: 31%; minorities: 4%; international: 4%
Acceptance rate (full time): 38%
Average GMAT (full time): 638
Average GMAT (part time): 566
Average GPA (full time): 3.30

Average age of entrants to full-time program: 27
Average months of prior work experience (full time): 40
TOEFL requirement: YES
Minimum TOEFL score: 600
Most popular departments: accounting, finance, marketing, management information systems, other
Mean starting base salary for 2002 full-time graduates: $75,646
Employment location for 2002 class: Intl. 0%; N.E. 15%; M.A. 5%; S. 0%; M.W. 80%; S.W. 0%; W. 0%

University of Northern Iowa[1]

Curris Business Building 325
Cedar Falls, IA 50614-0123
Public
Admissions: (319) 273-6243
E-mail: mba@uni.edu
Web site: http://www.cba.uni.edu/mba/
Internet application: http://www.cba.uni.edu/mba/admissions.htm
Financial aid: (319) 273-2700
Tuition: N/A
Room/board/expenses: N/A
Enrollment: N/A

KANSAS

Emporia State University

1200 Commercial
Campus Box 4059
Emporia, KS 66801-5087
Public
Admissions: (800) 950-4723
E-mail: gradinfo@emporia.edu
Web site: http://www.emporia.edu/grad/
Internet application: http://www.emporia.edu/grad/appinstr.htm
Financial aid: (620) 341-5457
Application deadline: 08/23
In-state tuition: full time: $3,378; part time: $129/credit hour
Out-of-state tuition: full time: $8,390
Room/board/expenses: $8,000
College-funded aid: YES
International student aid: YES
Research assistantships: 30
Teaching assistantships: 120
Full-time enrollment: 52
men: 69%; women: 31%; minorities: 2%; international: 52%
Part-time enrollment: 19
men: 53%; women: 47%; minorities: 0%; international: 26%
Acceptance rate (full time): 71%
Average GMAT (full time): 527
Average GMAT (part time): 420
Average GPA (full time): 3.18
Average age of entrants to full-time program: 27
TOEFL requirement: YES
Minimum TOEFL score: 550
Most popular departments: accounting, general management

Kansas State University

107 Calvin Hall
Manhattan, KS 66506
Public
Admissions: (785) 532-7190
E-mail: flynn@ksu.edu
Web site: http://www.cba.ksu.edu/cba/
Internet application: http://www.ksu.edu/grad/application/index.htm
Financial aid: (785) 532-6420
Application deadline: 03/01
In-state tuition: full time: $4,965; part time: $138/credit hour
Out-of-state tuition: full time: $12,190
Room/board/expenses: $10,000
College-funded aid: YES
International student aid: YES
Research assistantships: 20
Teaching assistantships: 20
Full-time enrollment: 48
men: 58%; women: 42%; minorities: 8%; international: 40%
Part-time enrollment: 21
men: 62%; women: 38%; minorities: 5%; international: 29%
Acceptance rate (full time): 49%
Average GMAT (full time): 538
Average GMAT (part time): 530
Average GPA (full time): 3.61
Average age of entrants to full-time program: 25
Average months of prior work experience (full time): 18
TOEFL requirement: YES
Minimum TOEFL score: 550
Most popular departments: finance, general management, human resources management, marketing, operations management
Employment location for 2002 class: Intl. N/A; N.E. 0%; M.A. 33%; S. 33%; M.W. N/A; S.W. N/A; W. 33%

Pittsburg State University (Kelce)[1]

1701 S. Broadway
Pittsburg, KS 66762
Public
Admissions: (620) 235-4222
E-mail: grad@pittstate.edu
Web site: http://www.pittstate.edu/kelce/graduate.html
Financial aid: (620) 235-4240
Tuition: N/A
Room/board/expenses: N/A
Enrollment: N/A

University of Kansas

1300 Sunnyside Avenue
Lawrence, KS 66045-7585
Public
Admissions: (785) 864-3844
E-mail: bschoolgrad@uk.edu
Web site: http://www.business.ku.edu
Internet application: http://www.embark.com
Financial aid: (785) 864-3844
Application deadline: 04/01
In-state tuition: full time: $134/credit hour; part time: $134/credit hour
Out-of-state tuition: full time: $389/credit hour
Room/board/expenses: $7,486
College-funded aid: YES
International student aid: YES
Fellowships: 0
Full-time enrollment: 89
men: 49%; women: 51%; minorities: 4%; international: 28%
Part-time enrollment: 478
men: 79%; women: 21%; minorities: 11%; international: 16%
Acceptance rate (full time): 50%
Average GMAT (full time): 608
Average GMAT (part time): 608
Average age of entrants to full-time program: 27
Average months of prior work experience (full time): 49
TOEFL requirement: YES
Minimum TOEFL score: 600
Most popular departments: finance, human resources management, international business, marketing, management information systems
Mean starting base salary for 2002 full-time graduates: $46,208
Employment location for 2002 class: Intl. 10%; N.E. N/A; M.A. N/A; S. 10%; M.W. 80%; S.W. N/A; W. N/A

Wichita State University (Barton)

1845 N. Fairmount
Box 48
Wichita, KS 67260-0048
Public
Admissions: (316) 978-3230
E-mail: gradbusiness@wichita.edu
Web site: http://www.wichita.edu/mba
Financial aid: (316) 978-3430
Application deadline: 06/01
In-state tuition: full time: $138/credit hour; part time: $138/credit hour
Out-of-state tuition: full time: $378/credit hour
Room/board/expenses: $14,748
College-funded aid: YES
International student aid: YES
Fellowships: 1
Research assistantships: 25
Teaching assistantships: 0
Full-time enrollment: 66
men: 53%; women: 47%; minorities: 8%; international: 38%
Part-time enrollment: 183
men: 62%; women: 38%; minorities: 7%; international: 7%
Acceptance rate (full time): 64%
Average GMAT (full time): 520
Average GMAT (part time): 547
Average GPA (full time): 3.23
Average age of entrants to full-time program: 26
Average months of prior work experience (full time): 36
TOEFL requirement: YES
Minimum TOEFL score: 570
Most popular departments: entrepreneurship, finance, health care administration, marketing, operations management

KENTUCKY

Murray State University

109 Business Building
Murray, KY 42071
Public
Admissions: (270) 762-6970
E-mail: admissions@murraystate.edu
Web site: http://www.murraystate.edu/cbpa
Internet application: http://www.murraystate.edu/adm/ad&rg/apps.htm
Financial aid: (270) 762-2546
Application deadline: 08/15
In-state tuition: full time: $3,159; part time: $185/credit hour
Out-of-state tuition: full time: $8,739
Room/board/expenses: $7,000
College-funded aid: YES
International student aid: YES
Full-time enrollment: 90
men: 63%; women: 37%; minorities: 33%; international: 51%
Part-time enrollment: 92
men: 48%; women: 52%; minorities: 12%; international: 2%
Acceptance rate (full time): 81%
Average GMAT (full time): 481
Average GMAT (part time): 494
Average GPA (full time): 3.15
Average age of entrants to full-time program: 24
TOEFL requirement: YES
Minimum TOEFL score: 525
Most popular departments: accounting, finance, general management, human resources management, marketing

Northern Kentucky University

Suite 401
BEP Center
Highland Heights, KY 41099
Public
Admissions: (859) 572-5165
E-mail: mbusiness@nku.edu
Web site: http://www.nku.edu/~mbusiness
Financial aid: (859) 572-6364
Application deadline: 08/01
In-state tuition: full time: N/A; part time: $211/credit hour
Out-of-state tuition: full time: N/A
Room/board/expenses: $21,246
College-funded aid: YES
International student aid: YES
Fellowships: 0
Research assistantships: 23
Teaching assistantships: 0
Full-time enrollment: N/A
men: N/A; women: N/A; minorities: N/A; international: N/A
Part-time enrollment: 262
men: 57%; women: 43%; minorities: 6%; international: 9%
Average GMAT (part time): 506
Average age of entrants to full-time program: N/A
Average months of prior work experience (full time): N/A
TOEFL requirement: YES
Minimum TOEFL score: 550
Most popular departments: entrepreneurship, finance, international business, marketing, management information systems

University of Kentucky (Gatton)

145 Gatton College of Business & Economics
Lexington, KY 40506-0034
Public
Admissions: (859) 257-5889
E-mail: ukmba@uky.edu
Web site: http://gatton.uky.edu
Internet application: http://gatton.uky.edu/Academic/MBA/Admissions.html?section=1
Financial aid: (859) 257-4221
Application deadline: 07/18
In-state tuition: full time: $4,654; part time: $231/credit hour
Out-of-state tuition: full time: $11,890
Room/board/expenses: $7,940
College-funded aid: YES
International student aid: YES
Fellowships: 58
Research assistantships: 0
Teaching assistantships: 0
Full-time enrollment: 152
men: 67%; women: 33%; minorities: 14%; international: 11%
Part-time enrollment: 105
men: 70%; women: 30%; minorities: 3%; international: 3%
Acceptance rate (full time): 44%
Average GMAT (full time): 615
Average GMAT (part time): 596
Average GPA (full time): 3.34
Average age of entrants to full-time program: 24
Average months of prior work experience (full time): 15
TOEFL requirement: YES
Minimum TOEFL score: 550
Most popular departments: accounting, finance, general management, international business, marketing
Mean starting base salary for 2002 full-time graduates: $50,659
Employment location for 2002 class: Intl. 0%; N.E. 0%; M.A. 0%; S. 71%; M.W. 21%; S.W. 0%; W. 7%

University of Louisville[1]

Belknap Campus
Louisville, KY 40292
Public
Admissions: (502) 852-6440
E-mail: gradadm@louisville.edu
Web site: http://cbpa.louisville.edu
Internet application: http://graduate.louisville.edu/app
Financial aid: (502) 852-5511
Tuition: N/A
Room/board/expenses: N/A
Enrollment: N/A

Western Kentucky University[1]

Gordon Ford College of Business
447 Grise Hall
Bowling Green, KY 42101
Public
Admissions: (270) 745-2446
E-mail: mba@wku.edu
Web site: http://www.wku.edu/Dept/Academic/COBA/MBA/
Financial aid: (270) 745-2755
Tuition: N/A
Room/board/expenses: N/A
Enrollment: N/A

LOUISIANA

Louisiana State University–Baton Rouge (Ourso)

3170 CEBA Building
Baton Rouge, LA 70803
Public
Admissions: (225) 578-8867
E-mail: busmba@lsu.edu
Web site: http://www.bus.lsu.edu/
Internet application: https://www.applyweb.com/apply/lsu/menu.html
Financial aid: (225) 578-3103
Application deadline: 05/15
In-state tuition: full time: $3,635; part time: N/A
Out-of-state tuition: full time: $8,935
Room/board/expenses: $8,000
College-funded aid: YES
International student aid: YES
Full-time enrollment: 163
men: 63%; women: 37%; minorities: 6%; international: 5%
Part-time enrollment: N/A
men: N/A; women: N/A; minorities: N/A; international: N/A
Acceptance rate (full time): 31%
Average GMAT (full time): 585
Average GPA (full time): 3.35
Average age of entrants to full-time program: 24
Average months of prior work experience (full time): 29
TOEFL requirement: YES
Minimum TOEFL score: 550
Most popular departments: accounting, finance, marketing, management information systems, other

KEY TO TERMINOLOGY ON PAGE 94

Louisiana State University–Shreveport[1]

1 University Place
Shreveport, LA 71115
Public
Admissions: (318) 797-5213
E-mail: swood@pilot.lsus.edu
Web site:
http://www.lsus.edu/ba/mba
Financial aid: (318) 797-5363
Tuition: N/A
Room/board/expenses: N/A
Enrollment: N/A

Louisiana Tech University

PO Box 10318
Ruston, LA 71272
Public
Admissions: (318) 257-4528
E-mail: cabgrad@latech.edu
Web site:
http://www.cab.latech.edu
Financial aid: (318) 257-2641
Application deadline: 08/01
In-state tuition: full time: $3,664;
part time: $1,168
Out-of-state tuition: full time:
$9,464
Room/board/expenses: $9,600
College-funded aid: YES
International student aid: YES
Fellowships: 3
Research assistantships: 17
Teaching assistantships: 16
**Average student indebtedness at
graduation:** $0
Full-time enrollment: 76
men: 51%; women: 49%; minori-
ties: 7%; international: 28%
Part-time enrollment: 24
men: 50%; women: 50%; minori-
ties: 21%; international: 0%
Acceptance rate (full time): 83%
Average GMAT (full time): 471
Average GMAT (part time): 550
Average GPA (full time): 3.23
**Average age of entrants to full-time
program:** 24
**Average months of prior work expe-
rience (full time):** N/A
TOEFL requirement: YES
Minimum TOEFL score: 550
Most popular departments: finance,
general management

Loyola University New Orleans (Butt)[1]

6363 St. Charles Avenue
Campus Box 15
New Orleans, LA 70118
Private
Admissions: (504) 864-7944
E-mail: mba@loyno.edu
Web site:
http://www.cba.loyno.edu
Internet application:
http://www.loyno.edu/cba/
applying.html
Financial aid: (504) 865-3231
Tuition: N/A
Room/board/expenses: N/A
Enrollment: N/A

McNeese State University (Burton)[1]

PO Box 91660
Lake Charles, LA 70609
Public
Admissions: (337) 475-5576
E-mail:
mbaprog@mail.mcneese.edu
Web site: http://www.mcneese.
edu/colleges/bus
Financial aid: (337) 475-5065
Tuition: N/A

Room/board/expenses: N/A
Enrollment: N/A

Nicholls State University

PO Box 2015
Thibodaux, LA 70310
Public
Admissions: (985) 448-4507
E-mail: esai-bl@nicholls.edu
Web site: http://www.nicholls.edu/
admission
Internet application:
http://www.nicholls.edu/
admission/application2.html
Financial aid: (985) 448-4048
Application deadline: 06/01
In-state tuition: full time: $2,500;
part time: N/A
Out-of-state tuition: full time:
$8,000
Room/board/expenses: N/A
College-funded aid: YES
International student aid: YES
Fellowships: 0
Research assistantships: 15
Teaching assistantships: 0
Full-time enrollment: 34
men: 56%; women: 44%; minori-
ties: 3%; international: 44%
Part-time enrollment: 95
men: 53%; women: 47%; minori-
ties: 0%; international: 0%
Acceptance rate (full time): 98%
Average GMAT (full time): 470
Average GPA (full time): 3.18
**Average age of entrants to full-time
program:** 26
TOEFL requirement: YES
Minimum TOEFL score: 550

Southeastern Louisiana University

SLU 10735
Hammond, LA 70402
Public
Admissions: (985) 549-2146
E-mail: jwalker@selu.edu
Web site: http://www.selu.edu/
Academics/Business/mba
Internet application:
http://www.selu.edu/enroll/
grad_app.htm
Financial aid: (985) 549-2244
Application deadline: 07/15
In-state tuition: full time: $2,482;
part time: $138/credit hour
Out-of-state tuition: full time:
$6,478
Room/board/expenses: $3,720
College-funded aid: YES
International student aid: YES
Fellowships: 5
Research assistantships: 157
Teaching assistantships: 14
Full-time enrollment: 205
men: 45%; women: 55%; minori-
ties: 8%; international: 23%
Part-time enrollment: N/A
men: N/A; women: N/A; minori-
ties: N/A; international: N/A
Average GMAT (full time): 477
Average GPA (full time): 3.10
**Average age of entrants to full-time
program:** 24
TOEFL requirement: YES
Minimum TOEFL score: 525
Most popular departments:
accounting, marketing

Southern University and A&M College

PO Box 9723
Baton Rouge, LA 70813
Public
Admissions: (225) 771-5390
E-mail: admit@subr.edu
Web site: http://www.subr.edu
Financial aid: (225) 771-2790

Application deadline: 05/01
In-state tuition: full time: $3,673;
part time: $2,458
Out-of-state tuition: full time:
$6,980
Room/board/expenses: $8,913
College-funded aid: YES
International student aid: YES
Full-time enrollment: 473
men: 28%; women: 72%; minori-
ties: 82%; international: 1%
Part-time enrollment: 748
men: 26%; women: 74%; minori-
ties: 86%; international: 1%
TOEFL requirement: YES
Minimum TOEFL score: 525

Tulane University (Freeman)

7 McAlister Drive
New Orleans, LA 70118-5669
Private
Admissions: (504) 865-5410
E-mail: freeman.admissions@
tulane.edu
Web site:
http://freeman.tulane.edu
Internet application:
http://freeman.tulane.edu/
admissions/application.htm
Financial aid: (504) 865-5410
Application deadline: 06/15
Tuition: full time: $966/credit hour;
part time: $966/credit hour
Room/board/expenses: $10,480
College-funded aid: YES
International student aid: YES
**Average student indebtedness at
graduation:** $35,000
Full-time enrollment: 203
men: 72%; women: 28%; minori-
ties: 10%; international: 34%
Part-time enrollment: 150
men: 69%; women: 31%; minori-
ties: 23%; international: 0%
Acceptance rate (full time): 54%
Average GMAT (full time): 663
Average GMAT (part time): 575
Average GPA (full time): 3.30
**Average age of entrants to full-time
program:** 28
**Average months of prior work expe-
rience (full time):** 67
TOEFL requirement: NO
Minimum TOEFL score: 600
Most popular departments: ac-
counting, finance, general man-
agement, marketing, management
information systems
**Mean starting base salary for 2002
full-time graduates:** $71,316
**Employment location for 2002
class:** Intl. 23%; N.E. 14%; M.A.
0%; S. 23%; M.W. 0%; S.W. 40%;
W. 0%

University of Louisiana–Lafayette[1]

USL Box 44568
Lafayette, LA 70504-4568
Public
Admissions: (337) 482-6965
E-mail: palmer@louisiana.edu
Web site:
http://www.louisiana.edu/
Academic/GradSchool/
programs.html
Financial aid: (337) 482-6497
Tuition: N/A
Room/board/expenses: N/A
Enrollment: N/A

University of Louisiana–Monroe[1]

700 University Avenue
Monroe, LA 71209
Public
Admissions: (318) 342-5252
E-mail: pena@ulm.edu
Web site: http://ele.ulm.edu
Internet application:
http://www.ulm.edu/enroll/
toapply.html
Financial aid: (318) 342-5320
Tuition: N/A
Room/board/expenses: N/A
Enrollment: N/A

University of New Orleans[1]

Lakefront, 2000 Lakeshore Drive
New Orleans, LA 70148
Public
Admissions: (504) 280-6393
E-mail: bamoran@uno.edu
Web site: http://www.uno.edu/~
admi/graduate.html
Financial aid: (504) 280-6603
Tuition: N/A
Room/board/expenses: N/A
Enrollment: N/A

University of Maine

Donald P. Corbett Business
Building
Orono, ME 04469-5723
Public
Admissions: (207) 581-1973
E-mail: mba@maine.edu
Web site:
http://www.umaine.edu/business
Internet application:
http://www.ume.maine.edu/~
graduate/onlineap.html
Financial aid: (207) 581-1324
Application deadline: rolling
In-state tuition: full time:
$218/credit hour; part time:
$218/credit hour
Out-of-state tuition: full time:
$623/credit hour
Room/board/expenses: $7,422
College-funded aid: YES
International student aid: YES
Fellowships: 2
Research assistantships: 6
Full-time enrollment: 54
men: 59%; women: 41%; minori-
ties: 4%; international: 35%
Part-time enrollment: 37
men: 49%; women: 51%; minori-
ties: 5%; international: 3%
Acceptance rate (full time): 60%
Average GMAT (full time): 550
Average GPA (full time): 3.22
**Average age of entrants to full-time
program:** 26
**Average months of prior work expe-
rience (full time):** 60
TOEFL requirement: YES
Minimum TOEFL score: 550
Most popular departments: ac-
counting, finance, general management, marketing, management
information systems

University of Southern Maine

PO Box 9300
Portland, ME 04104
Public
Admissions: (207) 780-4184
E-mail: mba@usm.maine.edu
Web site:
http://www.usm.maine.edu/sb
Internet application:
http://www.usm.maine.edu/grad
Financial aid: (207) 780-5250

Application deadline: 08/01
In-state tuition: full time:
$200/credit hour; part time:
$200/credit hour
Out-of-state tuition: full time:
$560/credit hour
Room/board/expenses: $15,466
College-funded aid: YES
International student aid: YES
Fellowships: 0
Research assistantships: 5
Teaching assistantships: 0
Full-time enrollment: N/A
men: N/A; women: N/A; minorities:
N/A; international: N/A
Part-time enrollment: 132
men: 66%; women: 34%; minori-
ties: 2%; international: 4%
Average GMAT (part time): 567
TOEFL requirement: YES
Minimum TOEFL score: 550
Most popular departments: ac-
counting, finance, leadership,
marketing, management informa-
tion systems

Loyola College in Maryland (Sellinger)

4501 N. Charles Street
Baltimore, MD 21210-2699
Private
Admissions: (410) 617-5020
E-mail: graduate@loyola.edu
Web site: http://www.loyola.edu
Internet application:
http://apply.embark.com/
MBAedge/Loyola/Sellinger/100
Financial aid: (410) 617-2576
Application deadline: 08/20
Tuition: full time: $435/credit hour;
part time: $435/credit hour
Room/board/expenses: N/A
College-funded aid: YES
International student aid: NO
Fellowships: 0
Research assistantships: 0
Teaching assistantships: 0
**Average student indebtedness at
graduation:** $25,550
Full-time enrollment: N/A
men: N/A; women: N/A; minorities:
N/A; international: N/A
Part-time enrollment: 955
men: 63%; women: 37%; minori-
ties: 8%; international: 3%
Average GMAT (part time): 518
**Average age of entrants to full-time
program:** N/A
**Average months of prior work expe-
rience (full time):** N/A
TOEFL requirement: YES
Minimum TOEFL score: 550
Most popular departments: finance,
general management, marketing,
management information systems,
other

Morgan State University (Graves)[1]

1700 E. Cold Spring Lane
Baltimore, MD 21239
Public
Admissions: (443) 885-3396
E-mail: mba@moac.morgan.edu
Web site: http://www.morgan.edu
Financial aid: (443) 885-3018
Tuition: N/A
Room/board/expenses: N/A
Enrollment: N/A

Salisbury University (Perdue)

1101 Camden Avenue
Salisbury, MD 21801
Public
Admissions: (410) 543-6161
E-mail: admissions@salisbury.edu
Web site: http://www.salisbury.edu/admissions
Internet application: http://apply.usmd.edu/
Financial aid: (410) 543-6165
Application deadline: 03/01
In-state tuition: full time: $184/credit hour; part time: $184/credit hour
Out-of-state tuition: full time: $380/credit hour
Room/board/expenses: $10,000
College-funded aid: YES
International student aid: YES
Fellowships: 0
Research assistantships: 5
Teaching assistantships: 0
Full-time enrollment: 49
men: 63%; women: 37%; minorities: 12%; international: 29%
Part-time enrollment: 58
men: 48%; women: 52%; minorities: 3%; international: 0%
Acceptance rate (full time): 89%
Average GMAT (full time): 452
Average GMAT (part time): 466
Average GPA (full time): 3.10
Average age of entrants to full-time program: 26
Average months of prior work experience (full time): N/A
TOEFL requirement: YES
Minimum TOEFL score: 550
Most popular departments: accounting, general management

University of Baltimore (Merrick)[1]

1420 N. Charles Street
Baltimore, MD 21201
Public
Admissions: (877) 277-5982
E-mail: admissions@ubmail.ubalt.edu
Web site: http://business.ubalt.edu
Financial aid: (410) 837-4763
Tuition: N/A
Room/board/expenses: N/A
Enrollment: N/A

University of Maryland–College Park (Smith)

2308 Van Munching Hall
College Park, MD 20742
Public
Admissions: (301) 405-2278
E-mail: mba_info@rhsmith.umd.edu
Web site: http://www.rhsmith.umd.edu
Internet application: http://www.embark.com
Financial aid: (301) 314-8297
Application deadline: 04/15
In-state tuition: full time: $14,121; part time: $698/credit hour
Out-of-state tuition: full time: $22,257
Room/board/expenses: $14,150
College-funded aid: YES
International student aid: YES
Fellowships: 25
Teaching assistantships: 45
Full-time enrollment: 419
men: 69%; women: 31%; minorities: 16%; international: 37%
Part-time enrollment: 839
men: 70%; women: 30%; minorities: 23%; international: 13%
Acceptance rate (full time): 23%
Average GMAT (full time): 656
Average GMAT (part time): 629
Average GPA (full time): 3.35
Average age of entrants to full-time program: 28
Average months of prior work experience (full time): 59
TOEFL requirement: YES
Minimum TOEFL score: 600
Most popular departments: consulting, entrepreneurship, finance, marketing, management information systems
Mean starting base salary for 2002 full-time graduates: $74,305
Employment location for 2002 class: Intl. 8%; N.E. 20%; M.A. 57%; S. 1%; M.W. 5%; S.W. 3%; W. 6%

MASSACHUSETTS

Babson College (Olin)

231 Forest Street
Babson Park, MA 02457-0310
Private
Admissions: (781) 239-4224
E-mail: mbaadmission@babson.edu
Web site: http://www.babson.edu/mba
Financial aid: (781) 239-4219
Application deadline: rolling
Tuition: full time: $27,912; part time: $819/credit hour
Room/board/expenses: $17,572
College-funded aid: YES
International student aid: YES
Fellowships: 37
Research assistantships: 6
Teaching assistantships: 0
Average student indebtedness at graduation: $43,492
Full-time enrollment: 440
men: 76%; women: 24%; minorities: 8%; international: 28%
Part-time enrollment: 1,149
men: 72%; women: 28%; minorities: 5%; international: 12%
Acceptance rate (full time): 39%
Average GMAT (full time): 643
Average GMAT (part time): 615
Average GPA (full time): 3.12
Average age of entrants to full-time program: 28
Average months of prior work experience (full time): 64
TOEFL requirement: YES
Minimum TOEFL score: 600
Most popular departments: consulting, entrepreneurship, finance, international business, marketing
Mean starting base salary for 2002 full-time graduates: $76,300
Employment location for 2002 class: Intl. 20%; N.E. 77%; M.A. 1%; S. 1%; M.W. 0%; S.W. 1%; W. 0%

Bentley College (McCallum)

175 Forest Street
Waltham, MA 02452-4705
Private
Admissions: (781) 891-2108
E-mail: dhaile@bentley.edu
Web site: http://www.bentley.edu
Internet application: http://www.bentley.edu/graduate/applying.cfm
Financial aid: (781) 891-3168
Application deadline: 06/01
Tuition: full time: $24,340; part time: $808/credit hour
Room/board/expenses: $12,950
College-funded aid: YES
International student aid: NO
Full-time enrollment: 178
men: 57%; women: 43%; minorities: 9%; international: 34%
Part-time enrollment: 497
men: 56%; women: 44%; minorities: 6%; international: 4%
Acceptance rate (full time): 61%
Average GMAT (full time): 582
Average GMAT (part time): 543
Average GPA (full time): 3.15
Average age of entrants to full-time program: 27
Average months of prior work experience (full time): 43
TOEFL requirement: YES
Minimum TOEFL score: 600
Most popular departments: finance, general management, marketing, management information systems, operations management
Mean starting base salary for 2002 full-time graduates: $67,125

Boston College (Carroll)

140 Commonwealth Avenue
Fulton Hall 320
Chestnut Hill, MA 02467
Private
Admissions: (617) 552-3920
E-mail: bcmba@bc.edu
Web site: http://www.bc.edu/mba
Internet application: http://www.bc.edu/bcmbaapply
Financial aid: (800) 294-0294
Application deadline: 04/01
Tuition: full time: $874/credit hour; part time: $874/credit hour
Room/board/expenses: $16,930
College-funded aid: YES
International student aid: YES
Average student indebtedness at graduation: $45,712
Full-time enrollment: 252
men: 61%; women: 39%; minorities: 8%; international: 19%
Part-time enrollment: 495
men: 68%; women: 32%; minorities: 8%; international: 1%
Acceptance rate (full time): 15%
Average GMAT (full time): 658
Average GMAT (part time): 615
Average GPA (full time): 3.33
Average age of entrants to full-time program: 28
Average months of prior work experience (full time): 49
TOEFL requirement: YES
Minimum TOEFL score: 600
Most popular departments: consulting, finance, general management, marketing, management information systems
Mean starting base salary for 2002 full-time graduates: $76,298
Employment location for 2002 class: Intl. 8%; N.E. 82%; M.A. 1%; S. 0%; M.W. 4%; S.W. 1%; W. 3%

Boston University

595 Commonwealth Avenue
Boston, MA 02215-1704
Private
Admissions: (617) 353-2670
E-mail: mba@bu.edu
Web site: http://management.bu.edu
Internet application: http://www.embark.com
Financial aid: (617) 353-2670
Application deadline: 04/01
Tuition: full time: $28,162; part time: $845/credit hour
Room/board/expenses: $14,886
College-funded aid: YES
International student aid: YES
Average student indebtedness at graduation: $47,412
Full-time enrollment: 384
men: 65%; women: 35%; minorities: 16%; international: 39%
Part-time enrollment: 462
men: 62%; women: 38%; minorities: 8%; international: 12%
Acceptance rate (full time): 34%
Average GMAT (full time): 632
Average GMAT (part time): 599
Average GPA (full time): 3.14
Average age of entrants to full-time program: 28
Average months of prior work experience (full time): 55
TOEFL requirement: YES
Minimum TOEFL score: 600
Most popular departments: finance, general management, healthcare administration, marketing, management information systems
Mean starting base salary for 2002 full-time graduates: $70,355
Employment location for 2002 class: Intl. 16%; N.E. 67%; M.A. 7%; S. 5%; M.W. 2%; S.W. 0%; W. 2%

Clark University

950 Main Street
Worcester, MA 01610
Private
Admissions: (508) 793-7406
E-mail: clarkmba@clarku.edu
Web site: http://www.clarku.edu/mba
Internet application: https://apply.embark.com/mbaedge/clark/mba
Financial aid: (508) 793-7406
Application deadline: 06/01
Tuition: total program: $18,800 (full time); part time: $783/credit hour
Room/board/expenses: $10,000
College-funded aid: YES
International student aid: YES
Fellowships: 0
Research assistantships: 10
Teaching assistantships: 10
Full-time enrollment: 108
men: 51%; women: 49%; minorities: 2%; international: 75%
Part-time enrollment: 193
men: 64%; women: 36%; minorities: 5%; international: 11%
Acceptance rate (full time): 75%
Average GMAT (full time): 524
Average GMAT (part time): 537
Average GPA (full time): 3.27
Average age of entrants to full-time program: 25
Average months of prior work experience (full time): 30
TOEFL requirement: YES
Minimum TOEFL score: 550
Most popular departments: finance, general management, healthcare administration, marketing, management information systems

Harvard University

Soldiers Field
Boston, MA 02163
Private
Admissions: (617) 495-6127
E-mail: admissions@hbs.edu
Web site: http://www.hbs.edu
Internet application: http://www.hbs.edu/mba/apply/index.html
Financial aid: (617) 495-6640
Application deadline: 03/11
Tuition: full time: $31,800; part time: N/A
Room/board/expenses: N/A
College-funded aid: YES
International student aid: YES
Full-time enrollment: 1,808
men: 64%; women: 36%; minorities: 24%; international: 36%
Part-time enrollment: N/A
men: N/A; women: N/A; minorities: N/A; international: N/A
Acceptance rate (full time): 10%
Average GMAT (full time): 705
Average GPA (full time): 3.60
Average age of entrants to full-time program: 27
Average months of prior work experience (full time): 52
TOEFL requirement: YES
Minimum TOEFL score: N/A
Mean starting base salary for 2002 full-time graduates: $93,898

Massachusetts Institute of Technology (Sloan)

50 Memorial Drive
Cambridge, MA 02142
Private
Admissions: (617) 258-5434
E-mail: mbaadmissions@sloan.mit.edu
Web site: http://mitsloan.mit.edu/mba
Internet application: http://mitsloan.mit.edu/mba/admissions/apply.php
Financial aid: (617) 253-4971
Application deadline: 11/13
Tuition: full time: $32,470; part time: N/A
Room/board/expenses: $25,000
College-funded aid: YES
International student aid: YES
Full-time enrollment: 744
men: 75%; women: 25%; minorities: 21%; international: 33%
Part-time enrollment: N/A
men: N/A; women: N/A; minorities: N/A; international: N/A
Acceptance rate (full time): 14%
Average GMAT (full time): 707
Average GPA (full time): 3.50
Average age of entrants to full-time program: 28
Average months of prior work experience (full time): 60
TOEFL requirement: NO
Minimum TOEFL score: N/A
Most popular departments: entrepreneurship, finance, marketing, technology, other
Mean starting base salary for 2002 full-time graduates: $87,729
Employment location for 2002 class: Intl. 23%; N.E. 45%; M.A. 2%; S. 2%; M.W. 7%; S.W. 7%; W. 13%

Northeastern University

350 Dodge Hall
360 Huntington Avenue
Boston, MA 02115
Private
Admissions: (617) 373-5992
E-mail: gsba@neu.edu
Web site: http://www.cba.neu.edu/graduate
Internet application: http://www.gradadmissions.neu.edu/adoverview.html
Financial aid: (617) 373-5899
Application deadline: 05/01
Tuition: full time: $610/credit hour; part time: $610/credit hour
Room/board/expenses: $14,900
College-funded aid: YES
International student aid: YES
Fellowships: 0
Research assistantships: 25
Teaching assistantships: 25
Average student indebtedness at graduation: $39,000
Full-time enrollment: 169
men: 64%; women: 36%; minorities: N/A; international: N/A
Part-time enrollment: 364
men: 64%; women: 36%; minorities: N/A; international: N/A
Acceptance rate (full time): 44%
Average GMAT (full time): 567

KEY TO TERMINOLOGY ON PAGE 94

Average GMAT (part time): 564
Average GPA (full time): 3.08
Average age of entrants to full-time program: 26
Average months of prior work experience (full time): 43
TOEFL requirement: YES
Minimum TOEFL score: 600
Most popular departments: entrepreneurship, finance, general management, marketing, supply chain management
Mean starting base salary for 2002 full-time graduates: $61,000
Employment location for 2002 class: Intl. 40%; N.E. 43%; M.A. 6%; S. 3%; M.W. 0%; S.W. 0%; W. 9%

Suffolk University (Sawyer)

8 Ashburton Place
Boston, MA 02108
Private
Admissions: (617) 573-8302
E-mail: grad.admission@suffolk.edu
Web site: http://www.sawyer.suffolk.edu
Internet application: http://www.suffolk.edu/gradadm/index.html
Financial aid: (617) 573-8470
Application deadline: 03/15
Tuition: full time: $21,560; part time: $715/credit hour
Room/board/expenses: $12,210
College-funded aid: YES
International student aid: YES
Fellowships: 148
Full-time enrollment: 184
men: 57%; women: 43%; minorities: 6%; international: 62%
Part-time enrollment: 723
men: 59%; women: 41%; minorities: 8%; international: 5%
Acceptance rate (full time): 79%
Average GMAT (full time): 511
Average GMAT (part time): 504
Average GPA (full time): 3.23
Average age of entrants to full-time program: 27
Average months of prior work experience (full time): 46
TOEFL requirement: YES
Minimum TOEFL score: 550
Most popular departments: accounting, finance, general management, international business, marketing
Mean starting base salary for 2002 full-time graduates: $63,500
Employment location for 2002 class: Intl. N/A; N.E. 93%; M.A. N/A; S. N/A; M.W. 7%; S.W. N/A; W. N/A

University of Massachusetts–Amherst (Isenberg)

305 Isenberg School of Management
Amherst, MA 01003
Public
Admissions: (413) 545-5608
E-mail: gradprog@som.umass.edu
Web site: http://www.umass.edu/mba
Internet application: http://www.umass.edu/gradschool/application/online/index.html
Financial aid: (413) 545-0801
Application deadline: 02/01
In-state tuition: full time: $7,138; part time: $490/credit hour
Out-of-state tuition: full time: $15,498
Room/board/expenses: $8,500

College-funded aid: YES
International student aid: YES
Fellowships: 17
Research assistantships: 9
Teaching assistantships: 38
Average student indebtedness at graduation: $15,925
Full-time enrollment: 70
men: 54%; women: 46%; minorities: 17%; international: 36%
Part-time enrollment: 209
men: 62%; women: 38%; minorities: 13%; international: 7%
Acceptance rate (full time): 33%
Average GMAT (full time): 615
Average GMAT (part time): 539
Average GPA (full time): 3.21
Average age of entrants to full-time program: 27
Average months of prior work experience (full time): 48
TOEFL requirement: YES
Minimum TOEFL score: 600
Most popular departments: finance, general management, marketing, operations management, sports business
Mean starting base salary for 2002 full-time graduates: $68,803
Employment location for 2002 class: Intl. 5%; N.E. 86%; M.A. 0%; S. 0%; M.W. 0%; S.W. 0%; W. 10%

University of Massachusetts–Boston

100 Morrissey Boulevard
Boston, MA 02125-3393
Public
Admissions: (617) 287-7720
E-mail: mba@umb.edu
Web site: http://www.mgmt.umb.edu
Internet application: http://www.mgmt.umb.edu/admission.html
Financial aid: (617) 287-6300
Application deadline: 06/01
In-state tuition: full time: $2,590; part time: $108/credit hour
Out-of-state tuition: full time: $9,758
Room/board/expenses: $10,100
College-funded aid: YES
International student aid: YES
Fellowships: 0
Research assistantships: 12
Teaching assistantships: 0
Average student indebtedness at graduation: $16,907
Full-time enrollment: 91
men: 47%; women: 53%; minorities: 11%; international: 55%
Part-time enrollment: 149
men: 60%; women: 40%; minorities: 7%; international: 7%
Acceptance rate (full time): 55%
Average GMAT (full time): 544
Average GMAT (part time): 570
Average GPA (full time): 3.29
Average age of entrants to full-time program: 28
Average months of prior work experience (full time): 58
TOEFL requirement: YES
Minimum TOEFL score: 600
Most popular departments: accounting, e-commerce, finance, general management, human resources management, international business, marketing, management information systems, operations management, other
Mean starting base salary for 2002 full-time graduates: $34,350
Employment location for 2002 class: Intl. 38%; N.E. 46%; M.A. 0%; S. 0%; M.W. 8%; S.W. 8%; W. 0%

University of Massachusetts–Dartmouth (Charlton)

285 Old Westport Road
North Dartmouth, MA 02747-2300
Public
Admissions: (508) 999-8604
E-mail: graduate@umassd.edu
Web site: http://www.umassd.edu/graduate
Financial aid: (508) 999-8632
Application deadline: 06/01
In-state tuition: full time: $6,266; part time: $261/credit hour
Out-of-state tuition: full time: $13,629
Room/board/expenses: $8,000
College-funded aid: YES
International student aid: YES
Research assistantships: 12
Teaching assistantships: 6
Average student indebtedness at graduation: $17,183
Full-time enrollment: 94
men: 51%; women: 49%; minorities: 2%; international: 47%
Part-time enrollment: N/A
men: N/A; women: N/A; minorities: N/A; international: N/A
Acceptance rate (full time): 84%
Average GMAT (full time): 474
Average age of entrants to full-time program: 27
TOEFL requirement: YES
Minimum TOEFL score: 500
Most popular departments: accounting, finance, general management, marketing, management information systems

University of Massachusetts–Lowell[1]

1 University Avenue
Lowell, MA 01854
Public
Admissions: (978) 934-2381
E-mail: graduate_school@uml.edu
Web site: http://www.uml.edu/grad
Financial aid: (978) 934-4220
Tuition: N/A
Room/board/expenses: N/A
Enrollment: N/A

Central Michigan University[1]

105 Grawn Hall
Mount Pleasant, MI 48859
Public
Admissions: (989) 774-3150
E-mail: pamela.stambersky@cmich.edu
Web site: http://www.cba.cmich.edu/mba/
Financial aid: (989) 774-3674
Tuition: N/A
Room/board/expenses: N/A
Enrollment: N/A

Eastern Michigan University

404 Gary M. Owen Building
Ypsilanti, MI 48197
Public
Admissions: (734) 487-4444
E-mail: cob.graduate@emich.edu
Web site: http://www.emich.edu
Internet application: http://www.emich.edu/public/admissions/admissions.html
Financial aid: (734) 487-0455
Application deadline: 05/15
In-state tuition: full time: $246/credit hour; part time: $246/credit hour

Out-of-state tuition: full time: $500/credit hour
Room/board/expenses: $8,000
College-funded aid: YES
International student aid: YES
Fellowships: 44
Research assistantships: 27
Teaching assistantships: 10
Full-time enrollment: N/A
men: N/A; women: N/A; minorities: N/A; international: N/A
Part-time enrollment: 499
men: 63%; women: 37%; minorities: 15%; international: 25%
Average GMAT (part time): 522
TOEFL requirement: YES
Minimum TOEFL score: 550
Most popular departments: finance, human resources management, international business, marketing, management information systems

Grand Valley State University (Seidman)

401 W. Fulton
Grand Rapids, MI 49504
Public
Admissions: (616) 331-7400
E-mail: go2gvmba@gvsu.edu
Web site: http://www.gvsu.edu
Internet application: http://admissions.gvsu.edu
Financial aid: (616) 331-3234
Application deadline: 08/01
In-state tuition: full time: N/A; part time: N/A
Out-of-state tuition: full time: N/A
Room/board/expenses: N/A
College-funded aid: YES
International student aid: YES
Fellowships: 0
Research assistantships: 10
Teaching assistantships: 0
Full-time enrollment: N/A
men: N/A; women: N/A; minorities: N/A; international: N/A
Part-time enrollment: 320
men: 71%; women: 29%; minorities: 5%; international: 6%
Average GMAT (part time): 562
TOEFL requirement: YES
Minimum TOEFL score: 550
Most popular departments: accounting, finance, human resources management, manufacturing and technology management, marketing

Michigan State University (Broad)

215 Eppley Center
East Lansing, MI 48824-1121
Public
Admissions: (800) 467-8622
E-mail: mba@msu.edu
Web site: http://mba.bus.msu.edu
Internet application: http://mba1.bus.msu.edu/admissions/
Financial aid: (517) 353-5940
Application deadline: 03/14
In-state tuition: full time: $13,416; part time: $37,016
Out-of-state tuition: full time: $19,416
Room/board/expenses: $10,000
College-funded aid: YES
International student aid: YES
Fellowships: 0
Research assistantships: 62
Teaching assistantships: 10
Average student indebtedness at graduation: $30,255
Full-time enrollment: 218
men: 77%; women: 23%; minorities: 15%; international: 34%
Part-time enrollment: 189
men: 81%; women: 19%; minorities: 18%; international: 9%
Acceptance rate (full time): 22%

Average GMAT (full time): 639
Average GMAT (part time): 607
Average GPA (full time): 3.30
Average age of entrants to full-time program: 28
Average months of prior work experience (full time): 60
TOEFL requirement: YES
Minimum TOEFL score: 600
Most popular departments: finance, general management, human resources management, marketing, supply chain management
Mean starting base salary for 2002 full-time graduates: $74,133
Employment location for 2002 class: Intl. 7%; N.E. 15%; M.A. 4%; S. 3%; M.W. 60%; S.W. 6%; W. 4%

Oakland University[1]

432 Elliott Hall
Rochester, MI 48309-4493
Public
Admissions: (248) 370-3287
E-mail: gbp@oakland.edu
Web site: http://www.sba.oakland.edu/mba
Internet application: http://www.sba.oakland.edu/mba/
Financial aid: (248) 370-3370
Tuition: N/A
Room/board/expenses: N/A
Enrollment: N/A

University of Detroit Mercy

PO Box 19900
4001 W. McNichols Road
Detroit, MI 48219-0900
Private
Admissions: (313) 993-1202
E-mail: bellja@udmercy.edu
Web site: http://www.business.udmercy.edu/
Financial aid: (313) 993-3350
Application deadline: 08/15
Tuition: full time: N/A; part time: N/A
Room/board/expenses: N/A
College-funded aid: YES
International student aid: YES
Fellowships: 0
Research assistantships: 5
Teaching assistantships: 0
Full-time enrollment: N/A
men: N/A; women: N/A; minorities: N/A; international: N/A
Part-time enrollment: 49
men: 51%; women: 49%; minorities: 69%; international: 31%
Average GMAT (part time): 515
TOEFL requirement: NO
Minimum TOEFL score: 600
Most popular departments: finance, general management, international business, marketing, management information systems

University of Michigan–Ann Arbor

701 Tappan Street
Ann Arbor, MI 48109
Public
Admissions: (734) 763-5796
E-mail: umbsmba@umich.edu
Web site: http://www.bus.umich.edu
Internet application: http://www.bus.umich.edu/apply
Financial aid: (734) 764-5139
Application deadline: 01/07
In-state tuition: full time: $27,686; part time: $900/credit hour
Out-of-state tuition: full time: $32,686
Room/board/expenses: $15,246
College-funded aid: YES
International student aid: YES

Average student indebtedness at graduation: $71,300
Full-time enrollment: 862
men: 72%; women: 28%; minorities: 21%; international: 29%
Part-time enrollment: 998
men: 80%; women: 20%; minorities: N/A; international: N/A
Acceptance rate (full time): 19%
Average GMAT (full time): 681
Average GMAT (part time): 660
Average GPA (full time): 3.40
Average age of entrants to full-time program: 28
Average months of prior work experience (full time): 66
TOEFL requirement: YES
Minimum TOEFL score: 600
Most popular departments: consulting, finance, general management, international business, marketing
Mean starting base salary for 2002 full-time graduates: $84,922
Employment location for 2002 class: Intl. 10%; N.E. 29%; M.A. 5%; S. 3%; M.W. 35%; S.W. 8%; W. 12%

University of Michigan–Dearborn

4901 Evergreen Road
Dearborn, MI 48128-1491
Public
Admissions: (313) 593-5460
E-mail: gradbusiness@umd.umich.edu
Web site: http://www.som.umd.umich.edu/grad
Internet application: http://www.som.umd.umich.edu/grad/graduateapp.pdf
Financial aid: (313) 593-5300
Application deadline: 08/01
In-state tuition: full time: N/A; part time: $326/credit hour
Out-of-state tuition: full time: N/A
Room/board/expenses: N/A
College-funded aid: YES
International student aid: YES
Full-time enrollment: N/A
men: N/A; women: N/A; minorities: N/A; international: N/A
Part-time enrollment: 439
men: 71%; women: 29%; minorities: 21%; international: N/A
Average GMAT (part time): 568
TOEFL requirement: YES
Minimum TOEFL score: 560
Most popular departments: accounting, finance, international business, marketing, operations management

University of Michigan–Flint[1]

303 E. Kearsley Street
Flint, MI 48502-1950
Public
Admissions: (810) 762-3163
E-mail: hack@umflint.edu
Web site: http://www.flint.umich.edu/departments/som/MBA
Internet application: http://www.flint.umich.edu/departments/som/MBA
Financial aid: (810) 762-3444
Tuition: N/A
Room/board/expenses: N/A
Enrollment: N/A

Wayne State University

5201 Cass Avenue
Prentis Building
Detroit, MI 48202
Public
Admissions: (313) 577-4510
E-mail: l.s.zaddach@wayne.edu
Web site: http://www.busadm.wayne.edu
Financial aid: (313) 577-3378
Application deadline: 07/01
In-state tuition: full time: $240/credit hour; part time: $240/credit hour
Out-of-state tuition: full time: $528/credit hour
Room/board/expenses: $12,200
College-funded aid: YES
International student aid: YES
Fellowships: 0
Research assistantships: 0
Teaching assistantships: 0
Average student indebtedness at graduation: $19,129
Full-time enrollment: 266
men: 57%; women: 43%; minorities: 11%; international: 28%
Part-time enrollment: 1,113
men: 60%; women: 40%; minorities: 18%; international: 4%
Acceptance rate (full time): 90%
Average GMAT (full time): 514
Average GMAT (part time): 514
Average GPA (full time): 3.09
Average age of entrants to full-time program: 28
Average months of prior work experience (full time): 60
TOEFL requirement: YES
Minimum TOEFL score: 550
Most popular departments: accounting, finance, human resources management, marketing, management information systems

Western Michigan University (Haworth)

1903 Oliver Street
Kalamazoo, MI 49008
Public
Admissions: (269) 387-5075
E-mail: business-adv-office@wmich.edu
Web site: http://www.hcob.wmich.edu
Internet application: http://www.wmich.edu/admigradapp/index.html
Financial aid: (269) 387-6000
Application deadline: 07/01
In-state tuition: full time: $205/credit hour; part time: $205/credit hour
Out-of-state tuition: full time: $503/credit hour
Room/board/expenses: $12,358
College-funded aid: YES
International student aid: YES
Fellowships: 1
Research assistantships: 11
Teaching assistantships: 8
Average student indebtedness at graduation: $22,504
Full-time enrollment: 369
men: 67%; women: 33%; minorities: 7%; international: 44%
Part-time enrollment: 191
men: 64%; women: 36%; minorities: 5%; international: 11%
Acceptance rate (full time): 86%
Average GMAT (full time): 527
Average GPA (full time): 3.20
Average age of entrants to full-time program: 28
TOEFL requirement: YES
Minimum TOEFL score: 550

Most popular departments: finance, general management, human resources management, international business, marketing

St. Cloud State University (Herberger)

720 Fourth Avenue S
St. Cloud, MN 56301
Public
Admissions: (320) 255-3212
E-mail: mpesch@stcloudstate.edu
Web site: http://bulletin.stcloudstate.edu/gb/programs/mba.asp
Financial aid: (320) 255-2047
Application deadline: rolling
In-state tuition: full time: $267/credit hour; part time: $267/credit hour
Out-of-state tuition: full time: $267/credit hour
Room/board/expenses: N/A
College-funded aid: YES
International student aid: YES
Full-time enrollment: 41
men: 66%; women: 34%; minorities: N/A; international: 59%
Part-time enrollment: 56
men: 55%; women: 45%; minorities: N/A; international: 9%
Acceptance rate (full time): 74%
Average GMAT (full time): 538
Average GPA (full time): 3.29
TOEFL requirement: YES
Minimum TOEFL score: 550
Most popular departments: economics, human resources management, marketing, management information systems, organizational behavior

University of Minnesota–Duluth

412 Library Drive
Duluth, MN 55812-2496
Public
Admissions: (218) 726-8839
E-mail: grad@d.umn.edu
Web site: http://www.d.umn.edu/sbe/degreeprogs/MBA/index.php
Internet application: http://www.d.umn.edu/grad/request.html
Financial aid: (218) 726-8000
Application deadline: 07/15
In-state tuition: full time: $540/credit hour; part time: $540/credit hour
Out-of-state tuition: full time: $540/credit hour
Room/board/expenses: $7,000
College-funded aid: YES
International student aid: YES
Fellowships: 0
Research assistantships: 4
Teaching assistantships: 0
Full-time enrollment: N/A
men: N/A; women: N/A; minorities: N/A; international: N/A
Part-time enrollment: 60
men: 48%; women: 52%; minorities: 7%; international: 7%
Average GMAT (part time): 530
TOEFL requirement: YES
Minimum TOEFL score: 550

University of Minnesota–Twin Cities (Carlson)

321 19th Avenue S
Office 4-300
Minneapolis, MN 55455
Public
Admissions: (612) 625-5555

E-mail: full-timembainfo@csom.umn.edu
Web site: http://www.carlsonmba.umn.edu
Internet application: http://www.csom.umn.edu/DegreesPrograms/FullTimeMBA/Admissions/Apply/Apply.cfm
Financial aid: (612) 624-1665
Application deadline: 04/01
In-state tuition: full time: $18,000; part time: $675/credit hour
Out-of-state tuition: full time: $25,000
Room/board/expenses: $14,950
College-funded aid: YES
International student aid: YES
Fellowships: 37
Average student indebtedness at graduation: $29,303
Full-time enrollment: 237
men: 73%; women: 27%; minorities: 10%; international: 30%
Part-time enrollment: 1,119
men: 69%; women: 31%; minorities: 9%; international: 8%
Acceptance rate (full time): 40%
Average GMAT (full time): 645
Average GMAT (part time): 610
Average GPA (full time): 3.20
Average age of entrants to full-time program: 30
Average months of prior work experience (full time): 66
TOEFL requirement: YES
Minimum TOEFL score: 580
Most popular departments: finance, general management, marketing, management information systems, operations management
Mean starting base salary for 2002 full-time graduates: $76,964
Employment location for 2002 class: Intl. 12%; N.E. 2%; M.A. 0%; S. 2%; M.W. 76%; S.W. 3%; W. 4%

Jackson State University (Moore)[1]

1400 JR Lynch Street
Jackson, MS 39217
Public
Admissions: (601) 432-6315
E-mail: gadmappl@ccaix.jsums.edu
Web site: http://www.jsums.edu/ccaix.jsums.edu/business
Internet application: http://ccaix.jsums.edu/~www/grad_form.htm
Financial aid: (601) 979-2227
Tuition: N/A
Room/board/expenses: N/A
Enrollment: N/A

Millsaps College (Else)[1]

1701 N. State Street
Jackson, MS 39210
Private
Admissions: (601) 974-1253
E-mail: mbamacc@millsaps.edu
Web site: http://millsaps.edu/esom
Internet application: http://millsaps.edu/esom/applynow.shtml
Financial aid: (601) 974-1220
Tuition: N/A
Room/board/expenses: N/A
Enrollment: N/A

Mississippi State University

PO Box 5288
Mississippi State, MS 39762
Public
Admissions: (662) 325-1891
E-mail: gsb@cobilan.msstate.edu

Web site: http://www.cbi.msstate.edu/cobi/gsb/index2.html
Internet application: https://www.uis.msstate.edu/pls/PROD/wwskblog.P_DisploginNon
Financial aid: (662) 325-2450
Application deadline: 07/01
In-state tuition: total program: $5,070 (full time); part time: $215/credit hour
Out-of-state tuition: total program: $11,491 (full time)
Room/board/expenses: $11,780
College-funded aid: YES
International student aid: YES
Research assistantships: 34
Teaching assistantships: 15
Average student indebtedness at graduation: $10,541
Full-time enrollment: 132
men: 64%; women: 36%; minorities: 20%; international: 6%
Part-time enrollment: N/A
men: N/A; women: N/A; minorities: N/A; international: N/A
Acceptance rate (full time): 49%
Average GMAT (full time): 510
Average GPA (full time): 3.42
Average age of entrants to full-time program: 25
Average months of prior work experience (full time): 15
TOEFL requirement: YES
Minimum TOEFL score: 575
Most popular departments: finance, general management, other

University of Mississippi

253 Holman Hall
University, MS 33677
Public
Admissions: (662) 915-5483
E-mail: jholleman@bus.olemiss.edu
Web site: http://www.mba.olemiss.edu/
Financial aid: (662) 915-7175
Application deadline: 04/01
In-state tuition: full time: $3,850; part time: N/A
Out-of-state tuition: full time: $8,600
Room/board/expenses: N/A
College-funded aid: YES
International student aid: YES
Fellowships: 25
Research assistantships: 25
Average student indebtedness at graduation: $13,000
Full-time enrollment: 101
men: 63%; women: 37%; minorities: 0%; international: 9%
Part-time enrollment: N/A
men: N/A; women: N/A; minorities: N/A; international: N/A
Acceptance rate (full time): 44%
Average GMAT (full time): 570
Average GPA (full time): 3.64
Average age of entrants to full-time program: 24
Average months of prior work experience (full time): 16
TOEFL requirement: YES
Minimum TOEFL score: 600
Most popular departments: entrepreneurship, finance, general management, marketing, management information systems
Mean starting base salary for 2002 full-time graduates: $51,439
Employment location for 2002 class: Intl. N/A; N.E. 6%; M.A. 3%; S. 91%; M.W. N/A; S.W. N/A; W. N/A

University of Southern Mississippi

Box 5096
Hattiesburg, MS 39406-5096
Public
Admissions: (601) 266-4653
E-mail: mba_mpa@cba.usm.edu
Web site:
http://www.usmmba.usm.edu
Internet application:
http://gradsch.mccain.usm.edu/
apply.htm
Financial aid: (601) 266-4774
Application deadline: 05/15
In-state tuition: full time: $4,912;
part time: $216/credit hour
Out-of-state tuition: full time:
$11,738
Room/board/expenses: $4,000
College-funded aid: YES
International student aid: YES
Fellowships: 0
Research assistantships: 33
Teaching assistantships: 0
Average student indebtedness at graduation: $1,000
Full-time enrollment: 38
men: 61%; women: 39%; minorities: 0%; international: 18%
Part-time enrollment: 24
men: 42%; women: 58%; minorities: 8%; international: 8%
Acceptance rate (full time): 80%
Average GMAT (full time): 530
Average GMAT (part time): 510
Average GPA (full time): 3.40
Average age of entrants to full-time program: 24
Average months of prior work experience (full time): 14
TOEFL requirement: YES
Minimum TOEFL score: 550
Most popular departments: accounting, finance, human resources management, international business, marketing

MISSOURI

Central Missouri State University (Harmon)[1]

Dockery 212
Warrensburg, MO 64093
Public
Admissions: (660) 543-8597
E-mail:
andrews@cmsu1.cmsu.edu
Web site:
http://www.cmsu.edu/hcba
Financial aid: (800) 729-2678
Tuition: N/A
Room/board/expenses: N/A
Enrollment: N/A

Southeast Missouri State University (Harrison)

1 University Plaza
Cape Girardeau, MO 63701
Public
Admissions: (573) 651-2192
E-mail: mba@semovm.semo.edu
Web site:
http://www2.semo.edu/gradschool
Internet application:
http://www2.semo.edu/
gradschool/download_forms.htm
Financial aid: (573) 651-2039
Application deadline: 07/01
In-state tuition: full time:
$164/credit hour; part time:
$164/credit hour
Out-of-state tuition: full time:
$292/credit hour
Room/board/expenses: $7,965
College-funded aid: YES
International student aid: YES

Fellowships: 1
Research assistantships: 112
Teaching assistantships: 70
Full-time enrollment: 63
men: 49%; women: 51%; minorities: 5%; international: 35%
Part-time enrollment: N/A
men: N/A; women: N/A; minorities: N/A; international: N/A
Acceptance rate (full time): 93%
Average GMAT (full time): 525
Average GPA (full time): 3.40
Average months of prior work experience (full time): 34
TOEFL requirement: YES
Minimum TOEFL score: 550
Most popular departments: accounting, general management, international business, other

Southwest Missouri State University

901 S. National Avenue
Springfield, MO 65804-0094
Public
Admissions: (417) 836-5335
E-mail:
graduatecollege@smsu.edu
Web site:
http://www.coba.smsu.edu
Financial aid: (417) 836-5262
Application deadline: 07/01
In-state tuition: full time:
$148/credit hour; part time:
$148/credit hour
Out-of-state tuition: full time:
$296/credit hour
Room/board/expenses: $8,000
College-funded aid: YES
International student aid: YES
Research assistantships: 108
Teaching assistantships: 322
Average student indebtedness at graduation: $12,500
Full-time enrollment: 160
men: 64%; women: 36%; minorities: N/A; international: 49%
Part-time enrollment: 169
men: 62%; women: 38%; minorities: N/A; international: 23%
Acceptance rate (full time): 80%
Average GMAT (full time): 520
Average GMAT (part time): 520
Average GPA (full time): 3.52
Average age of entrants to full-time program: 29
Average months of prior work experience (full time): 12
TOEFL requirement: YES
Minimum TOEFL score: 550
Most popular departments: accounting, finance, general management, marketing, management information systems
Employment location for 2002 class: Intl. N/A; N.E. 1%; M.A. 2%; S. 2%; M.W. 90%; S.W. 3%; W. 2%

St. Louis University (Cook)

3674 Lindell Boulevard
St. Louis, MO 63108
Private
Admissions: (314) 977-2013
E-mail: mba@slu.edu
Web site: http://mba.slu.edu
Internet application:
http://mba.slu.edu/
admissions.html
Financial aid: (314) 977-2350
Application deadline: 12/01
Tuition: full time: $25,660; part time: $725/credit hour
Room/board/expenses: $11,000
College-funded aid: YES
International student aid: YES
Fellowships: 0
Research assistantships: 17

Full-time enrollment: 53
men: 72%; women: 28%; minorities: 11%; international: 28%
Part-time enrollment: 228
men: 63%; women: 37%; minorities: 9%; international: 8%
Acceptance rate (full time): 41%
Average GMAT (full time): 604
Average GMAT (part time): 563
Average GPA (full time): 3.35
Average age of entrants to full-time program: 26
Average months of prior work experience (full time): 44
TOEFL requirement: YES
Minimum TOEFL score: 550
Most popular departments: e-commerce, entrepreneurship, finance, international business, marketing

Truman State University

100 E. Normal
Kirksville, MO 63501
Public
Admissions: (660) 785-4109
E-mail: gradinfo@truman.edu
Web site:
http://gradschool.truman.edu/
Internet application:
http://gradschool.truman.edu/
applications/onlineform.pdf
Financial aid: (660) 785-4130
Application deadline: 06/15
In-state tuition: total program:
$5,500 (full time); part time:
$185/credit hour
Out-of-state tuition: total program:
$10,200 (full time)
Room/board/expenses: $6,800
College-funded aid: YES
International student aid: YES
Teaching assistantships: 11
Average student indebtedness at graduation: $8,900
Full-time enrollment: 27
men: 56%; women: 44%; minorities: 0%; international: 7%
Part-time enrollment: 1
men: 0%; women: 100%; minorities: N/A; international: N/A
Acceptance rate (full time): 86%
Average GMAT (full time): 600
Average GMAT (part time): 600
Average GPA (full time): 3.55
Average age of entrants to full-time program: 23
Average months of prior work experience (full time): 12
TOEFL requirement: YES
Minimum TOEFL score: 550
Most popular departments: accounting
Mean starting base salary for 2002 full-time graduates: $43,000
Employment location for 2002 class: Intl. N/A; N.E. N/A; M.A. N/A; S. N/A; M.W. 100%; S.W. N/A; W. N/A

University of Missouri–Columbia

213 Cornell Hall
Columbia, MO 65211
Public
Admissions: (573) 882-2750
E-mail: mba@missouri.edu
Web site: http://mba.missouri.edu
Financial aid: (573) 882-7506
Application deadline: 08/01
In-state tuition: full time:
$194/credit hour; part time:
$194/credit hour
Out-of-state tuition: full time:
$604/credit hour
Room/board/expenses: $8,000
College-funded aid: YES
International student aid: YES
Fellowships: 12
Research assistantships: 30

Teaching assistantships: 30
Full-time enrollment: 205
men: 64%; women: 36%; minorities: 5%; international: 27%
Part-time enrollment: N/A
men: N/A; women: N/A; minorities: N/A; international: N/A
Acceptance rate (full time): 76%
Average GMAT (full time): 613
Average GPA (full time): 3.37
Average age of entrants to full-time program: 25
Average months of prior work experience (full time): 28
TOEFL requirement: YES
Minimum TOEFL score: 550
Most popular departments: e-commerce, finance, general management, marketing, management information systems
Mean starting base salary for 2002 full-time graduates: $51,000
Employment location for 2002 class: Intl. N/A; N.E. 3%; M.A. 3%; S. N/A; M.W. 92%; S.W. 3%; W. N/A

University of Missouri–Kansas City (Bloch)

5110 Cherry Street
Kansas City, MO 64110
Public
Admissions: (816) 235-1111
E-mail: admit@umkc.edu
Web site:
http://www.bsbpa.umkc.edu/
Internet application:
http://www.umkc.edu/admit/
app.html
Financial aid: (816) 235-1154
Application deadline: rolling
In-state tuition: full time:
$194/credit hour; part time:
$194/credit hour
Out-of-state tuition: full time:
$584/credit hour
Room/board/expenses: N/A
College-funded aid: YES
International student aid: YES
Research assistantships: 21
Teaching assistantships: 5
Average student indebtedness at graduation: $10,230
Full-time enrollment: N/A
men: N/A; women: N/A; minorities: N/A; international: N/A
Part-time enrollment: 411
men: 60%; women: 40%; minorities: 11%; international: 15%
Average GMAT (part time): 561
TOEFL requirement: YES
Minimum TOEFL score: 550
Most popular departments: entrepreneurship, general management, healthcare administration, marketing, management information systems

University of Missouri–St. Louis

8001 Natural Bridge Road
St. Louis, MO 63121
Public
Admissions: (314) 516-5458
E-mail: gradadm@umsl.edu
Web site: http://www1.uop.edu/
esb/mba/index.html
Internet application:
http://mba.umsl.edu
Financial aid: (314) 516-5526
Application deadline: 07/01
In-state tuition: full time:
$194/credit hour; part time:
$194/credit hour
Out-of-state tuition: full time:
$584/credit hour
Room/board/expenses: $4,575
College-funded aid: YES
International student aid: YES
Fellowships: 0

Research assistantships: 10
Teaching assistantships: 6
Full-time enrollment: 50
men: 62%; women: 38%; minorities: N/A; international: 74%
Part-time enrollment: 361
men: 55%; women: 45%; minorities: N/A; international: 20%
TOEFL requirement: YES
Minimum TOEFL score: 550

Washington University in St. Louis (Olin)

1 Brookings Drive
Campus Box 1133
St. Louis, MO 63130-4899
Private
Admissions: (314) 935-7301
E-mail: mba@olin.wustl.edu
Web site: http://www.olin.wustl.edu
Internet application:
http://www.olin.wustl.edu/
mba/adm/apply.cfm
Financial aid: (314) 935-6610
Application deadline: 04/25
Tuition: full time: $30,260; part time: $850/credit hour
Room/board/expenses: $20,075
College-funded aid: YES
International student aid: YES
Fellowships: 95
Full-time enrollment: 308
men: 80%; women: 20%; minorities: 16%; international: 35%
Part-time enrollment: 354
men: 73%; women: 27%; minorities: 11%; international: 6%
Acceptance rate (full time): 35%
Average GMAT (full time): 651
Average GMAT (part time): 591
Average GPA (full time): 3.26
Average age of entrants to full-time program: 29
Average months of prior work experience (full time): 66
TOEFL requirement: YES
Minimum TOEFL score: 590
Most popular departments: consulting, finance, general management, international business, operations management
Mean starting base salary for 2002 full-time graduates: $78,100
Employment location for 2002 class: Intl. 11%; N.E. 16%; M.A. 5%; S. 4%; M.W. 41%; S.W. 10%; W. 13%

MONTANA

Montana State University

PO Box 173040
Bozeman, MT 59717-3040
Public
Admissions: (406) 994-4683
E-mail: rsundby@montana.edu
Web site:
http://www.montana.edu/cob/
Internet application:
http://www.montana.edu/
gradstudies/apply.shtml
Financial aid: (406) 994-2845
Application deadline: 06/30
In-state tuition: full time: N/A; part time: N/A
Out-of-state tuition: full time: N/A
Room/board/expenses: N/A
Teaching assistantships: 4
Full-time enrollment: 40
men: 25%; women: 75%; minorities: 3%; international: 5%
Part-time enrollment: 2
men: 0%; women: 100%; minorities: N/A; international: N/A
Acceptance rate (full time): 97%
Average GMAT (full time): 520
Average GPA (full time): 3.70
Average age of entrants to full-time program: 23

Average months of prior work experience (full time): 2
TOEFL requirement: YES
Minimum TOEFL score: N/A
Most popular departments: accounting

University of Montana

School of Business Administration
Missoula, MT 59812
Public
Admissions: (406) 243-4983
E-mail: kathleen.spritzer@business.umt.edu
Web site: http://www.mba-macct.umt.edu
Internet application: www.umt.edu/grad/forms/default.htm
Financial aid: (406) 243-5373
Application deadline: 03/01
In-state tuition: full time: $4,920; part time: $208/credit hour
Out-of-state tuition: full time: $12,360
Room/board/expenses: $8,250
College-funded aid: YES
International student aid: YES
Fellowships: 0
Research assistantships: 7
Teaching assistantships: 0
Average student indebtedness at graduation: $21,820
Full-time enrollment: 72
men: 51%; women: 49%; minorities: 8%; international: 13%
Part-time enrollment: 24
men: 50%; women: 50%; minorities: 0%; international: 0%
Acceptance rate (full time): 79%
Average GMAT (full time): 560
Average GMAT (part time): 540
Average GPA (full time): 3.26
Average age of entrants to full-time program: 28
Average months of prior work experience (full time): 24
TOEFL requirement: YES
Minimum TOEFL score: 580
Most popular departments: accounting, entrepreneurship, finance, general management, marketing
Mean starting base salary for 2002 full-time graduates: $44,031

NEBRASKA

Creighton University

2500 California Plaza
Omaha, NE 68178-0130
Private
Admissions: (402) 280-2829
E-mail: cobagrad@creighton.edu
Web site: http://cobweb.creighton.edu/
Financial aid: (402) 280-2731
Application deadline: rolling
Tuition: full time: $507/credit hour; part time: $507/credit hour
Room/board/expenses: $12,000
College-funded aid: YES
International student aid: YES
Fellowships: 3
Research assistantships: 8
Teaching assistantships: 0
Average student indebtedness at graduation: $0
Full-time enrollment: N/A
men: N/A; women: N/A; minorities: N/A; international: N/A
Part-time enrollment: 119
men: 71%; women: 29%; minorities: 8%; international: 13%
Average GMAT (part time): 530
TOEFL requirement: YES
Minimum TOEFL score: 550
Most popular departments: e-commerce, finance, general management, marketing, management information systems

University of Nebraska–Lincoln

12th and R Streets
Lincoln, NE 68588-0405
Public
Admissions: (402) 472-2338
E-mail: cgraduate@unlnotes.unl.edu
Web site: http://www.cba.unl.edu
Internet application: http://www.unl.edu/gradstud/Prospective/Apply_Online.html
Financial aid: (402) 472-2030
Application deadline: 06/16
In-state tuition: full time: $148/credit hour; part time: $148/credit hour
Out-of-state tuition: full time: $398/credit hour
Room/board/expenses: $5,911
College-funded aid: YES
International student aid: YES
Fellowships: 15
Research assistantships: 5
Full-time enrollment: 66
men: 67%; women: 33%; minorities: 2%; international: 24%
Part-time enrollment: 91
men: 78%; women: 22%; minorities: 3%; international: 10%
Acceptance rate (full time): 45%
Average GMAT (full time): 594
Average GMAT (part time): 581
Average GPA (full time): 3.60
Average age of entrants to full-time program: 25
Average months of prior work experience (full time): 53
TOEFL requirement: YES
Minimum TOEFL score: 550
Most popular departments: finance, general management, human resources management, marketing, management information systems
Mean starting base salary for 2002 full-time graduates: $53,650
Employment location for 2002 class: Intl. N/A; N.E. N/A; M.A. N/A; S. N/A; M.W. 80%; S.W. 20%; W. N/A

University of Nebraska–Omaha

6001 Dodge Street
Omaha, NE 68182-0048
Public
Admissions: (402) 554-2303
E-mail: mba@unomaha.edu
Web site: http://mba.unomaha.edu
Internet application: http://www.ses.unomaha.edu/admissions/
Financial aid: (402) 554-2327
Application deadline: 07/01
In-state tuition: full time: N/A; part time: $127/credit hour
Out-of-state tuition: full time: N/A
Room/board/expenses: $13,086
College-funded aid: YES
International student aid: YES
Fellowships: 0
Research assistantships: 2
Teaching assistantships: 0
Average student indebtedness at graduation: $18,500
Full-time enrollment: N/A
men: N/A; women: N/A; minorities: N/A; international: N/A
Part-time enrollment: 339
men: 59%; women: 41%; minorities: 2%; international: 8%
Average GMAT (part time): 535
TOEFL requirement: YES
Minimum TOEFL score: 550
Most popular departments: e-commerce, economics, general management, human resources management, international business

NEVADA

University of Nevada–Las Vegas

4505 Maryland Parkway
PO Box 456031
Las Vegas, NV 89154-6031
Public
Admissions: (702) 895-3655
E-mail: cobmba@ccmail.nevada.edu
Web site: http://business.unlv.edu
Financial aid: (702) 895-3697
Application deadline: 06/01
In-state tuition: full time: $107/credit hour; part time: $107/credit hour
Out-of-state tuition: full time: $7,490
Room/board/expenses: $9,800
College-funded aid: YES
International student aid: YES
Average student indebtedness at graduation: $30,818
Full-time enrollment: N/A
men: N/A; women: N/A; minorities: N/A; international: N/A
Part-time enrollment: 179
men: 64%; women: 36%; minorities: 6%; international: 12%
Average GMAT (part time): 589
TOEFL requirement: YES
Minimum TOEFL score: 550
Most popular departments: finance, manufacturing and technology management, marketing

University of Nevada–Reno[1]

1664 N. Virginia Street
Reno, NV 89557
Public
Admissions: (775) 784-4912
E-mail: vkrentz@unr.edu
Web site: http://www.unr.edu/content/
Financial aid: (775) 784-4666
Tuition: N/A
Room/board/expenses: N/A
Enrollment: N/A

NEW HAMPSHIRE

Dartmouth College (Tuck)

100 Tuck Hall
Hanover, NH 03755-9000
Private
Admissions: (603) 646-3162
E-mail: tuck.admissions@dartmouth.edu
Web site: http://www.tuck.dartmouth.edu
Internet application: http://apply.embark.com/mbaedge/dartmouth
Financial aid: (603) 646-3748
Application deadline: 04/18
Tuition: full time: $32,490; part time: N/A
Room/board/expenses: $19,800
College-funded aid: YES
International student aid: YES
Research assistantships: 0
Teaching assistantships: 0
Average student indebtedness at graduation: $52,184
Full-time enrollment: 463
men: 72%; women: 28%; minorities: 18%; international: 29%
Part-time enrollment: N/A
men: N/A; women: N/A; minorities: N/A; international: N/A
Acceptance rate (full time): 14%
Average GMAT (full time): 695
Average GPA (full time): 3.40
Average age of entrants to full-time program: 28

Average months of prior work experience (full time): 57
TOEFL requirement: YES
Minimum TOEFL score: N/A
Most popular departments: accounting, economics, finance, organizational behavior, other
Mean starting base salary for 2002 full-time graduates: $89,661
Employment location for 2002 class: Intl. 13%; N.E. 58%; M.A. 5%; S. 6%; M.W. 8%; S.W. 3%; W. 6%

University of New Hampshire (Whittemore)

McConnell Hall
15 College Road
Durham, NH 03824
Public
Admissions: (603) 862-1367
E-mail: wsbe.grad@unh.edu
Web site: http://www.mba.unh.edu
Internet application: https://webcat.unh.edu/index_adm.html
Financial aid: (603) 862-3600
Application deadline: 07/01
In-state tuition: full time: $8,111; part time: $10,781
Out-of-state tuition: full time: $17,811
Room/board/expenses: $7,266
College-funded aid: YES
International student aid: YES
Fellowships: 5
Research assistantships: 24
Full-time enrollment: 37
men: 65%; women: 35%; minorities: 5%; international: 30%
Part-time enrollment: 174
men: 67%; women: 33%; minorities: 7%; international: 2%
Acceptance rate (full time): 75%
Average GMAT (full time): 545
Average GMAT (part time): 544
Average GPA (full time): 3.04
Average age of entrants to full-time program: 27
Average months of prior work experience (full time): 54
TOEFL requirement: YES
Minimum TOEFL score: 550
Most popular departments: accounting, entrepreneurship, finance, general management, statistics and operations research

NEW JERSEY

Fairleigh Dickinson University (Silberman)[1]

1000 River Road
Teaneck, NJ 07666
Private
Admissions: (201) 692-2426
E-mail: vaccaro@fdu.edu
Web site: http://www.fduinfo.com/depts/sctab.php
Internet application: http://www.fdu.edu/admissions/applyol.html
Financial aid: (201) 692-2363
Tuition: N/A
Room/board/expenses: N/A
Enrollment: N/A

Monmouth University

400 Cedar Avenue
West Long Branch, NJ 07764
Private
Admissions: (732) 571-3452
E-mail: gradadm@monmouth.edu
Web site: http://www.monmouth.edu
Financial aid: (732) 571-3463
Application deadline: 08/15

Tuition: full time: $549/credit hour; part time: $549/credit hour
Room/board/expenses: N/A
College-funded aid: YES
International student aid: YES
Full-time enrollment: N/A
men: N/A; women: N/A; minorities: N/A; international: N/A
Part-time enrollment: 311
men: 59%; women: 41%; minorities: 9%; international: 3%
Average GMAT (part time): 501
TOEFL requirement: YES
Minimum TOEFL score: 550
Most popular departments: healthcare administration, other

Montclair State University

Partridge Hall
Upper Montclair, NJ 07043
Public
Admissions: (973) 655-4148
E-mail: graduate.school@montclair.edu
Web site: http://www.montclair.edu/mba
Internet application: http://www.montclair.edu/admissions.shtml
Financial aid: (973) 655-4461
Application deadline: rolling
In-state tuition: full time: N/A; part time: N/A
Out-of-state tuition: full time: N/A
Room/board/expenses: N/A
College-funded aid: YES
International student aid: YES
Fellowships: 0
Full-time enrollment: 355
men: 60%; women: 40%; minorities: N/A; international: 22%
Part-time enrollment: N/A
men: N/A; women: N/A; minorities: N/A; international: N/A
Average GMAT (part time): 507
TOEFL requirement: YES
Minimum TOEFL score: 550
Most popular departments: accounting, finance, general management, marketing, management information systems

New Jersey Institute of Technology[1]

University Heights
Newark, NJ 07102
Public
Admissions: (973) 642-7499
E-mail: lipper@njit.edu
Web site: http://management/njit.edu
Internet application: http://www.njit.edu/admissions/graduate/apply_online.php
Financial aid: (973) 596-3479
Tuition: N/A
Room/board/expenses: N/A
Enrollment: N/A

Rider University

2083 Lawrenceville Road
Lawrenceville, NJ 08648-3099
Private
Admissions: (609) 896-5036
E-mail: grdsrv@rider.edu
Web site: http://www.rider.edu
Financial aid: (609) 896-5360
Application deadline: rolling
Tuition: full time: N/A; part time: $520/credit hour
Room/board/expenses: N/A
College-funded aid: YES
International student aid: YES
Fellowships: 0
Research assistantships: 15
Teaching assistantships: 0

Full-time enrollment: N/A
men: N/A; women: N/A; minorities: N/A; international: N/A
Part-time enrollment: 356
men: 50%; women: 50%; minorities: 13%; international: 1%
Average GMAT (part time): 517
TOEFL requirement: YES
Minimum TOEFL score: 580
Most popular departments: accounting, finance, healthcare administration, international business, marketing

Rutgers State University–Camden[1]
227 Penn Street
Camden, NJ 08102
Public
Admissions: (856) 225-6104
E-mail: camden@camuga.rutgers.edu
Web site: http://camden-sbc.rutgers.edu
Internet application: http://gradstudy.rutgers.edu/3ways.html
Financial aid: (856) 225-6039
Tuition: N/A
Room/board/expenses: N/A
Enrollment: N/A

Rutgers State University– New Brunswick and Newark
111 Washington Street
Newark, NJ 07102-1895
Public
Admissions: (973) 353-1234
E-mail: admit@business.rutgers.edu
Web site: http://business.rutgers.edu
Internet application: http://gradstudy.rutgers.edu/3ways.html
Financial aid: (973) 353-5152
Application deadline: 06/01
In-state tuition: full time: $12,436; part time: $471/credit hour
Out-of-state tuition: full time: $18,026
Room/board/expenses: $12,828
College-funded aid: YES
International student aid: NO
Full-time enrollment: 206
men: 60%; women: 40%; minorities: 27%; international: 36%
Part-time enrollment: 1,009
men: 69%; women: 31%; minorities: 29%; international: 7%
Acceptance rate (full time): 40%
Average GMAT (full time): 634
Average GMAT (part time): 577
Average GPA (full time): 3.27
Average age of entrants to full-time program: 28
Average months of prior work experience (full time): 52
TOEFL requirement: YES
Minimum TOEFL score: 600
Most popular departments: finance, marketing, management information systems, supply chain management, other
Mean starting base salary for 2002 full-time graduates: $70,026
Employment location for 2002 class: Intl. 0%; N.E. 100%; M.A. 0%; S. 0%; M.W. 0%; S.W. 0%; W. 0%

Seton Hall University (Stillman)[1]
400 S. Orange Avenue
South Orange, NJ 07079
Private
Admissions: (973) 761-9222
E-mail: stillman@shu.edu
Web site: http://www.business.shu.edu
Financial aid: (973) 761-9350
Tuition: N/A
Room/board/expenses: N/A
Enrollment: N/A

NEW MEXICO

New Mexico State University[1]
114 Guthrie Hall
MSC 3GSP
Las Cruces, NM 88003
Public
Admissions: (505) 646-8003
E-mail: mba@nmsu.edu
Web site: http://mba.nmsu.edu/
Financial aid: (505) 646-2447
Tuition: N/A
Room/board/expenses: N/A
Enrollment: N/A

University of New Mexico (Anderson)[1]
1924 Las Lomas NE
Albuquerque, NM 87131
Public
Admissions: (505) 277-3147
E-mail: mba@mgt.unm.edu
Web site: http://asm.unm.edu
Financial aid: (505) 277-7045
Tuition: N/A
Room/board/expenses: N/A
Enrollment: N/A

NEW YORK

Alfred University[1]
College of Business
Saxon Drive
Alfred, NY 14802
Private
Admissions: (800) 541-9229
E-mail: gradinquiry@alfred.edu
Web site: http://business.alfred.edu/mba.html
Internet application: http://www.alfred.edu/admissions/gradapp/
Financial aid: (607) 871-2159
Tuition: N/A
Room/board/expenses: N/A
Enrollment: N/A

Binghamton University
PO Box 6015
Binghamton, NY 13902-6015
Public
Admissions: (607) 777-2317
E-mail: somadvis@binghamton.edu
Web site: http://som.binghamton.edu/
Internet application: http://gradschool.binghamton.edu/graduate/Gradapp.htm
Financial aid: (607) 777-2470
Application deadline: rolling
In-state tuition: full time: $5,967; part time: $213/credit hour
Out-of-state tuition: full time: $9,283
Room/board/expenses: $9,974
College-funded aid: YES
International student aid: YES
Fellowships: 1
Research assistantships: 14
Teaching assistantships: 12

Average student indebtedness at graduation: $25,098
Full-time enrollment: 159
men: 59%; women: 41%; minorities: 5%; international: 64%
Part-time enrollment: 22
men: 64%; women: 36%; minorities: 5%; international: 45%
Acceptance rate (full time): 65%
Average GMAT (full time): 596
Average GMAT (part time): 570
Average GPA (full time): 3.30
Average age of entrants to full-time program: 25
Average months of prior work experience (full time): 30
TOEFL requirement: YES
Minimum TOEFL score: 580
Most popular departments: finance, marketing, management information systems
Mean starting base salary for 2002 full-time graduates: $45,500
Employment location for 2002 class: Intl. 23%; N.E. 77%; M.A. N/A; S. N/A; M.W. N/A; S.W. N/A; W. N/A

Canisius College (Wehle)
2001 Main Street
Buffalo, NY 14208
Private
Admissions: (800) 543-7906
E-mail: gradbus@canisius.edu
Web site: http://www.canisius.edu/business
Internet application: http://www.canisius.edu/business/online_application.asp
Financial aid: (716) 888-2300
Application deadline: rolling
Tuition: total program: $29,841 (full time); part time: $621/credit hour
Room/board/expenses: $8,100
College-funded aid: YES
International student aid: YES
Fellowships: 0
Research assistantships: 0
Teaching assistantships: 0
Average student indebtedness at graduation: $19,619
Full-time enrollment: 28
men: 68%; women: 32%; minorities: 18%; international: 7%
Part-time enrollment: 210
men: 64%; women: 36%; minorities: 4%; international: 9%
Acceptance rate (full time): 94%
Average GMAT (full time): 491
Average GMAT (part time): 516
Average GPA (full time): 3.00
Average age of entrants to full-time program: 23
Average months of prior work experience (full time): 23
TOEFL requirement: YES
Minimum TOEFL score: 500
Most popular departments: accounting, economics, finance, general management, human resources management

Clarkson University
Snell Hall 322E
CU Box 5770
Potsdam, NY 13699-5770
Private
Admissions: (315) 268-6613
E-mail: busgrad@clarkson.edu
Web site: http://www.clarkson.edu/business/graduate
Financial aid: (315) 268-7699
Application deadline: rolling
Tuition: full time: $26,185; part time: $26,185
Room/board/expenses: $8,600
College-funded aid: YES
International student aid: YES

Average student indebtedness at graduation: $24,349
Full-time enrollment: 77
men: 66%; women: 34%; minorities: 4%; international: 10%
Part-time enrollment: 6
men: 33%; women: 67%; minorities: N/A; international: 17%
Acceptance rate (full time): 65%
Average GMAT (full time): 552
Average GPA (full time): 3.32
Average age of entrants to full-time program: 24
Average months of prior work experience (full time): 24
TOEFL requirement: YES
Minimum TOEFL score: 600
Most popular departments: consulting, finance, general management, marketing, supply chain management
Employment location for 2002 class: Intl. 5%; N.E. 83%; M.A. 5%; S. N/A; M.W. 2%; S.W. 2%; W. 2%

Columbia University
3022 Broadway
216 Uris Hall
New York, NY 10027
Private
Admissions: (212) 854-1961
E-mail: apply@claven.gsb.columbia.edu
Web site: http://www.gsb.columbia.edu
Internet application: http://www.gsb.columbia.edu/admissions/online
Financial aid: (212) 854-4057
Application deadline: 04/20
Tuition: full time: $33,054; part time: N/A
Room/board/expenses: $22,131
College-funded aid: YES
International student aid: YES
Fellowships: 50
Research assistantships: 19
Teaching assistantships: 72
Full-time enrollment: 1,188
men: 65%; women: 35%; minorities: 23%; international: 27%
Part-time enrollment: N/A
men: N/A; women: N/A; minorities: N/A; international: N/A
Acceptance rate (full time): 11%
Average GMAT (full time): 711
Average GPA (full time): 3.50
Average age of entrants to full-time program: 27
Average months of prior work experience (full time): 48
TOEFL requirement: YES
Minimum TOEFL score: N/A
Most popular departments: entrepreneurship, finance, general management, international business, leadership
Mean starting base salary for 2002 full-time graduates: $92,000
Employment location for 2002 class: Intl. 100%; N.E. N/A; M.A. N/A; S. N/A; M.W. N/A; S.W. N/A; W. N/A

Cornell University (Johnson)
Sage Hall
Ithaca, NY 14853-6201
Private
Admissions: (607) 255-4526
E-mail: mba@cornell.edu
Web site: http://www.johnson.cornell.edu
Financial aid: (607) 255-6116
Application deadline: N/A
Tuition: full time: $32,016; part time: N/A
Room/board/expenses: $16,805
College-funded aid: YES
International student aid: YES

Fellowships: 65
Average student indebtedness at graduation: $60,500
Full-time enrollment: 572
men: 72%; women: 28%; minorities: 21%; international: 29%
Part-time enrollment: N/A
men: N/A; women: N/A; minorities: N/A; international: N/A
Acceptance rate (full time): 22%
Average GMAT (full time): 673
Average GPA (full time): 3.35
Average age of entrants to full-time program: 28
Average months of prior work experience (full time): 60
TOEFL requirement: YES
Minimum TOEFL score: 600
Most popular departments: entrepreneurship, finance, general management, leadership, marketing
Mean starting base salary for 2002 full-time graduates: $84,715
Employment location for 2002 class: Intl. 7%; N.E. 61%; M.A. 9%; S. 2%; M.W. 9%; S.W. 3%; W. 9%

CUNY Bernard M. Baruch College (Zicklin)
1 Bernard Baruch Way
New York, NY 10010
Public
Admissions: (646) 312-1300
E-mail: zicklingradadmissions@baruch.cuny.edu
Web site: http://zicklin.baruch.cuny.edu
Internet application: http://embark.com/MBAedge/baruch
Financial aid: (646) 312-1370
Application deadline: 05/31
In-state tuition: full time: $6,218; part time: $265/credit hour
Out-of-state tuition: full time: $475/credit hour
Room/board/expenses: $16,000
College-funded aid: YES
International student aid: YES
Fellowships: 40
Research assistantships: 70
Teaching assistantships: 30
Average student indebtedness at graduation: $16,600
Full-time enrollment: 128
men: 61%; women: 39%; minorities: 22%; international: 35%
Part-time enrollment: 1,325
men: 59%; women: 41%; minorities: 23%; international: 26%
Acceptance rate (full time): 19%
Average GMAT (full time): 644
Average GMAT (part time): 584
Average GPA (full time): 3.20
Average age of entrants to full-time program: 29
Average months of prior work experience (full time): 65
TOEFL requirement: YES
Minimum TOEFL score: 590
Most popular departments: accounting, finance, international business, marketing, management information systems
Mean starting base salary for 2002 full-time graduates: $60,237
Employment location for 2002 class: Intl. 10%; N.E. 90%; M.A. N/A; S. N/A; M.W. N/A; S.W. N/A; W. N/A

Fordham University

113 W. 60th Street
Room 624
New York, NY 10023
Private
Admissions: (800) 825-4422
E-mail: admissionsgb@fordham.edu
Web site: http://www.bnet.fordham.edu
Internet application: http://www.embark.com
Financial aid: (212) 636-6700
Application deadline: 06/01
Tuition: full time: $25,504; part time: $12,922
Room/board/expenses: $14,000
College-funded aid: YES
International student aid: YES
Fellowships: 0
Research assistantships: 80
Teaching assistantships: 0
Full-time enrollment: 395
men: 66%; women: 34%; minorities: 21%; international: 13%
Part-time enrollment: 1,037
men: 63%; women: 37%; minorities: 6%; international: 4%
Acceptance rate (full time): 51%
Average GMAT (full time): 590
Average GMAT (part time): 570
Average GPA (full time): 3.05
Average age of entrants to full-time program: 28
Average months of prior work experience (full time): 68
TOEFL requirement: YES
Minimum TOEFL score: 600
Most popular departments: finance, general management, international business, marketing, management information systems
Mean starting base salary for 2002 full-time graduates: $75,013
Employment location for 2002 class: Intl. 2%; N.E. 98%; M.A. N/A; S. N/A; M.W. N/A; S.W. N/A; W. N/A

Hofstra University (Zarb)

134 Hofstra University
Weller Hall
Hempstead, NY 11549
Private
Admissions: (866) 472-3463
E-mail: gradstudent@hofstra.edu
Web site: http://www.hofstra.edu/graduatestudies
Internet application: http://www.hofstra.edu/Academics/Graduate/GS_Admissions/gs_admissions_applying.cfm
Financial aid: (516) 463-6680
Application deadline: 05/01
Tuition: full time: $551/credit hour; part time: $551/credit hour
Room/board/expenses: $12,155
College-funded aid: YES
International student aid: NO
Fellowships: 30
Full-time enrollment: 123
men: 70%; women: 30%; minorities: 7%; international: 28%
Part-time enrollment: 365
men: 61%; women: 39%; minorities: 5%; international: 5%
Acceptance rate (full time): 70%
Average GMAT (full time): 529
Average GMAT (part time): 513
Average GPA (full time): 3.20
Average age of entrants to full-time program: 27
TOEFL requirement: YES
Minimum TOEFL score: 575
Most popular departments: finance, general management, international business, marketing, management information systems
Mean starting base salary for 2002 full-time graduates: $68,875
Employment location for 2002 class: Intl. 2%; N.E. 93%; M.A. 2%; S. 2%; M.W. N/A; S.W. N/A; W. N/A

Iona College (Hagan)

715 North Avenue
New Rochelle, NY 10801
Private
Admissions: (914) 633-2288
E-mail: kscarola@iona.edu
Web site: http://www.iona.edu/hagan
Internet application: http://www.applyweb.com/apply/hagan/menu.html
Financial aid: (914) 633-2497
Application deadline: rolling
Tuition: full time: $530/credit hour; part time: $530/credit hour
Room/board/expenses: N/A
Full-time enrollment: N/A
men: N/A; women: N/A; minorities: N/A; international: N/A
Part-time enrollment: 89
men: 51%; women: 49%; minorities: N/A; international: 11%
Average GMAT (part time): 489
TOEFL requirement: YES
Minimum TOEFL score: 550
Most popular departments: finance, general management, human resources management, marketing, management information systems

Long Island University–C.W. Post Campus

720 Northern Boulevard
Brookville, NY 11548-1300
Private
Admissions: (516) 299-2900
E-mail: enroll@cwpost.liu.edu
Web site: http://www.liu.edu
Financial aid: (516) 299-2338
Application deadline: 08/15
Tuition: full time: $612/credit hour; part time: $612/credit hour
Room/board/expenses: $3
College-funded aid: YES
International student aid: YES
Full-time enrollment: 152
men: 64%; women: 36%; minorities: N/A; international: 31%
Part-time enrollment: 346
men: 60%; women: 40%; minorities: N/A; international: 0%
Acceptance rate (full time): 39%
Average GMAT (full time): 500
Average GMAT (part time): 490
Average GPA (full time): 3.12
Average age of entrants to full-time program: 28
TOEFL requirement: YES
Minimum TOEFL score: 500
Most popular departments: accounting, finance, general management, international business, marketing, management information systems

Marist College

149 Dyson Center
Poughkeepsie, NY 12601
Private
Admissions: (845) 575-3800
E-mail: graduate@marist.edu
Web site: http://www.marist.edu/management/mba/
Internet application: http://www.marist.edu/management/mba/mbaadm.html
Financial aid: (845) 575-3230
Application deadline: 08/01
Tuition: full time: $504/credit hour; part time: $504/credit hour
Room/board/expenses: N/A
College-funded aid: YES
International student aid: NO
Fellowships: 0
Research assistantships: 0
Teaching assistantships: 0
Full-time enrollment: 15
men: N/A; women: N/A; minorities: N/A; international: N/A
Part-time enrollment: 191
men: N/A; women: N/A; minorities: N/A; international: N/A
Average GMAT (part time): 500
TOEFL requirement: YES
Minimum TOEFL score: 550

New York University (Stern)

44 W. Fourth Street
New York, NY 10012-1126
Private
Admissions: (212) 998-0600
E-mail: sternmba@stern.nyu.edu
Web site: http://www.stern.nyu.edu
Internet application: http://www.stern.nyu.edu/mba/admissions/
Financial aid: (212) 998-0790
Application deadline: 03/15
Tuition: full time: $32,280; part time: $1,130/credit hour
Room/board/expenses: $22,996
College-funded aid: YES
International student aid: YES
Fellowships: 200
Teaching assistantships: 410
Average student indebtedness at graduation: $60,239
Full-time enrollment: 817
men: 64%; women: 36%; minorities: 22%; international: 30%
Part-time enrollment: 1,734
men: 67%; women: 33%; minorities: 22%; international: 11%
Acceptance rate (full time): 15%
Average GMAT (full time): 700
Average GMAT (part time): 670
Average GPA (full time): 3.40
Average age of entrants to full-time program: 27
Average months of prior work experience (full time): 56
TOEFL requirement: YES
Minimum TOEFL score: 600
Most popular departments: accounting, finance, general management, international business, marketing
Mean starting base salary for 2002 full-time graduates: $82,970
Employment location for 2002 class: Intl. 13%; N.E. 79%; M.A. 3%; S. 2%; M.W. 1%; S.W. 0%; W. 2%

Niagara University[1]

Division of Graduate Studies
Niagara University, NY 14109
Private
Admissions: (716) 286-8051
E-mail: pscherer@niagara.edu
Web site: http://www.niagara.edu/mba
Internet application: http://www.niagara.edu/mba/app.htm
Financial aid: (716) 286-8686
Tuition: N/A
Room/board/expenses: N/A
Enrollment: N/A

Pace University (Lubin)

1 Pace Plaza
New York, NY 10038
Private
Admissions: (212) 346-1531
E-mail: gradwp@pace.edu
Web site: http://www.pace.edu
Financial aid: (212) 346-1300
Application deadline: 08/01
Tuition: full time: $668/credit hour; part time: $668/credit hour
Room/board/expenses: $10,700
College-funded aid: YES
International student aid: YES
Research assistantships: 93
Average student indebtedness at graduation: $29,867
Full-time enrollment: 547
men: 52%; women: 48%; minorities: 16%; international: 47%
Part-time enrollment: 931
men: 59%; women: 41%; minorities: 21%; international: 6%
Acceptance rate (full time): 53%
Average GMAT (full time): 528
Average GMAT (part time): 523
Average GPA (full time): 3.32
Average age of entrants to full-time program: 26
TOEFL requirement: YES
Minimum TOEFL score: 570
Most popular departments: accounting, finance, international business, marketing, management information systems
Mean starting base salary for 2002 full-time graduates: $47,197
Employment location for 2002 class: Intl. N/A; N.E. 97%; M.A. N/A; S. N/A; M.W. 3%; S.W. N/A; W. N/A

Rensselaer Polytechnic Institute (Lally)

Room 3218
Pittsburgh Building
Troy, NY 12180
Private
Admissions: (518) 276-6586
E-mail: lallymba@rpi.edu
Web site: http://lallymba.mgmt.rpi.edu
Internet application: http://apply.embark.com/grad/rpi/62/
Financial aid: (518) 276-6586
Application deadline: rolling
Tuition: full time: $27,837; part time: $1,320/credit hour
Room/board/expenses: $11,205
College-funded aid: YES
International student aid: YES
Full-time enrollment: 87
men: 61%; women: 39%; minorities: 10%; international: 39%
Part-time enrollment: 476
men: 68%; women: 32%; minorities: 16%; international: 7%
Acceptance rate (full time): 64%
Average GMAT (full time): 611
Average GMAT (part time): 591
Average GPA (full time): 3.18
Average age of entrants to full-time program: 27
Average months of prior work experience (full time): 34
TOEFL requirement: YES
Minimum TOEFL score: 600
Most popular departments: entrepreneurship, manufacturing and technology management, marketing, management information systems, technology
Mean starting base salary for 2002 full-time graduates: $76,643
Employment location for 2002 class: Intl. 18%; N.E. 68%; M.A. N/A; S. N/A; M.W. 5%; S.W. N/A; W. 9%

Rochester Institute of Technology

105 Lomb Memorial Drive
Rochester, NY 14623-5608
Private
Admissions: (585) 475-7284
E-mail: gradbus@rit.edu
Web site: http://www.cob.rit.edu
Internet application: http://www.rit.edu/~625www/
Financial aid: (585) 475-2186
Application deadline: 08/01
Tuition: full time: $22,382; part time: $613/credit hour
Room/board/expenses: $8,000
College-funded aid: YES
International student aid: YES
Fellowships: 0
Research assistantships: 37
Teaching assistantships: 0
Full-time enrollment: 68
men: 75%; women: 25%; minorities: 4%; international: 57%
Part-time enrollment: 21
men: 67%; women: 33%; minorities: 10%; international: 5%
Acceptance rate (full time): 76%
Average GMAT (full time): 576
Average GMAT (part time): 546
Average GPA (full time): 3.24
Average age of entrants to full-time program: 25
Average months of prior work experience (full time): 36
TOEFL requirement: YES
Minimum TOEFL score: 580
Most popular departments: finance, general management, marketing, management information systems, technology
Mean starting base salary for 2002 full-time graduates: $50,000
Employment location for 2002 class: Intl. 7%; N.E. 89%; M.A. N/A; S. N/A; M.W. 4%; S.W. N/A; W. N/A

St. John's University (Tobin)

8000 Utopia Parkway
Jamaica, NY 11439
Private
Admissions: (718) 990-1345
E-mail: mbaadmissions@stjohns.edu
Web site: http://www.stjohns.edu
Financial aid: (718) 990-2000
Application deadline: 06/01
Tuition: full time: N/A; part time: N/A
Room/board/expenses: N/A
College-funded aid: YES
International student aid: YES
Fellowships: 0
Research assistantships: 30
Teaching assistantships: 0
Full-time enrollment: 146
men: 52%; women: 48%; minorities: 11%; international: 52%
Part-time enrollment: 633
men: 59%; women: 41%; minorities: 21%; international: 2%
Acceptance rate (full time): 59%
Average GMAT (full time): 525
Average GMAT (part time): 520
Average GPA (full time): 3.30
Average age of entrants to full-time program: 25
TOEFL requirement: YES
Minimum TOEFL score: 550
Most popular departments: accounting, finance, general management, marketing

SUNY–Albany

1400 Washington Avenue
Albany, NY 12222
Public
Admissions: (518) 442-4961
E-mail: busapps@albany.edu
Web site: http://www.albany.edu/business
Internet application: http://www.albany.edu/admiss/grad/gradstud.html
Financial aid: (518) 442-5757
Application deadline: 05/01

KEY TO TERMINOLOGY ON PAGE 94

In-state tuition: full time: $5,511; part time: $213/credit hour
Out-of-state tuition: full time: $8,827
Room/board/expenses: $9,500
College-funded aid: YES
International student aid: YES
Fellowships: 5
Research assistantships: 31
Teaching assistantships: 0
Average student indebtedness at graduation: $21,000
Full-time enrollment: 94
men: 53%; women: 47%; minorities: 10%; international: 44%
Part-time enrollment: 325
men: 59%; women: 41%; minorities: 11%; international: 12%
Acceptance rate (full time): 42%
Average GMAT (full time): 558
Average GMAT (part time): 549
Average GPA (full time): 3.39
Average age of entrants to full-time program: 26
Average months of prior work experience (full time): 36
TOEFL requirement: YES
Minimum TOEFL score: 600
Most popular departments: finance, general management, human resources management, marketing, management information systems
Mean starting base salary for 2002 full-time graduates: $57,800
Employment location for 2002 class: Intl. 7%; N.E. 71%; M.A. 14%; S. 7%; M.W. N/A; S.W. N/A; W. N/A

Syracuse University

900 S. Crouse Avenue
Room 222
Syracuse, NY 13244-2130
Private
Admissions: (315) 443-9214
E-mail: MBAinfo@som.syr.edu
Web site: http://www.som.syr.edu
Internet application: https://apply.embark.com/MBAEdge/Syracuse/MBAMS/15/
Financial aid: (315) 443-9214
Application deadline: 05/01
Tuition: full time: $21,005; part time: $686/credit hour
Room/board/expenses: $12,919
College-funded aid: YES
International student aid: YES
Fellowships: 50
Research assistantships: 10
Teaching assistantships: 0
Average student indebtedness at graduation: $11,200
Full-time enrollment: 112
men: 72%; women: 28%; minorities: 13%; international: 59%
Part-time enrollment: 100
men: 72%; women: 28%; minorities: 10%; international: 4%
Acceptance rate (full time): 42%
Average GMAT (full time): 629
Average GMAT (part time): 553
Average GPA (full time): 3.18
Average age of entrants to full-time program: 27
Average months of prior work experience (full time): 47
TOEFL requirement: YES
Minimum TOEFL score: 600
Most popular departments: accounting, finance, manufacturing and technology management, marketing, supply chain management
Mean starting base salary for 2002 full-time graduates: $63,754
Employment location for 2002 class: Intl. 13%; N.E. 69%; M.A. 13%; S. 0%; M.W. 0%; S.W. 0%; W. 6%

Union College[1]

Schenectady, NY 12308-3107
Private
Admissions: (518) 388-6238
E-mail: mba@union.edu
Web site: http://www.mba.union.edu
Financial aid: (518) 388-6123
Tuition: N/A
Room/board/expenses: N/A
Enrollment: N/A

University at Buffalo

206 Jacobs Management Center
Box 604000
Buffalo, NY 14260-4000
Public
Admissions: (716) 645-3204
E-mail: som-mba@buffalo.edu
Web site: http://www.mgt.buffalo.edu
Internet application: http://www.mgt.buffalo.edu/mba/application.shtm
Financial aid: (716) 645-2450
Application deadline: 07/01
In-state tuition: full time: $6,060; part time: $500/credit hour
Out-of-state tuition: full time: $9,376
Room/board/expenses: $10,750
College-funded aid: YES
International student aid: NO
Fellowships: 4
Research assistantships: 0
Teaching assistantships: 6
Average student indebtedness at graduation: $13,049
Full-time enrollment: 299
men: 63%; women: 37%; minorities: 7%; international: 43%
Part-time enrollment: 169
men: 74%; women: 26%; minorities: 5%; international: 6%
Acceptance rate (full time): 38%
Average GMAT (full time): 601
Average GMAT (part time): 585
Average GPA (full time): 3.27
Average age of entrants to full-time program: 25
Average months of prior work experience (full time): 27
TOEFL requirement: YES
Minimum TOEFL score: 550
Most popular departments: accounting, finance, human resources management, marketing, management information systems
Mean starting base salary for 2002 full-time graduates: $44,130
Employment location for 2002 class: Intl. 22%; N.E. 69%; M.A. 3%; S. 3%; M.W. 3%; S.W. 0%; W. 0%

University of Rochester (Simon)

Schlegel Hall
Rochester, NY 14627
Private
Admissions: (585) 275-3533
E-mail: mbaadm@simon.rochester.edu
Web site: http://www.simon.rochester.edu
Financial aid: (585) 275-3533
Application deadline: 06/01
Tuition: full time: $30,660; part time: $1,010/credit hour
Room/board/expenses: $13,951
College-funded aid: YES
International student aid: YES
Teaching assistantships: 0
Average student indebtedness at graduation: $29,327
Full-time enrollment: 417
men: 76%; women: 24%; minorities: 8%; international: 50%

Part-time enrollment: 339
men: 67%; women: 33%; minorities: 4%; international: 16%
Acceptance rate (full time): 27%
Average GMAT (full time): 649
Average GPA (full time): 3.20
Average age of entrants to full-time program: 29
Average months of prior work experience (full time): 69
TOEFL requirement: YES
Minimum TOEFL score: 600
Most popular departments: accounting, consulting, finance, marketing, operations management
Mean starting base salary for 2002 full-time graduates: $78,136
Employment location for 2002 class: Intl. 61%; N.E. 28%; M.A. 3%; S. 1%; M.W. 5%; S.W. 0%; W. 2%

Appalachian State University (Walker)

ASU Box 32037
Boone, NC 28608
Public
Admissions: (828) 262-2922
E-mail: mba@appstate.edu
Web site: http://www.business.appstate.edu
Internet application: http://www.graduate.appstate.edu/gs/prospective/app_forms.shtml
Financial aid: (828) 262-2190
Application deadline: N/A
In-state tuition: full time: $2,896; part time: $2,498
Out-of-state tuition: full time: $13,288
Room/board/expenses: $3,836
College-funded aid: YES
International student aid: YES
Full-time enrollment: 50
men: 66%; women: 34%; minorities: 0%; international: 10%
Part-time enrollment: N/A
men: N/A; women: N/A; minorities: N/A; international: N/A
Acceptance rate (full time): 79%
Average GMAT (full time): 484
Average GPA (full time): 3.19
Average age of entrants to full-time program: 25
Average months of prior work experience (full time): 54
TOEFL requirement: YES
Minimum TOEFL score: 550

Duke University (Fuqua)

Box 90104
Durham, NC 27708-0104
Private
Admissions: (919) 660-7705
E-mail: admissions-info@fuqua.duke.edu
Web site: http://www.fuqua.duke.edu
Internet application: http://www.fuqua.duke.edu/daytime.html
Financial aid: (919) 660-7934
Application deadline: 03/13
Tuition: full time: $32,252; part time: N/A
Room/board/expenses: $13,720
College-funded aid: YES
International student aid: YES
Average student indebtedness at graduation: $56,537
Full-time enrollment: 697
men: 67%; women: 33%; minorities: 23%; international: 32%
Part-time enrollment: N/A
men: N/A; women: N/A; minorities: N/A; international: N/A

Acceptance rate (full time): 18%
Average GMAT (full time): 701
Average GPA (full time): 3.59
Average age of entrants to full-time program: 28
Average months of prior work experience (full time): 64
TOEFL requirement: YES
Minimum TOEFL score: 600
Most popular departments: finance, general management, healthcare administration, marketing, operations management
Mean starting base salary for 2002 full-time graduates: $88,650
Employment location for 2002 class: Intl. 12%; N.E. 36%; M.A. 7%; S. 16%; M.W. 13%; S.W. 10%; W. 6%

East Carolina University[1]

School of Business
Greenville, NC 27858-4353
Public
Admissions: (252) 328-6970
E-mail: gradbus@mail.ecu.edu
Web site: http://www.business.ecu.edu/grad/
Financial aid: (252) 328-6610
Tuition: N/A
Room/board/expenses: N/A
Enrollment: N/A

North Carolina State University

2124 Nelson Hall
Raleigh, NC 27695-7229
Public
Admissions: (919) 515-5584
E-mail: msm@ncsu.edu
Web site: http://www.mgt.ncsu.edu
Internet application: http://www.mba.ncsu.edu/prospective/ft_app.html#online
Financial aid: (919) 515-2421
Application deadline: 03/05
In-state tuition: full time: $6,536; part time: $4,949
Out-of-state tuition: full time: $18,185
Room/board/expenses: $11,500
College-funded aid: YES
International student aid: YES
Fellowships: 2
Research assistantships: 3
Teaching assistantships: 25
Average student indebtedness at graduation: $6,800
Full-time enrollment: 58
men: 67%; women: 33%; minorities: 9%; international: 24%
Part-time enrollment: 167
men: 72%; women: 28%; minorities: 17%; international: 0%
Acceptance rate (full time): 48%
Average GMAT (full time): 622
Average GMAT (part time): 613
Average GPA (full time): 3.37
Average age of entrants to full-time program: 27
Average months of prior work experience (full time): 43
TOEFL requirement: YES
Minimum TOEFL score: 620
Most popular departments: e-commerce, entrepreneurship, manufacturing and technology management, management information systems, supply chain management
Mean starting base salary for 2002 full-time graduates: $62,357
Employment location for 2002 class: Intl. 11%; N.E. 17%; M.A. 0%; S. 61%; M.W. 6%; S.W. 0%; W. 6%

University of North Carolina–Chapel Hill (Kenan-Flagler)

CB 3490
McColl Building
Chapel Hill, NC 27599-3490
Public
Admissions: (919) 962-3236
E-mail: mba_info@unc.edu
Web site: http://www.kenan-flagler.unc.edu
Internet application: http://www.kenan-flagler.unc.edu/application
Financial aid: (919) 962-8396
Application deadline: 04/02
In-state tuition: full time: $13,974; part time: N/A
Out-of-state tuition: full time: $28,929
Room/board/expenses: $17,052
College-funded aid: YES
International student aid: YES
Fellowships: 45
Research assistantships: 0
Teaching assistantships: 0
Full-time enrollment: 560
men: 71%; women: 29%; minorities: 16%; international: 29%
Part-time enrollment: N/A
men: N/A; women: N/A; minorities: N/A; international: N/A
Acceptance rate (full time): 30%
Average GMAT (full time): 671
Average GPA (full time): 3.20
Average age of entrants to full-time program: 28
Average months of prior work experience (full time): 62
TOEFL requirement: YES
Minimum TOEFL score: 600
Most popular departments: consulting, entrepreneurship, finance, general management, marketing
Mean starting base salary for 2002 full-time graduates: $79,076
Employment location for 2002 class: Intl. 9%; N.E. 25%; M.A. 14%; S. 33%; M.W. 4%; S.W. 6%; W. 9%

University of North Carolina–Charlotte (Belk)

316 Friday Building
9201 University City Boulevard
Charlotte, NC 28223
Public
Admissions: (704) 687-3366
E-mail: gradadm@email.uncc.edu
Web site: http://www.uncc.edu
Internet application: http://www.uncc.edu/gradmiss
Financial aid: (704) 687-2461
Application deadline: 07/01
In-state tuition: full time: $3,022; part time: $2,012
Out-of-state tuition: full time: $12,748
Room/board/expenses: $5,900
College-funded aid: YES
International student aid: YES
Fellowships: 0
Research assistantships: 0
Teaching assistantships: 18
Full-time enrollment: N/A
men: N/A; women: N/A; minorities: N/A; international: N/A
Part-time enrollment: 365
men: 67%; women: 33%; minorities: 13%; international: 10%
Average GMAT (part time): 569
TOEFL requirement: YES
Minimum TOEFL score: 550
Most popular departments: finance, general management, marketing, management information systems, real estate

University of North Carolina–Greensboro (Bryan)

PO Box 26165
Greensboro, NC 27402-6165
Public
Admissions: (336) 334-5390
E-mail: mba@uncg.edu
Web site:
http://www.uncg.edu/bae/mba
Internet application:
http://www.uncg.edu/grs/
Financial aid: (336) 334-5702
Application deadline: 07/01
In-state tuition: full time: $3,087;
part time: $1,907
Out-of-state tuition: full time:
$13,651
Room/board/expenses: $8,200
College-funded aid: YES
International student aid: YES
Fellowships: 3
Teaching assistantships: 16
Full-time enrollment: N/A
men: N/A; women: N/A; minorities:
N/A; international: N/A
Part-time enrollment: 215
men: 59%; women: 41%; minorities: 6%; international: 22%
Average GMAT (part time): 566
TOEFL requirement: YES
Minimum TOEFL score: 550
Most popular departments: finance, international business, manufacturing and technology management, marketing, supply chain management

University of North Carolina–Wilmington (Cameron)[1]

601 S. College Road
Wilmington, NC 28403
Public
Admissions: (910) 962-3544
E-mail: gradprograms@uncwil.edu
Web site: http://www.csb.uncwil.edu/indexie.htm
Internet application:
http://www.uncwil.edu/grad_info
Financial aid: (910) 962-3177
Tuition: N/A
Room/board/expenses: N/A
Enrollment: N/A

Wake Forest University (Babcock)

PO Box 7659
Winston-Salem, NC 27109
Private
Admissions: (336) 758-5422
E-mail: admissions@mba.wfu.edu
Web site: http://www.mba.wfu.edu
Internet application:
http://www.mba.wfu.edu/admapply.htm
Financial aid: (336) 758-4424
Application deadline: 04/01
Tuition: full time: $25,125; part time: $24,375
Room/board/expenses: $13,080
College-funded aid: YES
International student aid: YES
Fellowships: 0
Research assistantships: 0
Teaching assistantships: 0
Average student indebtedness at graduation: $42,911
Full-time enrollment: 225
men: 76%; women: 24%; minorities: 10%; international: 31%
Part-time enrollment: 279
men: 77%; women: 23%; minorities: 7%; international: 3%
Acceptance rate (full time): 47%
Average GMAT (full time): 639
Average GMAT (part time): 579

Average GPA (full time): 3.20
Average age of entrants to full-time program: 27
Average months of prior work experience (full time): 47
TOEFL requirement: YES
Minimum TOEFL score: 600
Most popular departments: consulting, entrepreneurship, finance, marketing, operations management
Mean starting base salary for 2002 full-time graduates: $72,000
Employment location for 2002 class: Intl. 5%; N.E. 16%; M.A. 5%; S. 64%; M.W. 5%; S.W. 4%; W. 2%

Western Carolina University

Forsyth Building
Cullowhee, NC 28723
Public
Admissions: (828) 227-3498
E-mail: plittle@email.wcu.edu
Web site: http://www.wcu.edu/cob/mba/index.htm
Financial aid: (828) 227-7290
Application deadline: 08/01
In-state tuition: full time: $2,610; part time: N/A
Out-of-state tuition: full time: $11,525
Room/board/expenses: $8,044
College-funded aid: YES
International student aid: YES
Fellowships: 0
Research assistantships: 0
Teaching assistantships: 35
Full-time enrollment: 69
men: 68%; women: 32%; minorities: 6%; international: 20%
Part-time enrollment: 63
men: 54%; women: 46%; minorities: 2%; international: 6%
Acceptance rate (full time): 92%
Average GMAT (full time): 507
Average GMAT (part time): 475
Average GPA (full time): 3.18
Average age of entrants to full-time program: 26
TOEFL requirement: YES
Minimum TOEFL score: 550
Most popular departments: accounting, entrepreneurship, finance, general management, healthcare administration

NORTH DAKOTA

North Dakota State University[1]

PO Box 5137
Fargo, ND 58105
Public
Admissions: (701) 231-7681
E-mail:
paul.brown@ndsu.nodak.edu
Web site: http://www.ndsu.nodak.edu/cba/mba
Financial aid: (800) 726-3188
Tuition: N/A
Room/board/expenses: N/A
Enrollment: N/A

University of North Dakota

PO Box 8098
Grand Forks, ND 58202-8098
Public
Admissions: (701) 777-2784
E-mail:
gradschool@mail.und.nodak.edu
Web site: http://www.und.nodak.edu/dept/grad/mbahome.htm
Financial aid: (701) 777-4409
Application deadline: 07/01
In-state tuition: full time: $3,782; part time: $183/credit hour

Out-of-state tuition: full time: $8,482
Room/board/expenses: $6,700
College-funded aid: YES
International student aid: YES
Full-time enrollment: 29
men: 55%; women: 45%; minorities: 3%; international: 17%
Part-time enrollment: 73
men: 70%; women: 30%; minorities: 5%; international: 5%
Acceptance rate (full time): 88%
Average GMAT (full time): 520
Average GMAT (part time): 520
Average GPA (full time): 3.10
Average age of entrants to full-time program: 26
Average months of prior work experience (full time): 18
TOEFL requirement: YES
Minimum TOEFL score: 550
Most popular departments: accounting, entrepreneurship, finance, marketing, management information systems

OHIO

Bowling Green State University

Graduate Studies in Business
Bowling Green, OH 43403
Public
Admissions: (800) 247-8622
E-mail: mba-info@cba.bgsu.edu
Web site:
http://www.cba.bgsu.edu/
Internet application:
http://www.bgsu.edu/colleges/gradcol/app/grad_app.pl
Financial aid: (419) 372-2651
Application deadline: 02/15
In-state tuition: full time: $8,523; part time: $404/credit hour
Out-of-state tuition: full time: $15,151
Room/board/expenses: N/A
College-funded aid: YES
International student aid: YES
Fellowships: 0
Research assistantships: 39
Teaching assistantships: 1
Full-time enrollment: 40
men: 33%; women: 68%; minorities: 10%; international: 55%
Part-time enrollment: 46
men: 78%; women: 22%; minorities: 7%; international: 11%
Acceptance rate (full time): 73%
Average GMAT (full time): 510
Average GMAT (part time): 497
Average GPA (full time): 3.14
Average age of entrants to full-time program: 25
Average months of prior work experience (full time): 41
TOEFL requirement: YES
Minimum TOEFL score: 550
Most popular departments: accounting, finance, marketing, management information systems, supply chain management

Case Western Reserve University (Weatherhead)

Peter B. Lewis Building
10900 Euclid Avenue
Cleveland, OH 44106-7235
Private
Admissions: (216) 368-2030
E-mail: questions@exchange.som.cwru.edu
Web site:
http://www.weatherhead.cwru.edu
Internet application:
http://apply.embark.com/mbaedge/cwru/default.asp
Financial aid: (216) 368-8907
Application deadline: 03/21

Tuition: full time: $26,460; part time: $1,102/credit hour
Room/board/expenses: $14,120
College-funded aid: YES
International student aid: YES
Fellowships: 50
Research assistantships: 0
Teaching assistantships: 0
Average student indebtedness at graduation: $37,711
Full-time enrollment: 322
men: 64%; women: 36%; minorities: 12%; international: 42%
Part-time enrollment: 652
men: 63%; women: 37%; minorities: 14%; international: 9%
Acceptance rate (full time): 48%
Average GMAT (full time): 610
Average GMAT (part time): 585
Average GPA (full time): 3.21
Average age of entrants to full-time program: 27.5
Average months of prior work experience (full time): 55
TOEFL requirement: YES
Minimum TOEFL score: 590
Most popular departments: finance, general management, marketing, management information systems, operations management
Mean starting base salary for 2002 full-time graduates: $67,300
Employment location for 2002 class: Intl. 18%; N.E. 5%; M.A. 12%; S. 6%; M.W. 55%; S.W. N/A; W. 5%

Cleveland State University (Nance)

1860 E. 18th Street
BU420
Cleveland, OH 44114
Public
Admissions: (216) 687-3730
E-mail: b.gottschalk@csuohio.edu
Web site:
http://www.csuohio.edu/mba
Internet application:
http://www.csuohio.edu/gradcollege/
Financial aid: (216) 687-3764
Application deadline: 07/01
In-state tuition: full time: $6,936; part time: $289/credit hour
Out-of-state tuition: full time: $13,704
Room/board/expenses: $10,600
College-funded aid: YES
International student aid: YES
Fellowships: 0
Research assistantships: 22
Teaching assistantships: 0
Average student indebtedness at graduation: $0
Full-time enrollment: 144
men: 57%; women: 43%; minorities: 15%; international: 34%
Part-time enrollment: 402
men: 63%; women: 37%; minorities: 16%; international: 3%
Acceptance rate (full time): 78%
Average GMAT (full time): 500
Average GMAT (part time): 495
Average GPA (full time): 3.12
Average age of entrants to full-time program: 27
Average months of prior work experience (full time): 52
TOEFL requirement: YES
Minimum TOEFL score: 525
Most popular departments: accounting, finance, general management, marketing, operations management

John Carroll University

20700 N. Park Boulevard
University Heights, OH 44118
Private
Admissions: (216) 397-1970
E-mail: jcumba@jcu.edu
Web site: http://bsob.jcu.edu
Financial aid: (216) 397-4248
Application deadline: 08/11
Tuition: full time: $676/credit hour; part time: $676/credit hour
Room/board/expenses: N/A
College-funded aid: YES
International student aid: NO
Fellowships: 0
Research assistantships: 6
Teaching assistantships: 0
Full-time enrollment: 34
men: 53%; women: 47%; minorities: 6%; international: 0%
Part-time enrollment: 223
men: 57%; women: 43%; minorities: 6%; international: 0%
TOEFL requirement: YES
Minimum TOEFL score: 550

Kent State University

PO Box 5190
Kent, OH 44242-0001
Public
Admissions: (330) 672-2282
E-mail: gradbus@bsa3.kent.edu
Web site: http://business.kent.edu
Internet application:
http://business.kent.edu/grad/application.asp
Financial aid: (330) 672-2972
Application deadline: 04/01
In-state tuition: full time: $6,780; part time: $309/credit hour
Out-of-state tuition: full time: $12,736
Room/board/expenses: $8,000
College-funded aid: YES
International student aid: YES
Research assistantships: 20
Full-time enrollment: 82
men: 54%; women: 46%; minorities: 9%; international: 38%
Part-time enrollment: 212
men: 62%; women: 38%; minorities: 7%; international: 4%
Acceptance rate (full time): 80%
Average GMAT (full time): 519
Average GMAT (part time): 500
Average GPA (full time): 3.22
Average age of entrants to full-time program: 25
Average months of prior work experience (full time): 22
TOEFL requirement: YES
Minimum TOEFL score: 550
Most popular departments: finance, human resources management, international business, marketing, management information systems

Miami University (Farmer)[1]

Laws Hall
Oxford, OH 45056
Public
Admissions: (513) 529-6643
E-mail: miamimba@muohio.edu
Web site:
http://www.sba.muohio.edu/mbaprogram
Internet application:
http://www.muohio.edu/graduateschool
Financial aid: (513) 529-8734
Tuition: N/A
Room/board/expenses: N/A
Enrollment: N/A

Ohio State University (Fisher)

100 Gerlach Hall
2108 Neil Avenue
Columbus, OH 43210-1144
Public
Admissions: (614) 292-8511
E-mail: fishergrad@cob.osu.edu
Web site:
http://fisher.osu.edu/mba
Internet application:
http://fisher.osu.edu/apply
Financial aid: (614) 292-4271
Application deadline: 04/30
In-state tuition: full time: $12,891;
part time: $14,388
Out-of-state tuition: full time:
$23,466
Room/board/expenses: $11,228
College-funded aid: YES
International student aid: YES
Fellowships: 16
Research assistantships: 0
Teaching assistantships: 55
Full-time enrollment: 289
men: 65%; women: 35%; minorities: 16%; international: 31%
Part-time enrollment: 290
men: 73%; women: 27%; minorities: 9%; international: 2%
Acceptance rate (full time): 25%
Average GMAT (full time): 655
Average GMAT (part time): 630
Average GPA (full time): 3.37
Average age of entrants to full-time program: 28
Average months of prior work experience (full time): 60
TOEFL requirement: YES
Minimum TOEFL score: 600
Most popular departments: accounting, finance, marketing, operations management, supply chain management
Mean starting base salary for 2002 full-time graduates: $80,069
Employment location for 2002 class: Intl. 16%; N.E. 6%; M.A. 3%; S. 4%; M.W. 66%; S.W. 0%; W. 6%

Ohio University

514 Copeland Hall
Athens, OH 45701
Public
Admissions: (740) 593-4320
E-mail: rossj@ohio.edu
Web site:
http://www.cob.ohiou.edu
Financial aid: (740) 593-4141
Application deadline: 03/01
In-state tuition: full time: $10,340;
part time: $299/credit hour
Out-of-state tuition: full time:
$19,240
Room/board/expenses: $15,000
College-funded aid: YES
International student aid: YES
Fellowships: 28
Research assistantships: 0
Teaching assistantships: 0
Full-time enrollment: 105
men: 55%; women: 45%; minorities: 7%; international: 24%
Part-time enrollment: 31
men: 71%; women: 29%; minorities: 16%; international: 6%
Acceptance rate (full time): 57%
Average GMAT (full time): 544
Average GPA (full time): 3.30
Average age of entrants to full-time program: 25
Average months of prior work experience (full time): 20
TOEFL requirement: YES
Minimum TOEFL score: 600
Most popular departments: accounting, finance, marketing, management information systems, sports business

University of Akron

259 S. Broadway
Room 412
Akron, OH 44325-4805
Public
Admissions: (330) 972-7043
E-mail: gradcba@uakron.edu
Web site:
http://www.uakron.edu/cba/grad/
Financial aid: (330) 972-7032
Application deadline: 08/01
In-state tuition: full time:
$279/credit hour; part time:
$279/credit hour
Out-of-state tuition: full time:
$459/credit hour
Room/board/expenses: $9,000
College-funded aid: YES
International student aid: YES
Fellowships: 7
Research assistantships: 50
Teaching assistantships: 0
Full-time enrollment: 119
men: 46%; women: 54%; minorities: 13%; international: 45%
Part-time enrollment: 156
men: 63%; women: 37%; minorities: 8%; international: 3%
Acceptance rate (full time): 54%
Average GMAT (full time): 575
Average GMAT (part time): 560
Average GPA (full time): 3.30
Average age of entrants to full-time program: 28
Average months of prior work experience (full time): 48
TOEFL requirement: YES
Minimum TOEFL score: 550
Most popular departments: e-commerce, finance, general management, international business, marketing
Mean starting base salary for 2002 full-time graduates: $52,560

University of Cincinnati

103 Lindner Hall
Cincinnati, OH 45221-0020
Public
Admissions: (513) 556-7024
E-mail: graduate@uc.edu
Web site: http://www.business.
uc.edu/mba
Internet application:
http://www.grad.uc.edu/
content/gradapp.cfm
Financial aid: (513) 556-6982
Application deadline: 03/30
In-state tuition: total program:
$15,844 (full time); part time:
$365/credit hour
Out-of-state tuition: total program:
$19,604 (full time)
Room/board/expenses: $15,600
College-funded aid: YES
International student aid: YES
Fellowships: 44
Average student indebtedness at graduation: $9,000
Full-time enrollment: 60
men: 67%; women: 33%; minorities: 18%; international: 27%
Part-time enrollment: 287
men: 74%; women: 26%; minorities: 14%; international: 9%
Acceptance rate (full time): 72%
Average GMAT (full time): 592
Average GMAT (part time): 570
Average GPA (full time): 3.20
Average age of entrants to full-time program: 27
Average months of prior work experience (full time): 43
TOEFL requirement: YES
Minimum TOEFL score: 600
Most popular departments: finance, general management, international business, marketing, operations management

Mean starting base salary for 2002 full-time graduates: $53,638
Employment location for 2002 class: Intl. 0%; N.E. 0%; M.A. 4%; S. 4%; M.W. 88%; S.W. 4%; W. 0%

University of Dayton

300 College Park Avenue
Dayton, OH 45469-2234
Private
Admissions: (937) 229-3733
E-mail: mba@udayton.edu
Web site:
http://www.sba.udayton.edu/mba
Internet application:
http://www.sba.udayton.edu/
mba/newstudents/admission.asp
Financial aid: (937) 229-4311
Application deadline: rolling
Tuition: full time: $515/credit hour;
part time: $515/credit hour
Room/board/expenses: $6,500
College-funded aid: YES
International student aid: YES
Research assistantships: 10
Full-time enrollment: 77
men: 47%; women: 53%; minorities: N/A; international: N/A
Part-time enrollment: 249
men: 62%; women: 38%; minorities: N/A; international: N/A
Average GMAT (full time): 555
Average GMAT (part time): 552
Average GPA (full time): 3.25
Average age of entrants to full-time program: 25
Average months of prior work experience (full time): 9
TOEFL requirement: YES
Minimum TOEFL score: 550
Most popular departments: finance, international business, marketing, management information systems, technology

University of Toledo

Room 1033 Stranahan Hall
Toledo, OH 43606-3390
Public
Admissions: (419) 530-2775
E-mail: mba@utoledo.edu
Web site: http://www.business.
utoledo.edu/degrees/mba
Financial aid: (419) 530-5800
Application deadline: 08/01
In-state tuition: full time:
$303/credit hour; part time:
$303/credit hour
Out-of-state tuition: full time:
$655/credit hour
Room/board/expenses: $7,500
College-funded aid: YES
International student aid: YES
Fellowships: 0
Research assistantships: 31
Teaching assistantships: 0
Full-time enrollment: 93
men: 60%; women: 40%; minorities: 6%; international: 48%
Part-time enrollment: 220
men: 68%; women: 32%; minorities: 5%; international: 16%
Average GMAT (full time): 525
Average GMAT (part time): 525
Average GPA (full time): 3.10
TOEFL requirement: YES
Minimum TOEFL score: 550
Most popular departments: accounting, finance, human resources management, international business, management information systems

Wright State University[1]

3640 Colonel Glenn Highway
Dayton, OH 45435
Public
Admissions: (937) 775-2437
E-mail:
mba_director@netscape.net
Web site:
http://www.wright.edu/coba/
Financial aid: (937) 775-5721
Tuition: N/A
Room/board/expenses: N/A
Enrollment: N/A

Xavier University (Williams)

3800 Victory Parkway
Cincinnati, OH 45207-3221
Private
Admissions: (513) 745-3525
E-mail: xumba@xu.edu
Web site:
http://www.xavier.edu/MBA
Internet application:
http://www.xu.edu/
cgi-bin/app_start_M.cgi
Financial aid: (513) 745-3142
Application deadline: 08/01
Tuition: full time: $450/credit hour;
part time: $450/credit hour
Room/board/expenses: N/A
College-funded aid: YES
International student aid: YES
Research assistantships: 9
Full-time enrollment: 97
men: 78%; women: 22%; minorities: 7%; international: 7%
Part-time enrollment: 892
men: 57%; women: 43%; minorities: 9%; international: 5%
Average GMAT (part time): 560
TOEFL requirement: YES
Minimum TOEFL score: 550
Most popular departments: e-commerce, finance, international business, marketing, management information systems

Youngstown State University (Williamson)

1 University Plaza
Youngstown, OH 44555
Public
Admissions: (330) 941-3091
E-mail: amgrad03@ysub.ysu.edu
Web site: http://www.cc.ysu.edu/
wcba/mba.htm
Internet application: http://www.applyweb.com/apply/ysu/menu.html
Financial aid: (330) 941-3505
Application deadline: 07/15
In-state tuition: full time: $6,100;
part time: $248/credit hour
Out-of-state tuition: full time:
$8,572
Room/board/expenses: $6,200
International student aid: YES
Research assistantships: 12
Full-time enrollment: N/A
men: N/A; women: N/A; minorities: N/A; international: N/A
Part-time enrollment: 164
men: 53%; women: 47%; minorities: 9%; international: 6%
Average GMAT (part time): 505
TOEFL requirement: YES
Minimum TOEFL score: 550
Most popular departments: accounting, e-commerce, finance, general management, human resources management

Oklahoma State University

102 Gundersen
Stillwater, OK 74078-4011
Public
Admissions: (405) 744-2951
E-mail: mba-osu@okstate.edu
Web site: http://mba.okstate.edu
Financial aid: (405) 744-6604
Application deadline: 07/01
In-state tuition: full time: $98/credit
hour; part time: $98/credit hour
Out-of-state tuition: full time:
$220/credit hour
Room/board/expenses: $12,500
College-funded aid: YES
International student aid: YES
Research assistantships: 30
Average student indebtedness at graduation: $32,500
Full-time enrollment: 113
men: 60%; women: 40%; minorities: 4%; international: 34%
Part-time enrollment: 247
men: 60%; women: 40%; minorities: N/A; international: N/A
Acceptance rate (full time): 68%
Average GMAT (full time): 602
Average GMAT (part time): 580
Average GPA (full time): 3.40
Average age of entrants to full-time program: 27
Average months of prior work experience (full time): 36
TOEFL requirement: YES
Minimum TOEFL score: 575
Most popular departments: accounting, finance, general management, international business, marketing
Mean starting base salary for 2002 full-time graduates: $61,923

University of Oklahoma (Price)

Adams Hall
Room 105K
Norman, OK 73019-4003
Public
Admissions: (405) 325-4107
E-mail: gamundson@ou.edu
Web site:
http://price.ou.edu/mba/index.asp
Financial aid: (405) 325-4521
Application deadline: 07/01
In-state tuition: full time:
$118/credit hour; part time:
$118/credit hour
Out-of-state tuition: full time:
$342/credit hour
Room/board/expenses: $9,445
College-funded aid: YES
International student aid: YES
Fellowships: 0
Research assistantships: 30
Teaching assistantships: 5
Average student indebtedness at graduation: $5,200
Full-time enrollment: 111
men: 72%; women: 28%; minorities: 9%; international: 29%
Part-time enrollment: 170
men: 66%; women: 34%; minorities: 9%; international: 8%
Acceptance rate (full time): 45%
Average GMAT (full time): 629
Average GMAT (part time): 583
Average GPA (full time): 3.59
Average age of entrants to full-time program: 26
Average months of prior work experience (full time): 35
TOEFL requirement: YES
Minimum TOEFL score: 550

Most popular departments: e-commerce, finance, general management, management information systems, supply chain management
Mean starting base salary for 2002 full-time graduates: $57,267
Employment location for 2002 class: Intl. N/A; N.E. N/A; M.A. N/A; S. 4%; M.W. 4%; S.W. 92%; W. N/A

University of Tulsa
600 S. College Avenue
Tulsa, OK 74104-3189
Private
Admissions: (918) 631-2242
E-mail: graduate-business@utulsa.edu
Web site: http://www.cba.utulsa.edu
Internet application: http://www.utulsa.edu/graduate
Financial aid: (918) 631-2526
Application deadline: 08/01
Tuition: full time: $560/credit hour; part time: $560/credit hour
Room/board/expenses: $8,086
College-funded aid: YES
International student aid: YES
Fellowships: 0
Research assistantships: 16
Teaching assistantships: 0
Full-time enrollment: 28
men: 57%; women: 43%; minorities: 0%; international: 32%
Part-time enrollment: 99
men: 64%; women: 36%; minorities: 15%; international: 7%
Acceptance rate (full time): 54%
Average GMAT (full time): 554
Average GMAT (part time): 509
Average GPA (full time): 3.34
Average age of entrants to full-time program: 24
Average months of prior work experience (full time): 12
TOEFL requirement: YES
Minimum TOEFL score: 575
Most popular departments: accounting, finance, general management, management information systems, tax

OREGON

Oregon State University
Bexell Hall 200
Corvallis, OR 97331
Public
Admissions: (541) 737-4411
E-mail: osuadmit@oregonstate.edu
Web site: http://www.bus.orst.edu/mba/
Internet application: http://oregonstate.edu/admissions/graduate/GRADoutline.html
Financial aid: (541) 737-2241
Application deadline: 03/15
In-state tuition: full time: $8,154; part time: $249/credit hour
Out-of-state tuition: full time: $13,611
Room/board/expenses: $9,145
College-funded aid: YES
International student aid: YES
Fellowships: 0
Research assistantships: 0
Full-time enrollment: 76
men: 70%; women: 30%; minorities: 8%; international: 22%
Part-time enrollment: 20
men: 80%; women: 20%; minorities: 0%; international: 0%
Acceptance rate (full time): 55%
Average GMAT (full time): 568
Average GPA (full time): 3.40

Average age of entrants to full-time program: 28
Average months of prior work experience (full time): 60
TOEFL requirement: YES
Minimum TOEFL score: 575
Most popular departments: general management

Portland State University
PO Box 751
Portland, OR 97207-0751
Public
Admissions: (503) 725-3511
E-mail: adm@pdx.edu
Web site: http://www.sba.pdx.edu
Financial aid: (503) 725-3461
Application deadline: 04/01
In-state tuition: full time: $7,758; part time: $6,597
Out-of-state tuition: full time: $12,780
Room/board/expenses: $14,624
College-funded aid: YES
International student aid: YES
Fellowships: 0
Research assistantships: 20
Teaching assistantships: 0
Average student indebtedness at graduation: $0
Full-time enrollment: 102
men: 55%; women: 45%; minorities: 13%; international: 37%
Part-time enrollment: 298
men: 68%; women: 32%; minorities: 10%; international: 5%
Acceptance rate (full time): 28%
Average GMAT (full time): 631
Average GMAT (part time): 605
Average GPA (full time): 3.39
Average age of entrants to full-time program: 28
Average months of prior work experience (full time): 60
TOEFL requirement: YES
Minimum TOEFL score: 550
Most popular departments: finance, general management, marketing, management information systems, organizational behavior
Mean starting base salary for 2002 full-time graduates: $60,338
Employment location for 2002 class: Intl. 25%; N.E. N/A; M.A. N/A; S. N/A; M.W. N/A; S.W. N/A; W. 75%

University of Oregon (Lundquist)
1208 University of Oregon
Eugene, OR 97403-1208
Public
Admissions: (541) 346-3306
E-mail: info@oregonmba.com
Web site: http://oregonmba.com
Internet application: http://apply.embark.com/mbaedge/uo/95
Financial aid: (541) 346-3221
Application deadline: 04/15
In-state tuition: full time: $9,513; part time: N/A
Out-of-state tuition: full time: $14,919
Room/board/expenses: $12,211
College-funded aid: YES
International student aid: YES
Average student indebtedness at graduation: $30,198
Full-time enrollment: 112
men: 71%; women: 29%; minorities: 10%; international: 29%
Part-time enrollment: N/A
men: N/A; women: N/A; minorities: N/A; international: N/A
Acceptance rate (full time): 47%
Average GMAT (full time): 632
Average GPA (full time): 3.06

Average age of entrants to full-time program: 28
Average months of prior work experience (full time): 54
TOEFL requirement: YES
Minimum TOEFL score: 600
Most popular departments: accounting, finance, leadership, sports business
Mean starting base salary for 2002 full-time graduates: $52,216
Employment location for 2002 class: Intl. 10%; N.E. 6%; M.A. 3%; S. 0%; M.W. 13%; S.W. 10%; W. 58%

University of Portland (Pamplin)
5000 N. Willamette Boulevard
Portland, OR 97203-5798
Private
Admissions: (503) 943-7225
E-mail: mba-up@up.edu
Web site: http://www.up.edu
Financial aid: (503) 943-7311
Application deadline: 07/15
Tuition: full time: $645/credit hour; part time: $645/credit hour
Room/board/expenses: $6,500
College-funded aid: YES
International student aid: YES
Fellowships: 7
Research assistantships: 0
Teaching assistantships: 0
Full-time enrollment: N/A
men: N/A; women: N/A; minorities: N/A; international: N/A
Part-time enrollment: 153
men: 58%; women: 42%; minorities: 18%; international: 25%
Average GMAT (part time): 525
Average age of entrants to full-time program: N/A
Average months of prior work experience (full time): N/A
TOEFL requirement: YES
Minimum TOEFL score: 570
Most popular departments: entrepreneurship, finance, general management, international business, marketing

Willamette University (Atkinson)
Willamette University
900 State Street
Salem, OR 97301-3922
Private
Admissions: (503) 370-6167
E-mail: agsm-admission@willamette.edu
Web site: www.willamette.edu/agsm
Internet application: www.willamette.edu/agsm/prospectus/onlineap.html
Financial aid: (503) 370-6273
Application deadline: rolling
Tuition: full time: $18,100; part time: $602/credit hour
Room/board/expenses: $11,000
College-funded aid: YES
International student aid: YES
Research assistantships: 12
Teaching assistantships: 0
Average student indebtedness at graduation: $32,523
Full-time enrollment: 159
men: 58%; women: 42%; minorities: 8%; international: 30%
Part-time enrollment: 13
men: 54%; women: 46%; minorities: 15%; international: 0%
Acceptance rate (full time): 95%
Average GMAT (full time): 544
Average GPA (full time): 3.22
Average age of entrants to full-time program: 27
Average months of prior work experience (full time): 32

TOEFL requirement: YES
Minimum TOEFL score: 570
Most popular departments: finance, general management, human resources management, marketing, public administration
Mean starting base salary for 2002 full-time graduates: $44,000
Employment location for 2002 class: Intl. 20%; N.E. 0%; M.A. 3%; S. 3%; M.W. 0%; S.W. 0%; W. 74%

PENNSYLVANIA

Carnegie Mellon University
5000 Forbes Avenue
Pittsburgh, PA 15213
Private
Admissions: (412) 268-2272
E-mail: mba-admissions@andrew.cmu.edu
Web site: http://wpweb2k.gsia.cmu.edu/mba/newmba/index2.htm
Internet application: https://wpweb2k.gsia.cmu.edu/mba/newmba/apply.htm
Financial aid: (412) 268-7581
Application deadline: 04/30
Tuition: full time: $29,960; part time: $329/credit hour
Room/board/expenses: $16,240
College-funded aid: YES
International student aid: NO
Research assistantships: 0
Average student indebtedness at graduation: $46,000
Full-time enrollment: 469
men: 77%; women: 23%; minorities: 23%; international: 35%
Part-time enrollment: 284
men: 85%; women: 15%; minorities: 10%; international: 13%
Acceptance rate (full time): 26%
Average GMAT (full time): 672
Average GMAT (part time): 631
Average GPA (full time): 3.30
Average age of entrants to full-time program: 28
Average months of prior work experience (full time): 66
TOEFL requirement: YES
Minimum TOEFL score: 600
Most popular departments: entrepreneurship, finance, marketing, management information systems, operations management
Mean starting base salary for 2002 full-time graduates: $80,099
Employment location for 2002 class: Intl. 11%; N.E. 32%; M.A. 21%; S. 3%; M.W. 14%; S.W. 12%; W. 8%

Clarion University of Pennsylvania
Still Hall
Clarion, PA 16214
Public
Admissions: (814) 393-2605
E-mail: mba@clarion.edu
Web site: http://www.clarion.edu/mba
Financial aid: (814) 393-2315
Application deadline: 07/01
In-state tuition: full time: $6,415; part time: $292/credit hour
Out-of-state tuition: full time: $9,569
Room/board/expenses: $6,744
College-funded aid: YES
International student aid: YES
Research assistantships: 18
Full-time enrollment: 54
men: 57%; women: 43%; minorities: 4%; international: 46%
Part-time enrollment: 4
men: 50%; women: 50%; minorities: N/A; international: N/A

Acceptance rate (full time): 89%
Average GMAT (full time): 485
Average GPA (full time): 3.28
Average age of entrants to full-time program: 27
Average months of prior work experience (full time): 27
TOEFL requirement: YES
Minimum TOEFL score: 550

Drexel University (LeBow)
3141 Chestnut Street
Philadelphia, PA 19104
Private
Admissions: (800) 237-3935
E-mail: admissions@drexel.edu
Web site: http://www.lebow.drexel.edu/
Financial aid: (215) 895-2537
Application deadline: 07/20
Tuition: full time: $27,984; part time: $583/credit hour
Room/board/expenses: $13,000
College-funded aid: YES
International student aid: YES
Fellowships: 53
Research assistantships: 48
Teaching assistantships: 48
Full-time enrollment: 257
men: 54%; women: 46%; minorities: 19%; international: 44%
Part-time enrollment: 646
men: 62%; women: 38%; minorities: 14%; international: 11%
Acceptance rate (full time): 42%
Average GMAT (full time): 602
Average GMAT (part time): 585
Average GPA (full time): 3.40
Average age of entrants to full-time program: 27
Average months of prior work experience (full time): 42
TOEFL requirement: YES
Minimum TOEFL score: 600
Most popular departments: accounting, economics, finance, manufacturing and technology management, management information systems

Duquesne University (Donahue)
704 Rockwell Hall
Pittsburgh, PA 15282
Private
Admissions: (412) 396-6276
E-mail: grad-bus@duq.edu
Web site: http://www.bus.duq.edu
Financial aid: (412) 396-6607
Application deadline: rolling
Tuition: full time: $621/credit hour; part time: $621/credit hour
Room/board/expenses: $12,500
College-funded aid: YES
International student aid: YES
Full-time enrollment: 94
men: 60%; women: 40%; minorities: N/A; international: N/A
Part-time enrollment: 377
men: 60%; women: 40%; minorities: N/A; international: N/A
Acceptance rate (full time): 80%
Average GMAT (full time): 508
Average GMAT (part time): 508
Average GPA (full time): 3.10
Average age of entrants to full-time program: 25
Average months of prior work experience (full time): 24
TOEFL requirement: YES
Minimum TOEFL score: 550
Most popular departments: finance, general management, international business, marketing, management information systems

Indiana University of Pennsylvania (Eberly)
ECB, Room 402
664 Pratt Drive
Indiana, PA 15705
Public
Admissions: (724) 357-2522
E-mail: kjdavis@iup.edu
Web site:
http://www.eberly.iup.edu/mba
Financial aid: (724) 357-2218
Application deadline: 07/15
In-state tuition: full time: $6,101;
part time: $292/credit hour
Out-of-state tuition: full time:
$9,255
Room/board/expenses: $3,010
College-funded aid: YES
International student aid: YES
Fellowships: 10
Research assistantships: 30
Teaching assistantships: 0
Full-time enrollment: 120
men: 63%; women: 38%; minorities: 3%; international: 58%
Part-time enrollment: 13
men: 69%; women: 31%; minorities: 0%; international: 0%
Acceptance rate (full time): 72%
Average GMAT (full time): 524
Average GMAT (part time): 511
Average GPA (full time): 3.21
Average age of entrants to full-time program: 24.8
Average months of prior work experience (full time): 3
TOEFL requirement: YES
Minimum TOEFL score: 520
Most popular departments: accounting, e-commerce, finance, international business, marketing, management information systems
Mean starting base salary for 2002 full-time graduates: $39,068
Employment location for 2002 class: Intl. 27%; N.E. 4%; M.A. 35%; S. 4%; M.W. 10%; S.W. 5%; W. 14%

La Salle University
1900 W. Olney Avenue
Philadelphia, PA 19141
Private
Admissions: (215) 951-1057
E-mail: mba@lasalle.edu
Web site:
http://www.lasalle.edu/sba.htm
Financial aid: (215) 951-1070
Application deadline: rolling
Tuition: full time: $10,080; part time: $595/credit hour
Room/board/expenses: N/A
College-funded aid: YES
International student aid: YES
Full-time enrollment: 40
men: 55%; women: 45%; minorities: 18%; international: 43%
Part-time enrollment: 598
men: 56%; women: 44%; minorities: 10%; international: 3%
Acceptance rate (full time): 41%
Average GMAT (full time): 476
Average GMAT (part time): 479
Average GPA (full time): 2.93
Average age of entrants to full-time program: 27
Average months of prior work experience (full time): 60
TOEFL requirement: YES
Minimum TOEFL score: 550
Most popular departments: accounting, finance, general management, marketing, management information systems

Lehigh University
621 Taylor Street
Bethlehem, PA 18015
Private
Admissions: (610) 758-5280
E-mail: incbgrad@lehigh.edu
Web site:
http://www.lehigh.edu/mba
Financial aid: (610) 758-4450
Application deadline: 05/01
Tuition: full time: $610/credit hour; part time: $610/credit hour
Room/board/expenses: $10,800
College-funded aid: YES
International student aid: YES
Fellowships: 2
Research assistantships: 0
Teaching assistantships: 22
Full-time enrollment: 51
men: 71%; women: 29%; minorities: 8%; international: 49%
Part-time enrollment: 237
men: 73%; women: 27%; minorities: 9%; international: 5%
Acceptance rate (full time): 75%
Average GMAT (full time): 596
Average GMAT (part time): 604
Average GPA (full time): 3.26
Average age of entrants to full-time program: 28
Average months of prior work experience (full time): 59
TOEFL requirement: YES
Minimum TOEFL score: 600
Most popular departments: entrepreneurship, finance, general management, marketing, supply chain management
Mean starting base salary for 2002 full-time graduates: $65,000
Employment location for 2002 class: Intl. N/A; N.E. N/A; M.A. 88%; S. 13%; M.W. N/A; S.W. N/A; W. N/A

Penn State University–Harrisburg[1]
777 W. Harrisburg Pike
Middletown, PA 17057-4898
Public
Admissions: (717) 948-6250
E-mail: mbahbg@psu.edu
Web site:
http://www.hbg.psu.edu/sbus
Internet application:
http://www.hbg.psu.edu/hbg/grdegapps.html
Financial aid: (717) 948-6307
Tuition: N/A
Room/board/expenses: N/A
Enrollment: N/A

Penn State University–University Park (Smeal)
106 Business Administration Building
University Park, PA 16802-3000
Public
Admissions: (814) 863-0474
E-mail: smealmba@psu.edu
Web site:
http://www.smeal.psu.edu/mba
Internet application:
http://www.smeal.psu.edu/mba/apply.html
Financial aid: (814) 865-6301
Application deadline: 04/15
In-state tuition: full time: $10,878; part time: N/A
Out-of-state tuition: full time: $20,256
Room/board/expenses: $14,930
College-funded aid: YES
International student aid: YES
Fellowships: 31
Research assistantships: 58
Teaching assistantships: 11

Average student indebtedness at graduation: $24,852
Full-time enrollment: 199
men: 74%; women: 26%; minorities: 14%; international: 36%
Part-time enrollment: N/A
men: N/A; women: N/A; minorities: N/A; international: N/A
Acceptance rate (full time): 24%
Average GMAT (full time): 645
Average GPA (full time): 3.35
Average age of entrants to full-time program: 28
Average months of prior work experience (full time): 59
TOEFL requirement: YES
Minimum TOEFL score: 600
Most popular departments: consulting, finance, management, portfolio management, supply chain management
Mean starting base salary for 2002 full-time graduates: $74,077
Employment location for 2002 class: Intl. 5%; N.E. 30%; M.A. 40%; S. 9%; M.W. 12%; S.W. 2%; W. 2%

St. Joseph's University (Haub)
5600 City Avenue
Philadelphia, PA 19131
Private
Admissions: (610) 660-1101
E-mail: admit@sju.edu
Web site: http://www.sju.edu
Internet application:
http://www.sju.edu/admissions/grad.html
Financial aid: (610) 660-1555
Application deadline: 07/15
Tuition: full time: $600/credit hour; part time: $600/credit hour
Room/board/expenses: N/A
College-funded aid: YES
International student aid: YES
Fellowships: 0
Research assistantships: 6
Teaching assistantships: 2
Average student indebtedness at graduation: $14,000
Full-time enrollment: 70
men: 60%; women: 40%; minorities: 14%; international: 86%
Part-time enrollment: 552
men: 60%; women: 40%; minorities: 7%; international: 0%
Average GMAT (part time): 534
TOEFL requirement: YES
Minimum TOEFL score: 550
Most popular departments: e-commerce, finance, international business, marketing, other

Temple University (Fox)
1810 N. 13th Street
Philadelphia, PA 19122-6083
Public
Admissions: (215) 204-7678
E-mail: foxgrad.info@temple.edu
Web site:
http://www.sbm.temple.edu/mbams
Internet application:
http://www.fox.temple.edu/mbams/admissions
Financial aid: (215) 204-8449
Application deadline: 04/15
In-state tuition: total program: $20,016 (full time); part time: $417/credit hour
Out-of-state tuition: total program: $29,568 (full time)
Room/board/expenses: $15,660
College-funded aid: YES
International student aid: YES
Fellowships: 20
Research assistantships: 0
Teaching assistantships: 0

Average student indebtedness at graduation: $27,725
Full-time enrollment: 197
men: 63%; women: 37%; minorities: 18%; international: 48%
Part-time enrollment: 547
men: 63%; women: 37%; minorities: 16%; international: 5%
Acceptance rate (full time): 55%
Average GMAT (full time): 611
Average GMAT (part time): 592
Average GPA (full time): 3.24
Average age of entrants to full-time program: 26
Average months of prior work experience (full time): 37
TOEFL requirement: YES
Minimum TOEFL score: 575
Most popular departments: finance, healthcare administration, international business, marketing, technology
Mean starting base salary for 2002 full-time graduates: $82,500
Employment location for 2002 class: Intl. 30%; N.E. 3%; M.A. 47%; S. 10%; M.W. 3%; S.W. N/A; W. 7%

University of Pennsylvania (Wharton)
420 Jon M. Huntsman Hall
3730 Walnut Street
Philadelphia, PA 19104
Private
Admissions: (215) 898-6183
E-mail: mba.admissions@wharton.upenn.edu
Web site: http://www.wharton.upenn.edu/mba
Internet application:
https://admissions.wharton.upenn.edu/admissions
Financial aid: (215) 898-6183
Application deadline: 10/24
Tuition: full time: $33,269; part time: N/A
Room/board/expenses: $19,382
College-funded aid: YES
International student aid: YES
Average student indebtedness at graduation: $82,000
Full-time enrollment: 1,601
men: 67%; women: 33%; minorities: 24%; international: 36%
Part-time enrollment: N/A
men: N/A; women: N/A; minorities: N/A; international: N/A
Acceptance rate (full time): 13%
Average GMAT (full time): 711
Average GPA (full time): 3.49
Average age of entrants to full-time program: 28
Average months of prior work experience (full time): 72
TOEFL requirement: YES
Minimum TOEFL score: N/A
Most popular departments: entrepreneurship, finance, general management, marketing, other
Mean starting base salary for 2002 full-time graduates: $90,718
Employment location for 2002 class: Intl. 23%; N.E. 47%; M.A. 6%; S. 3%; M.W. 8%; S.W. 4%; W. 10%

University of Pittsburgh (Katz)
372 Mervis Hall
Pittsburgh, PA 15260
Public
Admissions: (412) 648-1700
E-mail: mba@katz.pitt.edu
Web site: http://www.katz.pitt.edu
Financial aid: (412) 648-1700
Application deadline: 12/01

In-state tuition: total program: $23,852 (full time); part time: $617/credit hour
Out-of-state tuition: total program: $37,626 (full time)
Room/board/expenses: $13,900
College-funded aid: YES
International student aid: YES
Full-time enrollment: 162
men: 74%; women: 26%; minorities: 14%; international: 56%
Part-time enrollment: 538
men: 69%; women: 31%; minorities: 8%; international: 3%
Acceptance rate (full time): 54%
Average GMAT (full time): 613
Average GMAT (part time): 563
Average GPA (full time): 3.16
Average age of entrants to full-time program: 27
Average months of prior work experience (full time): 46
TOEFL requirement: YES
Minimum TOEFL score: 600
Most popular departments: finance, marketing, management information systems, organizational behavior, statistics and operations research
Mean starting base salary for 2002 full-time graduates: $70,000
Employment location for 2002 class: Intl. 5%; N.E. 12%; M.A. 54%; S. 11%; M.W. 14%; S.W. 2%; W. 2%

University of Scranton
800 Linden Street
Scranton, PA 18510-4632
Private
Admissions: (570) 941-7600
E-mail: goonanj1@scranton.edu
Web site:
http://matrix.scranton.edu/academics/ac_pr_graduate.shtml
Financial aid: (570) 941-7700
Application deadline: rolling
Tuition: full time: $564/credit hour; part time: $564/credit hour
Room/board/expenses: $10,000
College-funded aid: YES
International student aid: YES
Teaching assistantships: 75
Full-time enrollment: 40
men: 48%; women: 53%; minorities: 0%; international: 65%
Part-time enrollment: 66
men: 61%; women: 39%; minorities: 0%; international: 14%
Average GMAT (part time): 496
Average age of entrants to full-time program: 25
TOEFL requirement: YES
Minimum TOEFL score: 500
Most popular departments: accounting, finance, general management, international business, management information systems

Villanova University[1]
Bartley Hall
800 E. Lancaster Avenue
Villanova, PA 19085
Private
Admissions: (610) 519-4336
E-mail: mba@villanova.edu
Web site:
http://www.mba.villanova.edu
Financial aid: (610) 519-6456
Tuition: N/A
Room/board/expenses: N/A
Enrollment: N/A

Widener University

1 University Place
Chester, PA 19013
Private
Admissions: (610) 499-4305
E-mail:
gradbus.advise@widener.edu
Web site: http://www.widener.edu
Internet application:
http://www.applyweb.com/apply/
widener/indexa.html
Financial aid: (610) 499-4174
Application deadline: 08/01
Tuition: full time: $570/credit hour;
part time: $570/credit hour
Room/board/expenses: N/A
College-funded aid: YES
International student aid: YES
Research assistantships: 9
**Average student indebtedness at
graduation:** $29,115
Full-time enrollment: N/A
men: N/A; women: N/A; minorities:
N/A; international: N/A
Part-time enrollment: 201
men: 62%; women: 38%; minori-
ties: 10%; international: 4%
Average GMAT (part time): 501
TOEFL requirement: YES
Minimum TOEFL score: 550
Most popular departments: finance,
general management, healthcare
administration, human resources
management, management
information systems

RHODE ISLAND

Bryant College

1150 Douglas Pike
Smithfield, RI 02917
Private
Admissions: (401) 232-6230
E-mail: gradprog@bryant.edu
Web site: http://www.bryant.edu/
Internet application:
http://www.bryant.edu/
gradschool/gradprod/
gradapp.htm
Financial aid: (401) 232-6020
Application deadline: 07/15
Tuition: full time: $444/credit hour;
part time: $444/credit hour
Room/board/expenses: $13,000
College-funded aid: YES
International student aid: YES
Fellowships: 0
Research assistantships: 11
Teaching assistantships: 0
Full-time enrollment: 41
men: 59%; women: 41%; minori-
ties: 10%; international: 24%
Part-time enrollment: 264
men: 64%; women: 36%; minori-
ties: 5%; international: 2%
Acceptance rate (full time): 74%
Average GMAT (full time): 489
Average GMAT (part time): 516
Average GPA (full time): 3.26
**Average age of entrants to full-time
program:** 27
**Average months of prior work expe-
rience (full time):** 96
TOEFL requirement: YES
Minimum TOEFL score: 550
Most popular departments: accounting, e-commerce, finance,
general management, marketing,
management information systems,
operations management, tax

University of Rhode Island

210 Flagg Road
Kingston, RI 02881
Public
Admissions: (401) 874-5000
E-mail: hadz@uri.edu
Web site: http://www.cba.
uri.edu/graduate/mba.htm
Internet application:
http://www.uri.edu/gsadmis/
gsform.html
Financial aid: (401) 874-9500
Application deadline: 06/01
In-state tuition: total program:
$8,100 (full time); part time:
$225/credit hour
Out-of-state tuition: total program:
$23,250 (full time)
Room/board/expenses: $7,000
College-funded aid: YES
International student aid: YES
Fellowships: 0
Research assistantships: 0
Teaching assistantships: 0
Full-time enrollment: 24
men: 71%; women: 29%; minori-
ties: 8%; international: 38%
Part-time enrollment: 211
men: 68%; women: 32%; minori-
ties: 3%; international: 1%
Acceptance rate (full time): 59%
Average GMAT (full time): 583
Average GMAT (part time): 550
Average GPA (full time): 3.27
**Average age of entrants to full-time
program:** 25
TOEFL requirement: YES
Minimum TOEFL score: 575
Most popular departments: ac-
counting, finance, general man-
agement, marketing, management
information systems

SOUTH CAROLINA

The Citadel

171 Moultrie Street
Charleston, SC 29409
Public
Admissions: (843) 953-5089
E-mail: cgps@citadel.edu
Web site: http://www.citadel.edu
Internet application:
http://www.citadel.edu/
admission/gadmission/
gadapplication.html
Financial aid: (843) 953-5187
Application deadline: 08/01
In-state tuition: full time:
$187/credit hour; part time:
$187/credit hour
Out-of-state tuition: full time:
$348/credit hour
Room/board/expenses: N/A
College-funded aid: YES
International student aid: YES
Fellowships: 0
Research assistantships: 3
Teaching assistantships: 0
Full-time enrollment: 32
men: 75%; women: 25%; minori-
ties: 6%; international: 6%
Part-time enrollment: 209
men: 65%; women: 35%; minori-
ties: 11%; international: 3%
Acceptance rate (full time): 100%
Average GMAT (full time): 461
Average GMAT (part time): 484
**Average age of entrants to full-time
program:** 24
TOEFL requirement: YES
Minimum TOEFL score: 550
Most popular departments: consult-
ing, entrepreneurship, general
management, human resources
management, marketing

Clemson University

124 Sirrine Hall
Box 341315
Clemson, SC 29634-1315
Public
Admissions: (864) 656-3975
E-mail: mba@clemson.edu
Web site:
http://business.clemson.edu/mba
Internet application:
http://www.grad.clemson.edu
Financial aid: (864) 656-2280
Application deadline: 04/15
In-state tuition: full time: $5,834;
part time: $356/credit hour
Out-of-state tuition: full time:
$12,932
Room/board/expenses: $12,002
College-funded aid: YES
International student aid: YES
Fellowships: 0
Research assistantships: 14
Teaching assistantships: 0
**Average student indebtedness at
graduation:** $6,702
Full-time enrollment: 40
men: 73%; women: 28%; minori-
ties: 8%; international: 25%
Part-time enrollment: 73
men: 70%; women: 30%; minori-
ties: 10%; international: 11%
Acceptance rate (full time): 33%
Average GMAT (full time): 615
Average GMAT (part time): 582
Average GPA (full time): 3.35
**Average age of entrants to full-time
program:** 27
**Average months of prior work expe-
rience (full time):** 45
TOEFL requirement: YES
Minimum TOEFL score: 600
Most popular departments: e-com-
merce, finance, human resources
management, international
business, marketing
**Mean starting base salary for 2002
full-time graduates:** $65,099
**Employment location for 2002
class:** Intl. 12%; N.E. 15%; M.A.
3%; S. 55%; M.W. 9%; S.W. 6%;
W. 0%

College of Charleston[1]

Randolph Hall 310
Charleston, SC 29424
Public
Admissions: (843) 953-5614
E-mail: gradsch@cofc.edu
Web site: http://univchas.cofc.edu/
programs/index.html
Internet application:
http://www.applyweb.com/
apply/cofc/index.html
Financial aid: (843) 953-5540
Tuition: N/A
Room/board/expenses: N/A
Enrollment: N/A

Francis Marion University[1]

Box 100547
Florence, SC 29501
Public
Admissions: (843) 661-1419
E-mail: bkyer@fmarion.edu
Web site:
http://alpha1.fmarion.edu/~
gradmba/
Financial aid: (843) 661-1190
Tuition: N/A
Room/board/expenses: N/A
Enrollment: N/A

South Carolina State University[1]

300 College Street NE
Orangeburg, SC 29117
Public
Admissions: (803) 536-7064
E-mail: admissions@scsu.edu
Web site: http://www.scsu.edu
Financial aid: (803) 536-7067
Tuition: N/A
Room/board/expenses: N/A
Enrollment: N/A

University of South Carolina (Moore)

1705 College Street
Columbia, SC 29208
Public
Admissions: (803) 777-4346
E-mail: gradadmit@moore.sc.edu
Web site:
http://mooreschool.sc.edu/
Internet application:
http://www.gradschool.sc.edu
Financial aid: (803) 777-8134
Application deadline: 12/01
In-state tuition: full time: $11,000;
part time: $340/credit hour
Out-of-state tuition: full time:
$19,000
Room/board/expenses: $15,000
College-funded aid: YES
International student aid: YES
Fellowships: 60
Research assistantships: 110
Teaching assistantships: 0
**Average student indebtedness at
graduation:** $15,500
Full-time enrollment: 377
men: 70%; women: 30%; minori-
ties: 6%; international: 33%
Part-time enrollment: 230
men: 76%; women: 24%; minori-
ties: 11%; international: 5%
Acceptance rate (full time): 54%
Average GMAT (full time): 630
Average GMAT (part time): 590
Average GPA (full time): 3.21
**Average age of entrants to full-time
program:** 27
**Average months of prior work expe-
rience (full time):** 50
TOEFL requirement: YES
Minimum TOEFL score: 600
Most popular departments: finance,
international business, marketing,
management information systems,
operations management
**Mean starting base salary for 2002
full-time graduates:** $63,910
**Employment location for 2002
class:** Intl. 12%; N.E. 9%; M.A. 7%;
S. 46%; M.W. 10%; S.W. 9%; W.
7%

Winthrop University[1]

Room 213 Thurmond Building
Rock Hill, SC 29733
Public
Admissions: (803) 323-2409
E-mail: hagerp@winthrop.edu
Web site: http://cba.winthrop.edu
Internet application:
http://www.winthrop.edu/
graduate-studies/application.htm
Financial aid: (803) 323-2189
Tuition: N/A
Room/board/expenses: N/A
Enrollment: N/A

SOUTH DAKOTA

University of South Dakota[1]

414 E. Clark Street
Vermillion, SD 57069
Public
Admissions: (605) 677-5232
E-mail: mba@usd.edu
Web site: http://www.usd.edu/mba
Financial aid: (605) 677-5446
Tuition: N/A
Room/board/expenses: N/A
Enrollment: N/A

TENNESSEE

Belmont University[1]

1900 Belmont Boulevard
Nashville, TN 37212
Private
Admissions: (615) 460-6480
E-mail:
masseygrad@mail.belmont.edu
Web site: http://massey.belmont.
edu/prospmba.htm
Internet application: N/A
Financial aid: (615) 460-6403
Tuition: N/A
Room/board/expenses: N/A
Enrollment: N/A

East Tennessee State University

PO Box 70699
Johnson City, TN 37614
Public
Admissions: (423) 439-5314
E-mail: business@etsu.edu
Web site: http://business.etsu.edu
Internet application:
http://www2.etsu.edu:443/
sourcedocs001/mwagr_
contents.htm
Financial aid: (423) 439-4300
Application deadline: 06/01
In-state tuition: full time:
$201/credit hour; part time:
$201/credit hour
Out-of-state tuition: full time:
$502/credit hour
Room/board/expenses: $4,000
College-funded aid: YES
International student aid: YES
Fellowships: 0
Research assistantships: 18
Teaching assistantships: 0
**Average student indebtedness at
graduation:** $1,000
Full-time enrollment: 25
men: 52%; women: 48%; minori-
ties: 12%; international: 28%
Part-time enrollment: 114
men: 55%; women: 45%; minori-
ties: 4%; international: 30%
Acceptance rate (full time): 85%
Average GMAT (full time): 500
Average GMAT (part time): 500
Average GPA (full time): 3.10
**Average age of entrants to full-time
program:** 26
**Average months of prior work expe-
rience (full time):** 36
TOEFL requirement: YES
Minimum TOEFL score: 550
Most popular departments: finance,
general management, healthcare
administration, manufacturing
and technology management,
marketing

Middle Tennessee State University

PO Box 290
Murfreesboro, TN 37132
Public
Admissions: (615) 898-2964
E-mail: fester@mtsu.edu
Web site: http://www.mtsu.edu
Financial aid: (615) 898-2830
Application deadline: 07/01
In-state tuition: full time:
$265/credit hour; part time:
$240/credit hour
Out-of-state tuition: full time:
$566/credit hour
Room/board/expenses: $5,671
College-funded aid: YES
International student aid: YES
Fellowships: 10
Research assistantships: 30
Full-time enrollment: 200
men: 63%; women: 38%; minorities: N/A; international: N/A
Part-time enrollment: 600
men: 58%; women: 42%; minorities: N/A; international: N/A
Acceptance rate (full time): 80%
Average GMAT (full time): 480
Average GMAT (part time): 510
Average age of entrants to full-time program: 25
Average months of prior work experience (full time): 12
TOEFL requirement: YES
Minimum TOEFL score: 525
Most popular departments: consulting, finance, human resources management, marketing, management information systems

Tennessee State University[1]

330 N. 10th Avenue
Nashville, TN 37203
Public
Admissions: (615) 963-7121
E-mail: gbhartmann@tnstate.edu
Web site: http://www.tnstate.edu
Financial aid: (888) 328-4636
Tuition: N/A
Room/board/expenses: N/A
Enrollment: N/A

Tennessee Technological University

Box 5023
Cookeville, TN 38505
Public
Admissions: (931) 372-3600
E-mail: mbastudies@tntech.edu
Web site: http://www.tntech.edu
Internet application:
https://wserve.tntech.edu/
webdocs/ahomepg1.htm
Financial aid: (931) 372-3600
Application deadline: 07/30
In-state tuition: full time: $4,770;
part time: $194/credit hour
Out-of-state tuition: full time:
$11,728
Room/board/expenses: $5,400
College-funded aid: NO
International student aid: YES
Fellowships: 10
Research assistantships: 34
Teaching assistantships: 0
Full-time enrollment: 58
men: 69%; women: 31%; minorities: 0%; international: 10%
Part-time enrollment: 42
men: 45%; women: 55%; minorities: 5%; international: 5%
Acceptance rate (full time): 83%
Average GMAT (full time): 541
Average GMAT (part time): 491
Average GPA (full time): 3.07
Average age of entrants to full-time program: 25

Average months of prior work experience (full time): 24
TOEFL requirement: YES
Minimum TOEFL score: 550
Most popular departments: accounting, general management, management information systems
Employment location for 2002 class: Intl. N/A; N.E. N/A; M.A. N/A; S. 96%; M.W. N/A; S.W. N/A; W. 4%

University of Memphis (Fogelman)

Fogelman College of
Business & Economics
Memphis, TN 38152
Public
Admissions: (901) 678-2911
E-mail: kweddle@memphis.edu
Web site: http://www.memphis.edu
Internet application:
http://www.people.memphis.
edu/~gradsch/applicant.html
Financial aid: (901) 678-4825
Application deadline: 08/01
In-state tuition:
$268/credit hour; part time:
$268/credit hour
Out-of-state tuition: full time:
$563/credit hour
Room/board/expenses: $4,229
College-funded aid: YES
International student aid: NO
Average student indebtedness at graduation: $16,350
Full-time enrollment: 169
men: 53%; women: 47%; minorities: 14%; international: 30%
Part-time enrollment: 156
men: 62%; women: 38%; minorities: 16%; international: 8%
Average GMAT (part time): 530
TOEFL requirement: YES
Minimum TOEFL score: 550
Most popular departments: accounting, finance, marketing, management information systems, supply chain management

University of Tennessee–Chattanooga

615 McCallie Avenue
Chattanooga, TN 37403
Public
Admissions: (423) 425-4210
E-mail: kim-gee@utk.edu
Web site: http://www.utc.edu
Internet application:
http://www.utc.edu/gradstudies/
graduateforms.htm
Financial aid: (423) 425-4677
Application deadline: 07/01
In-state tuition: full time:
$246/credit hour; part time:
$246/credit hour
Out-of-state tuition: full time:
$636/credit hour
Room/board/expenses: $1,500
College-funded aid: YES
International student aid: YES
Research assistantships: 12
Full-time enrollment: N/A
men: N/A; women: N/A; minorities: N/A; international: N/A
Part-time enrollment: 314
men: 55%; women: 45%; minorities: N/A; international: N/A
Average GMAT (part time): 497
TOEFL requirement: YES
Minimum TOEFL score: 500
Most popular departments: finance, general management, human resources management, marketing, organizational behavior

University of Tennessee–Knoxville

527 Stokely Management Center
Knoxville, TN 37996-0552
Public
Admissions: (865) 974-5033
E-mail: mba@utk.edu
Web site: http://mba.utk.edu
Financial aid: (865) 974-3131
Application deadline: 03/01
In-state tuition: total program:
$9,089 (full time); part time: N/A
Out-of-state tuition: total program:
$24,270 (full time)
Room/board/expenses: $12,201
College-funded aid: YES
International student aid: YES
Fellowships: 25
Research assistantships: 25
Teaching assistantships: 0
Full-time enrollment: 90
men: 74%; women: 26%; minorities: 8%; international: 7%
Part-time enrollment: N/A
men: N/A; women: N/A; minorities: N/A; international: N/A
Acceptance rate (full time): 37%
Average GMAT (full time): 610
Average GPA (full time): 3.31
Average age of entrants to full-time program: 26
Average months of prior work experience (full time): 42
TOEFL requirement: YES
Minimum TOEFL score: 600
Most popular departments: finance, marketing, operations management, supply chain management
Mean starting base salary for 2002 full-time graduates: $62,800
Employment location for 2002 class: Intl. 2%; N.E. 2%; M.A. 11%; S. 66%; M.W. 15%; S.W. 2%; W. 2%

University of Tennessee–Martin[1]

103 Business Administration
Building
Martin, TN 38238
Public
Admissions: (731) 587-7012
E-mail: larant@utm.edu
Web site: http://www.utm.edu/
departments/soba/graduate/
gradprogmain.htm
Financial aid: (731) 587-7040
Tuition: N/A
Room/board/expenses: N/A
Enrollment: N/A

Vanderbilt University (Owen)

401 21st Avenue S
Nashville, TN 37203
Private
Admissions: (615) 322-6469
E-mail:
admissions@owen.vanderbilt.edu
Web site:
http://mba.vanderbilt.edu
Internet application:
http://mba.vanderbilt.edu/external/
Financial aid: (615) 343-8085
Application deadline: 04/15
Tuition: full time: $30,018; part time: N/A
Room/board/expenses: $16,162
College-funded aid: YES
International student aid: YES
Fellowships: 0
Research assistantships: 5
Teaching assistantships: 5
Average student indebtedness at graduation: $47,074
Full-time enrollment: 445
men: 76%; women: 24%; minorities: 8%; international: 26%

Part-time enrollment: N/A
men: N/A; women: N/A; minorities: N/A; international: N/A
Acceptance rate (full time): 46%
Average GMAT (full time): 648
Average GPA (full time): 3.29
Average age of entrants to full-time program: 28
Average months of prior work experience (full time): 57
TOEFL requirement: YES
Minimum TOEFL score: 600
Most popular departments: entrepreneurship, finance, marketing, operations management, organizational behavior
Mean starting base salary for 2002 full-time graduates: $72,020
Employment location for 2002 class: Intl. 9%; N.E. 13%; M.A. 7%; S. 42%; M.W. 12%; S.W. 4%; W. 12%

TEXAS

Baylor University (Hankamer)

PO Box 98013
Waco, TX 76798-8013
Private
Admissions: (254) 710-3718
E-mail: mba@hsb.baylor.edu
Web site:
http://gradbusiness.baylor.edu
Internet application:
https://apply.embark.com/
mbaedge/baylor/63/
Financial aid: (254) 710-2611
Application deadline: 07/01
Tuition: total program: $32,296
(full time); part time: N/A
Room/board/expenses: $15,000
College-funded aid: YES
International student aid: YES
Average student indebtedness at graduation: $22,800
Full-time enrollment: 125
men: 73%; women: 27%; minorities: 10%; international: 29%
Part-time enrollment: N/A
men: N/A; women: N/A; minorities: N/A; international: N/A
Acceptance rate (full time): 61%
Average GMAT (full time): 595
Average GPA (full time): 3.23
Average age of entrants to full-time program: 25
Average months of prior work experience (full time): 27
TOEFL requirement: YES
Minimum TOEFL score: 600
Most popular departments: consulting, entrepreneurship, finance, marketing, management information systems
Mean starting base salary for 2002 full-time graduates: $54,314
Employment location for 2002 class: Intl. 2%; N.E. 10%; M.A. 0%; S. 0%; M.W. 0%; S.W. 70%; W. 0%

Lamar University–Beaumont

4400 Martin Luther King Parkway
Beaumont, TX 77710
Public
Admissions: (409) 880-8349
E-mail: intladm@hal.lamar.edu
Web site:
http://www.mis.lamar.edu
Financial aid: (409) 880-8450
Application deadline: 06/01
In-state tuition: full time: $1,674;
part time: $670
Out-of-state tuition: full time:
$5,436
Room/board/expenses: $4,000
College-funded aid: YES
International student aid: YES

Fellowships: 0
Research assistantships: 5
Teaching assistantships: 0
Full-time enrollment: N/A
men: N/A; women: N/A; minorities: N/A; international: N/A
Part-time enrollment: N/A
men: N/A; women: N/A; minorities: N/A; international: N/A
Acceptance rate (full time): 68%
Average GMAT (full time): 540
Average GMAT (part time): 540
Average GPA (full time): 3.20
Average age of entrants to full-time program: 30
Average months of prior work experience (full time): 44
TOEFL requirement: YES
Minimum TOEFL score: 525
Most popular departments: accounting, finance, general management, marketing, management information systems

Rice University (Jones)

PO Box 2932
Houston, TX 77252-2932
Private
Admissions: (713) 348-4918
E-mail: ricemba@rice.edu
Web site:
http://www.jonesgsm.rice.edu
Internet application:
http://www.jonesgsm.rice.edu/
jonesgsm/Application_for_
Admission.asp
Financial aid: (713) 348-4958
Application deadline: 04/11
Tuition: full time: $24,080; part
time: N/A
Room/board/expenses: $11,855
College-funded aid: YES
International student aid: YES
Fellowships: 43
Research assistantships: 0
Teaching assistantships: 0
Average student indebtedness at graduation: $44,853
Full-time enrollment: 359
men: 64%; women: 36%; minorities: 22%; international: 23%
Part-time enrollment: N/A
men: N/A; women: N/A; minorities: N/A; international: N/A
Acceptance rate (full time): 39%
Average GMAT (full time): 630
Average GPA (full time): 3.30
Average age of entrants to full-time program: 28
Average months of prior work experience (full time): 60
TOEFL requirement: YES
Minimum TOEFL score: 600
Mean starting base salary for 2002 full-time graduates: $75,394
Employment location for 2002 class: Intl. 5%; N.E. 7%; M.A. 0%; S. 4%; M.W. 4%; S.W. 76%; W. 5%

Sam Houston State University

Box 2056
Huntsville, TX 77341
Public
Admissions: (936) 294-1246
E-mail: eco_mjm@shsu.edu
Web site: http://coba.shsu.edu/
Internet application:
http://www.shsu.edu/mba
Financial aid: (936) 294-1724
Application deadline: 08/01
In-state tuition: full time: $79/credit
hour; part time: $79/credit hour
Out-of-state tuition: full time:
$297/credit hour
Room/board/expenses: $2,500
College-funded aid: YES
International student aid: YES
Fellowships: 0

Research assistantships: 3
Teaching assistantships: 0
Full-time enrollment: 61
men: 46%; women: 54%; minorities: 15%; international: 21%
Part-time enrollment: 215
men: 54%; women: 46%; minorities: 16%; international: 0%
Acceptance rate (full time): 72%
Average GMAT (full time): 496
Average GMAT (part time): 483
Average GPA (full time): 3.32
Average age of entrants to full-time program: 24
TOEFL requirement: YES
Minimum TOEFL score: 550
Most popular departments: accounting, finance, general management, marketing, management information systems

Southern Methodist University (Cox)

PO Box 750333
Dallas, TX 75275-0333
Private
Admissions: (800) 472-3622
E-mail:
mbainfo@mail.cox.smu.edu
Web site: http://mba.cox.smu.edu/index.html
Internet application:
http://mba.cox.smu.edu/ftmba/mba_apply.html
Financial aid: (214) 768-2371
Application deadline: 04/30
Tuition: full time: $27,648; part time: $24,292
Room/board/expenses: $12,218
College-funded aid: YES
International student aid: YES
Fellowships: 0
Research assistantships: 0
Teaching assistantships: 0
Average student indebtedness at graduation: $0
Full-time enrollment: 239
men: 72%; women: 28%; minorities: 15%; international: 22%
Part-time enrollment: 658
men: 76%; women: 24%; minorities: 16%; international: 15%
Acceptance rate (full time): 30%
Average GMAT (full time): 660
Average GMAT (part time): 614
Average GPA (full time): 3.22
Average age of entrants to full-time program: 28
Average months of prior work experience (full time): 56
TOEFL requirement: YES
Minimum TOEFL score: 600
Most popular departments: consulting, entrepreneurship, finance, general management, marketing
Mean starting base salary for 2002 full-time graduates: $73,270
Employment location for 2002 class: Intl. 5%; N.E. 3%; M.A. 0%; S. 6%; M.W. 2%; S.W. 78%; W. 6%

Southwest Texas State University

601 University Drive
San Marcos, TX 78666-4616
Public
Admissions: (512) 245-3591
E-mail: ro02@swt.edu
Web site: http://www.swt.edu
Internet application:
http://www.gradcollege.swt.edu
Financial aid: (512) 245-2315
Application deadline: 06/15
In-state tuition: full time: $2,097; part time: $1,308
Out-of-state tuition: full time: $4,185
Room/board/expenses: $8,000
College-funded aid: YES
International student aid: YES

Research assistantships: 15
Full-time enrollment: N/A
men: N/A; women: N/A; minorities: N/A; international: N/A
Part-time enrollment: 388
men: 51%; women: 49%; minorities: 19%; international: 16%
Average GMAT (part time): 570
TOEFL requirement: YES
Minimum TOEFL score: 550
Most popular departments: accounting, finance, general management, manufacturing and technology management, management information systems

Stephen F. Austin State University

Box 13004, SFA Station
Nacogdoches, TX 75962
Public
Admissions: (936) 468-2807
E-mail: gschool@titan.sfasu.edu
Web site:
http://www.cob.sfasu.edu
Financial aid: (936) 468-2807
Application deadline: 07/15
In-state tuition: full time: $44/credit hour; part time: $44/credit hour
Out-of-state tuition: full time: $253/credit hour
Room/board/expenses: $12,000
College-funded aid: YES
International student aid: NO
Fellowships: 0
Research assistantships: 7
Teaching assistantships: 0
Average student indebtedness at graduation: $0
Full-time enrollment: 12
men: 42%; women: 58%; minorities: 8%; international: 17%
Part-time enrollment: 55
men: 60%; women: 40%; minorities: 7%; international: 7%
Average GMAT (full time): 473
Average GMAT (part time): 439
Average GPA (full time): 3.01
Average age of entrants to full-time program: 24
Average months of prior work experience (full time): 30
TOEFL requirement: YES
Minimum TOEFL score: 550
Most popular departments: accounting, finance, general management, international business, marketing

St. Mary's University[1]

1 Camino Santa Maria
San Antonio, TX 78228-8607
Private
Admissions: (210) 436-3708
E-mail:
jzertuch@alvin.stmarytx.edu
Web site: http://www.stmarytx.edu/acad/business
Financial aid: (210) 436-3141
Tuition: N/A
Room/board/expenses: N/A
Enrollment: N/A

Texas A&M International University

5201 University Boulevard
Pellegrino Hall, Suite 301
Laredo, TX 78041-1900
Public
Admissions: (956) 326-2200
E-mail: adms@tamiu.edu
Web site: http://www.tamiu.edu
Internet application:
https://www.applytexas.org/adappc/general/c_start.wb
Financial aid: (956) 326-2225
Application deadline: 07/01

In-state tuition: full time: $3,604; part time: $120/credit hour
Out-of-state tuition: full time: $11,127
Room/board/expenses: $4,500
Fellowships: 140
Research assistantships: 0
Teaching assistantships: 0
Average student indebtedness at graduation: $8,300
Full-time enrollment: 98
men: 67%; women: 33%; minorities: 16%; international: 84%
Part-time enrollment: 124
men: 67%; women: 33%; minorities: 79%; international: 21%
Acceptance rate (full time): 92%
Average GMAT (full time): 495
Average GMAT (part time): 495
Average GPA (full time): 3.35
Average age of entrants to full-time program: 27
Minimum TOEFL score: 550
Most popular departments: economics, finance, general management, international business, management information systems

Texas A&M University–College Station (Mays)

4117 TAMU
212 Wehner Building
College Station, TX 77843-4117
Public
Admissions: (979) 845-4714
E-mail: maysmba@tamu.edu
Web site: http://mba.tamu.edu
Internet application:
http://mba.tamu.edu/apply/
Financial aid: (979) 845-3236
Application deadline: 05/01
In-state tuition: total program: $9,797 (full time); part time: N/A
Out-of-state tuition: total program: $19,740 (full time)
Room/board/expenses: $11,804
College-funded aid: YES
International student aid: YES
Fellowships: 5
Research assistantships: 30
Teaching assistantships: 0
Average student indebtedness at graduation: $7,965
Full-time enrollment: 193
men: 76%; women: 24%; minorities: 7%; international: 27%
Part-time enrollment: N/A
men: N/A; women: N/A; minorities: N/A; international: N/A
Acceptance rate (full time): 29%
Average GMAT (full time): 626
Average GPA (full time): 3.36
Average age of entrants to full-time program: 28
Average months of prior work experience (full time): 59
TOEFL requirement: YES
Minimum TOEFL score: 600
Most popular departments: e-commerce, finance, human resources management, marketing, management information systems
Mean starting base salary for 2002 full-time graduates: $75,017
Employment location for 2002 class: Intl. 5%; N.E. 11%; M.A. 3%; S. 6%; M.W. 12%; S.W. 55%; W. 9%

Texas A&M University–Commerce

PO Box 3011
Commerce, TX 75429-3011
Public
Admissions: (903) 886-5163
E-mail: graduate_school@tamu-commerce.edu
Web site:
http://www.tamu-commerce.edu/mba

Internet application:
http://www7.tamu-commerce.edu/gradschool/gradmenu/ApplyOnline.asp
Financial aid: (903) 886-5096
Application deadline: rolling
In-state tuition: full time: $188/credit hour; part time: $188/credit hour
Out-of-state tuition: full time: $406/credit hour
Room/board/expenses: $5,660
College-funded aid: YES
International student aid: YES
Fellowships: 0
Research assistantships: 11
Teaching assistantships: 0
Full-time enrollment: 470
men: 56%; women: 44%; minorities: 25%; international: 36%
Part-time enrollment: N/A
men: N/A; women: N/A; minorities: N/A; international: N/A
TOEFL requirement: YES
Minimum TOEFL score: 500

Texas A&M University–Corpus Christi[1]

6300 Ocean Drive
Corpus Christi, TX 78412-5503
Public
Admissions: (361) 825-2177
E-mail: maria.martinez@mail.tamucc.edu
Web site: http://www.cob.tamucc.edu/graduate/
Internet application:
http://www.applytexas.org
Financial aid: (361) 825-2338
Tuition: N/A
Room/board/expenses: N/A
Enrollment: N/A

Texas Christian University (Neeley)

PO Box 298540
Fort Worth, TX 76129
Private
Admissions: (817) 257-7531
E-mail: mbainfo@tcu.edu
Web site: http://www.mba.tcu.edu
Financial aid: (817) 257-7872
Application deadline: 04/30
Tuition: full time: $15,345; part time: $11,250
Room/board/expenses: $11,000
College-funded aid: YES
International student aid: YES
Full-time enrollment: 116
men: 72%; women: 28%; minorities: 7%; international: 31%
Part-time enrollment: 143
men: 78%; women: 22%; minorities: 11%; international: 4%
Acceptance rate (full time): 63%
Average GMAT (full time): 613
Average GMAT (part time): 568
Average GPA (full time): 3.10
Average age of entrants to full-time program: 27
Average months of prior work experience (full time): 43
TOEFL requirement: YES
Minimum TOEFL score: 550
Most popular departments: consulting, finance, general management, marketing, supply chain management
Mean starting base salary for 2002 full-time graduates: $55,835
Employment location for 2002 class: Intl. 19%; N.E. 7%; M.A. 0%; S. 4%; M.W. 7%; S.W. 63%; W. 0%

Texas Southern University[1]

3100 Cleburne Avenue
Houston, TX 77004
Public
Admissions: (713) 313-7590
E-mail: richardson_bj@tsu.edu
Web site:
http://www.tsu.edu/business
Financial aid: (713) 313-7530
Tuition: N/A
Room/board/expenses: N/A
Enrollment: N/A

Texas Tech University (Rawls)

PO Box 42101
Lubbock, TX 79409-2101
Public
Admissions: (806) 742-3184
E-mail: bagrad@ba.ttu.edu
Web site: http://grad.ba.ttu.edu
Internet application:
http://grad.ba.ttu.edu/GSC_Applynow.asp
Financial aid: (806) 742-3681
Application deadline: 07/01
In-state tuition: full time: $4,899; part time: N/A
Out-of-state tuition: full time: $10,131
Room/board/expenses: $10,593
College-funded aid: YES
International student aid: YES
Fellowships: 150
Research assistantships: 9
Teaching assistantships: 14
Average student indebtedness at graduation: $27,199
Full-time enrollment: 146
men: 34%; women: 66%; minorities: 16%; international: 23%
Part-time enrollment: 158
men: 73%; women: 27%; minorities: 7%; international: 0%
Acceptance rate (full time): 29%
Average GMAT (full time): 580
Average GMAT (part time): 530
Average GPA (full time): 3.34
Average age of entrants to full-time program: 26
Average months of prior work experience (full time): 41
TOEFL requirement: YES
Minimum TOEFL score: 550
Most popular departments: finance, general management, healthcare administration, marketing, management information systems
Mean starting base salary for 2002 full-time graduates: $47,183
Employment location for 2002 class: Intl. 0%; N.E. 0%; M.A. 0%; S. 0%; M.W. 0%; S.W. 100%; W. 0%

University of Houston–Clear Lake

2700 Bay Area Boulevard
Box 71
Houston, TX 77058
Public
Admissions: (281) 283-2533
E-mail: admissions@cl.uh.edu
Web site: http://www.uhcl.edu
Internet application:
http://www.uhcl.edu/admissions/
Financial aid: (281) 283-2481
Application deadline: 08/01
In-state tuition: full time: N/A; part time: $88/credit hour
Out-of-state tuition: full time: N/A
Room/board/expenses: $18,520
College-funded aid: YES
International student aid: YES
Full-time enrollment: N/A
men: N/A; women: N/A; minorities: N/A; international: N/A

Part-time enrollment: 534
men: 56%; women: 44%; minorities: 24%; international: 14%
Average GMAT (part time): 523
TOEFL requirement: YES
Minimum TOEFL score: 550
Most popular departments: accounting, finance, general management, marketing, management information systems

University of Houston–Main Campus (Bauer)

334 Melcher Hall
Room 275
Houston, TX 77204-6021
Public
Admissions: (713) 743-4876
E-mail: houstonmba@uh.edu
Web site:
http://www.houstonmba.uh.edu
Internet application:
http://www.houstonmba.uh.edu
Financial aid: (713) 743-1010
Application deadline: 05/01
In-state tuition: full time: $132/credit hour; part time: $132/credit hour
Out-of-state tuition: full time: $350/credit hour
Room/board/expenses: $7,920
College-funded aid: YES
International student aid: YES
Teaching assistantships: 30
Full-time enrollment: N/A
men: N/A; women: N/A; minorities: N/A; international: N/A
Part-time enrollment: 200
men: 64%; women: 37%; minorities: 20%; international: 24%
Average GMAT (part time): 590
TOEFL requirement: YES
Minimum TOEFL score: 620
Most popular departments: accounting, finance, general management, marketing, management information systems

University of North Texas[1]

PO Box 311160
Denton, TX 76203
Public
Admissions: (940) 369-8977
E-mail: mba@cobaf.unt.edu
Web site: http://www.coba.unt.edu
Financial aid: (940) 565-2302
Tuition: N/A
Room/board/expenses: N/A
Enrollment: N/A

University of Texas–Arlington

UTA Box 19376
Arlington, TX 76019-0376
Public
Admissions: (817) 272-3005
E-mail: admit@uta.edu
Web site:
http://www2.uta.edu/gradbiz/
Internet application:
http://grad.uta.edu/
leftMenuPages/admissions.asp
Financial aid: (817) 272-3561
Application deadline: 06/15
In-state tuition: full time: $7,674; part time: $4,995
Out-of-state tuition: full time: $14,418
Room/board/expenses: $12,000
College-funded aid: YES
International student aid: YES
Full-time enrollment: 180
men: 56%; women: 44%; minorities: 17%; international: 46%
Part-time enrollment: 407
men: 64%; women: 36%; minorities: 20%; international: 9%
Acceptance rate (full time): 56%

Average GMAT (full time): 547
Average GMAT (part time): 557
Average GPA (full time): 3.34
Average age of entrants to full-time program: 28
TOEFL requirement: YES
Minimum TOEFL score: 550
Most popular departments: accounting, finance, general management, marketing, management information systems

University of Texas–Austin (McCombs)

MBA Program
1 University Station, B6004
Austin, TX 78712
Public
Admissions: (512) 471-7612
E-mail:
McCombsMBA@bus.utexas.edu
Web site: http://texasmba.bus.
utexas.edu/admissions
Internet application:
http://texasmba.bus.utexas.edu/
admissions/adm/
Financial aid: (512) 471-7607
Application deadline: 03/15
In-state tuition: full time: $11,925; total program: $51,600 (part time)
Out-of-state tuition: full time: $25,005
Room/board/expenses: $15,638
College-funded aid: YES
International student aid: YES
Fellowships: 50
Research assistantships: 0
Teaching assistantships: 0
Average student indebtedness at graduation: $28,836
Full-time enrollment: 804
men: 76%; women: 24%; minorities: 15%; international: 26%
Part-time enrollment: 79
men: 78%; women: 22%; minorities: 19%; international: 19%
Acceptance rate (full time): 29%
Average GMAT (full time): 678
Average GMAT (part time): 660
Average GPA (full time): 3.37
Average age of entrants to full-time program: 28
Average months of prior work experience (full time): 62
TOEFL requirement: YES
Minimum TOEFL score: 620
Most popular departments: entrepreneurship, finance, general management, marketing, management information systems
Mean starting base salary for 2002 full-time graduates: $79,175
Employment location for 2002 class: Intl. 11%; N.E. 7%; M.A. 6%; S. 3%; M.W. 11%; S.W. 54%; W. 8%

University of Texas–Dallas

PO Box 830688
Richardson, TX 75083-0688
Public
Admissions: (972) 883-2342
E-mail: enrollment@utdallas.edu
Web site: http://www.utdallas.edu/
Internet application:
http://www.utdallas.edu/student/
admissions/application.htm
Financial aid: (972) 883-2941
Application deadline: 07/01
In-state tuition: full time: $3,743; part time: $88/credit hour
Out-of-state tuition: full time: $7,667
Room/board/expenses: $8,736
College-funded aid: YES
International student aid: YES
Fellowships: 0
Research assistantships: 2

Teaching assistantships: 128
Full-time enrollment: 82
men: 56%; women: 44%; minorities: 16%; international: 41%
Part-time enrollment: 817
men: 65%; women: 35%; minorities: 24%; international: 24%
Acceptance rate (full time): 48%
Average GMAT (full time): 641
Average GMAT (part time): 560
Average age of entrants to full-time program: 27
TOEFL requirement: YES
Minimum TOEFL score: 550
Most popular departments: accounting, finance, international business, marketing, management information systems
Mean starting base salary for 2002 full-time graduates: $61,625
Employment location for 2002 class: Intl. 15%; N.E. 0%; M.A. 0%; S. 0%; M.W. 8%; S.W. 69%; W. 8%

University of Texas–El Paso

500 W. University Drive
El Paso, TX 79968
Public
Admissions: (915) 747-5491
E-mail: gradschool@utep.edu
Web site: http://www.utep.edu
Financial aid: (915) 747-5204
Application deadline: 07/31
In-state tuition: full time: $2,649; part time: $114/credit hour
Out-of-state tuition: full time: $6,429
Room/board/expenses: $7,908
College-funded aid: YES
International student aid: YES
Full-time enrollment: 128
men: 59%; women: 41%; minorities: 57%; international: 29%
Part-time enrollment: 253
men: 59%; women: 41%; minorities: 66%; international: 5%
Acceptance rate (full time): 97%
Average GMAT (full time): 451
Average age of entrants to full-time program: 32
TOEFL requirement: YES
Minimum TOEFL score: 600
Most popular departments: accounting, finance, general management, management information systems

University of Texas–Pan American[1]

1201 W. University Drive
Edinburg, TX 78539
Public
Admissions: (956) 381-3313
E-mail: mbaprog@panam.edu
Web site:
http://www.coba.panam.edu/
mba/index
Financial aid: (956) 381-2501
Tuition: N/A
Room/board/expenses: N/A
Enrollment: N/A

University of Texas–San Antonio

6900 N. Loop 1604 W
San Antonio, TX 78249
Public
Admissions: (210) 458-4330
E-mail: graduatestudies@utsa.edu
Web site:
http://www.utsa.edu/graduate
Financial aid: (210) 458-8000
Application deadline: 07/01
In-state tuition: full time: $4,258; part time: $2,860
Out-of-state tuition: full time: $8,982
Room/board/expenses: N/A

College-funded aid: YES
International student aid: YES
Full-time enrollment: N/A
men: N/A; women: N/A; minorities: N/A; international: N/A
Part-time enrollment: 362
men: 54%; women: 46%; minorities: 35%; international: 8%
Average GMAT (part time): 560
TOEFL requirement: YES
Minimum TOEFL score: 500
Most popular departments: finance, general management, international business, marketing, management information systems

University of Texas–Tyler[1]

3900 University Boulevard
Tyler, TX 75799
Public
Admissions: (903) 566-7142
E-mail: gsmith@mail.uttyler.edu
Web site:
http://www.uttyl.edu/cbt/mba.htm
Internet application:
http://www.uttyler.edu/mainsite/
onlineapp.html
Financial aid: (903) 566-7180
Tuition: N/A
Room/board/expenses: N/A
Enrollment: N/A

UTAH

Brigham Young University (Marriott)

640 TNRB
Provo, UT 84602
Private
Admissions: (801) 422-3701
E-mail: mba@byu.edu
Web site:
http://marriottschool.byu.edu/mba
Internet application:
http://marriottschool.byu.edu/
apply.cfm
Financial aid: (801) 422-6824
Application deadline: 03/01
Tuition: full time: $6,200; part time: $342/credit hour
Room/board/expenses: $12,750
College-funded aid: YES
International student aid: YES
Fellowships: 0
Research assistantships: 10
Teaching assistantships: 50
Average student indebtedness at graduation: $18,667
Full-time enrollment: 265
men: 85%; women: 15%; minorities: 4%; international: 11%
Part-time enrollment: N/A
men: N/A; women: N/A; minorities: N/A; international: N/A
Acceptance rate (full time): 44%
Average GMAT (full time): 650
Average GPA (full time): 3.62
Average age of entrants to full-time program: 28
Average months of prior work experience (full time): 36
TOEFL requirement: YES
Minimum TOEFL score: 580
Most popular departments: finance, human resources management, marketing, operations management, supply chain management
Mean starting base salary for 2002 full-time graduates: $63,379
Employment location for 2002 class: Intl. 8%; N.E. 6%; M.A. 1%; S. 4%; M.W. 23%; S.W. 6%; W. 52%

University of Utah (Eccles)

1645 E. Campus Center Drive
Room 101
Salt Lake City, UT 84112-9301
Public
Admissions: (801) 581-7785
E-mail:
masters@business.utah.edu
Web site: http://www.business.
utah.edu/masters
Internet application:
http://www.business.utah.edu/
masters/admissions/
onlineapp-real.htm
Financial aid: (801) 581-7785
Application deadline: 03/15
In-state tuition: full time: $5,204; part time: $4,997
Out-of-state tuition: full time: $13,993
Room/board/expenses: $12,000
College-funded aid: YES
International student aid: YES
Fellowships: 71
Research assistantships: 5
Teaching assistantships: 13
Full-time enrollment: 179
men: 71%; women: 29%; minorities: 8%; international: 22%
Part-time enrollment: 218
men: 87%; women: 13%; minorities: 4%; international: 6%
Acceptance rate (full time): 75%
Average GMAT (full time): 615
Average GMAT (part time): 588
Average GPA (full time): 3.48
Average age of entrants to full-time program: 26
Average months of prior work experience (full time): 12
TOEFL requirement: YES
Minimum TOEFL score: 600
Most popular departments: entrepreneurship, finance, international business, marketing, management information systems
Mean starting base salary for 2002 full-time graduates: $46,280
Employment location for 2002 class: Intl. 9%; N.E. 2%; M.A. 2%; S. 2%; M.W. 4%; S.W. 0%; W. 81%

Utah State University

3535 Old Main Hill
Logan, UT 84322-3535
Public
Admissions: (435) 797-2360
E-mail: maryjo.blahna@usu.edu
Web site: http://www.usu.edu
Financial aid: (435) 797-0173
Application deadline: 03/15
In-state tuition: full time: $4,114; part time: $2,672
Out-of-state tuition: full time: $11,322
Room/board/expenses: $5,865
College-funded aid: YES
International student aid: YES
Full-time enrollment: 96
men: N/A; women: N/A; minorities: N/A; international: N/A
Part-time enrollment: 184
men: N/A; women: N/A; minorities: N/A; international: N/A
TOEFL requirement: YES
Minimum TOEFL score: 550
Most popular departments: accounting, entrepreneurship, general management, human resources management, management information systems

Weber State University (Goddard)

3801 University Circle
Ogden, UT 84408-3801
Public
Admissions: (801) 626-7545
E-mail: mba@weber.edu
Web site:
http://goddard.weber.edu/dp/mba
Internet application:
http://goddard.weber.edu/dp/
mba/mba-application.asp
Financial aid: (801) 626-7569
Application deadline: 06/01
In-state tuition: total program:
$5,874 (full time); $5,874 (part
time)
Out-of-state tuition: total program:
$13,905 (full time)
Room/board/expenses: $9,200
College-funded aid: YES
International student aid: YES
Fellowships: 0
Research assistantships: 0
Teaching assistantships: 0
**Average student indebtedness at
graduation:** $0
Full-time enrollment: 101
men: 80%; women: 20%; minorities: 2%; international: 8%
Part-time enrollment: N/A
men: N/A; women: N/A; minorities: N/A; international: N/A
Acceptance rate (full time): 78%
Average GMAT (full time): 570
Average GPA (full time): 3.38
Average age of entrants to full-time program: 32
Average months of prior work experience (full time): 64
TOEFL requirement: YES
Minimum TOEFL score: 550
Most popular departments: accounting, economics, finance,
general management, marketing

VERMONT

University of Vermont

55 Colchester Avenue
Burlington, VT 05405
Public
Admissions: (802) 656-2699
E-mail: mba@uvm.edu
Web site:
http://www.bsad.uvm.edu/mba
Internet application:
http://www.uvm.edu/~
gradcoll/?Page=apply.
html&SM=admissionsmenu.html
Financial aid: (802) 656-8793
Application deadline: 04/01
In-state tuition: full time: N/A; part
time: $347/credit hour
Out-of-state tuition: full time: N/A
Room/board/expenses: $300
College-funded aid: YES
International student aid: YES
Fellowships: 0
Research assistantships: 0
Teaching assistantships: 6
Full-time enrollment: N/A
men: N/A; women: N/A; minorities: N/A; international: N/A
Part-time enrollment: 74
men: 65%; women: 35%; minorities: 4%; international: 5%
Average GMAT (part time): 602
TOEFL requirement: YES
Minimum TOEFL score: 550
Most popular departments: general
management

VIRGINIA

College of William and Mary

PO Box 8795
Williamsburg, VA 23187-8795
Public
Admissions: (757) 221-2900
E-mail:
admissions@business.wm.edu
Web site: http://business.wm.edu
Internet application:
http://business.wm.edu/mba/
admissions
Financial aid: (757) 221-2900
Application deadline: 03/15
In-state tuition: full time: $9,978;
part time: $306/credit hour
Out-of-state tuition: full time:
$21,258
Room/board/expenses: $16,330
College-funded aid: YES
International student aid: YES
Fellowships: 53
Research assistantships: 46
**Average student indebtedness at
graduation:** $28,507
Full-time enrollment: 179
men: 68%; women: 32%; minorities: 9%; international: 38%
Part-time enrollment: 143
men: 75%; women: 25%; minorities: 6%; international: 1%
Acceptance rate (full time): 73%
Average GMAT (full time): 607
Average GMAT (part time): 607
**Average age of entrants to full-time
program:** 28
Average months of prior work experience (full time): 52
TOEFL requirement: YES
Minimum TOEFL score: 600
Most popular departments: finance,
general management, marketing,
management information systems,
operations management
**Mean starting base salary for 2002
full-time graduates:** $70,663
**Employment location for 2002
class:** Intl. 0%; N.E. 12%; M.A.
44%; S. 21%; M.W. 15%; S.W. 3%;
W. 6%

George Mason University

4400 University Drive
Fairfax, VA 22030
Public
Admissions: (703) 993-2136
E-mail: masonmba@som.gmu.edu
Web site:
http://www.som.gmu.edu
Internet application:
http://www.applyweb.com/
apply/gmumba/menu.html
Financial aid: (703) 993-2353
Application deadline: 04/01
In-state tuition: full time: N/A; part
time: $366/credit hour
Out-of-state tuition: full time: N/A
Room/board/expenses: N/A
College-funded aid: YES
International student aid: NO
Fellowships: 0
Research assistantships: 0
Teaching assistantships: 0
Full-time enrollment: N/A
men: N/A; women: N/A; minorities: N/A; international: N/A
Part-time enrollment: 260
men: 29%; women: 71%; minorities: 23%; international: 3%
Average GMAT (part time): 605
TOEFL requirement: YES
Minimum TOEFL score: 580
Most popular departments: entrepreneurship, finance, general
management, marketing,
management information systems

James Madison University

Showker Hall
Harrisonburg, VA 22807
Public
Admissions: (540) 568-3009
E-mail: bahnkb@jmu.edu
Web site:
http://www.jmu.edu/mba/
Financial aid: (540) 568-8059
Application deadline: 06/01
In-state tuition: full time:
$170/credit hour; part time:
$170/credit hour
Out-of-state tuition: full time:
$565/credit hour
Room/board/expenses: $10,000
College-funded aid: YES
International student aid: YES
Fellowships: 0
Research assistantships: 22
Teaching assistantships: 0
**Average student indebtedness at
graduation:** $2,500
Full-time enrollment: N/A
men: N/A; women: N/A; minorities: N/A; international: N/A
Part-time enrollment: 122
men: 57%; women: 43%; minorities: 15%; international: 10%
Average GMAT (part time): 575
**Average age of entrants to full-time
program:** N/A
Average months of prior work experience (full time): N/A
TOEFL requirement: YES
Minimum TOEFL score: 550
Most popular departments: e-commerce, finance, organizational
behavior, other

Old Dominion University

203A Technology Building
Norfolk, VA 23529
Public
Admissions: (757) 683-3585
E-mail: mbainfo@odu.edu
Web site: http://www.odu.edu
Internet application:
http://www.odu-cbpa.org
Financial aid: (757) 683-3683
Application deadline: 06/01
In-state tuition: full time:
$228/credit hour; part time:
$228/credit hour
Out-of-state tuition: full time:
$586/credit hour
Room/board/expenses: $10,728
College-funded aid: YES
International student aid: YES
Fellowships: 0
Research assistantships: 17
Teaching assistantships: 3
Full-time enrollment: 143
men: 50%; women: 50%; minorities: 10%; international: 59%
Part-time enrollment: 221
men: 57%; women: 43%; minorities: 21%; international: 2%
Average GPA (full time): 3.10
TOEFL requirement: YES
Minimum TOEFL score: 550
Most popular departments: finance,
general management, portfolio
management, technology,
transportation

Radford University

Graduate College
PO Box 6956
Radford, VA 24142
Public
Admissions: (540) 831-5431
E-mail: rumba@radford.edu
Web site: http://www.radford.edu
Financial aid: (540) 831-5408
Application deadline: N/A

In-state tuition: full time:
$200/credit hour; part time:
$200/credit hour
Out-of-state tuition: full time:
$365/credit hour
Room/board/expenses: $9,054
College-funded aid: YES
International student aid: YES
Fellowships: 73
Research assistantships: 96
Teaching assistantships: 88
**Average student indebtedness at
graduation:** $12,189
Full-time enrollment: 16
men: 50%; women: 50%; minorities: 38%; international: N/A
Part-time enrollment: 9
men: 56%; women: 44%; minorities: 22%; international: N/A
Average GMAT (full time): 426
Average GMAT (part time): 531
Average GPA (full time): 3.25
**Average age of entrants to full-time
program:** N/A
TOEFL requirement: YES
Minimum TOEFL score: 550

University of Richmond (Robins)[1]

Richard S. Reynolds Graduate
School
Richmond, VA 23173
Private
Admissions: (804) 289-8553
E-mail: mba@richmond.edu
Web site:
http://www.richmond.edu
Financial aid: (804) 289-8438
Tuition: N/A
Room/board/expenses: N/A
Enrollment: N/A

University of Virginia (Darden)

PO Box 6550
Charlottesville, VA 22906
Public
Admissions: (434) 924-7281
E-mail: darden@virginia.edu
Web site:
http://www.darden.virginia.edu
Internet application:
http://www2.darden.virginia.edu/
admissions/
Financial aid: (434) 924-7739
Application deadline: 03/25
In-state tuition: full time: $26,343;
part time: N/A
Out-of-state tuition: full time:
$31,343
Room/board/expenses: $14,000
College-funded aid: YES
International student aid: YES
Fellowships: 140
Research assistantships: 0
Teaching assistantships: 0
**Average student indebtedness at
graduation:** $37,937
Full-time enrollment: 564
men: 72%; women: 28%; minorities: 16%; international: 28%
Part-time enrollment: N/A
men: N/A; women: N/A; minorities: N/A; international: N/A
Acceptance rate (full time): 18%
Average GMAT (full time): 683
Average GPA (full time): 3.34
**Average age of entrants to full-time
program:** 27
Average months of prior work experience (full time): 67
TOEFL requirement: YES
Minimum TOEFL score: 600
Most popular departments: entrepreneurship, finance, general
management, marketing, organizational behavior
**Mean starting base salary for 2002
full-time graduates:** $84,563

**Employment location for 2002
class:** Intl. 9%; N.E. 37%; M.A.
26%; S. 11%; M.W. 6%; S.W. 7%;
W. 3%

Virginia Commonwealth University

1015 Floyd Avenue
PO Box 844000
Richmond, VA 23284-4000
Public
Admissions: (804) 828-4622
E-mail: gsib@vcu.edu
Web site:
http://www.bus.vcu.edu/gsib
Internet application:
http://www.vcu.edu/gradweb/
admission.htm
Financial aid: (804) 828-6669
Application deadline: 06/01
In-state tuition: full time: $6,397;
part time: $300/credit hour
Out-of-state tuition: full time:
$15,465
Room/board/expenses: $8,500
College-funded aid: YES
International student aid: YES
Fellowships: 0
Research assistantships: 15
Teaching assistantships: 0
**Average student indebtedness at
graduation:** $19,839
Full-time enrollment: 61
men: 64%; women: 36%; minorities: 8%; international: 34%
Part-time enrollment: 193
men: 72%; women: 28%; minorities: 5%; international: 10%
Acceptance rate (full time): 61%
Average GMAT (full time): 554
Average GMAT (part time): 554
Average GPA (full time): 3.30
**Average age of entrants to full-time
program:** 26
Average months of prior work experience (full time): 97
TOEFL requirement: YES
Minimum TOEFL score: 600
Most popular departments: accounting, finance, general management, marketing, management
information systems

Virginia Tech (Pamplin)

1044 Pamplin Hall (0209)
Blacksburg, VA 24061
Public
Admissions: (540) 231-6152
E-mail: mba_info@vt.edu
Web site: http://www.mba.vt.edu
Internet application:
https://www.applyweb.com/
apply/vtmba/indexa.html
Financial aid: (540) 231-5179
Application deadline: 02/01
In-state tuition: full time: $6,523;
part time: $296/credit hour
Out-of-state tuition: full time:
$9,758
Room/board/expenses: $10,000
College-funded aid: YES
International student aid: YES
**Average student indebtedness at
graduation:** $19,581
Full-time enrollment: 103
men: 66%; women: 34%; minorities: 8%; international: 42%
Part-time enrollment: 200
men: 63%; women: 38%; minorities: 7%; international: 11%
Acceptance rate (full time): 36%
Average GMAT (full time): 635
Average GMAT (part time): 598
Average GPA (full time): 3.24
**Average age of entrants to full-time
program:** 25
Average months of prior work experience (full time): 32

TOEFL requirement: YES
Minimum TOEFL score: 550
Most popular departments: e-commerce, economics, leadership, marketing, management information systems
Mean starting base salary for 2002 full-time graduates: $55,909
Employment location for 2002 class: Intl. 0%; N.E. 14%; M.A. 57%; S. 21%; M.W. 0%; S.W. 7%; W. 0%

WASHINGTON

Eastern Washington University

668 N. Riverpoint Boulevard
Suite A
Spokane, WA 99202-1660
Public
Admissions: (509) 358-2270
E-mail: mbaprogram@ewu.edu
Web site:
http://www.cbpa.ewu.edu
Internet application:
http://grad.ewu.edu/prospective_
students/prospective_students/
Financial aid: (509) 359-2314
Application deadline: 09/01
In-state tuition: full time: $5,656; part time: $180/credit hour
Out-of-state tuition: full time: $16,248
Room/board/expenses: $7,000
College-funded aid: YES
International student aid: YES
Fellowships: 0
Research assistantships: 2
Teaching assistantships: 2
Full-time enrollment: 28
men: 64%; women: 36%; minorities: 11%; international: 21%
Part-time enrollment: 29
men: 52%; women: 48%; minorities: 7%; international: 34%
Acceptance rate (full time): 81%
Average GMAT (full time): 540
Average GMAT (part time): 515
Average GPA (full time): 3.33
Average age of entrants to full-time program: 23
Average months of prior work experience (full time): 25
TOEFL requirement: YES
Minimum TOEFL score: 580
Most popular departments:
accounting, entrepreneurship, finance, general management, statistics and operations research

Gonzaga University

School of Business Administration
Spokane, WA 99258
Private
Admissions: (509) 323-3414
E-mail:
wilson@jepson.gonzaga.edu
Web site:
http://www.gonzaga.edu/
Academics/Colleges+and+
Schools/School+of+Business+
Administration/default.htm
Financial aid: (509) 323-6582
Application deadline: rolling
Tuition: full time: $495/credit hour; part time: $495/credit hour
Room/board/expenses: N/A
College-funded aid: YES
International student aid: YES
Full-time enrollment: 192
men: 68%; women: 32%; minorities: N/A; international: 23%
Part-time enrollment: N/A
men: N/A; women: N/A; minorities: N/A; international: N/A
Acceptance rate (full time): 86%
Average age of entrants to full-time program: 30

Average months of prior work experience (full time): 48
TOEFL requirement: YES
Minimum TOEFL score: 550
Most popular departments: accounting, finance, general management, marketing, management information systems

Pacific Lutheran University

School of Business
Tacoma, WA 98447
Private
Admissions: (253) 535-7151
E-mail: business@plu.edu
Web site:
http://www.plu.edu/~busa/mba
Internet application:
http://plu.edu/~admi/apply.html
Financial aid: (253) 535-7161
Application deadline: rolling
Tuition: full time: $13,872; part time: $578/credit hour
Room/board/expenses: $6,745
College-funded aid: YES
International student aid: YES
Fellowships: 1
Research assistantships: 11
Teaching assistantships: 0
Full-time enrollment: 63
men: 67%; women: 33%; minorities: 10%; international: 29%
Part-time enrollment: 28
men: 54%; women: 46%; minorities: 11%; international: 4%
Acceptance rate (full time): 89%
Average GMAT (full time): 530
Average GPA (full time): 3.20
Average age of entrants to full-time program: 29
Average months of prior work experience (full time): 89
TOEFL requirement: YES
Minimum TOEFL score: 550
Most popular departments: general management, technology

Seattle Pacific University

3307 Third Avenue W
Seattle, WA 98119
Private
Admissions: (206) 281-2753
E-mail: djwysom@spu.edu
Web site: http://www.spu.edu/sbe
Financial aid: (206) 281-2061
Application deadline: 08/01
Tuition: full time: $482/credit hour; part time: $482/credit hour
Room/board/expenses: $9,500
College-funded aid: NO
International student aid: NO
Full-time enrollment: N/A
men: N/A; women: N/A; minorities: N/A; international: N/A
Part-time enrollment: 124
men: 56%; women: 44%; minorities: 10%; international: 15%
Average GMAT (part time): 508
TOEFL requirement: YES
Minimum TOEFL score: 565
Most popular departments: e-commerce, general management, human resources management, management information systems

Seattle University (Albers)

900 Broadway
Seattle, WA 98122-4340
Private
Admissions: (206) 296-5700
E-mail: carpms@seattleu.edu
Web site:
http://www.seattleu.edu/asbe
Financial aid: (206) 296-5840
Application deadline: 08/20

Tuition: full time: $544/credit hour; part time: $544/credit hour
Room/board/expenses: $11,134
College-funded aid: YES
International student aid: NO
Fellowships: 0
Research assistantships: 0
Teaching assistantships: 0
Full-time enrollment: N/A
men: N/A; women: N/A; minorities: N/A; international: N/A
Part-time enrollment: 519
men: 61%; women: 39%; minorities: 13%; international: 10%
Average GMAT (part time): 561
TOEFL requirement: YES
Minimum TOEFL score: 580
Most popular departments: accounting, finance, general management, international business, marketing

University of Washington

Box 353200
Seattle, WA 98195-3200
Public
Admissions: (206) 543-4661
E-mail: mba@u.washington.edu
Web site:
http://depts.washington.edu/mba/
Financial aid: (206) 543-4661
Application deadline: 03/01
In-state tuition: full time: $8,469; part time: $8,469
Out-of-state tuition: full time: $17,569
Room/board/expenses: $16,990
College-funded aid: YES
International student aid: YES
Average student indebtedness at graduation: $30,030
Full-time enrollment: 258
men: 67%; women: 33%; minorities: 13%; international: 27%
Part-time enrollment: 139
men: 78%; women: 22%; minorities: 19%; international: 6%
Acceptance rate (full time): 31%
Average GMAT (full time): 671
Average GMAT (part time): 668
Average GPA (full time): 3.40
Average age of entrants to full-time program: 29
Average months of prior work experience (full time): 64
TOEFL requirement: YES
Minimum TOEFL score: 600
Most popular departments: entrepreneurship, finance, international business, marketing, operations management
Mean starting base salary for 2002 full-time graduates: $68,474
Employment location for 2002 class: Intl. 7%; N.E. 3%; M.A. 1%; S. N/A; M.W. 1%; S.W. N/A; W. 88%

Washington State University

PO Box 4744
Pullman, WA 99164-4744
Public
Admissions: (509) 335-7617
E-mail: mba@wsu.edu
Web site:
http://www.cbe.wsu.edu/graduate
Internet application:
http://www.gradsch.wsu.edu/
howtoapply.htm
Financial aid: (509) 335-9711
Application deadline: 04/15
In-state tuition: full time: $7,218; part time: $287/credit hour
Out-of-state tuition: full time: $16,004
Room/board/expenses: $6,500
College-funded aid: YES
International student aid: NO

Fellowships: 0
Research assistantships: 15
Teaching assistantships: 15
Full-time enrollment: 156
men: 57%; women: 43%; minorities: 7%; international: 33%
Part-time enrollment: N/A
men: N/A; women: N/A; minorities: N/A; international: N/A
Acceptance rate (full time): 47%
Average GMAT (full time): 582
Average GPA (full time): 3.47
Average age of entrants to full-time program: 27
Average months of prior work experience (full time): 28
TOEFL requirement: YES
Minimum TOEFL score: 580
Most popular departments: finance, international business, management information systems, technology

Western Washington University

516 High Street, MS 9072
Bellingham, WA 98225-9072
Public
Admissions: (360) 650-3898
E-mail: mba@wwu.edu
Web site:
http://www.cbe.wwu.edu/mba/
Internet application:
http://www.cbe.wwu.edu/mba/
Financial aid: (360) 650-3470
Application deadline: 05/01
In-state tuition: full time: $166/credit hour; part time: $166/credit hour
Out-of-state tuition: full time: $505/credit hour
Room/board/expenses: $3,500
College-funded aid: YES
International student aid: YES
Full-time enrollment: 47
men: 64%; women: 36%; minorities: 9%; international: 23%
Part-time enrollment: 15
men: 80%; women: 20%; minorities: 7%; international: 7%
Acceptance rate (full time): 85%
Average GMAT (full time): 542
Average GMAT (part time): 561
Average GPA (full time): 3.32
Average age of entrants to full-time program: 29
Average months of prior work experience (full time): 60
TOEFL requirement: YES
Minimum TOEFL score: 567
Most popular departments: accounting, finance, general management, leadership, marketing

WEST VIRGINIA

Marshall University (Lewis)[1]

1 John Marshall Drive
Huntington, WV 25755-2020
Public
Admissions: (800) 642-9842
E-mail: shumlas@marshall.edu
Web site: http://lcob.marshall.edu
Internet application:
http://www.marshall.edu/
mugc/grad_app.shtml
Financial aid: (800) 438-5390
Tuition: N/A
Room/board/expenses: N/A
Enrollment: N/A

West Virginia University[1]

PO Box 6025
Morgantown, WV 26506
Public
Admissions: (304) 293-5408
E-mail: mba@wvu.edu
Web site: http://www.be.wvu.edu
Financial aid: (304) 293-5242
Tuition: N/A
Room/board/expenses: N/A
Enrollment: N/A

WISCONSIN

Marquette University

606 N. 13th Street
Milwaukee, WI 53233
Private
Admissions: (414) 288-7145
E-mail: mba@Marquette.edu
Web site:
http://www.busadm.mu.edu
Internet application:
http://www.grad.marquette.edu
Financial aid: (414) 288-7137
Application deadline: 07/15
Tuition: full time: $615/credit hour; part time: $615/credit hour
Room/board/expenses: N/A
College-funded aid: YES
International student aid: YES
Research assistantships: 13
Full-time enrollment: N/A
men: N/A; women: N/A; minorities: N/A; international: N/A
Part-time enrollment: 575
men: 69%; women: 31%; minorities: N/A; international: N/A
Average GMAT (part time): 547
TOEFL requirement: YES
Minimum TOEFL score: N/A
Most popular departments: e-commerce, finance, general management, human resources management, marketing

University of Wisconsin–Eau Claire

Schneider Hall 309
Eau Claire, WI 54702-4004
Public
Admissions: (715) 836-6019
E-mail: cob@uwec.edu
Web site: http://www.uwec.edu/
academic/cob/
Internet application:
http://www.uwec.edu/
cob/programs/mba/
framembahome.htm
Financial aid: (715) 836-3373
Application deadline: 08/01
In-state tuition: full time: $300/credit hour; part time: $300/credit hour
Out-of-state tuition: full time: $891/credit hour
Room/board/expenses: $3,500
College-funded aid: YES
International student aid: YES
Fellowships: 2
Research assistantships: 5
Full-time enrollment: N/A
men: N/A; women: N/A; minorities: N/A; international: N/A
Part-time enrollment: 100
men: 55%; women: 45%; minorities: 3%; international: 6%
Average GMAT (part time): 530
TOEFL requirement: YES
Minimum TOEFL score: 550
Most popular departments: accounting, general management, human resources management, marketing, management information systems

University of Wisconsin–La Crosse

1725 State Street
La Crosse, WI 54601
Public
Admissions: (608) 785-8090
E-mail: admissions@uwlax.edu
Web site: http://www.uwlax.edu
Financial aid: (608) 785-8604
Application deadline: 05/01
In-state tuition: full time: $5,566;
part time: $307/credit hour
Out-of-state tuition: full time:
$16,176
Room/board/expenses: $6,400
College-funded aid: YES
International student aid: YES
Fellowships: 0
Research assistantships: 4
Teaching assistantships: 0
Full-time enrollment: N/A
men: N/A; women: N/A; minorities:
N/A; international: N/A
Part-time enrollment: N/A
men: N/A; women: N/A; minorities:
N/A; international: N/A
Average GMAT (part time): 520
TOEFL requirement: YES
Minimum TOEFL score: 550

University of Wisconsin–Madison

3150 Grainger Hall
975 University Avenue
Madison, WI 53706-1323
Public
Admissions: (608) 262-4000
E-mail: uwmadmba@bus.wisc.edu
Web site:
http://www.bus.wisc.edu/
Internet application:
http://www.bus.wisc.edu/
graduateprograms/apply
Financial aid: (608) 262-4000
Application deadline: 04/01
In-state tuition: full time: $8,902;
part time: $13,112
Out-of-state tuition: full time:
$24,272

Room/board/expenses: $17,916
College-funded aid: YES
International student aid: YES
Fellowships: 31
Research assistantships: 149
Teaching assistantships: 63
**Average student indebtedness at
graduation:** $22,788
Full-time enrollment: 355
men: 70%; women: 30%; minori-
ties: 13%; international: 35%
Part-time enrollment: 115
men: 64%; women: 36%; minori-
ties: 7%; international: 7%
Acceptance rate (full time): 27%
Average GMAT (full time): 632
Average GMAT (part time): 573
Average GPA (full time): 3.30
**Average age of entrants to full-time
program:** 28
**Average months of prior work expe-
rience (full time):** 55
TOEFL requirement: YES
Minimum TOEFL score: 600
Most popular departments: entre-
preneurship, finance, marketing,
operations management, real
estate
**Mean starting base salary for 2002
full-time graduates:** $69,013
**Employment location for 2002
class:** Intl. 10%; N.E. 9%; M.A. 3%;
S. 4%; M.W. 60%; S.W. 5%; W.
10%

University of Wisconsin–Milwaukee

PO Box 742
Milwaukee, WI 53201
Public
Admissions: (414) 229-5403
E-mail:
umbusmasters@csd.uwm.edu
Web site: http://www.uwm.edu/
Dept/Business
Internet application:
http://www.uwm.edu/Dept/
Grad_Sch/Prospective/
onlineapp.html
Financial aid: (414) 229-4541

Application deadline: 01/01
In-state tuition: full time: N/A; part
time: N/A
Out-of-state tuition: full time: N/A
Room/board/expenses: N/A
College-funded aid: YES
International student aid: YES
Full-time enrollment: 53
men: 64%; women: 36%; minori-
ties: 19%; international: 17%
Part-time enrollment: 237
men: 59%; women: 41%; minori-
ties: 7%; international: 5%
Acceptance rate (full time): 63%
Average GMAT (full time): 540
Average GMAT (part time): 541
Average GPA (full time): 2.91
**Average age of entrants to full-time
program:** 27
**Average months of prior work expe-
rience (full time):** 28
TOEFL requirement: YES
Minimum TOEFL score: 550
Most popular departments: ac-
counting, finance, marketing,
management information systems,
organizational behavior

University of Wisconsin–Oshkosh[1]

800 Algoma Boulevard
Oshkosh, WI 54901
Public
Admissions: (800) 633-1430
E-mail: mba@uwosh.edu
Web site:
http://www.uwosh.edu/coba/
Financial aid: (920) 424-3377
Tuition: N/A
Room/board/expenses: N/A
Enrollment: N/A

University of Wisconsin–Parkside[1]

Box 2000
Kenosha, WI 53141-2000
Public
Admissions: (262) 595-2046
E-mail: piazza@uwp.edu
Web site: http://www.uwp.edu/
academic/business.technology/
business.html
Financial aid: (262) 595-2574
Tuition: N/A
Room/board/expenses: N/A
Enrollment: N/A

University of Wisconsin–Whitewater

800 W. Main Street
Whitewater, WI 53190
Public
Admissions: (262) 472-1945
E-mail: zahnd@uww.edu
Web site: http://www.uww.edu/
Financial aid: (262) 472-1130
Application deadline: 07/15
In-state tuition: full time:
$301/credit hour; part time:
$301/credit hour
Out-of-state tuition: full time:
$892/credit hour
Room/board/expenses: $5,000
College-funded aid: YES
International student aid: YES
Fellowships: 0
Research assistantships: 14
Teaching assistantships: 0
Full-time enrollment: 92
men: 40%; women: 60%; minori-
ties: 24%; international: 33%
Part-time enrollment: 328
men: 49%; women: 51%; minori-
ties: 5%; international: 2%
Acceptance rate (full time): 82%
Average GMAT (full time): 460
Average GMAT (part time): 491
Average GPA (full time): 3.09

**Average age of entrants to full-time
program:** 22
**Average months of prior work expe-
rience (full time):** 22
TOEFL requirement: YES
Minimum TOEFL score: 550
Most popular departments: finance,
general management,
international business, marketing

WYOMING

University of Wyoming

PO Box 3275
Laramie, WY 82071-3275
Public
Admissions: (307) 766-2449
E-mail: mba@uwyo.edu
Web site: http://business.uwyo.
edu/MBA_index.html
Internet application:
http://business.uwyo.edu/
MBA_apply.html
Financial aid: (307) 766-3886
Application deadline: 02/01
In-state tuition: full time: $3,286;
part time: $166/credit hour
Out-of-state tuition: full time:
$8,974
Room/board/expenses: $6,212
College-funded aid: YES
International student aid: YES
Full-time enrollment: 33
men: 64%; women: 36%; minori-
ties: N/A; international: 18%
Part-time enrollment: 30
men: 47%; women: 53%; minori-
ties: N/A; international: N/A
Acceptance rate (full time): 87%
Average GMAT (full time): 532
Average GMAT (part time): 584
Average GPA (full time): 3.24
**Average age of entrants to full-time
program:** 25
TOEFL requirement: YES
Minimum TOEFL score: 525

EDUCATION

The education school directory lists 188 schools nationwide that offer doctoral programs. One hundred fifty-five schools responded to the *U.S. News* survey, which was conducted in the fall of 2002. Their data, including information on accreditation, entrance requirements, enrollment, the cost of attendance, fellowships and assistantships, and areas of student specialization, are reported below. Schools that did not respond to the survey have abbreviated entries.

TERMINOLOGY

1 A school whose name has been footnoted with the numeral 1 did not return the *U.S. News* statistical survey; limited data appear in its entry.

N/A. Not available from the school or not applicable.

NCATE. National Council for Accreditation of Teacher Education. "Yes," "no," or "applying" indicates NCATE accreditation status as of February 2003. This is the organization that accredits teacher-education schools, colleges, and departments in the United States.

Admissions. The office phone number.

E-mail. The electronic address of the admissions office. If, instead of an E-mail address, a Web site address is listed, the Web site will automatically present an E-mail screen programmed to reach the admissions office.

Internet application. The electronic address for online applications.

Financial aid. The financial aid office phone number.

Application deadline. For fall 2004 enrollment. "Rolling" means there is no application deadline; the school acts on applications as they are received. "Varies" means deadlines vary according to department or whether applicants are U.S. citizens or foreign nationals.

Tuition. For the 2002–2003 academic year. Includes fees.

Room/board/expenses. For the 2002–2003 academic year.

Credit hour. The cost per credit hour for the 2002–2003 academic year.

Enrollment. Full and part time for fall 2002.

Minorities. For fall 2002, percent of students who are Asian-American, African-American, Hispanic, or American Indian. (When the U.S. Department of Education calculates minority enrollment percentages, these are the demographic groupings it uses.)

Acceptance rate. Percent of applicants who were accepted for fall 2002 master's and doctoral programs.

TOEFL requirement. A "yes" means that students from non-English-speaking countries must submit scores for the Test of English as a Foreign Language.

Minimum TOEFL score. The lowest score accepted for admission. The score listed is the minimum acceptable score for the paper TOEFL. (The computer-administered TOEFL is graded on a different scale.)

Entrance test requirement. "GRE" means that Graduate Record Examinations scores are required by some or all departments. "MAT" means that the Miller Analogies Test is required by some or all departments. "GRE or MAT" means that some or all departments require either GRE or MAT scores.

Average GRE scores. Average verbal and quantitative scores for students who entered in fall 2002. Averages are based on the number of students who provided the school with scores. That number may be less than the total number of students entering in fall 2002. The GRE scores published in the ranking table refer to the scores of a school's entering doctoral students and may not be the same as the average GRE scores for the overall entering class printed in the directory.

Total fellowships, teaching assistantships, and research assistantships. For the 2002–2003 academic year.

Students reporting specialty. The percent of graduate students, both full and part time, reporting a program specialization in fall 2002. If this figure is less than 50 percent, this entry and the following do not appear for the school.

Student specialties. Proportion of students in the specialty-reporting population (not necessarily the entire student body) who are enrolled in a particular specialty. Numbers may not add up to 100 because of rounding. The largest specialty areas in graduate education are listed.

ALABAMA

Auburn University–Main Campus
3084 Haley Center
Auburn University, AL 36849
Public
NCATE accredited: YES
Admissions: (334) 844-4700
Web site: http://www.auburn.edu/
Financial aid: (334) 844-4723
Application deadline: N/A
In-state tuition: full time: $3,784; part time: $151/credit hour
Out-of-state tuition: full time: $11,084
Room/board/expenses: $8,126
Full-time enrollment: 288
doctoral students: 28%; master's students: 71%; education specialists: 1%; men: 29%; women: 71%; minorities: 16%; international: 5%
Part-time enrollment: 306
doctoral students: 49%; master's students: 47%; education specialists: 4%; men: 31%; women: 69%; minorities: 18%; international: 1%
Acceptance rate (master's): 69%
Acceptance rate (doctoral): 57%
Entrance test required: GRE
Avg. GRE (of all entering students with scores): quantitative: 498; verbal 444
TOEFL requirement: YES
Minimum TOEFL score: 550
Teaching assistantships: 65
Research assistantships: 18
Students reporting specialty: 96%
Students specializing in: admin.: 6%; counseling: 10%; educational psych.: 2%; elementary: 4%; higher education admin.: 9%; secondary: 16%; special: 8%; technical (vocational): 4%; instructional media design: 2%; other: 40%

University of Alabama–Birmingham[1]
1530 Third Avenue N
EB 217
Birmingham, AL 35294
Public
NCATE accredited: YES
Admissions: (205) 934-8227
E-mail: gradschool@uab.edu
Web site: http://www.uab.edu/graduate
Internet application: http://www.uab.edu/graduate/apply/frame.htm
Financial aid: (205) 934-8223
Tuition: N/A
Room/board/expenses: N/A
Enrollment: N/A

University of Alabama–Tuscaloosa
Box 870231
Tuscaloosa, AL 35487-0231
Public
NCATE accredited: YES
Admissions: (205) 348-5921
E-mail: usgradapply@aalan.ua.edu
Web site: http://graduate.ua.edu
Financial aid: (205) 348-6756
Application deadline: 06/15
In-state tuition: full time: $3,556; part time: N/A

Out-of-state tuition: full time: $9,624
Room/board/expenses: $6,938
Full-time enrollment: 295
doctoral students: 40%; master's students: 54%; education specialists: 7%; men: 32%; women: 68%; minorities: 13%; international: 7%
Part-time enrollment: 492
doctoral students: 33%; master's students: 40%; education specialists: 26%; men: 29%; women: 71%; minorities: 12%; international: 1%
Acceptance rate (master's): 64%
Acceptance rate (doctoral): 56%
Entrance test required: GRE or MAT
Avg. GRE (of all entering students with scores): quantitative: 554; verbal 453
TOEFL requirement: YES
Minimum TOEFL score: 550
Fellowships: 0
Teaching assistantships: 41
Research assistantships: 56
Students reporting specialty: 100%
Students specializing in: admin.: 27%; counseling: 9%; evaluation/research/statistics: 2%; educational psych.: 5%; elementary: 16%; higher education admin.: 8%; secondary: 22%; special: 7%; other: 4%

University of South Alabama
UCOM 3600
Mobile, AL 36688
Public
NCATE accredited: YES
Admissions: (251) 460-6141
E-mail: admiss@usouthal.edu
Web site: http://www.southalabama.edu
Internet application: http://www.southalabama.edu/admissions/
Financial aid: (251) 460-6231
Application deadline: N/A
In-state tuition: full time: $135/credit hour; part time: $135/credit hour
Out-of-state tuition: full time: $270/credit hour
Room/board/expenses: $1,840
Full-time enrollment: 456
doctoral students: 8%; master's students: 92%; education specialists: N/A; men: 20%; women: 80%; minorities: 27%; international: 3%
Part-time enrollment: 600
doctoral students: 10%; master's students: 81%; education specialists: 10%; men: 19%; women: 81%; minorities: 18%; international: 1%
Acceptance rate (master's): 85%
Acceptance rate (doctoral): 50%
Entrance test required: N/A
Avg. GRE (of all entering students with scores): quantitative: N/A; verbal N/A
TOEFL requirement: YES
Minimum TOEFL score: 500
Students reporting specialty: N/A
Students specializing in: N/A

ARIZONA

Arizona State University–Main Campus
Box 870211
Tempe, AZ 85287-0211
Public
NCATE accredited: NO
Admissions: (480) 965-6113
E-mail: asugrad@asu.edu
Web site:
http://www.asu.edu/graduate
Internet application:
http://www.asu.edu/graduate/
forms/
Financial aid: (480) 965-3521
Application deadline: rolling
In-state tuition: full time: $2,584;
part time: $131/credit hour
Out-of-state tuition: full time:
$11,104
Room/board/expenses: $10,996
Full-time enrollment: 460
doctoral students: 56%; master's
students: 44%; education special-
ists: N/A; men: 30%; women: 70%;
minorities: 23%; international: 15%
Part-time enrollment: 722
doctoral students: 37%; master's
students: 63%; education special-
ists: N/A; men: 24%; women: 76%;
minorities: 17%; international: 3%
Acceptance rate (master's): 42%
Acceptance rate (doctoral): 21%
Entrance test required: GRE or
MAT
**Avg. GRE (of all entering students
with scores):** quantitative: 593;
verbal 576
TOEFL requirement: YES
Minimum TOEFL score: 550
Fellowships: 32
Teaching assistantships: 80
Research assistantships: 97
Students reporting specialty: 100%
Students specializing in: admin.:
14%; counseling: 15%; curricu-
lum/instr.: 31%; social/philosophi-
cal foundations: 1%; policy: 4%;
educational psych.: 8%; elemen-
tary: 9%; higher education admin.:
7%; secondary: 1%; special: 3%;
instructional media design: 8%

Northern Arizona University
College of Education
PO Box 5774
Flagstaff, AZ 86011-5774
Public
NCATE accredited: NO
Admissions: (928) 523-4348
E-mail:
Graduate.College@nau.edu
Web site:
http://www.nau.edu/gradcol
Internet application:
http://www.nau.edu/gradcol/
appoptions.htm
Financial aid: (928) 523-4951
Application deadline: 03/15
In-state tuition: full time: $2,663;
part time: $142/credit hour
Out-of-state tuition: full time:
$11,183
Room/board/expenses: $11,178
Full-time enrollment: 774
doctoral students: 6%; master's
students: 94%; education special-
ists: 0%; men: 26%; women: 74%;
minorities: 27%; international: 2%
Part-time enrollment: 2,889
doctoral students: 6%; master's
students: 94%; education specialists: N/A; men: 25%; women: 75%;
minorities: 24%; international: 0%
Acceptance rate (master's): 81%
Acceptance rate (doctoral): 48%

Entrance test required: GRE or
MAT
**Avg. GRE (of all entering students
with scores):** quantitative: 472;
verbal 457
Minimum TOEFL score: 550
Fellowships: 0
Teaching assistantships: 22
Research assistantships: 3
Students reporting specialty: N/A
Students specializing in: N/A

University of Arizona
Box 210069
1430 E. Second Street
Tucson, AZ 85721-0069
Public
NCATE accredited: NO
Admissions: (520) 621-3132
E-mail: gradadm@lorax.admin.ari-
zona.edu
Web site:
http://www.ed.arizona.edu
Internet application:
http://www.arizona.edu/
html/grad.html
Financial aid: (520) 621-1858
Application deadline: 06/01
In-state tuition: full time: $2,680;
part time: $131/credit hour
Out-of-state tuition: full time:
$11,200
Room/board/expenses: $9,581
Full-time enrollment: 399
doctoral students: 36%; master's
students: 58%; education special-
ists: 6%; men: 28%; women: 72%;
minorities: 20%; international: 13%
Part-time enrollment: 481
doctoral students: 52%; master's
students: 47%; education special-
ists: 1%; men: 26%; women: 74%;
minorities: 30%; international: 6%
Acceptance rate (master's): 77%
Acceptance rate (doctoral): 62%
Entrance test required: GRE or
MAT
**Avg. GRE (of all entering students
with scores):** quantitative: 537;
verbal 480
TOEFL requirement: YES
Minimum TOEFL score: 550
Fellowships: 261
Teaching assistantships: 45
Research assistantships: 28
Students reporting specialty: 97%
Students specializing in: counsel-
ing: 4%; curriculum/instr.: 15%;
evaluation/research/statistics: 4%;
policy: 5%; educational psych.:
12%; higher education admin.:
14%; special: 25%; other: 21%

ARKANSAS

University of Arkansas–Fayetteville
324 Graduate Education Building
Fayetteville, AR 72701
Public
NCATE accredited: YES
Admissions: (479) 575-4401
E-mail: gradinfo@cavern.uark.edu
Web site: http://www.uark.edu
Internet application:
http://www.uark.edu/depts/
gradinfo/
Financial aid: (479) 575-3806
Application deadline: N/A
In-state tuition: full time:
$211/credit hour; part time:
$211/credit hour
Out-of-state tuition: full time:
$500/credit hour
Room/board/expenses: $6,750
Full-time enrollment: 292
doctoral students: 20%; master's
students: 79%; education special-
ists: 2%; men: 27%; women: 73%;
minorities: 17%; international: 7%

Part-time enrollment: 404
doctoral students: 32%; master's
students: 63%; education special-
ists: 4%; men: 34%; women: 66%;
minorities: 17%; international: 3%
Acceptance rate (master's): 75%
Acceptance rate (doctoral): 63%
Entrance test required: GRE or
MAT
**Avg. GRE (of all entering students
with scores):** quantitative: 517;
verbal 439
TOEFL requirement: YES
Minimum TOEFL score: 550
Fellowships: 11
Teaching assistantships: 25
Research assistantships: 11
Students reporting specialty: 100%
Students specializing in: admin.:
9%; counseling: 7%;
curriculum/instr.: 5%; elementary:
8%; higher education admin.:
11%; junior high: 2%; secondary:
5%; special: 3%; technical (voca-
tional): 4%; instructional media design: 4%; other: 41%

University of Arkansas–Little Rock[1]
2801 S. University Avenue
Little Rock, AR 72204
Public
NCATE accredited: YES
Admissions: (501) 569-3127
E-mail: gradinfo@ualr.edu
Web site: http://www.ualr.
edu/%7Egraddept/gsprodegs.html
Internet application:
http://www.ualr.
edu/%7Egraddept/forms.html
Financial aid: (501) 569-3450
Tuition: N/A
Room/board/expenses: N/A
Enrollment: N/A

CALIFORNIA

Alliant International University
10455 Pomerado Road
San Diego, CA 92131
Private
NCATE accredited: APPLYING
Admissions: (866) 825-5426
E-mail: admissions@alliant.edu
Web site: http://www.alliant.edu/
Internet application:
http://www.alliant.edu/apply/
Financial aid: (858) 635-4559
Application deadline: 08/01
Tuition: full time: $350/credit hour;
part time: $350/credit hour
Room/board/expenses: $17,240
Full-time enrollment: 67
doctoral students: 33%; master's
students: 67%; education special-
ists: 0%; men: 21%; women: 79%;
minorities: 49%; international: 1%
Part-time enrollment: 231
doctoral students: 46%; master's
students: 54%; education special-
ists: 0%; men: 22%; women: 78%;
minorities: 38%; international: 2%
Acceptance rate (master's): 78%
Acceptance rate (doctoral): 56%
Entrance test required: NONE
**Avg. GRE (of all entering students
with scores):** quantitative: N/A;
verbal N/A
TOEFL requirement: YES
Minimum TOEFL score: 550
Fellowships: 1
Teaching assistantships: 5
Research assistantships: 2
Students reporting specialty: 100%
Students specializing in: admin.:
9%; curriculum/instr.: 0%; educa-
tional psych.: 6%; other: 85%

Claremont Graduate University[1]
150 E. 10th Street
Claremont, CA 91711
Private
NCATE accredited: NO
Admissions: (909) 621-8069
E-mail: barbara.jefferson@cgu.edu
Web site: http://www.cgu.edu/ces/
Internet application:
http://www.applyweb.com/aw?cgu
Financial aid: (909) 621-8337
Tuition: N/A
Room/board/expenses: N/A
Enrollment: N/A

Fielding Graduate Institute
2112 Santa Barbara Street
Santa Barbara, CA 93105
Private
NCATE accredited: NO
Admissions: (800) 340-1099
E-mail: admissions@fielding.edu
Web site: http://www.fielding.edu
Financial aid: (805) 898-4008
Application deadline: 08/11
Tuition: full time: $13,740; part
time: N/A
Room/board/expenses: $22,354
Full-time enrollment: 273
doctoral students: 100%; master's
students: 0%; education special-
ists: N/A; men: 29%; women: 71%;
minorities: 62%; international: 2%
Part-time enrollment: N/A
doctoral students: N/A; master's
students: N/A; education special-
ists: N/A; men: N/A; women: N/A;
minorities: N/A; international: N/A
Acceptance rate (master's): N/A
Acceptance rate (doctoral): 75%
Entrance test required: N/A
**Avg. GRE (of all entering students
with scores):** quantitative: N/A;
verbal N/A
TOEFL requirement: NO
Minimum TOEFL score: N/A
Fellowships: 0
Teaching assistantships: 0
Research assistantships: 1
Students reporting specialty: 100%
Students specializing in:
admin.: 100%

Pepperdine University[1]
24255 Pacific Coast Highway
Malibu, CA 90263-4301
Private
NCATE accredited: NO
Admissions: (310) 568-5600
E-mail: gsep@pepperdine.edu
Web site:
http://gsep.pepperdine.edu/
Internet application:
http://gsep.pepperdine.edu/
programs/application/
Financial aid: (310) 258-2848
Tuition: N/A
Room/board/expenses: N/A
Enrollment: N/A

San Diego State University
College of Education
San Diego, CA 92812
Public
NCATE accredited: YES
Admissions: (619) 594-6544
E-mail:
cnecoechea@mail.sdsu.edu
Web site: http://www.sdsu.edu
Internet application:
http://www.csumentor.edu/
admissionapp/
Financial aid: (619) 594-6323
Application deadline: 11/01

In-state tuition: full time: $1,948;
part time: $1,318
Out-of-state tuition: full time:
$4,986
Room/board/expenses: $11,476
Full-time enrollment: 326
doctoral students: 1%; master's
students: 99%; education special-
ists: N/A; men: 33%; women: 67%;
minorities: 58%; international: 8%
Part-time enrollment: 965
doctoral students: 13%; master's
students: 87%; education special-
ists: N/A; men: 27%; women: 73%;
minorities: 32%; international: 14%
Acceptance rate (master's): 56%
Acceptance rate (doctoral): 51%
Entrance test required: GRE
**Avg. GRE (of all entering students
with scores):** quantitative: 492;
verbal 465
TOEFL requirement: YES
Minimum TOEFL score: 550
Fellowships: 79
Teaching assistantships: 9
Research assistantships: 12
Students reporting specialty: 100%
Students specializing in: admin.:
17%; counseling: 7%;
curriculum/instr.: 34%; special:
3%; instructional media design:
8%; other: 30%

Stanford University
School of Education
485 Lasuen Mall
Stanford, CA 94305-3096
Private
NCATE accredited: YES
Admissions: (650) 723-4794
E-mail: info@edumail.stanford.edu
Web site:
http://ed.stanford.edu/suse/
index.html
Internet application:
https://apply.embark.com/
grad/stanford
Financial aid: (650) 723-4794
Application deadline: 01/02
Tuition: full time: $27,404; part
time: N/A
Room/board/expenses: $15,495
Full-time enrollment: 361
doctoral students: 53%; master's
students: 47%; education special-
ists: 0%; men: 32%; women: 68%;
minorities: 30%; international: 13%
Part-time enrollment: N/A
doctoral students: N/A; master's
students: N/A; education special-
ists: N/A; men: N/A; women: N/A;
minorities: N/A; international: N/A
Acceptance rate (master's): 54%
Acceptance rate (doctoral): 11%
Entrance test required: GRE
**Avg. GRE (of all entering students
with scores):** quantitative: 646;
verbal 552
TOEFL requirement: YES
Minimum TOEFL score: 600
Fellowships: 126
Teaching assistantships: 62
Research assistantships: 101
Students reporting specialty: 100%
Students specializing in: admin.:
1%; curriculum/instr.: 15%; evalua-
tion/research/statistics: 5%; so-
cial/philosophical foundations:
18%; policy: 8%; educational
psych.: 13%; higher education
admin.: 2%; secondary: 17%; instructional media design: 5%;
other: 15%

University of California–Berkeley
1600 Tolman Hall
MC #1670
Berkeley, CA 94720-1670
Public
NCATE accredited: NO
Admissions: (510) 642-0841
E-mail: gse_info@uclink4.berkeley.edu
Web site: http://gse.berkeley.edu
Internet application: http://gse.berkeley.edu/admin/sas/requirements.html
Financial aid: (510) 643-1720
Application deadline: 12/15
In-state tuition: full time: $4,431; part time: N/A
Out-of-state tuition: full time: $15,563
Room/board/expenses: $17,936
Full-time enrollment: 453
doctoral students: 55%; master's students: 45%; education specialists: 0%; men: 26%; women: 74%; minorities: 41%; international: 6%
Part-time enrollment: N/A
doctoral students: N/A; master's students: N/A; education specialists: N/A; men: N/A; women: N/A; minorities: N/A; international: N/A
Acceptance rate (master's): 37%
Acceptance rate (doctoral): 20%
Entrance test required: GRE
Avg. GRE (of all entering students with scores): quantitative: 613; verbal 557
TOEFL requirement: YES
Minimum TOEFL score: 570
Fellowships: 290
Teaching assistantships: 30
Research assistantships: 140
Students reporting specialty: 100%
Students specializing in: admin.: 11%; evaluation/research/statistics: 4%; social/philosophical foundations: 6%; policy: 6%; educational psych.: 13%; elementary: 11%; secondary: 17%; special: 6%; other: 27%

University of California–Davis
2077 Academic Surge
1 Shields Avenue
Davis, CA 95616
Public
NCATE accredited: NO
Admissions: (530) 752-0761
E-mail: kbray@ucdavis.edu
Web site: http://education.ucdavis.edu
Internet application: http://gradstudies.ucdavis.edu
Financial aid: (530) 752-9246
Application deadline: 12/15
In-state tuition: full time: $4,890; part time: $4,890
Out-of-state tuition: full time: $16,022
Room/board/expenses: N/A
Full-time enrollment: 61
doctoral students: 90%; master's students: 10%; education specialists: N/A; men: 38%; women: 62%; minorities: 2%; international: N/A
Part-time enrollment: 2
doctoral students: 100%; master's students: 0%; education specialists: N/A; men: 100%; women: N/A; minorities: N/A; international: N/A
Acceptance rate (master's): 41%
Acceptance rate (doctoral): 31%
Entrance test required: GRE or MAT
Avg. GRE (of all entering students with scores): quantitative: 500; verbal 605
TOEFL requirement: YES
Minimum TOEFL score: 550
Fellowships: 45
Teaching assistantships: 25
Research assistantships: 9
Students reporting specialty: 78%
Students specializing in: curriculum/instr.: 59%; policy: 24%; educational psych.: 14%; other: 2%

University of California–Los Angeles
1009 Moore Hall
MB 951521
Los Angeles, CA 90095-1521
Public
NCATE accredited: NO
Admissions: (310) 825-8326
E-mail: info@gseis.ucla.edu
Web site: http://www.gseis.ucla.edu
Internet application: http://www.gdnet.ucla.edu/
Financial aid: (310) 206-0400
Application deadline: 12/15
In-state tuition: full time: $4,549; part time: $4,549
Out-of-state tuition: full time: $15,681
Room/board/expenses: $16,428
Full-time enrollment: 686
doctoral students: 39%; master's students: 61%; education specialists: 0%; men: 27%; women: 73%; minorities: 55%; international: 4%
Part-time enrollment: 80
doctoral students: 100%; master's students: 0%; education specialists: 0%; men: 54%; women: 46%; minorities: 40%; international: N/A
Acceptance rate (master's): 51%
Acceptance rate (doctoral): 27%
Entrance test required: GRE or MAT
Avg. GRE (of all entering students with scores): quantitative: 589; verbal 535
TOEFL requirement: YES
Minimum TOEFL score: 560
Fellowships: 349
Teaching assistantships: 12
Research assistantships: 203
Students reporting specialty: 100%
Students specializing in: admin.: 17%; counseling: 2%; curriculum/instr.: 5%; evaluation/research/statistics: 5%; social/philosophical foundations: 9%; policy: 3%; educational psych.: 8%; elementary: 26%; higher education admin.: 7%; secondary: 17%; special: 1%; instructional media design: 1%

University of California–Riverside
Graduate School of Education
Riverside, CA 92521
Public
NCATE accredited: NO
Admissions: (909) 787-6332
E-mail: edgrad@citrus.ucr.edu
Web site: http://www.education.ucr.edu
Financial aid: (909) 787-6362
Application deadline: 05/01
In-state tuition: full time: $10,350; part time: N/A
Out-of-state tuition: full time: $22,317
Room/board/expenses: $10,000
Full-time enrollment: N/A
doctoral students: N/A; master's students: N/A; education specialists: N/A; men: N/A; women: N/A; minorities: N/A; international: N/A
Part-time enrollment: N/A
doctoral students: N/A; master's students: N/A; education specialists: N/A; men: N/A; women: N/A; minorities: N/A; international: N/A
Acceptance rate (master's): 49%
Acceptance rate (doctoral): 40%
Entrance test required: N/A
Avg. GRE (of all entering students with scores): quantitative: 458; verbal 411
TOEFL requirement: YES
Minimum TOEFL score: 550
Students reporting specialty: N/A
Students specializing in: N/A

University of California–Santa Barbara (Gevirtz)
Gevirtz Graduate School of Education
Santa Barbara, CA 93106-9490
Public
NCATE accredited: NO
Admissions: (805) 893-2137
E-mail: vzumdahl@education.ucsb.edu
Web site: http://www.education.ucsb.edu
Internet application: http://www.graddiv.ucsb.edu/eapp/
Financial aid: (805) 893-2432
Application deadline: N/A
In-state tuition: full time: $5,166; part time: N/A
Out-of-state tuition: full time: $16,488
Room/board/expenses: $16,030
Full-time enrollment: 378
doctoral students: 61%; master's students: 37%; education specialists: 2%; men: 22%; women: 78%; minorities: 29%; international: 6%
Part-time enrollment: N/A
doctoral students: N/A; master's students: N/A; education specialists: N/A; men: N/A; women: N/A; minorities: N/A; international: N/A
Acceptance rate (master's): 55%
Acceptance rate (doctoral): 37%
Entrance test required: GRE or MAT
Avg. GRE (of all entering students with scores): quantitative: 567; verbal 505
TOEFL requirement: YES
Minimum TOEFL score: N/A
Fellowships: 525
Teaching assistantships: 119
Research assistantships: 82
Students reporting specialty: 100%
Students specializing in: counseling: 3%; curriculum/instr.: 17%; evaluation/research/statistics: 2%; policy: 11%; elementary: 13%; secondary: 15%; special: 8%; other: 31%

University of La Verne
1950 Third Street
La Verne, CA 91750
Private
NCATE accredited: NO
Admissions: (909) 593-3511
E-mail: bakerj@ulv.edu
Web site: http://www.ulv.edu
Financial aid: (909) 593-3511
Application deadline: rolling
Tuition: full time: $600/credit hour; part time: $600/credit hour
Room/board/expenses: N/A
Full-time enrollment: 765
doctoral students: 25%; master's students: 75%; education specialists: 0%; men: 27%; women: 73%; minorities: 35%; international: 0%
Part-time enrollment: 523
doctoral students: 25%; master's students: 75%; education specialists: 0%; men: 27%; women: 73%; minorities: 35%; international: 0%
Acceptance rate (master's): N/A
Acceptance rate (doctoral): 62%
Entrance test required: GRE or MAT
Avg. GRE (of all entering students with scores): quantitative: N/A; verbal N/A
TOEFL requirement: YES
Minimum TOEFL score: 550
Students reporting specialty: 100%
Students specializing in: admin.: 39%; counseling: 15%; other: 46%

University of San Diego
5998 Alcala Park
San Diego, CA 92110-2492
Private
NCATE accredited: APPLYING
Admissions: (619) 260-4506
E-mail: grads@sandiego.edu
Web site: http://www.sandiego.edu/soe
Internet application: http://www.sandiego.edu/gradmiss/application.html
Financial aid: (619) 260-4514
Application deadline: 05/01
Tuition: full time: $775/credit hour; part time: $775/credit hour
Room/board/expenses: $12,152
Full-time enrollment: 129
doctoral students: 5%; master's students: 95%; education specialists: N/A; men: 25%; women: 75%; minorities: 31%; international: 2%
Part-time enrollment: 263
doctoral students: 54%; master's students: 46%; education specialists: N/A; men: 32%; women: 68%; minorities: 22%; international: 3%
Acceptance rate (master's): 83%
Acceptance rate (doctoral): 77%
Entrance test required: GRE or MAT
Avg. GRE (of all entering students with scores): quantitative: N/A; verbal N/A
TOEFL requirement: YES
Minimum TOEFL score: 580
Fellowships: 9
Teaching assistantships: 1
Research assistantships: 4
Students reporting specialty: 100%
Students specializing in: admin.: 41%; counseling: 20%; curriculum/instr.: 39%

University of San Francisco
2130 Fulton Street
San Francisco, CA 94117-1080
Private
NCATE accredited: NO
Admissions: (415) 422-6563
E-mail: admissions@usfca.edu
Web site: http://www.usfca.edu
Internet application: http://www.usfca.edu/acadserv/admission/gradandadult/apply.html
Financial aid: (415) 422-6303
Application deadline: N/A
Tuition: full time: $28,800; part time: $28,800
Room/board/expenses: $11,440
Full-time enrollment: 648
doctoral students: 25%; master's students: 75%; education specialists: N/A; men: 26%; women: 74%; minorities: 28%; international: 10%
Part-time enrollment: 356
doctoral students: 40%; master's students: 60%; education specialists: N/A; men: 27%; women: 73%; minorities: 27%; international: 3%
Acceptance rate (master's): 76%
Acceptance rate (doctoral): 72%
Entrance test required: GRE or MAT
Avg. GRE (of all entering students with scores): quantitative: N/A; verbal N/A
TOEFL requirement: YES
Minimum TOEFL score: 570
Teaching assistantships: 16
Research assistantships: 10
Students reporting specialty: 100%
Students specializing in: admin.: 6%; counseling: 7%; curriculum/instr.: 4%; educational psych.: 16%; elementary: 22%; higher education admin.: 13%; secondary: 7%; special: 5%; instructional media design: 2%; other: 18%

University of Southern California (Rossier)
3470 Trousdale Parkway
Waite Phillips Hall
Los Angeles, CA 90089-0031
Private
NCATE accredited: NO
Admissions: (213) 740-2606
E-mail: soeinfo@usc.edu
Web site: http://www.usc.edu/dept/education/
Internet application: http://www.usc.edu/dept/education/admission_graduate.html
Financial aid: (213) 740-2157
Application deadline: 12/01
Tuition: full time: $891/credit hour; part time: $891/credit hour
Room/board/expenses: $11,948
Full-time enrollment: 641
doctoral students: 64%; master's students: 36%; education specialists: N/A; men: 27%; women: 73%; minorities: 41%; international: 12%
Part-time enrollment: 334
doctoral students: 66%; master's students: 34%; education specialists: N/A; men: 38%; women: 62%; minorities: 43%; international: 5%
Acceptance rate (master's): 67%
Acceptance rate (doctoral): 38%
Entrance test required: GRE
Avg. GRE (of all entering students with scores): quantitative: 598; verbal 500
TOEFL requirement: NO
Minimum TOEFL score: N/A
Fellowships: 17
Teaching assistantships: 15
Research assistantships: 14
Students reporting specialty: 100%
Students specializing in: admin.: 38%; curriculum/instr.: 28%; policy: 7%; educational psych.: 5%; higher education admin.: 6%; special: 1%; other: 15%

COLORADO

Colorado State University
Graduate School
Fort Collins, CO 80523-2015
Public
NCATE accredited: YES
Admissions: (970) 491-6909
E-mail: gschool@grad.colostate.edu
Web site: http://www.colostate.edu/
Internet application: http://www.colostate.edu/Depts/Grad
Financial aid: (970) 491-6321
Application deadline: N/A

In-state tuition: full time: $3,838; part time: $170/credit hour
Out-of-state tuition: full time: $13,218
Room/board/expenses: $9,520
Full-time enrollment: 122
doctoral students: 28%; master's students: 72%; education specialists: N/A; men: 35%; women: 65%; minorities: 2%; international: 1%
Part-time enrollment: 360
doctoral students: 46%; master's students: 54%; education specialists: N/A; men: 37%; women: 63%; minorities: N/A; international: N/A
Acceptance rate (master's): 54%
Acceptance rate (doctoral): 74%
Entrance test required: GRE
Avg. GRE (of all entering students with scores): quantitative: N/A; verbal N/A
TOEFL requirement: YES
Minimum TOEFL score: 550
Fellowships: 5
Teaching assistantships: 14
Research assistantships: 5
Students reporting specialty: 100%
Students specializing in: admin.: 8%; counseling: 32%; curriculum/instr.: 3%; policy: 12%; higher education admin.: 22%; secondary: 7%; other: 15%

University of Colorado–Boulder

Campus Box 249
Boulder, CO 80309-0249
Public
NCATE accredited: YES
Admissions: (303) 492-6555
E-mail: edadvise@colorado.edu
Web site: http://www.colorado.edu/education
Internet application: http://www.colorado.edu/education/admissions/index.html
Financial aid: (303) 492-5091
Application deadline: 02/01
In-state tuition: full time: $2,428; part time: $618/credit hour
Out-of-state tuition: full time: $10,438
Room/board/expenses: $12,198
Full-time enrollment: 211
doctoral students: 28%; master's students: 72%; education specialists: N/A; men: 28%; women: 72%; minorities: 8%; international: 1%
Part-time enrollment: 216
doctoral students: 6%; master's students: 94%; education specialists: N/A; men: 11%; women: 89%; minorities: 16%; international: N/A
Acceptance rate (master's): 80%
Acceptance rate (doctoral): 41%
Entrance test required: GRE or MAT
Avg. GRE (of all entering students with scores): quantitative: 623; verbal 573
TOEFL requirement: YES
Minimum TOEFL score: 500
Fellowships: 10
Teaching assistantships: 54
Research assistantships: 68
Students reporting specialty: 100%
Students specializing in: curriculum/instr.: 36%; evaluation/research/statistics: 2%; policy: 6%; educational psych.: 4%; elementary: 10%; secondary: 13%; other: 30%

University of Colorado–Denver

Campus Box 106
PO Box 173364
Denver, CO 80217-3364
Public
NCATE accredited: YES
Admissions: (303) 556-8854
E-mail: lori_sisneros@ceo.cudenver.edu
Web site: http://www.cudenver.edu
Internet application: http://carbon.cudenver.edu/public/education
Financial aid: (303) 556-2886
Application deadline: 02/15
In-state tuition: full time: $4,506; part time: $1,792
Out-of-state tuition: full time: $15,922
Room/board/expenses: $7,895
Full-time enrollment: 471
doctoral students: 11%; master's students: 81%; education specialists: 8%; men: 18%; women: 82%; minorities: 11%; international: 1%
Part-time enrollment: 870
doctoral students: 2%; master's students: 90%; education specialists: 8%; men: 20%; women: 80%; minorities: 11%; international: 1%
Acceptance rate (master's): 81%
Acceptance rate (doctoral): 51%
Entrance test required: GRE or MAT
Avg. GRE (of all entering students with scores): quantitative: 564; verbal 466
TOEFL requirement: YES
Minimum TOEFL score: 500
Fellowships: 18
Teaching assistantships: 0
Research assistantships: 20
Students reporting specialty: 100%
Students specializing in: admin.: 15%; counseling: 0%; curriculum/instr.: 17%; evaluation/research/statistics: 0%; educational psych.: 3%; elementary: 19%; secondary: 8%; special: 6%; instructional media design: 3%; other: 28%

University of Denver

Graduate Office
A. Hyde Building
Denver, CO 80208
Private
NCATE accredited: NO
Admissions: (303) 871-2509
E-mail: educ03@denver.du.edu
Web site: http://www.du.edu/education/
Financial aid: (303) 871-4900
Application deadline: N/A
Tuition: full time: $630/credit hour; part time: $630/credit hour
Room/board/expenses: N/A
Full-time enrollment: 136
doctoral students: 44%; master's students: 44%; education specialists: 12%; men: 20%; women: 80%; minorities: 10%; international: 4%
Part-time enrollment: 187
doctoral students: 42%; master's students: 55%; education specialists: 3%; men: 23%; women: 77%; minorities: 16%; international: 2%
Acceptance rate (master's): 47%
Acceptance rate (doctoral): 43%
Entrance test required: GRE
Avg. GRE (of all entering students with scores): quantitative: 500; verbal 550
Minimum TOEFL score: 550
Fellowships: 15
Teaching assistantships: 5
Research assistantships: 18
Students reporting specialty: 99%
Students specializing in: admin.: 15%; counseling: 23%; curriculum/instr.: 11%; evaluation/research/statistics: 2%; educational psych.: 10%; elementary: 13%; higher education admin.: 11%; special: 1%; other: 14%

University of Northern Colorado

College of Education
Greeley, CO 80639
Public
NCATE accredited: YES
Admissions: (970) 351-2831
E-mail: gradsch@unco.edu
Web site: http://www.unco.edu/grad/
Internet application: http://www.unco.edu/grad/admissions/admissions.htm
Financial aid: (970) 351-2502
Application deadline: N/A
In-state tuition: full time: $3,343; part time: $151/credit hour
Out-of-state tuition: full time: $11,903
Room/board/expenses: $8,643
Full-time enrollment: 272
doctoral students: 32%; master's students: 64%; education specialists: 4%; men: 24%; women: 76%; minorities: 8%; international: 8%
Part-time enrollment: 338
doctoral students: 15%; master's students: 80%; education specialists: 5%; men: 20%; women: 80%; minorities: 7%; international: 2%
Acceptance rate (master's): 70%
Acceptance rate (doctoral): 46%
Entrance test required: GRE or MAT
Avg. GRE (of all entering students with scores): quantitative: 527; verbal 449
TOEFL requirement: YES
Minimum TOEFL score: 550
Teaching assistantships: 10
Students reporting specialty: 100%
Students specializing in: admin.: 8%; counseling: 25%; educational psych.: 2%; elementary: 12%; special: 40%; technical (vocational): 9%; other: 4%

CONNECTICUT

University of Connecticut (Neag)

249 Glenbrook Road
Storrs, CT 06269-2064
Public
NCATE accredited: YES
Admissions: (860) 486-3617
E-mail: gradschool@uconn.edu
Web site: http://www.grad.uconn.edu
Financial aid: (860) 486-2819
Application deadline: 02/01
In-state tuition: full time: $6,836; part time: $316/credit hour
Out-of-state tuition: full time: $15,928
Room/board/expenses: $9,814
Full-time enrollment: 909
doctoral students: 34%; master's students: 59%; education specialists: 7%; men: 32%; women: 68%; minorities: 16%; international: 10%
Part-time enrollment: 539
doctoral students: 34%; master's students: 35%; education specialists: 31%; men: 27%; women: 73%; minorities: 12%; international: 1%
Acceptance rate (master's): 95%
Acceptance rate (doctoral): 56%
Entrance test required: GRE or MAT
Avg. GRE (of all entering students with scores): quantitative: 629; verbal 681
TOEFL requirement: YES
Minimum TOEFL score: 550
Fellowships: 32
Teaching assistantships: 41
Research assistantships: 82
Students reporting specialty: 100%
Students specializing in: admin.: 14%; counseling: 12%; curriculum/instr.: 5%; evaluation/research/statistics: 2%; educational psych.: 0%; elementary: 5%; higher education admin.: 4%; secondary: 10%; special: 19%; technical (vocational): 3%; instructional media design: 7%; other: 20%

University of Hartford[1]

200 Bloomfield Avenue
Room 200
West Hartford, CT 06117
Private
NCATE accredited: YES
Admissions: (860) 768-4371
E-mail: gettoknow@mail.hartford.edu
Web site: http://www.hartford.edu/admission/graduate/college_edu.htm
Internet application: http://www.hartford.edu/admission/graduate/gradform.htm
Financial aid: (860) 768-4296
Tuition: N/A
Room/board/expenses: N/A
Enrollment: N/A

DELAWARE

University of Delaware

113 Willard Hall Education Building
Newark, DE 19716
Public
NCATE accredited: YES
Admissions: (302) 831-2129
E-mail: marym@udel.edu
Web site: http://www.udel.edu/gradoffice/applicants/degreesmajors.html
Internet application: http://www.udel.edu/gradoffice/applicants/index.html
Financial aid: (302) 831-2129
Application deadline: 07/01
In-state tuition: full time: $5,520; part time: $282/credit hour
Out-of-state tuition: full time: $15,050
Room/board/expenses: $7,330
Full-time enrollment: 126
doctoral students: 44%; master's students: 56%; education specialists: 0%; men: 26%; women: 74%; minorities: 10%; international: 11%
Part-time enrollment: 390
doctoral students: 38%; master's students: 62%; education specialists: 0%; men: 23%; women: 77%; minorities: 10%; international: N/A
Acceptance rate (master's): 52%
Acceptance rate (doctoral): 36%
Entrance test required: GRE
Avg. GRE (of all entering students with scores): quantitative: 601; verbal 514
TOEFL requirement: YES
Minimum TOEFL score: 600
Fellowships: 7
Teaching assistantships: 16
Research assistantships: 27
Students reporting specialty: 100%
Students specializing in: admin.: 22%; counseling: 6%; curriculum/instr.: 51%; evaluation/research/statistics: 2%; policy: 0%; educational psych.: 2%; special: 9%; instructional media design: 5%; other: 2%

Wilmington College

320 DuPont Highway
Wilmington, DE 19720
Private
NCATE accredited: NO
Admissions: (302) 328-9407
E-mail: inquire@wilmcoll.edu
Web site: http://www.wilmcoll.edu/education/
Internet application: http://www.wilmcoll.edu/admission/applications.html
Financial aid: (302) 328-9437
Application deadline: rolling
Tuition: full time: $274/credit hour; part time: $274/credit hour
Room/board/expenses: $750
Full-time enrollment: 164
doctoral students: 2%; master's students: 91%; education specialists: 7%; men: 29%; women: 71%; minorities: 1%; international: N/A
Part-time enrollment: 1,712
doctoral students: 13%; master's students: 77%; education specialists: 10%; men: 31%; women: 69%; minorities: 4%; international: N/A
Acceptance rate (master's): N/A
Acceptance rate (doctoral): 68%
Entrance test required: NONE
Avg. GRE (of all entering students with scores): quantitative: N/A; verbal N/A
TOEFL requirement: YES
Minimum TOEFL score: N/A
Students reporting specialty: 99%
Students specializing in: admin.: 31%; counseling: 15%; curriculum/instr.: 11%; elementary: 16%; junior high: 11%; special: 10%; instructional media design: 6%

DISTRICT OF COLUMBIA

American University[1]

4400 Massachusetts Avenue NW
Washington, DC 20016-8030
Private
NCATE accredited: YES
Admissions: (202) 885-3720
E-mail: casgrad@american.edu
Web site: http://www.american.edu/cas/department_education.shtml
Internet application: http://app.applyyourself.com/?id=au-cas
Financial aid: (202) 885-6100
Tuition: N/A
Room/board/expenses: N/A
Enrollment: N/A

Catholic University of America

Department of Education
Cardinal Station
Washington, DC 20064
Private
NCATE accredited: YES
Admissions: (202) 319-5057
E-mail: cua-admissions@cua.edu
Web site: http://www.cua.edu
Internet application: http://admissions.cua.edu/graduate/
Financial aid: (202) 319-5307
Application deadline: rolling
Tuition: full time: $21,890; part time: $810/credit hour
Room/board/expenses: $13,508
Full-time enrollment: 9
doctoral students: 33%; master's students: 67%; education specialists: N/A; men: 11%; women: 89%; minorities: 33%; international: N/A
Part-time enrollment: 52
doctoral students: 48%; master's students: 52%; education specialists: N/A; men: 38%; women: 62%; minorities: 56%; international: 6%

Acceptance rate (master's): 49%
Acceptance rate (doctoral): 63%
Entrance test required: GRE or MAT
Avg. GRE (of all entering students with scores): quantitative: 550; verbal 540
TOEFL requirement: YES
Minimum TOEFL score: 580
Teaching assistantships: 2
Research assistantships: 2
Students reporting specialty: 100%
Students specializing in: admin.: 23%; counseling: 8%; educational psych.: 13%; elementary: 5%; secondary: 3%; special: 5%; other: 43%

Gallaudet University

GSPP-HM S-450
800 Florida Avenue NE
Washington, DC 20002-3695
Private
NCATE accredited: YES
Admissions: (202) 651-5717
E-mail: graduate.school@gallaudet.edu
Web site: http://gradschool.gallaudet.edu
Internet application: http://gradschool.gallaudet.edu/gradschool/prospective/application.html
Financial aid: (202) 651-5290
Application deadline: 02/15
Tuition: full time: $10,737; part time: $515/credit hour
Room/board/expenses: $8,800
Full-time enrollment: 104
doctoral students: 15%; master's students: 74%; education specialists: 11%; men: 13%; women: 88%; minorities: 10%; international: 1%
Part-time enrollment: 49
doctoral students: 55%; master's students: 33%; education specialists: 12%; men: 22%; women: 78%; minorities: 22%; international: 2%
Acceptance rate (master's): 42%
Acceptance rate (doctoral): 47%
Entrance test required: GRE or MAT
Avg. GRE (of all entering students with scores): quantitative: 411; verbal 384
TOEFL requirement: YES
Minimum TOEFL score: N/A
Teaching assistantships: 8
Research assistantships: 7
Students reporting specialty: 100%
Students specializing in: counseling: 16%; educational psych.: 11%; special: 73%

George Washington University

2134 G Street NW
Washington, DC 20052
Private
NCATE accredited: YES
Admissions: (202) 994-9283
E-mail: gsehdapp@gwu.edu
Web site: http://www.gwu.edu/~gsehd
Internet application: http://www.gwu.edu/~gradinfo
Financial aid: (202) 994-6822
Application deadline: 04/01
Tuition: full time: $810/credit hour; part time: $810/credit hour
Room/board/expenses: $16,680
Full-time enrollment: 425
doctoral students: 40%; master's students: 58%; education specialists: 3%; men: 25%; women: 75%; minorities: 31%; international: 7%

Part-time enrollment: 1,152
doctoral students: 38%; master's students: 56%; education specialists: 6%; men: 30%; women: 70%; minorities: 32%; international: 3%
Acceptance rate (master's): 68%
Acceptance rate (doctoral): 67%
Entrance test required: GRE or MAT
Avg. GRE (of all entering students with scores): quantitative: 540; verbal 493
TOEFL requirement: YES
Minimum TOEFL score: 550
Fellowships: 103
Teaching assistantships: 0
Research assistantships: 6
Students reporting specialty: 100%
Students specializing in: admin.: 14%; counseling: 28%; curriculum/instr.: 5%; policy: 1%; elementary: 2%; higher education admin.: 11%; secondary: 10%; special: 17%; instructional media design: 8%; other: 4%

Howard University[1]

2441 Fourth Street NW
Washington, DC 20059
Private
NCATE accredited: YES
Admissions: (202) 806-7340
E-mail: hugsadmission@howard.edu
Web site: http://www.gs.howard.edu/gp-educationproginfo.htm
Internet application: http://www.howard.edu/banner/applyonline.asp
Financial aid: (202) 806-2820
Tuition: N/A
Room/board/expenses: N/A
Enrollment: N/A

FLORIDA

Barry University[1]

11300 N.E. Second Avenue
Miami Shores, FL 33161-6695
Private
NCATE accredited: NO
Admissions: (305) 899-3100
E-mail: admissions@mail.barry.edu
Web site: http://www.barry.edu/ed/
Financial aid: (305) 899-3673
Tuition: N/A
Room/board/expenses: N/A
Enrollment: N/A

Florida A&M University[1]

College of Education
Tallahassee, FL 32307
Public
NCATE accredited: YES
Admissions: (850) 599-3482
E-mail: adm@famu.edu
Web site: http://www.famu.edu/acad/colleges/ced/
Financial aid: (850) 599-3730
Tuition: N/A
Room/board/expenses: N/A
Enrollment: N/A

Florida Atlantic University

777 Glades Road
PO Box 3091
Boca Raton, FL 33431-0991
Public
NCATE accredited: YES
Admissions: (561) 297-3624
E-mail: gradadm@fau.edu
Web site: http://www.fau.edu
Financial aid: (561) 297-3530
Application deadline: rolling

In-state tuition: full time: $187/credit hour; part time: $187/credit hour
Out-of-state tuition: full time: $678/credit hour
Room/board/expenses: $10,685
Full-time enrollment: 260
doctoral students: 19%; master's students: 75%; education specialists: 6%; men: 22%; women: 78%; minorities: N/A; international: N/A
Part-time enrollment: 583
doctoral students: 22%; master's students: 72%; education specialists: 7%; men: 22%; women: 78%; minorities: N/A; international: N/A
Acceptance rate (master's): 39%
Acceptance rate (doctoral): 36%
Entrance test required: GRE
Avg. GRE (of all entering students with scores): quantitative: 498; verbal 450
TOEFL requirement: YES
Minimum TOEFL score: 500
Teaching assistantships: 5
Research assistantships: 47
Students reporting specialty: 100%
Students specializing in: admin.: 41%; counseling: 18%; elementary: 26%; special: 15%

Florida International University

11200 S.W. Eighth Street
Miami, FL 33199
Public
NCATE accredited: YES
Admissions: (305) 348-2363
E-mail: admiss@fiu.edu
Web site: http://www.fiu.edu
Financial aid: (305) 348-2489
Application deadline: rolling
In-state tuition: full time: $177/credit hour; part time: $177/credit hour
Out-of-state tuition: full time: $666/credit hour
Room/board/expenses: $10,404
Full-time enrollment: 206
doctoral students: 15%; master's students: 70%; education specialists: 15%; men: 25%; women: 75%; minorities: 58%; international: 14%
Part-time enrollment: 713
doctoral students: 32%; master's students: 62%; education specialists: 6%; men: 23%; women: 77%; minorities: 63%; international: 2%
Acceptance rate (master's): 52%
Acceptance rate (doctoral): 24%
Entrance test required: GRE
Avg. GRE (of all entering students with scores): quantitative: 482; verbal 434
TOEFL requirement: YES
Minimum TOEFL score: 550
Students reporting specialty: 47%
Students specializing in: N/A

Florida State University

236 Stone Building
Tallahassee, FL 32306-4450
Public
NCATE accredited: YES
Admissions: (850) 644-3760
E-mail: admissions@admin.fsu.edu
Web site: http://admissions.fsu.edu
Internet application: http://admissions.fsu.edu/online.html
Financial aid: (850) 644-0539
Application deadline: 07/01
In-state tuition: full time: $178/credit hour; part time: $178/credit hour

Out-of-state tuition: full time: $671/credit hour
Room/board/expenses: $9,248
Full-time enrollment: 638
doctoral students: 37%; master's students: 60%; education specialists: 3%; men: 39%; women: 61%; minorities: 20%; international: 19%
Part-time enrollment: 509
doctoral students: 43%; master's students: 54%; education specialists: 4%; men: 35%; women: 65%; minorities: 20%; international: 5%
Acceptance rate (master's): 53%
Acceptance rate (doctoral): 35%
Entrance test required: GRE
Avg. GRE (of all entering students with scores): quantitative: 549; verbal 453
TOEFL requirement: YES
Minimum TOEFL score: 550
Fellowships: 34
Teaching assistantships: 221
Research assistantships: 536
Students reporting specialty: 100%
Students specializing in: admin.: 6%; counseling: 10%; evaluation/research/statistics: 1%; social/philosophical foundations: 3%; educational psych.: 3%; elementary: 9%; higher education admin.: 7%; secondary: 12%; special: 10%; technical (vocational): 1%; instructional media design: 12%; other: 26%

Nova Southeastern University

3301 College Avenue
Fort Lauderdale, FL 33314
Private
NCATE accredited: NO
Admissions: (954) 262-8500
Web site: http://www.fgse.nova.edu
Financial aid: (954) 262-3380
Application deadline: rolling
Tuition: full time: $325/credit hour; part time: $325/credit hour
Room/board/expenses: $14,743
Full-time enrollment: 1,789
doctoral students: 15%; master's students: 73%; education specialists: 13%; men: 23%; women: 77%; minorities: 52%; international: 3%
Part-time enrollment: 5,888
doctoral students: 48%; master's students: 47%; education specialists: 6%; men: 25%; women: 75%; minorities: 47%; international: 1%
Acceptance rate (master's): 100%
Acceptance rate (doctoral): 100%
Entrance test required: GRE or MAT
Avg. GRE (of all entering students with scores): quantitative: N/A; verbal N/A
TOEFL requirement: YES
Minimum TOEFL score: 550
Fellowships: 3
Teaching assistantships: 7
Research assistantships: 2
Students reporting specialty: 57%
Students specializing in: admin.: 58%; counseling: 2%; curriculum/instr.: 2%; elementary: 12%; higher education admin.: 6%; special: 10%; technical (vocational): 7%; instructional media design: 4%

University of Central Florida

4000 Central Florida Boulevard
Orlando, FL 32816-1250
Public
NCATE accredited: YES
Admissions: (407) 823-2766
E-mail: graduate@mail.ucf.edu
Web site: http://www.graduate.ucf.edu
Internet application: http://www.ucf.edu/admission.html
Financial aid: (407) 823-2827
Application deadline: 02/01
In-state tuition: full time: $181/credit hour; part time: $181/credit hour
Out-of-state tuition: full time: $667/credit hour
Room/board/expenses: $11,780
Full-time enrollment: 470
doctoral students: 25%; master's students: 64%; education specialists: 10%; men: 20%; women: 80%; minorities: 19%; international: 6%
Part-time enrollment: 803
doctoral students: 24%; master's students: 74%; education specialists: 2%; men: 22%; women: 78%; minorities: 15%; international: 0%
Acceptance rate (master's): 71%
Acceptance rate (doctoral): 67%
Entrance test required: GRE
Avg. GRE (of all entering students with scores): quantitative: 528; verbal 473
TOEFL requirement: YES
Minimum TOEFL score: 550
Fellowships: 101
Teaching assistantships: 7
Research assistantships: 115
Students reporting specialty: 100%
Students specializing in: admin.: 19%; counseling: 10%; curriculum/instr.: 14%; educational psych.: 4%; elementary: 12%; higher education admin.: 2%; special: 9%; technical (vocational): 1%; instructional media design: 7%; other: 22%

University of Florida

125 Norman Hall
PO Box 117043
Gainesville, FL 32611-7043
Public
NCATE accredited: YES
Admissions: (352) 392-1275
E-mail: edugrad@coe.ufl.edu
Web site: http://www.coe.ufl.edu
Internet application: http://gradschool.rgp.ufl.edu/education/toapply.html
Financial aid: (352) 392-2315
Application deadline: rolling
In-state tuition: full time: $179/credit hour; part time: $179/credit hour
Out-of-state tuition: full time: $667/credit hour
Room/board/expenses: $10,890
Full-time enrollment: 948
doctoral students: 39%; master's students: 49%; education specialists: 12%; men: N/A; women: N/A; minorities: N/A; international: N/A
Part-time enrollment: N/A
doctoral students: N/A; master's students: N/A; education specialists: N/A; men: N/A; women: N/A; minorities: N/A; international: N/A
Acceptance rate (master's): 61%
Acceptance rate (doctoral): 38%
Entrance test required: GRE
Avg. GRE (of all entering students with scores): quantitative: 578; verbal 495
TOEFL requirement: YES

Minimum TOEFL score: 550
Fellowships: 52
Teaching assistantships: 92
Research assistantships: 71
Students reporting specialty: 100%
Students specializing in: admin.: 8%; counseling: 8%; curriculum/instr.: 16%; evaluation/research/statistics: 1%; social/philosophical foundations: 1%; educational psych.: 6%; elementary: 18%; higher education admin.: 8%; secondary: 2%; special: 11%; other: 20%

University of Miami

PO Box 248065
Coral Gables, FL 33124
Private
NCATE accredited: YES
Admissions: (305) 284-3711
E-mail: soe@umiami.ir.miami.edu
Web site: http://www.education.miami.edu
Financial aid: (305) 284-5212
Application deadline: 01/02
Tuition: full time: $24,810; part time: $1,010/credit hour
Room/board/expenses: $11,167
Full-time enrollment: 205
doctoral students: 39%; master's students: 60%; education specialists: 0%; men: 24%; women: 76%; minorities: 45%; international: 7%
Part-time enrollment: 231
doctoral students: 2%; master's students: 93%; education specialists: 5%; men: 13%; women: 87%; minorities: 68%; international: 20%
Acceptance rate (master's): 71%
Acceptance rate (doctoral): 17%
Entrance test required: GRE
Avg. GRE (of all entering students with scores): quantitative: 549; verbal 463
TOEFL requirement: YES
Minimum TOEFL score: 550
Fellowships: 1
Teaching assistantships: 0
Research assistantships: 0
Students reporting specialty: 100%
Students specializing in: admin.: 2%; counseling: 22%; elementary: 5%; higher education admin.: 2%; secondary: 0%; special: 36%; other: 33%

University of South Florida

4202 E. Fowler Avenue
EDU 162
Tampa, FL 33620
Public
NCATE accredited: YES
Admissions: (813) 974-8800
E-mail: admissions@grad.usf.edu
Web site: http://www.grad.usf.edu
Internet application: http://www.usf.edu/apply.html
Financial aid: (813) 974-4700
Application deadline: N/A
In-state tuition: full time: $184/credit hour; part time: $184/credit hour
Out-of-state tuition: full time: $676/credit hour
Room/board/expenses: $10,410
Full-time enrollment: 566
doctoral students: 26%; master's students: 72%; education specialists: 2%; men: 25%; women: 75%; minorities: 25%; international: 4%
Part-time enrollment: 1,151
doctoral students: 25%; master's students: 72%; education specialists: 3%; men: 25%; women: 75%; minorities: 17%; international: 1%
Acceptance rate (master's): 67%
Acceptance rate (doctoral): 53%
Entrance test required: GRE

Avg. GRE (of all entering students with scores): quantitative: 522; verbal 478
TOEFL requirement: YES
Minimum TOEFL score: 550
Fellowships: 11
Teaching assistantships: 46
Research assistantships: 55
Students reporting specialty: N/A
Students specializing in: N/A

Emory University[1]

North Decatur Building
Suite 240
Atlanta, GA 30322
Private
NCATE accredited: YES
Admissions: (404) 727-6468
E-mail: gavant@emory.edu
Web site: http://www.emory.edu/EDUCATION/
Internet application: http://www.emory.edu/gsoas/application.html
Financial aid: (404) 727-6039
Tuition: N/A
Room/board/expenses: N/A
Enrollment: N/A

Georgia State University[1]

MSC6A1005
33 Gilmer St SE, Unit 6
Atlanta, GA 30303-3086
Public
NCATE accredited: YES
Admissions: (404) 651-2525
E-mail: educadmissions@gsu.edu
Web site: http://education.gsu.edu/coe/index.htm
Financial aid: (404) 651-2227
Tuition: N/A
Room/board/expenses: N/A
Enrollment: N/A

University of Georgia

College of Education
G-3 Aderhold Hall
Athens, GA 30602
Public
NCATE accredited: YES
Admissions: (706) 542-1739
E-mail: gradadm@arches.uga.edu
Web site: http://www.gradsch.uga.edu
Internet application: http://www.gradsch.uga.edu/admissions
Financial aid: (706) 542-3476
Application deadline: 07/01
In-state tuition: full time: $3,348; part time: $140/credit hour
Out-of-state tuition: full time: $14,392
Room/board/expenses: $8,738
Full-time enrollment: 1,187
doctoral students: 40%; master's students: 55%; education specialists: 4%; men: 28%; women: 72%; minorities: 11%; international: 13%
Part-time enrollment: 1,007
doctoral students: 33%; master's students: 51%; education specialists: 17%; men: 30%; women: 70%; minorities: 6%; international: 2%
Acceptance rate (master's): 49%
Acceptance rate (doctoral): 41%
Entrance test required: GRE or MAT
Avg. GRE (of all entering students with scores): quantitative: 575; verbal 500
TOEFL requirement: YES
Minimum TOEFL score: 550
Fellowships: 56

Teaching assistantships: 89
Research assistantships: 47
Students reporting specialty: 100%
Students specializing in: admin.: 21%; counseling: 6%; evaluation/research/statistics: 1%; social/philosophical foundations: 1%; educational psych.: 1%; elementary: 4%; junior high: 2%; special: 4%; technical (vocational): 9%; instructional media design: 10%; other: 41%

University of Hawaii–Manoa

1776 University Avenue
Wist Annex 2-128
Honolulu, HI 96822
Public
NCATE accredited: YES
Admissions: (808) 956-8544
E-mail: admissions@grad.hawaii.edu
Web site: http://www.hawaii.edu/graduate/
Financial aid: (808) 956-7251
Application deadline: rolling
In-state tuition: full time: $4,452; part time: $180/credit hour
Out-of-state tuition: full time: $10,524
Room/board/expenses: $8,353
Full-time enrollment: 274
doctoral students: 15%; master's students: 85%; education specialists: 0%; men: 33%; women: 67%; minorities: 53%; international: 10%
Part-time enrollment: 485
doctoral students: 22%; master's students: 78%; education specialists: 0%; men: 27%; women: 73%; minorities: 68%; international: 5%
Acceptance rate (master's): 72%
Acceptance rate (doctoral): 68%
Entrance test required: GRE
Avg. GRE (of all entering students with scores): quantitative: 558; verbal 476
TOEFL requirement: YES
Minimum TOEFL score: 500
Fellowships: 6
Teaching assistantships: 13
Research assistantships: 20
Students reporting specialty: 100%
Students specializing in: admin.: 13%; counseling: 11%; curriculum/instr.: 25%; social/philosophical foundations: 9%; educational psych.: 8%; special: 7%; instructional media design: 5%; other: 21%

University of Idaho

College of Education
Moscow, ID 83844-3080
Public
NCATE accredited: YES
Admissions: (208) 885-4001
E-mail: gadms@uidaho.edu
Web site: http://www.uidaho.edu/
Internet application: http://www.uidaho.edu/cogs/
Financial aid: (208) 885-6312
Application deadline: 07/01
In-state tuition: full time: $3,044; part time: $181/credit hour
Out-of-state tuition: full time: $9,764
Room/board/expenses: $10,562
Full-time enrollment: 236
doctoral students: 25%; master's students: 66%; education specialists: 9%; men: 41%; women: 59%; minorities: 5%; international: 16%

Part-time enrollment: 607
doctoral students: 23%; master's students: 63%; education specialists: 13%; men: 39%; women: 61%; minorities: 5%; international: 3%
Acceptance rate (master's): 58%
Acceptance rate (doctoral): 45%
Entrance test required: GRE
Avg. GRE (of all entering students with scores): quantitative: 469; verbal 486
TOEFL requirement: YES
Minimum TOEFL score: 525
Fellowships: 18
Teaching assistantships: 23
Students reporting specialty: 77%
Students specializing in: admin.: 14%; counseling: 20%; curriculum/instr.: 14%; elementary: 2%; higher education admin.: 2%; secondary: 1%; special: 5%; technical (vocational): 9%; other: 34%

Illinois State University

Campus Box 5300
Normal, IL 61790-5300
Public
NCATE accredited: YES
Admissions: (309) 438-2181
E-mail: gradinfo@ilstu.edu
Web site: http://www.ilstu.edu
Internet application: https://www.arr.ilstu.edu/OnApp/GradApp/
Financial aid: (309) 438-2231
Application deadline: 06/18
In-state tuition: full time: $4,094; part time: $122/credit hour
Out-of-state tuition: full time: $7,514
Room/board/expenses: $8,034
Full-time enrollment: 212
doctoral students: 39%; master's students: 54%; education specialists: 7%; men: 28%; women: 72%; minorities: 13%; international: 16%
Part-time enrollment: 700
doctoral students: 33%; master's students: 66%; education specialists: 1%; men: 28%; women: 72%; minorities: 11%; international: 2%
Acceptance rate (master's): 80%
Acceptance rate (doctoral): 60%
Entrance test required: GRE
Avg. GRE (of all entering students with scores): quantitative: 557; verbal 445
TOEFL requirement: YES
Minimum TOEFL score: 550
Teaching assistantships: 65
Research assistantships: 23
Students reporting specialty: 100%
Students specializing in: admin.: 37%; curriculum/instr.: 18%; special: 9%; instructional media design: 1%; other: 36%

Loyola University Chicago

820 N. Michigan Avenue
Chicago, IL 60611
Private
NCATE accredited: APPLYING
Admissions: (312) 915-6722
E-mail: mrosind@luc.edu
Web site: http://www.luc.edu/
Internet application: http://www.luc.edu/schools/education
Financial aid: (773) 508-3155
Application deadline: N/A
Tuition: full time: $548/credit hour; part time: $548/credit hour
Room/board/expenses: N/A

Full-time enrollment: 580
doctoral students: 58%; master's students: 42%; education specialists: 0%; men: 26%; women: 74%; minorities: 25%; international: 5%
Part-time enrollment: 645
doctoral students: 39%; master's students: 55%; education specialists: 6%; men: 24%; women: 76%; minorities: 32%; international: 1%
Acceptance rate (master's): 82%
Acceptance rate (doctoral): 54%
Entrance test required: GRE or MAT
Avg. GRE (of all entering students with scores): quantitative: 532; verbal 472
TOEFL requirement: YES
Minimum TOEFL score: 550
Fellowships: 11
Research assistantships: 17
Students reporting specialty: 100%
Students specializing in: admin.: 8%; counseling: 15%; curriculum/instr.: 24%; evaluation/research/statistics: 1%; policy: 7%; educational psych.: 7%; elementary: 3%; higher education admin.: 22%; secondary: 6%; special: 1%; other: 5%

Northern Illinois University

College of Education
DeKalb, IL 60115
Public
NCATE accredited: YES
Admissions: (815) 753-0395
E-mail: gradsch@niu.edu
Web site: http://www.cedu.niu.edu
Internet application: http://www.grad.niu.edu/apply.htm
Financial aid: (815) 753-1395
Application deadline: 06/01
In-state tuition: full time: $3,258; part time: $136/credit hour
Out-of-state tuition: full time: $6,516
Room/board/expenses: $5,476
Full-time enrollment: 82
doctoral students: 12%; master's students: 88%; education specialists: 0%; men: 33%; women: 67%; minorities: 11%; international: 6%
Part-time enrollment: 1,976
doctoral students: 28%; master's students: 70%; education specialists: 2%; men: 26%; women: 74%; minorities: 12%; international: 2%
Acceptance rate (master's): 61%
Acceptance rate (doctoral): 59%
Entrance test required: GRE or MAT
Avg. GRE (of all entering students with scores): quantitative: 508; verbal 452
TOEFL requirement: YES
Minimum TOEFL score: 550
Fellowships: 10
Teaching assistantships: 52
Research assistantships: 134
Students reporting specialty: 100%
Students specializing in: admin.: 20%; counseling: 9%; curriculum/instr.: 16%; evaluation/research/statistics: 0%; social/philosophical foundations: 1%; educational psych.: 3%; elementary: 7%; special: 7%; instructional media design: 12%; other: 26%

Northwestern University
2120 Campus Drive
Evanston, IL 60208
Private
NCATE accredited: NO
Admissions: (847) 491-3790
E-mail: sesp@northwestern.edu
Web site: http://www.sesp.northwestern.edu
Internet application: http://www.northwestern.edu/graduate/
Financial aid: (847) 491-3790
Application deadline: 12/31
Tuition: full time: $29,474; part time: $2,948/credit hour
Room/board/expenses: N/A
Full-time enrollment: 129
doctoral students: 50%; master's students: 50%; education specialists: N/A; men: 23%; women: 77%; minorities: 16%; international: 9%
Part-time enrollment: 110
doctoral students: 0%; master's students: 100%; education specialists: N/A; men: 19%; women: 81%; minorities: 19%; international: 1%
Acceptance rate (master's): 76%
Acceptance rate (doctoral): 16%
Entrance test required: GRE
Avg. GRE (of all entering students with scores): quantitative: 677; verbal 596
TOEFL requirement: YES
Minimum TOEFL score: 560
Fellowships: 14
Teaching assistantships: 15
Research assistantships: 45
Students reporting specialty: 61%
Students specializing in: elementary: 14%; higher education admin.: 3%; secondary: 10%; other: 73%

Southern Illinois University–Carbondale
Wham Building 115
Carbondale, IL 62901-4624
Public
NCATE accredited: YES
Admissions: (618) 536-7791
E-mail: gradschl@siu.edu
Web site: http://web.coehs.siu.edu/Public/
Internet application: http://www.siu.edu/gradschl/admissions.htm
Financial aid: (618) 453-4334
Application deadline: 05/23
In-state tuition: full time: $137/credit hour; part time: $69/credit hour
Out-of-state tuition: full time: $274/credit hour
Room/board/expenses: $5,967
Full-time enrollment: 590
doctoral students: 17%; master's students: 83%; education specialists: N/A; men: 24%; women: 76%; minorities: 13%; international: 9%
Part-time enrollment: 733
doctoral students: 35%; master's students: 65%; education specialists: N/A; men: 33%; women: 67%; minorities: 10%; international: 6%
Acceptance rate (master's): 51%
Acceptance rate (doctoral): 27%
Entrance test required: GRE or MAT
Avg. GRE (of all entering students with scores): quantitative: 445; verbal 452
TOEFL requirement: YES
Minimum TOEFL score: 550
Fellowships: 7
Teaching assistantships: 115
Research assistantships: 156
Students reporting specialty: N/A
Students specializing in: N/A

University of Illinois–Chicago
1040 W. Harrison Street
Chicago, IL 60607-7133
Public
NCATE accredited: NO
Admissions: (312) 996-4532
E-mail: scoleman@uic.edu
Web site: http://www.uic.edu/educ/index.html/admissions/index.html
Internet application: http://www.uic.edu/depts/ims/uiconline/uic_appl_strt.htm
Financial aid: (312) 996-3126
Application deadline: 02/15
In-state tuition: full time: $7,156; part time: $5,362
Out-of-state tuition: full time: $15,138
Room/board/expenses: $9,120
Full-time enrollment: 152
doctoral students: 26%; master's students: 74%; education specialists: N/A; men: 22%; women: 78%; minorities: 33%; international: 5%
Part-time enrollment: 596
doctoral students: 28%; master's students: 72%; education specialists: N/A; men: 21%; women: 79%; minorities: 39%; international: 3%
Acceptance rate (master's): 77%
Acceptance rate (doctoral): 78%
Entrance test required: GRE
Avg. GRE (of all entering students with scores): quantitative: 529; verbal 500
TOEFL requirement: YES
Minimum TOEFL score: 550
Fellowships: 18
Teaching assistantships: 39
Research assistantships: 228
Students reporting specialty: 100%
Students specializing in: admin.: 9%; curriculum/instr.: 13%; evaluation/research/statistics: 0%; social/philosophical foundations: 1%; educational psych.: 7%; elementary: 20%; higher education admin.: 2%; secondary: 10%; special: 14%; other: 25%

University of Illinois–Urbana-Champaign
1310 S. Sixth Street
Champaign, IL 61820
Public
NCATE accredited: APPLYING
Admissions: (217) 333-0964
E-mail: admissions@mail.ed.uiuc.edu
Web site: http://www.ed.uiuc.edu/ipo
Internet application: http://www.grad.uiuc.edu/forms/formsGC.html
Financial aid: (217) 333-0964
Application deadline: rolling
In-state tuition: full time: $6,454; part time: $4,804
Out-of-state tuition: full time: $14,338
Room/board/expenses: $9,124
Full-time enrollment: 476
doctoral students: 65%; master's students: 35%; education specialists: 0%; men: 33%; women: 67%; minorities: 21%; international: 41%
Part-time enrollment: 525
doctoral students: 30%; master's students: 70%; education specialists: 0%; men: 27%; women: 73%; minorities: 14%; international: 5%
Acceptance rate (master's): 62%
Acceptance rate (doctoral): 46%
Entrance test required: GRE
Avg. GRE (of all entering students with scores): quantitative: 602; verbal 498
TOEFL requirement: YES
Minimum TOEFL score: 590
Fellowships: 116
Teaching assistantships: 172
Research assistantships: 140
Students reporting specialty: 100%
Students specializing in: admin.: 17%; counseling: 3%; curriculum/instr.: 26%; policy: 10%; educational psych.: 13%; elementary: 2%; secondary: 3%; special: 10%; technical (vocational): 16%

INDIANA

Ball State University
Teachers College
Muncie, IN 47306
Public
NCATE accredited: YES
Admissions: (765) 285-1297
E-mail: whitenac@bsu.edu
Web site: http://www.bsu.edu/gradschool/
Internet application: http://www.bsu.edu/gradschool/application.htm
Financial aid: (765) 295-5600
Application deadline: N/A
In-state tuition: full time: N/A; part time: N/A
Out-of-state tuition: full time: N/A
Room/board/expenses: N/A
Full-time enrollment: 214
doctoral students: 27%; master's students: 69%; education specialists: 4%; men: 30%; women: 70%; minorities: N/A; international: N/A
Part-time enrollment: 437
doctoral students: 27%; master's students: 70%; education specialists: 3%; men: 29%; women: 71%; minorities: N/A; international: N/A
Acceptance rate (master's): 69%
Acceptance rate (doctoral): 52%
Entrance test required: GRE
Avg. GRE (of all entering students with scores): quantitative: 556; verbal 477
TOEFL requirement: YES
Minimum TOEFL score: 550
Teaching assistantships: 125
Research assistantships: 8
Students reporting specialty: 99%
Students specializing in: admin.: 18%; counseling: 30%; curriculum/instr.: 1%; evaluation/research/statistics: 7%; elementary: 13%; junior high: 0%; secondary: 4%; special: 11%; other: 15%

Indiana State University
School of Education
Terre Haute, IN 47809
Public
NCATE accredited: YES
Admissions: (812) 237-3111
E-mail: grdstudies@indstate.edu
Web site: http://web.indstate.edu/sogs/
Internet application: http://web.indstate.edu/sogs/GradNewtemp/usform.html
Financial aid: (800) 841-4744
Application deadline: rolling
In-state tuition: full time: $178/credit hour; part time: $178/credit hour
Out-of-state tuition: full time: $405/credit hour
Room/board/expenses: $6,310
Full-time enrollment: 185
doctoral students: 45%; master's students: 52%; education specialists: 3%; men: 29%; women: 71%; minorities: 12%; international: 13%
Part-time enrollment: 120
doctoral students: 34%; master's students: 55%; education specialists: 11%; men: 32%; women: 68%; minorities: 13%; international: 2%
Acceptance rate (master's): 49%
Acceptance rate (doctoral): 46%
Entrance test required: GRE
Avg. GRE (of all entering students with scores): quantitative: N/A; verbal N/A
TOEFL requirement: YES
Minimum TOEFL score: 550
Fellowships: 23
Research assistantships: 47
Students reporting specialty: 94%
Students specializing in: admin.: 15%; counseling: 7%; curriculum/instr.: 11%; educational psych.: 7%; elementary: 7%; higher education admin.: 18%; secondary: 6%; special: 3%; technical (vocational): 1%; instructional media design: 3%; other: 23%

Indiana University–Bloomington
201 N. Rose Avenue
Bloomington, IN 47405-1006
Public
NCATE accredited: YES
Admissions: (812) 856-8504
E-mail: educate@indiana.edu
Web site: http://education.indiana.edu/
Internet application: http://www.indiana.edu/~educate/appadvice.html
Financial aid: (812) 855-3278
Application deadline: 01/15
In-state tuition: full time: $197/credit hour; part time: $197/credit hour
Out-of-state tuition: full time: $573/credit hour
Room/board/expenses: $10,486
Full-time enrollment: 586
doctoral students: 43%; master's students: 55%; education specialists: 2%; men: 33%; women: 67%; minorities: 14%; international: 26%
Part-time enrollment: 599
doctoral students: 72%; master's students: 25%; education specialists: 2%; men: 36%; women: 64%; minorities: 11%; international: 16%
Acceptance rate (master's): 51%
Acceptance rate (doctoral): 24%
Entrance test required: GRE
Avg. GRE (of all entering students with scores): quantitative: 585; verbal 495
TOEFL requirement: YES
Minimum TOEFL score: 550
Fellowships: 154
Teaching assistantships: 178
Research assistantships: 50
Students reporting specialty: 100%
Students specializing in: admin.: 7%; counseling: 16%; curriculum/instr.: 12%; evaluation/research/statistics: 0%; social/philosophical foundations: 1%; policy: 3%; educational psych.: 7%; elementary: 6%; higher education admin.: 10%; secondary: 4%; special: 4%; instructional media design: 19%; other: 11%

Purdue University–West Lafayette
100 N. University Street
West Lafayette, IN 47907-2098
Public
NCATE accredited: YES
Admissions: (765) 494-2345
E-mail: gradoffice@soe.purdue.edu
Web site: http://www.soe.purdue.edu/
Internet application: http://www.purdue.edu/GradSchool/Admissions/admissions.html
Financial aid: (765) 494-5050
Application deadline: 01/15
In-state tuition: full time: $5,680; part time: $200/credit hour
Out-of-state tuition: full time: $16,360
Room/board/expenses: $8,510
Full-time enrollment: 142
doctoral students: 46%; master's students: 54%; education specialists: N/A; men: 33%; women: 67%; minorities: 14%; international: 23%
Part-time enrollment: 345
doctoral students: 59%; master's students: 40%; education specialists: 1%; men: 40%; women: 60%; minorities: 9%; international: 7%
Acceptance rate (master's): 46%
Acceptance rate (doctoral): 31%
Entrance test required: GRE or MAT
Avg. GRE (of all entering students with scores): quantitative: 603; verbal 494
TOEFL requirement: YES
Minimum TOEFL score: 550
Fellowships: 14
Teaching assistantships: 79
Research assistantships: 46
Students reporting specialty: 100%
Students specializing in: admin.: 19%; counseling: 13%; curriculum/instr.: 32%; educational psych.: 5%; elementary: 1%; higher education admin.: 9%; special: 5%; technical (vocational): 4%; instructional media design: 11%

IOWA

Drake University
3206 University Avenue
Des Moines, IA 50311
Private
NCATE accredited: APPLYING
Admissions: (515) 271-3871
E-mail: gradadmission@drake.edu
Web site: http://www.educ.drake.edu/
Internet application: http://www.applyweb.com/aw?drakeg
Financial aid: (515) 271-2905
Application deadline: rolling
Tuition: full time: $18,830; part time: $290/credit hour
Room/board/expenses: $10,200
Full-time enrollment: 6
doctoral students: 0%; master's students: 100%; education specialists: 0%; men: 33%; women: 67%; minorities: N/A; international: N/A
Part-time enrollment: 632
doctoral students: 4%; master's students: 86%; education specialists: 9%; men: 37%; women: 63%; minorities: 2%; international: N/A
Acceptance rate (master's): 83%
Acceptance rate (doctoral): 43%
Entrance test required: GRE or MAT
Avg. GRE (of all entering students with scores): quantitative: 567; verbal 501

TOEFL requirement: YES
Minimum TOEFL score: 550
Fellowships: 0
Teaching assistantships: 0
Research assistantships: 0
Students reporting specialty: 91%
Students specializing in: admin.: 27%; counseling: 17%; curriculum/instr.: 14%; elementary: 7%; junior high: 6%; secondary: 7%; other: 22%

Iowa State University

E262 Lagomarcino Hall
Ames, IA 50011
Public
NCATE accredited: NO
Admissions: (515) 294-5836
E-mail: admissions@iastate.edu
Web site:
http://www.grad-college.
iastate.edu/
Internet application:
http://www.public.iastate.edu/~adm_info/
Financial aid: (515) 294-2223
Application deadline: rolling
In-state tuition: full time: $4,698; part time: $244/credit hour
Out-of-state tuition: full time: $13,224
Room/board/expenses: $8,335
Full-time enrollment: 179
doctoral students: 43%; master's students: 57%; education specialists: 0%; men: 45%; women: 55%; minorities: 15%; international: 22%
Part-time enrollment: 235
doctoral students: 32%; master's students: 68%; education specialists: 0%; men: 40%; women: 60%; minorities: 6%; international: 5%
Acceptance rate (master's): 80%
Acceptance rate (doctoral): 70%
Entrance test required: GRE or MAT
Avg. GRE (of all entering students with scores): quantitative: 574; verbal 466
TOEFL requirement: YES
Minimum TOEFL score: 560
Fellowships: 5
Teaching assistantships: 40
Research assistantships: 27
Students reporting specialty: 100%
Students specializing in: admin.: 16%; counseling: 8%; evaluation/research/statistics: 10%; higher education admin.: 27%; special: 6%; instructional media design: 14%; other: 20%

University of Iowa

Lindquist Center
Iowa City, IA 52242
Public
NCATE accredited: NO
Admissions: (319) 335-5359
E-mail: coe-tess@uiowa.edu
Web site:
http://www.education.uiowa.edu
Internet application:
http://www.uiowa.edu/admissions/apply.html
Financial aid: (319) 335-1450
Application deadline: 07/15
In-state tuition: full time: $4,887; part time: $244/credit hour
Out-of-state tuition: full time: $14,271
Room/board/expenses: $7,536
Full-time enrollment: 557
doctoral students: 48%; master's students: 51%; education specialists: 1%; men: 28%; women: 72%; minorities: 12%; international: 17%

Part-time enrollment: 478
doctoral students: 47%; master's students: 50%; education specialists: 3%; men: 33%; women: 67%; minorities: 9%; international: 5%
Acceptance rate (master's): 77%
Acceptance rate (doctoral): 46%
Entrance test required: GRE
Avg. GRE (of all entering students with scores): quantitative: 631; verbal 531
TOEFL requirement: YES
Minimum TOEFL score: 550
Fellowships: 10
Teaching assistantships: 94
Research assistantships: 114
Students reporting specialty: 100%
Students specializing in: admin.: 7%; counseling: 8%; curriculum/instr.: 2%; evaluation/research/statistics: 5%; social/philosophical foundations: 5%; policy: 2%; educational psych.: 2%; elementary: 9%; higher education admin.: 6%; secondary: 27%; special: 12%; instructional media design: 2%; other: 13%

University of Northern Iowa[1]

1227 W. 27th Street
Cedar Falls, IA 50614-0615
Public
NCATE accredited: N/A
Admissions: (319) 273-2717
E-mail: admissions@uni.edu
Web site: http://www.uni.edu/coe
Financial aid: (800) 772-2736
Tuition: N/A
Room/board/expenses: N/A

KANSAS

Kansas State University[1]

2 Bluemont Hall
Manhattan, KS 66506
Public
NCATE accredited: YES
Admissions: (785) 532-5595
E-mail:
gradstudy@mail.educ.ksu.edu
Web site: http://www.educ.ksu.edu/departments/grad/home.html
Financial aid: (785) 532-6420
Tuition: N/A
Room/board/expenses: N/A
Enrollment: N/A

University of Kansas

210 Joseph R. Pearson Hall
Lawrence, KS 66045
Public
NCATE accredited: YES
Admissions: (785) 864-4510
E-mail: fredrod@ku.edu
Web site:
http://www.soe.ukans.edu
Financial aid: (785) 864-4700
Application deadline: N/A
In-state tuition: full time: $134/credit hour; part time: $134/credit hour
Out-of-state tuition: full time: $389/credit hour
Room/board/expenses: N/A
Full-time enrollment: 1,273
doctoral students: 32%; master's students: 66%; education specialists: 1%; men: 29%; women: 71%; minorities: 7%; international: 6%

Part-time enrollment: N/A
doctoral students: N/A; master's students: N/A; education specialists: N/A; men: N/A; women: N/A; minorities: N/A; international: N/A
Acceptance rate (master's): 93%
Acceptance rate (doctoral): 60%
Entrance test required: GRE or MAT
Avg. GRE (of all entering students with scores): quantitative: 560; verbal 500
TOEFL requirement: YES
Minimum TOEFL score: 570
Teaching assistantships: 64
Research assistantships: 32
Students reporting specialty: 100%
Students specializing in: admin.: 2%; counseling: 8%; curriculum/instr.: 33%; evaluation/research/statistics: 2%; social/philosophical foundations: 0%; educational psych.: 3%; higher education admin.: 14%; special: 19%; other: 19%

KENTUCKY

University of Kentucky

351 Patterson Office Tower
Lexington, KY 40506-0027
Public
NCATE accredited: YES
Admissions: (859) 257-4905
Web site:
http://www.rgs.uky.edu/gs
Internet application:
http://www.rgs.uky.edu/gs/gsapplication.html
Financial aid: (859) 257-3172
Application deadline: 07/25
In-state tuition: full time: $4,647; part time: $227/credit hour
Out-of-state tuition: full time: $11,565
Room/board/expenses: $7,500
Full-time enrollment: 474
doctoral students: 49%; master's students: 48%; education specialists: 3%; men: 34%; women: 66%; minorities: 15%; international: 4%
Part-time enrollment: 430
doctoral students: 30%; master's students: 63%; education specialists: 8%; men: 26%; women: 74%; minorities: 8%; international: 0%
Acceptance rate (master's): 65%
Acceptance rate (doctoral): 53%
Entrance test required: GRE
Avg. GRE (of all entering students with scores): quantitative: 510; verbal 448
TOEFL requirement: YES
Minimum TOEFL score: 550
Fellowships: 16
Teaching assistantships: 53
Research assistantships: 66
Students reporting specialty: 100%
Students specializing in: admin.: 20%; counseling: 8%; curriculum/instr.: 5%; evaluation/research/statistics: 9%; elementary: 2%; junior high: 1%; secondary: 8%; special: 8%; technical (vocational): 5%; other: 34%

University of Louisville

College of Education & Human Development
Louisville, KY 40292
Public
NCATE accredited: YES
Admissions: (502) 852-3101
E-mail: gradadm@louisville.edu
Web site: http://www.louisville.edu
Internet application: http://graduate.louisville.edu/app/
Financial aid: (502) 852-5511
Application deadline: rolling

In-state tuition: full time: $4,442; part time: $247/credit hour
Out-of-state tuition: full time: $12,236
Room/board/expenses: $12,196
Full-time enrollment: 514
doctoral students: 20%; master's students: 79%; education specialists: 1%; men: 25%; women: 75%; minorities: 11%; international: 10%
Part-time enrollment: 739
doctoral students: 17%; master's students: 79%; education specialists: 4%; men: 24%; women: 76%; minorities: 12%; international: 3%
Acceptance rate (master's): 90%
Acceptance rate (doctoral): 93%
Entrance test required: GRE or MAT
Avg. GRE (of all entering students with scores): quantitative: 500; verbal 452
TOEFL requirement: YES
Minimum TOEFL score: 550
Fellowships: 2
Teaching assistantships: 9
Research assistantships: 50
Students reporting specialty: 100%
Students specializing in: admin.: 13%; counseling: 17%; curriculum/instr.: 4%; elementary: 10%; higher education admin.: 4%; junior high: 2%; secondary: 9%; special: 15%; other: 27%

LOUISIANA

Grambling State University[1]

PO Box 805
Grambling, LA 71245
Public
NCATE accredited: YES
Admissions: (318) 274-2457
E-mail: admissions@gram.edu
Web site:
http://www.gram.edu/sogs/school-of-graduate-studies.htm
Financial aid: (318) 274-6056
Tuition: N/A
Room/board/expenses: N/A
Enrollment: N/A

Louisiana State University–Baton Rouge

221 Peabody Hall
Baton Rouge, LA 70803
Public
NCATE accredited: YES
Admissions: (225) 578-1641
E-mail: gradadm@lsu.edu
Web site:
http://obelix.ednet.lsu.edu
Financial aid: (225) 578-3103
Application deadline: rolling
In-state tuition: full time: $3,485; part time: $2,026
Out-of-state tuition: full time: $8,785
Room/board/expenses: $8,920
Full-time enrollment: 214
doctoral students: 35%; master's students: 60%; education specialists: 5%; men: 29%; women: 71%; minorities: 18%; international: 7%
Part-time enrollment: 297
doctoral students: 34%; master's students: 33%; education specialists: 33%; men: 18%; women: 82%; minorities: 24%; international: 1%
Acceptance rate (master's): 53%
Acceptance rate (doctoral): 38%
Entrance test required: GRE
Avg. GRE (of all entering students with scores): quantitative: 530; verbal 438

TOEFL requirement: YES
Minimum TOEFL score: 550
Fellowships: 6
Teaching assistantships: 34
Research assistantships: 19
Students reporting specialty: 100%
Students specializing in: admin.: 17%; counseling: 1%; curriculum/instr.: 13%; evaluation/research/statistics: 0%; secondary: 14%; other: 55%

Louisiana Tech University

PO Box 3163
Ruston, LA 71272-0001
Public
NCATE accredited: YES
Admissions: (318) 257-3036
E-mail: gschool@latech.edu
Web site:
http://www.latech.edu/tech/education/
Internet application:
http://www.latech.edu/tech/gradschool/admit.html
Financial aid: (318) 257-2641
Application deadline: rolling
In-state tuition: full time: $2,112; part time: $951/credit hour
Out-of-state tuition: full time: $4,797
Room/board/expenses: $4,305
Full-time enrollment: 362
doctoral students: 12%; master's students: 88%; education specialists: N/A; men: N/A; women: N/A; minorities: N/A; international: N/A
Part-time enrollment: 751
doctoral students: 5%; master's students: 95%; education specialists: N/A; men: N/A; women: N/A; minorities: N/A; international: N/A
Acceptance rate (master's): N/A
Acceptance rate (doctoral): N/A
Entrance test required: GRE
Avg. GRE (of all entering students with scores): quantitative: 480; verbal 445
TOEFL requirement: YES
Minimum TOEFL score: 500
Fellowships: 7
Teaching assistantships: 12
Research assistantships: 9
Students reporting specialty: 100%
Students specializing in: admin.: 2%; counseling: 14%; curriculum/instr.: 8%; other: 75%

University of Louisiana–Monroe

Strauss Hall
Monroe, LA 71209-0001
Public
NCATE accredited: YES
Admissions: (318) 342-5252
E-mail: admissions@ulm.edu
Web site: http://www.ulm.edu
Internet application:
http://www.ulm.edu/enrollment/admissions.html
Financial aid: (318) 342-5320
Application deadline: 07/01
In-state tuition: full time: $1,215; part time: $128/credit hour
Out-of-state tuition: full time: $4,194
Room/board/expenses: $1,935
Full-time enrollment: 159
doctoral students: 9%; master's students: 82%; education specialists: 9%; men: N/A; women: N/A; minorities: N/A; international: N/A
Part-time enrollment: 32
doctoral students: 100%; master's students: N/A; education specialists: N/A; men: N/A; women: N/A; minorities: N/A; international: N/A
Acceptance rate (master's): N/A

Acceptance rate (doctoral): 55%
Entrance test required: GRE
Avg. GRE (of all entering students with scores): quantitative: N/A; verbal N/A
TOEFL requirement: YES
Minimum TOEFL score: 480
Teaching assistantships: 12
Research assistantships: 31
Students reporting specialty: 100%
Students specializing in: admin.: 15%; counseling: 11%; curriculum/instr.: 6%; elementary: 23%; secondary: 11%; special: 12%; other: 22%

University of New Orleans

College of Education
New Orleans, LA 70148
Public
NCATE accredited: YES
Admissions: (504) 280-6595
E-mail: admissions@uno.edu
Web site: http//www.uno.edu
Internet application: http://www.uno.edu/~admi/app.html
Financial aid: (504) 280-6603
Application deadline: 08/31
In-state tuition: full time: $3,026; part time: $1,940
Out-of-state tuition: full time: $10,070
Room/board/expenses: $6,540
Full-time enrollment: 288
doctoral students: 26%; master's students: 74%; education specialists: N/A; men: 21%; women: 79%; minorities: 45%; international: 3%
Part-time enrollment: 1,012
doctoral students: 14%; master's students: 86%; education specialists: N/A; men: 20%; women: 80%; minorities: 38%; international: 0%
Acceptance rate (master's): 74%
Acceptance rate (doctoral): 61%
Entrance test required: GRE
Avg. GRE (of all entering students with scores): quantitative: 457; verbal 441
TOEFL requirement: YES
Minimum TOEFL score: 550
Students reporting specialty: 100%
Students specializing in: admin.: 12%; counseling: 11%; curriculum/instr.: 18%; special: 8%; other: 51%

MAINE

University of Maine–Orono

Shibles Hall
Orono, ME 04469
Public
NCATE accredited: YES
Admissions: (207) 581-3218
E-mail: graduate@maine.maine.edu
Web site: http://www.umaine.edu/graduate/
Internet application: http://www.umaine.edu/graduate/onlineap.htm
Financial aid: (207) 581-1324
Application deadline: rolling
In-state tuition: full time: $218/credit hour; part time: $218/credit hour
Out-of-state tuition: full time: $623/credit hour
Room/board/expenses: $7,372
Full-time enrollment: 207
doctoral students: 7%; master's students: 88%; education specialists: 5%; men: 27%; women: 73%; minorities: 4%; international: 1%

Part-time enrollment: 449
doctoral students: 8%; master's students: 69%; education specialists: 24%; men: 28%; women: 72%; minorities: 2%; international: N/A
Acceptance rate (master's): 84%
Acceptance rate (doctoral): 60%
Entrance test required: GRE or MAT
Avg. GRE (of all entering students with scores): quantitative: 491; verbal 447
TOEFL requirement: YES
Minimum TOEFL score: 550
Fellowships: 1
Teaching assistantships: 20
Research assistantships: 5
Students reporting specialty: 82%
Students specializing in: admin.: 17%; counseling: 14%; curriculum/instr.: 9%; elementary: 4%; higher education admin.: 6%; secondary: 4%; special: 12%; instructional media design: 5%; other: 28%

MARYLAND

Johns Hopkins University[1]

7150 Columbia Gateway Drive
Suite A/B
Columbia, MD 21046
Private
NCATE accredited: APPLYING
Admissions: (410) 872-1234
E-mail: edspsbe@jhu.edu
Web site: http://www.spsbe.jhu.edu/programs/grad_edu.cfm
Internet application: http://apply.spsbe.jhu.edu/
Financial aid: (410) 872-1230
Tuition: N/A
Room/board/expenses: N/A
Enrollment: N/A

Morgan State University[1]

1700 E. Cold Spring Lane
Baltimore, MD 21251
Public
NCATE accredited: YES
Admissions: (443) 885-3185
E-mail: jwaller@moac.morgan.edu
Web site: http://www.morgan.edu/academics/Grad-Studies/default.asp
Internet application: http://www.morgan.edu/academics/Grad-Studies/apply.asp
Financial aid: (443) 885-3170
Tuition: N/A
Room/board/expenses: N/A
Enrollment: N/A

University of Maryland–College Park

3119 Benjamin Building
College Park, MD 20742-1121
Public
NCATE accredited: YES
Admissions: (301) 405-2359
E-mail: kangel@deans.umd.edu
Web site: http://www.education.umd.edu
Internet application: http://www.gradschool.umd.edu/Admit/web.html
Financial aid: (301) 314-9000
Application deadline: 11/01
In-state tuition: full time: $312/credit hour; part time: $312/credit hour

Out-of-state tuition: full time: $494/credit hour
Room/board/expenses: $8,257
Full-time enrollment: 546
doctoral students: 64%; master's students: 36%; education specialists: 0%; men: 19%; women: 81%; minorities: 25%; international: 13%
Part-time enrollment: 510
doctoral students: 40%; master's students: 60%; education specialists: 0%; men: 19%; women: 81%; minorities: 25%; international: 1%
Acceptance rate (master's): 46%
Acceptance rate (doctoral): 42%
Entrance test required: GRE or MAT
Avg. GRE (of all entering students with scores): quantitative: 603; verbal 526
TOEFL requirement: YES
Minimum TOEFL score: 575
Fellowships: 150
Teaching assistantships: 40
Research assistantships: 112
Students reporting specialty: 100%
Students specializing in: admin.: 7%; counseling: 23%; evaluation/research/statistics: 3%; social/philosophical foundations: 6%; policy: 4%; educational psych.: 13%; elementary: 9%; higher education admin.: 6%; secondary: 20%; special: 9%; other: 0%

MASSACHUSETTS

Boston College (Lynch)

Campion Hall
Chestnut Hill, MA 02467-3813
Private
NCATE accredited: YES
Admissions: (617) 552-4214
E-mail: grad.ed.info@bc.edu
Web site: http://www.bc.edu/education
Internet application: http://www.bc.edu/bc_org/avp/soe/admissions
Financial aid: (617) 552-3300
Application deadline: 01/01
Tuition: full time: $760/credit hour; part time: $760/credit hour
Room/board/expenses: $13,358
Full-time enrollment: 436
doctoral students: 26%; master's students: 72%; education specialists: 2%; men: 25%; women: 75%; minorities: 14%; international: 10%
Part-time enrollment: 607
doctoral students: 30%; master's students: 68%; education specialists: 2%; men: 25%; women: 75%; minorities: 14%; international: 9%
Acceptance rate (master's): 69%
Acceptance rate (doctoral): 33%
Entrance test required: GRE or MAT
Avg. GRE (of all entering students with scores): quantitative: 593; verbal 517
TOEFL requirement: YES
Minimum TOEFL score: 550
Fellowships: 797
Teaching assistantships: 115
Research assistantships: 200
Students reporting specialty: 100%
Students specializing in: admin.: 12%; counseling: 20%; curriculum/instr.: 13%; evaluation/research/statistics: 3%; educational psych.: 7%; elementary: 8%; higher education admin.: 12%; secondary: 10%; special: 7%; other: 8%

Boston University

2 Sherborn Street
Boston, MA 02215
Private
NCATE accredited: NO
Admissions: (617) 353-4237
E-mail: sedgrad@bu.edu
Web site: http://www.bu.edu/education/
Financial aid: (617) 353-4238
Application deadline: rolling
Tuition: full time: $27,306; part time: $423/credit hour
Room/board/expenses: $14,050
Full-time enrollment: 268
doctoral students: 13%; master's students: 86%; education specialists: 1%; men: 21%; women: 79%; minorities: 6%; international: 22%
Part-time enrollment: 253
doctoral students: 32%; master's students: 66%; education specialists: 2%; men: 23%; women: 77%; minorities: 10%; international: 11%
Acceptance rate (master's): 80%
Acceptance rate (doctoral): 57%
Entrance test required: GRE or MAT
Avg. GRE (of all entering students with scores): quantitative: 594; verbal 514
TOEFL requirement: YES
Minimum TOEFL score: 550
Fellowships: 10
Teaching assistantships: 27
Research assistantships: 12
Students reporting specialty: 98%
Students specializing in: admin.: 15%; counseling: 12%; curriculum/instr.: 8%; elementary: 3%; secondary: 7%; special: 12%; other: 43%

Harvard University

Appian Way
Cambridge, MA 02138
Private
NCATE accredited: NO
Admissions: (617) 495-3414
E-mail: gseadmissions@harvard.edu
Web site: http://www.gse.harvard.edu
Financial aid: (617) 495-3416
Application deadline: 01/02
Tuition: full time: $26,914; part time: $14,342
Room/board/expenses: $18,838
Full-time enrollment: 854
doctoral students: 41%; master's students: 59%; education specialists: N/A; men: 26%; women: 74%; minorities: 27%; international: 11%
Part-time enrollment: 179
doctoral students: 39%; master's students: 61%; education specialists: N/A; men: 22%; women: 78%; minorities: 18%; international: 2%
Acceptance rate (master's): 54%
Acceptance rate (doctoral): 13%
Entrance test required: GRE or MAT
Avg. GRE (of all entering students with scores): quantitative: 634; verbal 581
TOEFL requirement: YES
Minimum TOEFL score: 600
Fellowships: 133
Teaching assistantships: 153
Research assistantships: 55
Students reporting specialty: 100%
Students specializing in: admin.: 16%; curriculum/instr.: 13%; evaluation/research/statistics: 0%; social/philosophical foundations: 0%; policy: 3%; educational psych.: 20%; higher education admin.: 3%; secondary: 6%; instructional media design: 4%; other: 34%

University of Massachusetts–Amherst

Furcolo Hall
813 North Pleasant Street
Amherst, MA 01003-9308
Public
NCATE accredited: YES
Admissions: (413) 545-0721
E-mail: gradadm@resgs.umass.edu
Web site: http://www.umass.edu/education
Internet application: http://www.umass.edu/gradschool
Financial aid: (413) 577-0555
Application deadline: 01/15
In-state tuition: full time: $6,753; part time: $110/credit hour
Out-of-state tuition: full time: $14,050
Room/board/expenses: $8,000
Full-time enrollment: 397
doctoral students: 28%; master's students: 72%; education specialists: N/A; men: 28%; women: 72%; minorities: 14%; international: 25%
Part-time enrollment: 532
doctoral students: 52%; master's students: 48%; education specialists: N/A; men: 32%; women: 68%; minorities: 11%; international: 14%
Acceptance rate (master's): 63%
Acceptance rate (doctoral): 45%
Entrance test required: NONE
Avg. GRE (of all entering students with scores): quantitative: 543; verbal 512
TOEFL requirement: YES
Minimum TOEFL score: 550
Fellowships: 13
Teaching assistantships: 152
Research assistantships: 131
Students reporting specialty: 100%
Students specializing in: admin.: 4%; counseling: 13%; curriculum/instr.: 37%; evaluation/research/statistics: 2%; policy: 11%; elementary: 9%; higher education admin.: 4%; secondary: 10%; special: 3%; instructional media design: 2%; other: 6%

University of Massachusetts–Lowell

1 University Avenue
Lowell, MA 01854
Public
NCATE accredited: YES
Admissions: (978) 934-4601
E-mail: donald_pierson@uml.edu
Web site: http://www.uml.edu/grad/
Internet application: http://gse.uml.edu
Financial aid: (978) 934-4220
Application deadline: rolling
In-state tuition: full time: $91/credit hour; part time: $91/credit hour
Out-of-state tuition: full time: $357/credit hour
Room/board/expenses: N/A
Full-time enrollment: 99
doctoral students: 4%; master's students: 96%; education specialists: 0%; men: 19%; women: 81%; minorities: 4%; international: 3%
Part-time enrollment: 334
doctoral students: 57%; master's students: 43%; education specialists: 0%; men: 29%; women: 71%; minorities: 4%; international: 1%
Acceptance rate (master's): 75%
Acceptance rate (doctoral): 70%
Entrance test required: GRE
Avg. GRE (of all entering students with scores): quantitative: 543; verbal 508

TOEFL requirement: YES
Minimum TOEFL score: 500
Fellowships: 6
Teaching assistantships: 4
Research assistantships: 7
Students reporting specialty: 100%
Students specializing in: admin.: 54%; curriculum/instr.: 22%; elementary: 11%; higher education admin.: 2%; secondary: 10%

MICHIGAN

Andrews University
School of Education
Berrien Springs, MI 49104-0100
Private
NCATE accredited: YES
Admissions: (800) 253-2874
E-mail: enroll@andrews.edu
Web site: http://www.andrews.edu/
Financial aid: (616) 471-3334
Application deadline: N/A
Tuition: full time: $650/credit hour; part time: $650/credit hour
Room/board/expenses: $5,690
Full-time enrollment: 162
doctoral students: 66%; master's students: 31%; education specialists: 2%; men: 38%; women: 62%; minorities: 39%; international: 27%
Part-time enrollment: 134
doctoral students: 63%; master's students: 28%; education specialists: 9%; men: 40%; women: 60%; minorities: 26%; international: 16%
Acceptance rate (master's): 58%
Acceptance rate (doctoral): 36%
Entrance test required: GRE
Avg. GRE (of all entering students with scores): quantitative: 439; verbal 410
TOEFL requirement: YES
Minimum TOEFL score: 550
Fellowships: 0
Teaching assistantships: 10
Research assistantships: 10
Students reporting specialty: 95%
Students specializing in: admin.: 8%; counseling: 23%; curriculum/instr.: 13%; educational psych.: 11%; elementary: 5%; higher education admin.: 4%; other: 37%

Michigan State University
501 Erickson Hall
East Lansing, MI 48824-1034
Public
NCATE accredited: NO
Admissions: (517) 355-8332
E-mail: admis@msu.edu
Web site: http://www.educ.msu.edu
Internet application: http://www.msu.edu/user/gradschl/apply.htm
Financial aid: (517) 353-5940
Application deadline: rolling
In-state tuition: full time: $265/credit hour; part time: $265/credit hour
Out-of-state tuition: full time: $536/credit hour
Room/board/expenses: $10,540
Full-time enrollment: 499
doctoral students: 68%; master's students: 29%; education specialists: 2%; men: 32%; women: 68%; minorities: 15%; international: 21%
Part-time enrollment: 820
doctoral students: 11%; master's students: 87%; education specialists: 2%; men: 28%; women: 72%; minorities: 10%; international: 4%
Acceptance rate (master's): 62%
Acceptance rate (doctoral): 36%
Entrance test required: GRE

Avg. GRE (of all entering students with scores): quantitative: 613; verbal 535
TOEFL requirement: YES
Minimum TOEFL score: 550
Fellowships: 221
Teaching assistantships: 155
Research assistantships: 157
Students reporting specialty: 100%
Students specializing in: admin.: 14%; counseling: 10%; curriculum/instr.: 42%; evaluation/research/statistics: 2%; social/philosophical foundations: 1%; policy: 1%; educational psych.: 3%; elementary: 2%; higher education admin.: 13%; secondary: 1%; special: 4%; other: 6%

Oakland University
415 Education Building
Rochester, MI 48309-4494
Public
NCATE accredited: YES
Admissions: (248) 370-3167
E-mail: applygrad@oakland.edu
Web site: http://www.oakland.edu/sehs
Financial aid: (248) 370-3370
Application deadline: N/A
In-state tuition: full time $6,930; part time: $269/credit hour
Out-of-state tuition: full time: $12,678
Room/board/expenses: $6,488
Full-time enrollment: 364
doctoral students: 7%; master's students: 93%; education specialists: 0%; men: 14%; women: 86%; minorities: 10%; international: 4%
Part-time enrollment: 1,187
doctoral students: 6%; master's students: 88%; education specialists: 6%; men: 12%; women: 88%; minorities: 7%; international: 1%
Acceptance rate (master's): 86%
Acceptance rate (doctoral): 63%
Entrance test required: N/A
Avg. GRE (of all entering students with scores): quantitative: N/A; verbal N/A
TOEFL requirement: YES
Minimum TOEFL score: 550
Fellowships: 12
Teaching assistantships: 22
Research assistantships: 167
Students reporting specialty: 100%
Students specializing in: admin.: 7%; counseling: 26%; special: 9%; other: 58%

University of Michigan–Ann Arbor
610 E. University Street
Ann Arbor, MI 48109-1259
Public
NCATE accredited: NO
Admissions: (734) 764-7563
E-mail: ed.grad.admit@umich.edu
Web site: http://www.soe.umich.edu/
Internet application: http://www.rackham.umich.edu
Financial aid: (734) 764-7563
Application deadline: 12/01
In-state tuition: full time: $12,431; part time: $2,062/credit hour
Out-of-state tuition: full time: $25,007
Room/board/expenses: $12,800
Full-time enrollment: 433
doctoral students: 63%; master's students: 37%; education specialists: N/A; men: 33%; women: 67%; minorities: 23%; international: 10%
Part-time enrollment: 40
doctoral students: 45%; master's students: 55%; education specialists: N/A; men: 15%; women: 85%; minorities: 13%; international: 13%

Acceptance rate (master's): 69%
Acceptance rate (doctoral): 37%
Entrance test required: GRE
Avg. GRE (of all entering students with scores): quantitative: 619; verbal 544
TOEFL requirement: YES
Minimum TOEFL score: 600
Fellowships: 691
Teaching assistantships: 88
Research assistantships: 228
Students reporting specialty: 100%
Students specializing in: admin.: 4%; curriculum/instr.: 19%; evaluation/research/statistics: 1%; social/philosophical foundations: 8%; educational psych.: 7%; elementary: 13%; higher education admin.: 23%; secondary: 11%; special: 2%; instructional media design: 8%; other: 4%

Wayne State University
College of Education
Detroit, MI 48202-3489
Public
NCATE accredited: NO
Admissions: (313) 577-1605
Web site: http://www.coe.wayne.edu/
Internet application: http://www.admissions.wayne.edu/
Financial aid: (313) 577-3378
Application deadline: 04/01
In-state tuition: full time: $239/credit hour; part time: $239/credit hour
Out-of-state tuition: full time: $528/credit hour
Room/board/expenses: $11,282
Full-time enrollment: 926
doctoral students: 7%; master's students: 86%; education specialists: 6%; men: 28%; women: 72%; minorities: N/A; international: N/A
Part-time enrollment: 1,891
doctoral students: 12%; master's students: 79%; education specialists: 9%; men: 28%; women: 72%; minorities: N/A; international: N/A
Acceptance rate (master's): 72%
Acceptance rate (doctoral): 35%
Entrance test required: GRE or MAT
Avg. GRE (of all entering students with scores): quantitative: 425; verbal 425
TOEFL requirement: YES
Minimum TOEFL score: 550
Fellowships: 0
Teaching assistantships: 6
Research assistantships: 3
Students reporting specialty: 100%
Students specializing in: admin.: 12%; counseling: 10%; curriculum/instr.: 4%; evaluation/research/statistics: 1%; social/philosophical foundations: 0%; policy: 2%; educational psych.: 2%; elementary: 23%; secondary: 17%; special: 3%; technical (vocational): 0%; instructional media design: 6%; other: 20%

Western Michigan University
1903 W. Michigan Avenue
Kalamazoo, MI 49008
Public
NCATE accredited: YES
Admissions: (269) 387-2000
E-mail: ask-wmu@wmich.edu
Web site: http://www.wmich.edu/coe
Internet application: http://www.wmich.edu/grad/
Financial aid: (269) 387-6000
Application deadline: rolling

In-state tuition: full time: $205/credit hour; part time: $205/credit hour
Out-of-state tuition: full time: $503/credit hour
Room/board/expenses: $12,358
Full-time enrollment: 713
doctoral students: 17%; master's students: 83%; education specialists: 0%; men: 24%; women: 76%; minorities: 15%; international: 6%
Part-time enrollment: 981
doctoral students: 7%; master's students: 92%; education specialists: 0%; men: 26%; women: 74%; minorities: 8%; international: 1%
Acceptance rate (master's): 87%
Acceptance rate (doctoral): 69%
Entrance test required: N/A
Avg. GRE (of all entering students with scores): quantitative: 530; verbal 461
TOEFL requirement: YES
Minimum TOEFL score: 550
Fellowships: 1
Teaching assistantships: 39
Research assistantships: 16
Students reporting specialty: 100%
Students specializing in: admin.: 22%; counseling: 23%; evaluation/research/statistics: 1%; elementary: 2%; junior high: 0%; special: 5%; other: 47%

MINNESOTA

University of Minnesota–Twin Cities
104 Burton Hall
178 Pillsbury Drive SE
Minneapolis, MN 55455
Public
NCATE accredited: YES
Admissions: (612) 625-6501
E-mail: spsinfo@umn.edu
Web site: http://education.umn.edu
Internet application: http://www.grad.umn.edu/admissions/index.html
Financial aid: (612) 624-1111
Application deadline: 12/01
In-state tuition: full time: $6,802; part time: $567/credit hour
Out-of-state tuition: full time: $13,359
Room/board/expenses: $9,110
Full-time enrollment: 1,314
doctoral students: 34%; master's students: 65%; education specialists: 1%; men: 28%; women: 72%; minorities: 9%; international: 14%
Part-time enrollment: 875
doctoral students: 44%; master's students: 56%; education specialists: 0%; men: 30%; women: 70%; minorities: 5%; international: 3%
Acceptance rate (master's): 75%
Acceptance rate (doctoral): 34%
Entrance test required: GRE
Avg. GRE (of all entering students with scores): quantitative: 623; verbal 522
TOEFL requirement: YES
Minimum TOEFL score: 550
Fellowships: 71
Teaching assistantships: 122
Research assistantships: 221
Students reporting specialty: 100%
Students specializing in: admin.: 7%; counseling: 5%; curriculum/instr.: 7%; evaluation/research/statistics: 1%; social/philosophical foundations: 4%; educational psych.: 2%; elementary: 9%; higher education admin.: 3%; secondary: 22%; special: 10%; instructional media design: 1%; other: 29%

MISSISSIPPI

Mississippi State University
PO Box 9710
Mississippi State, MS 39762
Public
NCATE accredited: YES
Admissions: (662) 325-2224
E-mail: admit@admissions.msstate.edu
Web site: http://www.msstate.edu/dept/coe/
Financial aid: (662) 325-2450
Application deadline: 04/01
In-state tuition: full time: $4,262; part time: $215/credit hour
Out-of-state tuition: full time: $9,168
Room/board/expenses: $4,780
Full-time enrollment: 314
doctoral students: 25%; master's students: 65%; education specialists: 11%; men: 30%; women: 70%; minorities: 31%; international: 2%
Part-time enrollment: 499
doctoral students: 43%; master's students: 47%; education specialists: 10%; men: 21%; women: 79%; minorities: 31%; international: 1%
Acceptance rate (master's): 75%
Acceptance rate (doctoral): 48%
Entrance test required: GRE
Avg. GRE (of all entering students with scores): quantitative: 459; verbal 402
TOEFL requirement: YES
Minimum TOEFL score: 550
Fellowships: 2
Teaching assistantships: 26
Research assistantships: 14
Students reporting specialty: 83%
Students specializing in: admin.: 10%; counseling: 25%; elementary: 6%; secondary: 3%; special: 4%; technical (vocational): 26%; other: 27%

University of Mississippi
Office of the Dean
164 Education
University, MS 38677
Public
NCATE accredited: YES
Admissions: (662) 915-7226
E-mail: bhoworth@olemiss.edu
Web site: http://www.olemiss.edu/depts/educ_school
Internet application: http://www.olemiss.edu/depts/graduate_school/apply.html
Financial aid: (662) 915-7175
Application deadline: rolling
In-state tuition: full time: $3,916; part time: $2,176
Out-of-state tuition: full time: $8,826
Room/board/expenses: $11,028
Full-time enrollment: 151
doctoral students: 28%; master's students: 69%; education specialists: 3%; men: 26%; women: 74%; minorities: N/A; international: 8%
Part-time enrollment: 376
doctoral students: 27%; master's students: 65%; education specialists: 8%; men: 26%; women: 74%; minorities: N/A; international: 1%
Acceptance rate (master's): 69%
Acceptance rate (doctoral): 43%
Entrance test required: GRE
Avg. GRE (of all entering students with scores): quantitative: 469; verbal 435
TOEFL requirement: YES
Minimum TOEFL score: 525

Fellowships: 15
Teaching assistantships: 3
Students reporting specialty: 48%
Students specializing in: N/A

University of Southern Mississippi[1]

Box 5023
Hattiesburg, MS 39406
Public
NCATE accredited: YES
Admissions: (601) 266-4369
E-mail: admissions@gradsch.mccain.usm.edu
Web site: http://www.usm.edu
Internet application: http://gradsch.mccain.usm.edu
Financial aid: (601) 266-4774
Tuition: N/A
Room/board/expenses: N/A
Enrollment: N/A

MISSOURI

St. Louis University

3750 Lindell Boulevard
St. Louis, MO 63108-3412
Private
NCATE accredited: YES
Admissions: (314) 977-2240
E-mail: grequest@slu.edu
Web site: http://www.slu.edu/colleges/cops
Financial aid: (314) 977-2350
Application deadline: 07/01
Tuition: full time: $660/credit hour; part time: $660/credit hour
Room/board/expenses: $8,180
Full-time enrollment: 68
doctoral students: 38%; master's students: 62%; education specialists: 0%; men: 21%; women: 79%; minorities: 22%; international: 1%
Part-time enrollment: 410
doctoral students: 78%; master's students: 22%; education specialists: N/A; men: 38%; women: 62%; minorities: 18%; international: 0%
Acceptance rate (master's): 100%
Acceptance rate (doctoral): 95%
Entrance test required: GRE or MAT
Avg. GRE (of all entering students with scores): quantitative: N/A; verbal N/A
TOEFL requirement: YES
Minimum TOEFL score: 550
Fellowships: 4
Teaching assistantships: 3
Research assistantships: 1
Students reporting specialty: 100%
Students specializing in: admin.: 60%; counseling: 11%; curriculum/instr.: 12%; higher education admin.: 15%; other: 1%

University of Missouri–Columbia

118 Hill Hall
Columbia, MO 65211
Public
NCATE accredited: APPLYING
Admissions: (573) 882-2961
E-mail: pullism@missouri.edu
Web site: http://www.coe.missouri.edu
Financial aid: (573) 882-7506
Application deadline: 03/01
In-state tuition: full time: $194/credit hour; part time: $194/credit hour
Out-of-state tuition: full time: $584/credit hour
Room/board/expenses: $12,885

Full-time enrollment: 659
doctoral students: 20%; master's students: 78%; education specialists: 2%; men: 27%; women: 73%; minorities: 9%; international: 15%
Part-time enrollment: 1,090
doctoral students: 36%; master's students: 60%; education specialists: 4%; men: 33%; women: 67%; minorities: 7%; international: 5%
Acceptance rate (master's): 65%
Acceptance rate (doctoral): 35%
Entrance test required: GRE or MAT
Avg. GRE (of all entering students with scores): quantitative: 571; verbal 497
TOEFL requirement: YES
Minimum TOEFL score: 500
Fellowships: 76
Teaching assistantships: 63
Research assistantships: 113
Students reporting specialty: N/A
Students specializing in: N/A

University of Missouri–Kansas City

5100 Rockhill Road
Kansas City, MO 64110
Public
NCATE accredited: YES
Admissions: (816) 235-1111
E-mail: admit@umkc.edu
Web site: http://www.umkc.edu/
Financial aid: (816) 235-1154
Application deadline: rolling
In-state tuition: full time: $194/credit hour; part time: $194/credit hour
Out-of-state tuition: full time: $584/credit hour
Room/board/expenses: $13,640
Full-time enrollment: 219
doctoral students: 11%; master's students: 81%; education specialists: 8%; men: 22%; women: 78%; minorities: 91%; international: 4%
Part-time enrollment: 798
doctoral students: 6%; master's students: 82%; education specialists: 13%; men: 22%; women: 78%; minorities: N/A; international: N/A
Acceptance rate (master's): 85%
Acceptance rate (doctoral): 10%
Entrance test required: GRE or MAT
Avg. GRE (of all entering students with scores): quantitative: 503; verbal 469
TOEFL requirement: YES
Minimum TOEFL score: 550
Fellowships: 1
Teaching assistantships: 0
Research assistantships: 0
Students reporting specialty: 100%
Students specializing in: admin.: 22%; counseling: 18%; curriculum/instr.: 29%; educational psych.: 3%; higher education admin.: 6%; special: 8%; other: 14%

University of Missouri–St. Louis

8001 Natural Bridge
St. Louis, MO 63121
Public
NCATE accredited: YES
Admissions: (314) 516-5458
E-mail: gradadm@umsl.edu
Web site: http://www.umsl.edu
Internet application: http://www.umsl.edu/divisions/graduate/
Financial aid: (314) 516-5526
Application deadline: rolling

In-state tuition: full time: $194/credit hour; part time: $194/credit hour
Out-of-state tuition: full time: $584/credit hour
Room/board/expenses: $14,080
Full-time enrollment: 112
doctoral students: 18%; master's students: 82%; education specialists: N/A; men: 27%; women: 73%; minorities: 14%; international: 6%
Part-time enrollment: 855
doctoral students: 17%; master's students: 83%; education specialists: N/A; men: 19%; women: 81%; minorities: 18%; international: 1%
Acceptance rate (master's): 75%
Acceptance rate (doctoral): 53%
Entrance test required: GRE
Avg. GRE (of all entering students with scores): quantitative: 519; verbal 455
TOEFL requirement: YES
Minimum TOEFL score: 500
Fellowships: 0
Teaching assistantships: 6
Research assistantships: 10
Students reporting specialty: 94%
Students specializing in: admin.: 21%; counseling: 25%; educational psych.: 1%; elementary: 21%; higher education admin.: 3%; secondary: 18%; special: 6%; instructional media design: 1%; other: 4%

Washington University in St. Louis

1 Brookings Drive
Box 1187
St. Louis, MO 63130
Private
NCATE accredited: YES
Admissions: (314) 935-6776
E-mail: bcmiller@artsci.wustl.edu
Web site: http://www.artsci.wustl.edu/~educ/
Financial aid: (314) 935-5900
Application deadline: 01/15
Tuition: full time: $27,350; part time: $325/credit hour
Room/board/expenses: $11,500
Full-time enrollment: 14
doctoral students: 14%; master's students: 86%; education specialists: N/A; men: 21%; women: 79%; minorities: 14%; international: 7%
Part-time enrollment: 14
doctoral students: 21%; master's students: 79%; education specialists: N/A; men: 29%; women: 71%; minorities: 14%; international: 7%
Acceptance rate (master's): 88%
Acceptance rate (doctoral): 29%
Entrance test required: GRE or MAT
Avg. GRE (of all entering students with scores): quantitative: 674; verbal 568
TOEFL requirement: YES
Minimum TOEFL score: 550
Fellowships: 3
Teaching assistantships: 2
Research assistantships: 0
Students reporting specialty: 100%
Students specializing in: policy: 7%; elementary: 21%; secondary: 21%; other: 50%

MONTANA

Montana State University

215 Reid Hall
Bozeman, MT 59717
Public
NCATE accredited: YES
Admissions: (406) 994-4145
E-mail: gradstudy@montana.edu

Web site: http://www.montana.edu/wwwdg
Internet application: http://www.montana.edu/wwwdg/apply.shtml
Financial aid: (406) 994-2845
Application deadline: N/A
In-state tuition: full time: $217/credit hour; part time: $217/credit hour
Out-of-state tuition: full time: $535/credit hour
Room/board/expenses: $8,320
Full-time enrollment: 161
doctoral students: 27%; master's students: 73%; education specialists: N/A; men: 45%; women: 55%; minorities: N/A; international: N/A
Part-time enrollment: 19
doctoral students: 26%; master's students: 68%; education specialists: 5%; men: 47%; women: 53%; minorities: N/A; international: N/A
Acceptance rate (master's): 100%
Acceptance rate (doctoral): 80%
Entrance test required: GRE
Avg. GRE (of all entering students with scores): quantitative: N/A; verbal N/A
TOEFL requirement: YES
Minimum TOEFL score: 550
Fellowships: 0
Teaching assistantships: 8
Research assistantships: 0
Students reporting specialty: N/A
Students specializing in: N/A

University of Montana[1]

Education Building
Room 108
Missoula, MT 59812
Public
NCATE accredited: YES
Admissions: (406) 243-5304
E-mail: lisa.blank@mso.umt.edu
Web site: http://www.soe.umt.edu
Financial aid: (406) 243-5373
Tuition: N/A
Room/board/expenses: N/A
Enrollment: N/A

NEBRASKA

University of Nebraska–Lincoln

116 Henzlik Hall
Lincoln, NE 68588-0385
Public
NCATE accredited: YES
Admissions: (402) 472-5333
E-mail: graduate@unl.edu
Web site: http://tc.unl.edu/
Internet application: https://frontier-s.unl.edu/universityofnebraskalinco-12/mck-cgi/gform.cgi
Financial aid: (402) 472-2030
Application deadline: rolling
In-state tuition: full time: $148/credit hour; part time: $148/credit hour
Out-of-state tuition: full time: $398/credit hour
Room/board/expenses: $6,340
Full-time enrollment: 323
doctoral students: 43%; master's students: 54%; education specialists: 4%; men: 28%; women: 72%; minorities: 12%; international: 14%
Part-time enrollment: 582
doctoral students: 62%; master's students: 37%; education specialists: 1%; men: 36%; women: 64%; minorities: 7%; international: 4%
Acceptance rate (master's): N/A
Acceptance rate (doctoral): N/A
Entrance test required: GRE or MAT
Avg. GRE (of all entering students with scores): quantitative: N/A; verbal N/A

TOEFL requirement: YES
Minimum TOEFL score: 550
Fellowships: 37
Teaching assistantships: 74
Research assistantships: 128
Students reporting specialty: N/A
Students specializing in: N/A

University of Nebraska–Omaha

6001 Dodge Street
Omaha, NE 68182
Public
NCATE accredited: YES
Admissions: (402) 554-2341
E-mail: graduate@unomaha.edu
Web site: http://www.unomaha.edu
Internet application: https://ebruno.unomaha.edu/grapp.html
Financial aid: (402) 554-3408
Application deadline: rolling
In-state tuition: full time: $127/credit hour; part time: $127/credit hour
Out-of-state tuition: full time: $334/credit hour
Room/board/expenses: $1,100
Full-time enrollment: 123
doctoral students: 2%; master's students: 97%; education specialists: 1%; men: 27%; women: 73%; minorities: 9%; international: 11%
Part-time enrollment: 720
doctoral students: 9%; master's students: 90%; education specialists: 1%; men: 23%; women: 77%; minorities: 7%; international: 0%
Acceptance rate (master's): 74%
Acceptance rate (doctoral): 46%
Entrance test required: GRE or MAT
Avg. GRE (of all entering students with scores): quantitative: 492; verbal 411
TOEFL requirement: YES
Minimum TOEFL score: 550
Fellowships: 0
Teaching assistantships: 0
Research assistantships: 4
Students reporting specialty: 88%
Students specializing in: admin.: 26%; counseling: 22%; elementary: 17%; secondary: 12%; special: 6%; other: 17%

NEVADA

University of Nevada–Las Vegas[1]

4505 Maryland Parkway
Box 453001
Las Vegas, NV 89154-3001
Public
NCATE accredited: YES
Admissions: (702) 895-3320
E-mail: gradcollege@ccmail.nevada.edu
Web site: http://www.unlv.edu/colleges/graduate
Financial aid: (702) 895-3424
Tuition: N/A
Room/board/expenses: N/A
Enrollment: N/A

University of Nevada–Reno[1]

MS278
Reno, NV 89557
Public
NCATE accredited: YES
Admissions: (775) 784-6869
E-mail: gradadmissions@unr.edu
Web site: http://www.unr.edu/grad
Financial aid: (775) 784-4666
Tuition: N/A

Room/board/expenses: N/A
Enrollment: N/A

NEW HAMPSHIRE

University of New Hampshire

Morrill Hall
Durham, NH 03824
Public
NCATE accredited: NO
Admissions: (603) 862-2311
E-mail: ruthe@cisunix.unh.edu
Web site: http://www.unh.edu/education/
Internet application: http://www.gradschool.unh.edu
Financial aid: (603) 862-3600
Application deadline: N/A
In-state tuition: full time: $7,771; part time: $369/credit hour
Out-of-state tuition: full time: $17,471
Room/board/expenses: $7,929
Full-time enrollment: 184
doctoral students: 20%; master's students: 79%; education specialists: 1%; men: 22%; women: 78%; minorities: 2%; international: 1%
Part-time enrollment: 290
doctoral students: 8%; master's students: 84%; education specialists: 8%; men: 25%; women: 75%; minorities: 3%; international: 3%
Acceptance rate (master's): 82%
Acceptance rate (doctoral): 46%
Entrance test required: GRE or MAT
Avg. GRE (of all entering students with scores): quantitative: 520; verbal 475
TOEFL requirement: YES
Minimum TOEFL score: 550
Fellowships: 2
Teaching assistantships: 20
Research assistantships: 1
Students reporting specialty: 46%
Students specializing in: N/A

NEW JERSEY

Rutgers State University–New Brunswick

10 Seminary Place
New Brunswick, NJ 08901-1183
Public
NCATE accredited: NO
Admissions: (732) 932-7711
E-mail: graduateadmissions@rutgers.edu
Web site: http://www.gse.rutgers.edu
Internet application: http://gradstudy.rutgers.edu
Financial aid: (732) 932-7057
Application deadline: 03/01
In-state tuition: full time: $8,994; part time: $338/credit hour
Out-of-state tuition: full time: $12,822
Room/board/expenses: $10,600
Full-time enrollment: 255
doctoral students: 16%; master's students: 84%; education specialists: N/A; men: 20%; women: 80%; minorities: 18%; international: 7%
Part-time enrollment: 553
doctoral students: 40%; master's students: 60%; education specialists: N/A; men: 25%; women: 75%; minorities: 12%; international: 3%
Acceptance rate (master's): 62%
Acceptance rate (doctoral): 27%
Entrance test required: GRE
Avg. GRE (of all entering students with scores): quantitative: 557; verbal 486
TOEFL requirement: YES
Minimum TOEFL score: 550
Fellowships: 3
Teaching assistantships: 12
Research assistantships: 24
Students reporting specialty: 100%
Students specializing in: admin.: 16%; counseling: 7%; curriculum/instr.: 1%; evaluation/research/statistics: 1%; social/philosophical foundations: 7%; policy: 1%; educational psych.: 7%; elementary: 14%; secondary: 27%; special: 8%; other: 11%

Seton Hall University

400 S. Orange Avenue
South Orange, NJ 07079
Private
NCATE accredited: APPLYING
Admissions: (973) 761-9668
E-mail: educate@shu.edu
Web site: http://education.shu.edu
Internet application: http://education.shu.edu/admissions/applyonline.html
Financial aid: (973) 761-9332
Application deadline: rolling
Tuition: full time: $649/credit hour; part time: $649/credit hour
Room/board/expenses: $10,750
Full-time enrollment: 231
doctoral students: 42%; master's students: 48%; education specialists: 10%; men: 40%; women: 60%; minorities: 19%; international: 3%
Part-time enrollment: 778
doctoral students: 24%; master's students: 70%; education specialists: 6%; men: 40%; women: 60%; minorities: 10%; international: 1%
Acceptance rate (master's): 97%
Acceptance rate (doctoral): 60%
Entrance test required: GRE or MAT
Avg. GRE (of all entering students with scores): quantitative: 489; verbal 428
TOEFL requirement: YES
Minimum TOEFL score: 550
Fellowships: 17
Students reporting specialty: 100%
Students specializing in: admin.: 31%; elementary: 2%; higher education admin.: 4%; secondary: 1%; other: 61%

NEW MEXICO

New Mexico State University

College of Education
Las Cruces, NM 88003-8001
Public
NCATE accredited: YES
Admissions: (505) 646-2736
E-mail: gradinfo@nmsu.edu
Web site: http://www.nmsu.edu/~gradcolg
Financial aid: (505) 646-4105
Application deadline: rolling
In-state tuition: full time: $4,344; part time: $144/credit hour
Out-of-state tuition: full time: $11,964
Room/board/expenses: $9,246
Full-time enrollment: 222
doctoral students: 27%; master's students: 68%; education specialists: 5%; men: 28%; women: 72%; minorities: 36%; international: 8%
Part-time enrollment: 466
doctoral students: 23%; master's students: 69%; education specialists: 8%; men: 29%; women: 71%; minorities: 50%; international: 1%
Acceptance rate (master's): 48%
Acceptance rate (doctoral): 43%
Entrance test required: GRE or MAT
Avg. GRE (of all entering students with scores): quantitative: 485; verbal 490
TOEFL requirement: YES
Minimum TOEFL score: 530
Teaching assistantships: 64
Research assistantships: 11
Students reporting specialty: 93%
Students specializing in: admin.: 17%; counseling: 9%; curriculum/instr.: 55%; special: 19%

University of New Mexico

College of Education
Albuquerque, NM 87131
Public
NCATE accredited: YES
Admissions: (505) 277-2711
E-mail: gradstud@unm.edu
Web site: http://www.unm.edu
Internet application: http://www.applyweb.com/apply/unm/
Financial aid: (505) 277-7395
Application deadline: N/A
In-state tuition: full time: $2,915; part time: $121/credit hour
Out-of-state tuition: full time: $11,207
Room/board/expenses: $11,440
Full-time enrollment: 439
doctoral students: 37%; master's students: 61%; education specialists: 3%; men: 26%; women: 74%; minorities: 31%; international: 6%
Part-time enrollment: 660
doctoral students: 29%; master's students: 67%; education specialists: 4%; men: 26%; women: 74%; minorities: 34%; international: 3%
Acceptance rate (master's): 72%
Acceptance rate (doctoral): 40%
Entrance test required: GRE or MAT
Avg. GRE (of all entering students with scores): quantitative: 530; verbal 444
TOEFL requirement: YES
Minimum TOEFL score: 550
Fellowships: 6
Teaching assistantships: 113
Research assistantships: 18
Students reporting specialty: 100%
Students specializing in: admin.: 7%; counseling: 7%; curriculum/instr.: 21%; social/philosophical foundations: 9%; educational psych.: 2%; elementary: 15%; secondary: 6%; special: 17%; instructional media design: 9%; other: 6%

NEW YORK

Binghamton University

School of Education & Human Development
Binghamton, NY 13902-6000
Public
NCATE accredited: NO
Admissions: (607) 777-2151
E-mail: gradad@binghamton.edu
Web site: http://www.binghamton.edu
Internet application: http://gradschool.binghamton.edu/graduate/Gradapp.htm
Financial aid: (607) 777-2428
Application deadline: rolling
In-state tuition: full time: $5,853; part time: $213/credit hour
Out-of-state tuition: full time: $9,169
Room/board/expenses: $11,885
Full-time enrollment: 135
doctoral students: 6%; master's students: 94%; education specialists: N/A; men: 33%; women: 67%; minorities: 8%; international: 3%
Part-time enrollment: 140
doctoral students: 26%; master's students: 74%; education specialists: N/A; men: 36%; women: 64%; minorities: 1%; international: 1%
Acceptance rate (master's): 66%
Acceptance rate (doctoral): 54%
Entrance test required: GRE
Avg. GRE (of all entering students with scores): quantitative: 531; verbal 485
TOEFL requirement: YES
Minimum TOEFL score: 550
Fellowships: 9
Teaching assistantships: 4
Research assistantships: 4
Students reporting specialty: 78%
Students specializing in: curriculum/instr.: 21%; elementary: 10%; junior high: 16%; secondary: 30%; special: 19%; other: 3%

Cornell University

Kennedy Hall
Ithaca, NY 14853
Private
NCATE accredited: APPLYING
Admissions: (607) 255-4278
E-mail: edgrfld@cornell.edu
Web site: http://www.cals.cornell.edu/dept/education
Internet application: http://www.gradschool.cornell.edu/
Financial aid: (607) 255-6521
Application deadline: 02/15
Tuition: full time: $15,250; part time: N/A
Room/board/expenses: $14,850
Full-time enrollment: 72
doctoral students: 38%; master's students: 63%; education specialists: N/A; men: 33%; women: 67%; minorities: 1%; international: 6%
Part-time enrollment: 7
doctoral students: 71%; master's students: 29%; education specialists: N/A; men: N/A; women: 100%; minorities: N/A; international: N/A
Acceptance rate (master's): 51%
Acceptance rate (doctoral): 16%
Entrance test required: GRE
Avg. GRE (of all entering students with scores): quantitative: 630; verbal 536
TOEFL requirement: YES
Minimum TOEFL score: 550
Fellowships: 3
Teaching assistantships: 15
Research assistantships: 15
Students reporting specialty: 100%
Students specializing in: admin.: 6%; curriculum/instr.: 15%; educational psych.: 8%; secondary: 47%; other: 24%

Fordham University

113 W. 60th Street
New York, NY 10023
Private
NCATE accredited: YES
Admissions: (212) 636-6400
E-mail: gse_admiss@fordham.edu
Web site: http://www.fordham.edu/gse
Financial aid: (212) 636-6400
Application deadline: rolling
Tuition: full time: $645/credit hour; part time: $645/credit hour
Room/board/expenses: $17,505
Full-time enrollment: 186
doctoral students: 19%; master's students: 66%; education specialists: 16%; men: 12%; women: 88%; minorities: 18%; international: 3%
Part-time enrollment: 1,191
doctoral students: 23%; master's students: 69%; education specialists: 8%; men: 19%; women: 81%; minorities: 32%; international: 3%
Acceptance rate (master's): 85%
Acceptance rate (doctoral): 43%
Entrance test required: GRE or MAT
Avg. GRE (of all entering students with scores): quantitative: 589; verbal 525
TOEFL requirement: YES
Minimum TOEFL score: 575
Research assistantships: 52
Students reporting specialty: 95%
Students specializing in: admin.: 16%; counseling: 28%; curriculum/instr.: 14%; educational psych.: 3%; elementary: 23%; special: 4%; other: 12%

Hofstra University

Mason Hall
145 Hofstra University
Hempstead, NY 11549
Private
NCATE accredited: YES
Admissions: (516) 463-6700
E-mail: hofstra@hofstra.edu
Web site: http://www.hofstra.edu
Internet application: http://www.hofstra.edu/application
Financial aid: (516) 463-6680
Application deadline: rolling
Tuition: full time: $551/credit hour; part time: $551/credit hour
Room/board/expenses: $12,155
Full-time enrollment: 395
doctoral students: 0%; master's students: 100%; education specialists: N/A; men: 30%; women: 70%; minorities: N/A; international: 0%
Part-time enrollment: 1,171
doctoral students: 7%; master's students: 93%; education specialists: N/A; men: 22%; women: 78%; minorities: N/A; international: 1%
Acceptance rate (master's): N/A
Acceptance rate (doctoral): 46%
Entrance test required: GRE or MAT
Avg. GRE (of all entering students with scores): quantitative: N/A; verbal N/A
TOEFL requirement: YES
Minimum TOEFL score: 550
Research assistantships: 3
Students reporting specialty: 100%
Students specializing in: admin.: 4%; counseling: 5%; social/philosophical foundations: 1%; elementary: 19%; secondary: 0%; special: 9%; other: 63%

New York University

82 Washington Square E
Fourth Floor
New York, NY 10003
Private
NCATE accredited: NO
Admissions: (212) 998-5030
E-mail: ed.gradadmissions@nyu.edu
Web site: http://www.education.nyu.edu/
Internet application: http://www.education.nyu.edu/graduate.admissions
Financial aid: (212) 998-4444
Application deadline: 02/01
Tuition: full time: $21,586; part time: $834/credit hour
Room/board/expenses: $19,305
Full-time enrollment: 1,687
doctoral students: 14%; master's students: 86%; education specialists: N/A; men: 18%; women: 82%; minorities: 21%; international: 22%

KEY TO TERMINOLOGY ON PAGE 126

Part-time enrollment: 2,229
doctoral students: 21%; master's students: 79%; education specialists: N/A; men: 20%; women: 80%; minorities: 26%; international: 9%
Acceptance rate (master's): 51%
Acceptance rate (doctoral): 12%
Entrance test required: GRE
Avg. GRE (of all entering students with scores): quantitative: 628; verbal 594
TOEFL requirement: YES
Minimum TOEFL score: 600
Fellowships: 91
Teaching assistantships: 72
Research assistantships: 35
Students reporting specialty: 100%
Students specializing in: admin.: 2%; counseling: 5%; curriculum/instr.: 7%; social/philosophical foundations: 1%; educational psych.: 4%; elementary: 5%; higher education admin.: 3%; junior high: 0%; secondary: 10%; special: 1%; instructional media design: 2%; other: 60%

St. John's University

8000 Utopia Parkway
Jamaica, NY 11439
Private
NCATE accredited: NO
Admissions: (718) 990-2304
E-mail: ronaynek@stjohns.edu
Web site: http://www.stjohns.edu
Financial aid: (718) 990-2000
Application deadline: rolling
Tuition: full time: $15,320; part time: $630/credit hour
Room/board/expenses: $8,850
Full-time enrollment: 101
doctoral students: 3%; master's students: 94%; education specialists: 3%; men: 26%; women: 74%; minorities: N/A; international: 3%
Part-time enrollment: 1,134
doctoral students: 11%; master's students: 79%; education specialists: 10%; men: 20%; women: 80%; minorities: N/A; international: 2%
Acceptance rate (master's): 84%
Acceptance rate (doctoral): 65%
Entrance test required: GRE
Avg. GRE (of all entering students with scores): quantitative: 593; verbal 535
TOEFL requirement: YES
Minimum TOEFL score: 500
Fellowships: 7
Teaching assistantships: 2
Students reporting specialty: 100%
Students specializing in: admin.: 13%; counseling: 17%; curriculum/instr.: 6%; elementary: 17%; special: 4%; technical (vocational): 39%; other: 4%

SUNY–Albany

1400 Washington Avenue
ED 212
Albany, NY 12222
Public
NCATE accredited: NO
Admissions: (518) 442-3980
E-mail:
graduate@uamail.albany.edu
Web site: http://www.albany.edu
Internet application:
http://www.albany.edu/admiss/grad/index.html
Financial aid: (518) 442-5757
Application deadline: rolling
In-state tuition: full time: $6,090; part time: $213/credit hour
Out-of-state tuition: full time: $9,406
Room/board/expenses: $9,120
Full-time enrollment: 406
doctoral students: 28%; master's students: 61%; education specialists: 11%; men: 25%; women: 75%; minorities: 12%; international: 9%
Part-time enrollment: 1,055
doctoral students: 22%; master's students: 71%; education specialists: 7%; men: 25%; women: 75%; minorities: 6%; international: 2%
Acceptance rate (master's): 62%
Acceptance rate (doctoral): 30%
Entrance test required: GRE
Avg. GRE (of all entering students with scores): quantitative: 591; verbal 509
TOEFL requirement: YES
Minimum TOEFL score: 600
Fellowships: 33
Teaching assistantships: 0
Research assistantships: 160
Students reporting specialty: 100%
Students specializing in: admin.: 19%; counseling: 10%; curriculum/instr.: 19%; evaluation/research/statistics: 0%; educational psych.: 5%; junior high: 31%; secondary: 9%; special: 3%; other: 3%

Syracuse University

270 Huntington Hall
Syracuse, NY 13244-2340
Private
NCATE accredited: APPLYING
Admissions: (315) 443-2505
E-mail: gradrcrt@gwmail.syr.edu
Web site: http://soeweb.syr.edu
Internet application:
http://apply.embark.com/grad/syracuse
Financial aid: (315) 443-1513
Application deadline: 02/01
Tuition: full time: $686/credit hour; part time: $686/credit hour
Room/board/expenses: $15,014
Full-time enrollment: 292
doctoral students: 60%; master's students: 40%; education specialists: N/A; men: 31%; women: 69%; minorities: 8%; international: 18%
Part-time enrollment: 360
doctoral students: 9%; master's students: 91%; education specialists: N/A; men: 24%; women: 76%; minorities: 11%; international: 6%
Acceptance rate (master's): 77%
Acceptance rate (doctoral): 42%
Entrance test required: GRE
Avg. GRE (of all entering students with scores): quantitative: 587; verbal 488
TOEFL requirement: YES
Minimum TOEFL score: 600
Fellowships: 28
Teaching assistantships: 61
Research assistantships: 37
Students reporting specialty: 100%
Students specializing in: admin.: 2%; counseling: 10%; curriculum/instr.: 3%; social/philosophical foundations: 7%; elementary: 5%; higher education admin.: 8%; secondary: 32%; special: 11%; instructional media design: 12%; other: 9%

Teachers College, Columbia University

525 W. 120th Street
New York, NY 10027
Private
NCATE accredited: APPLYING
Admissions: (212) 678-3710
E-mail: tcinfo@columbia.edu
Web site:
http://www.tc.columbia.edu/
Internet application: http://www.tc.columbia.edu/admissions/
Financial aid: (212) 678-3714
Application deadline: rolling
Tuition: full time: $780/credit hour; part time: $780/credit hour
Room/board/expenses: $18,637
Full-time enrollment: 1,397
doctoral students: 36%; master's students: 64%; education specialists: N/A; men: 21%; women: 79%; minorities: 27%; international: 12%
Part-time enrollment: 3,324
doctoral students: 38%; master's students: 62%; education specialists: N/A; men: 24%; women: 76%; minorities: 27%; international: 12%
Acceptance rate (master's): 61%
Acceptance rate (doctoral): 25%
Entrance test required: GRE or MAT
Avg. GRE (of all entering students with scores): quantitative: 613; verbal 532
TOEFL requirement: YES
Minimum TOEFL score: 600
Students reporting specialty: 100%
Students specializing in: admin.: 5%; counseling: 16%; curriculum/instr.: 7%; evaluation/research/statistics: 1%; social/philosophical foundations: 10%; policy: 1%; educational psych.: 7%; elementary: 11%; higher education admin.: 5%; secondary: 16%; special: 6%; instructional media design: 5%; other: 10%

University at Buffalo

367 Baldy Hall
Buffalo, NY 14260-1000
Public
NCATE accredited: NO
Admissions: (716) 645-2110
E-mail: gse-info@buffalo.edu
Web site:
http://www.gse.buffalo.edu
Internet application:
http://www.gse.buffalo.edu
Financial aid: (716) 645-2450
Application deadline: rolling
In-state tuition: full time: $6,153; part time: $213/credit hour
Out-of-state tuition: full time: $9,469
Room/board/expenses: $8,086
Full-time enrollment: 663
doctoral students: 40%; master's students: 60%; education specialists: N/A; men: N/A; women: N/A; minorities: N/A; international: N/A
Part-time enrollment: 599
doctoral students: 16%; master's students: 84%; education specialists: N/A; men: N/A; women: N/A; minorities: N/A; international: N/A
Acceptance rate (master's): 73%
Acceptance rate (doctoral): 64%
Entrance test required: GRE or MAT
Avg. GRE (of all entering students with scores): quantitative: 585; verbal 527
TOEFL requirement: YES
Minimum TOEFL score: 550
Fellowships: 16
Teaching assistantships: 84
Research assistantships: 21
Students reporting specialty: 100%
Students specializing in: admin.: 7%; counseling: 1%; social/philosophical foundations: 6%; educational psych.: 2%; elementary: 20%; higher education admin.: 5%; secondary: 43%; special: 1%; other: 16%

University of Rochester (Warner)[1]

2-147 Dewey Hall
Rochester, NY 14627
Private
NCATE accredited: NO
Admissions: (716) 275-3950
E-mail:
tmug@dbl.cc.rochester.edu
Web site:
http://www.rochester.edu/warner/
Financial aid: (716) 275-3226
Tuition: N/A
Room/board/expenses: N/A
Enrollment: N/A

Yeshiva University (Azrieli)[1]

245 Lexington Avenue
New York, NY 10016
Private
NCATE accredited: NO
Admissions: (212) 340-7705
Web site:
http://www.yu.edu/azrieli/
Financial aid: (212) 960-5269
Tuition: N/A
Room/board/expenses: N/A
Enrollment: N/A

NORTH CAROLINA

North Carolina State University–Raleigh

College of Education
Box 7801
Raleigh, NC 27695-7801
Public
NCATE accredited: YES
Admissions: (919) 515-2872
E-mail:
graduate_admissions@ncsu.edu
Web site: http://ced.ncsu.edu/
Internet application:
http://www2.acs.ncsu.edu/grad/prospect.htm
Financial aid: (919) 515-3325
Application deadline: N/A
In-state tuition: full time: $4,036; part time: $3,283
Out-of-state tuition: full time: $15,685
Room/board/expenses: $7,896
Full-time enrollment: 299
doctoral students: 31%; master's students: 69%; education specialists: N/A; men: 31%; women: 69%; minorities: 32%; international: 3%
Part-time enrollment: 637
doctoral students: 46%; master's students: 54%; education specialists: N/A; men: 33%; women: 67%; minorities: 18%; international: 0%
Acceptance rate (master's): 53%
Acceptance rate (doctoral): 32%
Entrance test required: GRE or MAT
Avg. GRE (of all entering students with scores): quantitative: 546; verbal 488
TOEFL requirement: YES
Minimum TOEFL score: 550
Fellowships: 8
Teaching assistantships: 22
Research assistantships: 36
Students reporting specialty: 100%
Students specializing in: admin.: 36%; counseling: 11%; curriculum/instr.: 8%; evaluation/research/statistics: 4%; elementary: 1%; higher education admin.: 10%; junior high: 1%; secondary: 6%; special: 6%; technical (vocational): 2%; instructional media design: 2%; other: 15%

University of North Carolina–Chapel Hill

CB#3500
101 Peabody Hall
Chapel Hill, NC 27599-3500
Public
NCATE accredited: YES
Admissions: (919) 966-7000
E-mail: ed@unc.edu
Web site:
http://www.unc.edu/depts/ed/
Internet application:
http://www.ais.unc.edu/sis/admissions/grad/gradhome.html
Financial aid: (919) 966-1346
Application deadline: 01/01
In-state tuition: full time: $5,074; part time: $4,249
Out-of-state tuition: full time: $16,723
Room/board/expenses: $9,520
Full-time enrollment: 284
doctoral students: 29%; master's students: 71%; education specialists: N/A; men: 24%; women: 76%; minorities: 23%; international: 4%
Part-time enrollment: 252
doctoral students: 48%; master's students: 52%; education specialists: N/A; men: 15%; women: 85%; minorities: 22%; international: 3%
Acceptance rate (master's): 62%
Acceptance rate (doctoral): 41%
Entrance test required: GRE or MAT
Avg. GRE (of all entering students with scores): quantitative: 588; verbal 531
TOEFL requirement: YES
Minimum TOEFL score: 550
Fellowships: 15
Teaching assistantships: 15
Research assistantships: 50
Students reporting specialty: 100%
Students specializing in: admin.: 25%; counseling: 13%; curriculum/instr.: 5%; evaluation/research/statistics: 21%; social/philosophical foundations: 1%; policy: 0%; educational psych.: 2%; secondary: 14%; other: 19%

University of North Carolina–Greensboro

329 Curry Building
Greensboro, NC 27402
Public
NCATE accredited: YES
Admissions: (336) 334-5596
E-mail: inquiries@uncg.edu
Web site: http://www.uncg.edu/grs
Internet application:
http://www.uncg.edu/grs/request.html
Financial aid: (336) 334-5702
Application deadline: 07/01
In-state tuition: full time: $2,814; part time: $1,914
Out-of-state tuition: full time: $13,378
Room/board/expenses: $7,624
Full-time enrollment: 278
doctoral students: 21%; master's students: 78%; education specialists: 0%; men: 20%; women: 80%; minorities: 19%; international: 5%
Part-time enrollment: 441
doctoral students: 34%; master's students: 64%; education specialists: 1%; men: 23%; women: 77%; minorities: 16%; international: 1%
Acceptance rate (master's): 57%
Acceptance rate (doctoral): 39%
Entrance test required: GRE
Avg. GRE (of all entering students with scores): quantitative: 524; verbal 489

TOEFL requirement: YES
Minimum TOEFL score: 550
Fellowships: 21
Teaching assistantships: 28
Research assistantships: 19
Students reporting specialty: 100%
Students specializing in: admin.: 22%; counseling: 16%; curriculum/instr.: 34%; evaluation/research/statistics: 4%; elementary: 0%; higher education admin.: 0%; junior high: 0%; special: 5%; other: 19%

NORTH DAKOTA

University of North Dakota

Box 7189
Grand Forks, ND 58202-7189
Public
NCATE accredited: YES
Admissions: (701) 777-2945
E-mail: gradschool@mail.und.nodak.edu
Web site: http://www.und.edu/dept/grad/index.htm
Internet application: http://www.und.edu/dept/grad/gradapp.htm
Financial aid: (701) 777-3121
Application deadline: rolling
In-state tuition: full time: $3,886; part time: $183/credit hour
Out-of-state tuition: full time: $9,196
Room/board/expenses: $7,133
Full-time enrollment: 30
doctoral students: 50%; master's students: 50%; education specialists: N/A; men: 37%; women: 63%; minorities: 17%; international: N/A
Part-time enrollment: 354
doctoral students: 35%; master's students: 65%; education specialists: N/A; men: 27%; women: 73%; minorities: 9%; international: N/A
Acceptance rate (master's): 96%
Acceptance rate (doctoral): 80%
Entrance test required: GRE or MAT
Avg. GRE (of all entering students with scores): quantitative: 490; verbal 478
TOEFL requirement: YES
Minimum TOEFL score: 550
Students reporting specialty: N/A
Students specializing in: N/A

OHIO

Bowling Green State University[1]

444 Education Building
Bowling Green, OH 43403
Public
NCATE accredited: YES
Admissions: (419) 372-2791
E-mail: prospct@bgnet.bgsu.edu
Web site: http://www.bgsu.edu/colleges/gradcol/
Internet application: http://www.bgsu.edu/colleges/gradcol/adms/admsindex.html
Financial aid: (419) 372-2651
Tuition: N/A
Room/board/expenses: N/A
Enrollment: N/A

Kent State University[1]

PO Box 5190
Kent, OH 44242-0001
Public
NCATE accredited: YES
Admissions: (330) 672-2862
E-mail: oas@educ.kent.edu
Web site: http://www.educ.kent.edu

Internet application: http://oas.educ.kent.edu
Financial aid: (330) 672-2972
Tuition: N/A
Room/board/expenses: N/A
Enrollment: N/A

Miami University–Oxford

200 McGuffey Hall
Oxford, OH 45056
Public
NCATE accredited: YES
Admissions: (513) 529-4125
E-mail: jacobsrb@muohio.edu
Web site: http://www.muohio.edu/graduateschool/
Financial aid: (513) 529-8734
Application deadline: N/A
In-state tuition: full time: $7,874; part time: $324/credit hour
Out-of-state tuition: full time: $16,598
Room/board/expenses: $10,740
Full-time enrollment: 160
doctoral students: 9%; master's students: 84%; education specialists: 7%; men: 24%; women: 76%; minorities: 17%; international: N/A
Part-time enrollment: 265
doctoral students: 14%; master's students: 86%; education specialists: 0%; men: 27%; women: 73%; minorities: 17%; international: N/A
Acceptance rate (master's): N/A
Acceptance rate (doctoral): 67%
Entrance test required: N/A
Avg. GRE (of all entering students with scores): quantitative: 558; verbal 457
TOEFL requirement: YES
Minimum TOEFL score: 550
Fellowships: 0
Teaching assistantships: 10
Research assistantships: 75
Students reporting specialty: N/A
Students specializing in: N/A

Ohio State University–Columbus

1945 N. High Street
Columbus, OH 43210-1172
Public
NCATE accredited: YES
Admissions: (614) 292-2581
E-mail: domestic.grad@osu.edu
Web site: http://www.coe.ohio-state.edu
Internet application: http://www.afa.adm.ohio-state.edu/grad/index.html
Financial aid: (614) 292-0300
Application deadline: 01/15
In-state tuition: full time: $7,342; part time: $289/credit hour
Out-of-state tuition: full time: $18,974
Room/board/expenses: $11,583
Full-time enrollment: 736
doctoral students: 34%; master's students: 66%; education specialists: 0%; men: 33%; women: 67%; minorities: 31%; international: 37%
Part-time enrollment: 729
doctoral students: 23%; master's students: 77%; education specialists: 0%; men: 23%; women: 77%; minorities: 20%; international: 10%
Acceptance rate (master's): 57%
Acceptance rate (doctoral): 44%
Entrance test required: GRE
Avg. GRE (of all entering students with scores): quantitative: 569; verbal 464
TOEFL requirement: YES
Minimum TOEFL score: 550
Fellowships: 42
Teaching assistantships: 138
Research assistantships: 71

Students reporting specialty: 100%
Students specializing in: admin.: 11%; counseling: 2%; curriculum/instr.: 8%; evaluation/research/statistics: 2%; social/philosophical foundations: 1%; elementary: 9%; higher education admin.: 5%; junior high: 2%; secondary: 33%; special: 6%; technical (vocational): 4%; instructional media design: 2%; other: 15%

Ohio University

133 McCracken Hall
Athens, OH 45701
Public
NCATE accredited: YES
Admissions: (740) 593-2800
E-mail: gradstu@www.ohiou.edu
Web site: http://www.ohiou.edu/graduate
Application deadline: 03/01
In-state tuition: full time: $2,839; part time: $299/credit hour
Out-of-state tuition: full time: $5,063
Room/board/expenses: $8,277
Full-time enrollment: 260
doctoral students: 30%; master's students: 70%; education specialists: 0%; men: 30%; women: 70%; minorities: 9%; international: 28%
Part-time enrollment: 247
doctoral students: 28%; master's students: 72%; education specialists: 0%; men: 37%; women: 63%; minorities: N/A; international: N/A
Acceptance rate (master's): 90%
Acceptance rate (doctoral): 82%
Entrance test required: GRE or MAT
Avg. GRE (of all entering students with scores): quantitative: 517; verbal 468
TOEFL requirement: YES
Minimum TOEFL score: 550
Fellowships: 0
Teaching assistantships: 10
Research assistantships: 78
Students reporting specialty: 100%
Students specializing in: admin.: 15%; counseling: 23%; curriculum/instr.: 8%; evaluation/research/statistics: 2%; social/philosophical foundations: 2%; elementary: 2%; higher education admin.: 13%; junior high: 3%; secondary: 9%; special: 13%; instructional media design: 10%

University of Akron

College of Education Graduate Studies
Akron, OH 44325-4201
Public
NCATE accredited: YES
Admissions: (330) 972-7663
E-mail: gradschool@uakron.edu
Web site: http://www.uakron.edu/gradsch
Internet application: http://www.uakron.edu/gradsch/index.html
Financial aid: (330) 972-7032
Application deadline: 03/01
In-state tuition: full time: $7,572; part time: $252/credit hour
Out-of-state tuition: full time: $12,990
Room/board/expenses: $6,709
Full-time enrollment: 234
doctoral students: 26%; master's students: 74%; education specialists: N/A; men: 26%; women: 74%; minorities: 16%; international: 4%

University of Dayton[1]

300 College Park
Dayton, OH 45469-0510
Private
NCATE accredited: YES
Admissions: (937) 229-2398
E-mail: Nancy.Wilson@notes.udayton.edu
Web site: http://www.udayton.edu/~gradsch/main.htm
Internet application: http://131.238.53.158/gradschool/instructions.asp

Part-time enrollment: 777
doctoral students: 16%; master's students: 84%; education specialists: N/A; men: 26%; women: 74%; minorities: 10%; international: 1%
Acceptance rate (master's): 92%
Acceptance rate (doctoral): 60%
Entrance test required: GRE or MAT
Avg. GRE (of all entering students with scores): quantitative: 600; verbal 600
TOEFL requirement: YES
Minimum TOEFL score: 550
Fellowships: 1
Teaching assistantships: 14
Research assistantships: 73
Students reporting specialty: 100%
Students specializing in: admin.: 16%; counseling: 10%; social/philosophical foundations: 8%; elementary: 15%; higher education admin.: 5%; secondary: 18%; special: 2%; technical (vocational): 1%; other: 25%

University of Cincinnati

PO Box 210002
Cincinnati, OH 45221-0002
Public
NCATE accredited: YES
Admissions: (513) 556-3857
E-mail: donald.wagner@uc.edu
Web site: http://www.education.uc.edu
Internet application: http://www.grad.uc.edu/content/gradapp.cfm
Financial aid: (513) 556-6982
Application deadline: 02/12
In-state tuition: full time: $7,743; part time: $270/credit hour
Out-of-state tuition: full time: $14,580
Room/board/expenses: $14,300
Full-time enrollment: 451
doctoral students: 39%; master's students: 61%; education specialists: 0%; men: 27%; women: 73%; minorities: 21%; international: 1%
Part-time enrollment: 412
doctoral students: 17%; master's students: 83%; education specialists: 0%; men: 33%; women: 67%; minorities: 16%; international: 1%
Acceptance rate (master's): 63%
Acceptance rate (doctoral): 57%
Entrance test required: GRE
Avg. GRE (of all entering students with scores): quantitative: 523; verbal 457
TOEFL requirement: YES
Minimum TOEFL score: 550
Fellowships: 1
Teaching assistantships: 37
Research assistantships: 20
Students reporting specialty: 100%
Students specializing in: admin.: 10%; counseling: 11%; curriculum/instr.: 11%; social/philosophical foundations: 6%; educational psych.: 6%; elementary: 5%; junior high: 2%; secondary: 6%; special: 7%; other: 36%

Financial aid: (937) 229-4311
Tuition: N/A
Room/board/expenses: N/A
Enrollment: N/A

University of Toledo

2801 W. Bancroft Street
Toledo, OH 43606
Public
NCATE accredited: YES
Admissions: (419) 530-4723
E-mail: grdsch@utnet.utoledo.edu
Web site: http://www.utoledo.edu/grad-school/
Internet application: http://www.utoledo.edu/grad-school/siteMap.html
Financial aid: (419) 530-5812
Application deadline: rolling
In-state tuition: full time: $7,276; part time: $303/credit hour
Out-of-state tuition: full time: $15,728
Room/board/expenses: $10,463
Full-time enrollment: 92
doctoral students: 11%; master's students: 88%; education specialists: 1%; men: 25%; women: 75%; minorities: 10%; international: 7%
Part-time enrollment: 631
doctoral students: 10%; master's students: 87%; education specialists: 4%; men: 21%; women: 79%; minorities: 10%; international: 1%
Acceptance rate (master's): N/A
Acceptance rate (doctoral): 61%
Entrance test required: GRE
Avg. GRE (of all entering students with scores): quantitative: N/A; verbal N/A
TOEFL requirement: YES
Minimum TOEFL score: 550
Fellowships: 0
Teaching assistantships: 12
Research assistantships: 36
Students reporting specialty: N/A
Students specializing in: N/A

Youngstown State University[1]

1 University Plaza
Youngstown, OH 44555
Public
NCATE accredited: YES
Admissions: (330) 742-3091
E-mail: graduateschool@cc.ysu.edu
Web site: http://www.coe.ysu.edu/
Financial aid: (330) 941-3505
Tuition: N/A
Room/board/expenses: N/A
Enrollment: N/A

OKLAHOMA

Oklahoma State University

339 Willard
Stillwater, OK 74078-4033
Public
NCATE accredited: YES
Admissions: (405) 744-6368
E-mail: grad-i@okstate.edu
Web site: http://www.pio.okstate.edu
Financial aid: (405) 744-6604
Application deadline: rolling
In-state tuition: full time: $98/credit hour; part time: $98/credit hour
Out-of-state tuition: full time: $220/credit hour
Room/board/expenses: $4,300
Full-time enrollment: 292
doctoral students: 40%; master's students: 55%; education specialists: 4%; men: 34%; women: 66%; minorities: 22%; international: 8%

Part-time enrollment: 658
doctoral students: 51%; master's students: 48%; education specialists: 1%; men: 35%; women: 65%; minorities: 18%; international: 4%
Acceptance rate (master's): 66%
Acceptance rate (doctoral): 36%
Entrance test required: GRE or MAT
Avg. GRE (of all entering students with scores): quantitative: 508; verbal 463
TOEFL requirement: YES
Minimum TOEFL score: 550
Fellowships: 0
Teaching assistantships: 68
Research assistantships: 75
Students reporting specialty: N/A
Students specializing in: N/A

University of Oklahoma

820 Van Vleet Oval
No. 100
Norman, OK 73019-2041
Public
NCATE accredited: YES
Admissions: (405) 325-2252
E-mail: admission@ou.edu
Web site:
http://www.ou.edu/education
Internet application:
http://www.ou.edu/bulletins/application/grad.htm
Financial aid: (405) 325-4521
Application deadline: rolling
In-state tuition: full time: $2,982; part time: $98/credit hour
Out-of-state tuition: full time: $8,355
Room/board/expenses: $11,747
Full-time enrollment: 403
doctoral students: 42%; master's students: 58%; education specialists: N/A; men: 29%; women: 71%; minorities: 29%; international: 6%
Part-time enrollment: 157
doctoral students: 66%; master's students: 34%; education specialists: N/A; men: 32%; women: 68%; minorities: 20%; international: 3%
Acceptance rate (master's): 13%
Acceptance rate (doctoral): 19%
Entrance test required: GRE or MAT
Avg. GRE (of all entering students with scores): quantitative: 540; verbal 510
TOEFL requirement: YES
Minimum TOEFL score: 550
Fellowships: 5
Teaching assistantships: 66
Research assistantships: 80
Students reporting specialty: 100%
Students specializing in: admin.: 22%; counseling: 13%; curriculum/instr.: 28%; evaluation/research/statistics: 11%; social/philosophical foundations: 7%; higher education admin.: 15%; special: 3%

OREGON

Oregon State University

School of Education
Corvallis, OR 97331-3502
Public
NCATE accredited: YES
Admissions: (541) 737-4411
E-mail:
osuadmit@oregonstate.edu
Web site:
http://oregonstate.edu/admissions
Financial aid: (541) 737-2241
Application deadline: 06/15
In-state tuition: full time: $7,854; part time: $249/credit hour
Out-of-state tuition: full time: $13,311
Room/board/expenses: $9,135
Full-time enrollment: 130
doctoral students: 15%; master's students: 85%; education specialists: N/A; men: 21%; women: 79%; minorities: N/A; international: N/A
Part-time enrollment: 228
doctoral students: 33%; master's students: 67%; education specialists: N/A; men: 34%; women: 66%; minorities: N/A; international: N/A
Acceptance rate (master's): N/A
Acceptance rate (doctoral): N/A
Entrance test required: N/A
Avg. GRE (of all entering students with scores): quantitative: N/A; verbal N/A
TOEFL requirement: YES
Minimum TOEFL score: 550
Students reporting specialty: N/A
Students specializing in: N/A

Portland State University

PO Box 751
Portland, OR 97207-0751
Public
NCATE accredited: YES
Admissions: (503) 725-3511
E-mail: adm@pdx.edu
Web site: http://www.pdx.edu
Internet application:
http://www.ed.pdx.edu
Financial aid: (503) 725-3461
Application deadline: rolling
In-state tuition: full time: $7,212; part time: $230/credit hour
Out-of-state tuition: full time: $12,228
Room/board/expenses: $10,875
Full-time enrollment: 388
doctoral students: 5%; master's students: 95%; education specialists: N/A; men: 24%; women: 76%; minorities: 12%; international: 4%
Part-time enrollment: 517
doctoral students: 9%; master's students: 91%; education specialists: N/A; men: 25%; women: 75%; minorities: 14%; international: 1%
Acceptance rate (master's): 72%
Acceptance rate (doctoral): 53%
Entrance test required: GRE or MAT
Avg. GRE (of all entering students with scores): quantitative: 527; verbal 546
TOEFL requirement: YES
Minimum TOEFL score: 550
Teaching assistantships: 2
Research assistantships: 3
Students reporting specialty: 100%
Students specializing in: admin.: 1%; counseling: 17%; curriculum/instr.: 17%; policy: 11%; elementary: 16%; higher education admin.: 3%; junior high: 6%; secondary: 11%; special: 17%; instructional media design: 1%; other: 0%

University of Oregon

1215 University of Oregon
Eugene, OR 97403-1215
Public
NCATE accredited: NO
Admissions: (541) 346-3201
E-mail:
uoadmit@oregon.uoregon.edu
Web site:
http://education.uoregon.edu/path.htm?setpath=19
Financial aid: (541) 346-3221
Application deadline: 05/15
In-state tuition: full time: $7,818; part time: $242/credit hour
Out-of-state tuition: full time: $13,224
Room/board/expenses: $9,747
Full-time enrollment: 482
doctoral students: 27%; master's students: 73%; education specialists: 0%; men: 26%; women: 74%; minorities: 20%; international: 5%
Part-time enrollment: 269
doctoral students: 30%; master's students: 70%; education specialists: 0%; men: 39%; women: 61%; minorities: 12%; international: 26%
Acceptance rate (master's): 64%
Acceptance rate (doctoral): 19%
Entrance test required: GRE or MAT
Avg. GRE (of all entering students with scores): quantitative: 537; verbal 504
TOEFL requirement: YES
Minimum TOEFL score: 500
Fellowships: 118
Students reporting specialty: 100%
Students specializing in: admin.: 22%; counseling: 23%; policy: 5%; elementary: 1%; higher education admin.: 1%; secondary: 26%; special: 11%; other: 10%

PENNSYLVANIA

Indiana University of Pennsylvania

104 Stouffer Hall
Indiana, PA 15705-1083
Public
NCATE accredited: YES
Admissions: (724) 357-2222
E-mail: graduate-admissions@iup.edu
Web site:
http://www.iup.edu/graduate
Internet application:
http://www.iup.edu/graduate/admit
Financial aid: (724) 357-2218
Application deadline: rolling
In-state tuition: full time: $6,201; part time: $292/credit hour
Out-of-state tuition: full time: $9,355
Room/board/expenses: $7,663
Full-time enrollment: 266
doctoral students: 24%; master's students: 65%; education specialists: 11%; men: 23%; women: 77%; minorities: 6%; international: 5%
Part-time enrollment: 473
doctoral students: 18%; master's students: 67%; education specialists: 16%; men: 28%; women: 72%; minorities: 5%; international: 1%
Acceptance rate (master's): 83%
Acceptance rate (doctoral): 60%
Entrance test required: GRE or MAT
Avg. GRE (of all entering students with scores): quantitative: N/A; verbal N/A
TOEFL requirement: YES
Minimum TOEFL score: 500
Fellowships: 3
Teaching assistantships: 3
Research assistantships: 81
Students reporting specialty: 100%
Students specializing in: admin.: 9%; counseling: 29%; curriculum/instr.: 7%; educational psych.: 5%; elementary: 2%; higher education admin.: 9%; special: 9%; other: 30%

Lehigh University

111 Research Drive
Bethlehem, PA 18015
Private
NCATE accredited: NO
Admissions: (610) 758-3231
E-mail: ineduc@lehigh.edu
Web site: http://www.lehigh.edu/collegeofeducation
Financial aid: (610) 758-3181
Application deadline: rolling
Tuition: full time: $480/credit hour; part time: $480/credit hour
Room/board/expenses: $10,250
Full-time enrollment: 189
doctoral students: 34%; master's students: 57%; education specialists: 9%; men: 25%; women: 75%; minorities: 13%; international: N/A
Part-time enrollment: 316
doctoral students: 28%; master's students: 72%; education specialists: 1%; men: 30%; women: 70%; minorities: 9%; international: N/A
Acceptance rate (master's): 83%
Acceptance rate (doctoral): 27%
Entrance test required: GRE or MAT
Avg. GRE (of all entering students with scores): quantitative: 597; verbal 530
TOEFL requirement: YES
Minimum TOEFL score: 600
Fellowships: 2
Teaching assistantships: 0
Research assistantships: 61
Students reporting specialty: 100%
Students specializing in: admin.: 22%; counseling: 18%; curriculum/instr.: 2%; educational psych.: 11%; elementary: 7%; secondary: 9%; special: 14%; instructional media design: 9%; other: 8%

Penn State University–University Park

274 Chambers Building
University Park, PA 16802-3206
Public
NCATE accredited: YES
Admissions: (814) 865-1795
E-mail: gadm@psu.edu
Web site: http://www.ed.psu.edu
Internet application:
http://www.gradsch.psu.edu/enroll/program.cfm
Financial aid: (814) 863-1489
Application deadline: N/A
In-state tuition: full time: $9,894; part time: $402/credit hour
Out-of-state tuition: full time: $18,702
Room/board/expenses: $8,805
Full-time enrollment: 504
doctoral students: 67%; master's students: 33%; education specialists: 0%; men: 33%; women: 67%; minorities: 17%; international: 27%
Part-time enrollment: 389
doctoral students: 68%; master's students: 32%; education specialists: 0%; men: 39%; women: 61%; minorities: 7%; international: 13%
Acceptance rate (master's): 52%
Acceptance rate (doctoral): 48%
Entrance test required: GRE or MAT
Avg. GRE (of all entering students with scores): quantitative: 567; verbal 472
TOEFL requirement: YES
Minimum TOEFL score: 550
Fellowships: 38
Teaching assistantships: 135
Research assistantships: 38
Students reporting specialty: 81%
Students specializing in: admin.: 7%; counseling: 28%; curriculum/instr.: 19%; social/philosophical foundations: 5%; educational psych.: 4%; higher education admin.: 8%; special: 11%; technical (vocational): 6%; instructional media design: 9%; other: 3%

Temple University

College of Education
OSS RA238
Philadelphia, PA 19122
Public
NCATE accredited: YES
Admissions: (215) 204-8011
E-mail:
educate@blue.vm.temple.edu
Web site: http://www.temple.edu/
Financial aid: (215) 204-1492
Application deadline: N/A
In-state tuition: full time: $402/credit hour; part time: $402/credit hour
Out-of-state tuition: full time: $582/credit hour
Room/board/expenses: $10,750
Full-time enrollment: 212
doctoral students: 39%; master's students: 61%; education specialists: 0%; men: 33%; women: 67%; minorities: 25%; international: 13%
Part-time enrollment: 1,344
doctoral students: 34%; master's students: 66%; education specialists: 0%; men: 32%; women: 68%; minorities: 29%; international: 14%
Acceptance rate (master's): 55%
Acceptance rate (doctoral): 36%
Entrance test required: GRE or MAT
Avg. GRE (of all entering students with scores): quantitative: 539; verbal 528
TOEFL requirement: YES
Minimum TOEFL score: 575
Fellowships: 12
Teaching assistantships: 49
Research assistantships: 38
Students reporting specialty: 100%
Students specializing in: admin.: 9%; counseling: 16%; curriculum/instr.: 36%; educational psych.: 8%; elementary: 4%; higher education admin.: 5%; secondary: 3%; special: 4%; technical (vocational): 3%; other: 13%

University of Pennsylvania

3700 Walnut Street
Philadelphia, PA 19104-6216
Private
NCATE accredited: NO
Admissions: (215) 898-6455
E-mail:
admissions@gse.upenn.edu
Web site:
http://www.gse.upenn.edu
Internet application:
http://www.gse.upenn.edu/adm_fin/application.html
Financial aid: (215) 898-9789
Application deadline: 01/10
Tuition: full time: $28,580; part time: $3,407/credit hour
Room/board/expenses: $15,668
Full-time enrollment: 414
doctoral students: 30%; master's students: 70%; education specialists: N/A; men: 23%; women: 77%; minorities: 11%; international: 24%
Part-time enrollment: 426
doctoral students: 72%; master's students: 28%; education specialists: N/A; men: 29%; women: 71%; minorities: 19%; international: 8%
Acceptance rate (master's): 65%
Acceptance rate (doctoral): 21%
Entrance test required: GRE
Avg. GRE (of all entering students with scores): quantitative: 620; verbal 548
TOEFL requirement: YES
Minimum TOEFL score: 550
Fellowships: 32
Teaching assistantships: 58
Research assistantships: 57
Students reporting specialty: 100%

Students specializing in: admin.: 10%; counseling: 8%; curriculum/instr.: 38%; evaluation/research/statistics: 2%; social/philosophical foundations: 7%; policy: 2%; educational psych.: 3%; elementary: 5%; higher education admin.: 19%; secondary: 6%

University of Pittsburgh

5T01 Wesley W. Posvar Hall
Pittsburgh, PA 15260
Public
NCATE accredited: NO
Admissions: (412) 648-2230
E-mail: soeinfo@pitt.edu
Web site: http://www.education.pitt.edu
Internet application: http://www.education.pitt.edu/students/admissions/application.asp
Financial aid: (412) 648-2230
Application deadline: rolling
In-state tuition: full time: $11,322; part time: $438/credit hour
Out-of-state tuition: full time: $21,872
Room/board/expenses: $9,800
Full-time enrollment: 540
doctoral students: 30%; master's students: 70%; education specialists: 0%; men: 29%; women: 71%; minorities: 13%; international: 23%
Part-time enrollment: 601
doctoral students: 55%; master's students: 45%; education specialists: 0%; men: 32%; women: 68%; minorities: N/A; international: N/A
Acceptance rate (master's): 84%
Acceptance rate (doctoral): 71%
Entrance test required: GRE
Avg. GRE (of all entering students with scores): quantitative: 563; verbal 600
TOEFL requirement: YES
Minimum TOEFL score: 550
Fellowships: 60
Teaching assistantships: 58
Research assistantships: 65
Students reporting specialty: 100%
Students specializing in: admin.: 16%; counseling: 2%; social/philosophical foundations: 9%; educational psych.: 7%; elementary: 9%; higher education admin.: 9%; secondary: 25%; special: 12%; instructional media design: 1%; other: 11%

Widener University

1 University Place
Chester, PA 19013
Private
NCATE accredited: APPLYING
Admissions: (610) 499-4251
E-mail: j.j.edgette@widener.edu
Web site: http://www.widener.edu
Internet application: http://muse.widener.edu/Center-Education/index.html
Financial aid: (610) 499-4174
Application deadline: rolling
Tuition: full time: $425/credit hour; part time: $425/credit hour
Room/board/expenses: $350
Full-time enrollment: 111
doctoral students: 81%; master's students: 19%; education specialists: 0%; men: N/A; women: N/A; minorities: N/A; international: N/A
Part-time enrollment: 407
doctoral students: 37%; master's students: 63%; education specialists: 0%; men: N/A; women: N/A; minorities: N/A; international: N/A
Acceptance rate (master's): 91%
Acceptance rate (doctoral): 92%
Entrance test required: GRE or MAT

Avg. GRE (of all entering students with scores): quantitative: 490; verbal 512
TOEFL requirement: YES
Minimum TOEFL score: 550
Fellowships: 0
Teaching assistantships: 0
Research assistantships: 5
Students reporting specialty: 92%
Students specializing in: admin.: 27%; counseling: 10%; educational psych.: 1%; elementary: 9%; higher education admin.: 14%; secondary: 7%; special: 5%; instructional media design: 0%; other: 25%

RHODE ISLAND

University of Rhode Island/Rhode Island College[1]

104 Horace Mann Hall
Providence, RI 02908
Public
NCATE accredited: YES
Admissions: (401) 874-4165
E-mail: lheifetz@uri.edu
Web site: http://www.ed.uri.edu/phd_program
Financial aid: (401) 874-4165
Tuition: N/A
Room/board/expenses: N/A
Enrollment: N/A

SOUTH CAROLINA

Clemson University

102 Tillman Hall
Clemson, SC 29634-0702
Public
NCATE accredited: YES
Admissions: (864) 656-3195
E-mail: grdapp@clemson.edu
Web site: http://www.grad.clemson.edu
Internet application: http://www.grad.clemson.edu/f_grad.html
Financial aid: (864) 656-2280
Application deadline: rolling
In-state tuition: full time: $6,404; part time: $300/credit hour
Out-of-state tuition: full time: $13,252
Room/board/expenses: $6,862
Full-time enrollment: 125
doctoral students: 11%; master's students: 87%; education specialists: 2%; men: 28%; women: 72%; minorities: 21%; international: 3%
Part-time enrollment: 346
doctoral students: 19%; master's students: 77%; education specialists: 4%; men: 30%; women: 70%; minorities: 16%; international: 0%
Acceptance rate (master's): 69%
Acceptance rate (doctoral): 42%
Entrance test required: GRE or MAT
Avg. GRE (of all entering students with scores): quantitative: 513; verbal 433
TOEFL requirement: YES
Minimum TOEFL score: 500
Fellowships: 0
Teaching assistantships: 11
Research assistantships: 24
Students reporting specialty: 100%
Students specializing in: admin.: 20%; counseling: 46%; curriculum/instr.: 6%; elementary: 3%; secondary: 3%; special: 3%; technical (vocational): 13%; other: 6%

South Carolina State University[1]

School of Education
Orangeburg, SC 29117
Public
NCATE accredited: YES
Admissions: (803) 536-7186
E-mail: admissions@scsu.edu
Web site: http://www.scsu.edu
Internet application: http://www.applyweb.com/aw?scsu
Financial aid: (803) 536-7067
Tuition: N/A
Room/board/expenses: N/A
Enrollment: N/A

University of South Carolina–Columbia

College of Education
Columbia, SC 29208
Public
NCATE accredited: YES
Admissions: (803) 777-4243
E-mail: gradapp@sc.edu
Web site: http://www.ed.sc.edu
Internet application: http://www.gradschool.sc.edu
Financial aid: (803) 777-8134
Application deadline: 07/01
In-state tuition: full time: $5,410; part time: $266/credit hour
Out-of-state tuition: full time: $11,698
Room/board/expenses: $10,425
Full-time enrollment: 601
doctoral students: 14%; master's students: 73%; education specialists: 13%; men: 25%; women: 75%; minorities: 19%; international: 2%
Part-time enrollment: 572
doctoral students: 38%; master's students: 41%; education specialists: 21%; men: 27%; women: 73%; minorities: 18%; international: 1%
Acceptance rate (master's): 53%
Acceptance rate (doctoral): 51%
Entrance test required: GRE or MAT
Avg. GRE (of all entering students with scores): quantitative: 515; verbal 450
TOEFL requirement: YES
Minimum TOEFL score: 570
Fellowships: 37
Teaching assistantships: 17
Research assistantships: 42
Students reporting specialty: 100%
Students specializing in: admin.: 25%; counseling: 10%; curriculum/instr.: 4%; evaluation/research/statistics: 3%; social/philosophical foundations: 1%; educational psych.: 2%; elementary: 13%; higher education admin.: 4%; secondary: 24%; special: 4%; instructional media design: 1%; other: 8%

SOUTH DAKOTA

University of South Dakota

414 E. Clark Street
Vermillion, SD 57069
Public
NCATE accredited: YES
Admissions: (605) 677-6287
E-mail: gradsch@usd.edu
Web site: http://www.usd.edu
Internet application: http://www.usd.edu/gradsch/admisApp.cfm
Financial aid: (605) 677-5446
Application deadline: rolling

In-state tuition: full time: $99/credit hour; part time: $99/credit hour
Out-of-state tuition: full time: $291/credit hour
Room/board/expenses: $4,427
Full-time enrollment: 219
doctoral students: 31%; master's students: 56%; education specialists: 13%; men: 38%; women: 62%; minorities: 58%; international: 14%
Part-time enrollment: 295
doctoral students: 36%; master's students: 48%; education specialists: 16%; men: 31%; women: 69%; minorities: 68%; international: 6%
Acceptance rate (master's): 99%
Acceptance rate (doctoral): 94%
Entrance test required: GRE or MAT
Avg. GRE (of all entering students with scores): quantitative: 509; verbal 443
TOEFL requirement: YES
Minimum TOEFL score: 550
Fellowships: 0
Teaching assistantships: 25
Research assistantships: 27
Students reporting specialty: 81%
Students specializing in: admin.: 37%; counseling: 22%; curriculum/instr.: 7%; elementary: 6%; secondary: 7%; special: 6%; instructional media design: 14%

TENNESSEE

East Tennessee State University

PO Box 70720
Graduate Studies
Johnson City, TN 37614-0720
Public
NCATE accredited: YES
Admissions: (423) 439-4221
E-mail: gradsch@mail.etsu.edu
Web site: http://www.etsu.edu/
Internet application: http://www.etsu.edu/gradstud
Financial aid: (423) 439-4300
Application deadline: 06/01
In-state tuition: full time: $4,253; part time: $194/credit hour
Out-of-state tuition: full time: $11,211
Room/board/expenses: $9,319
Full-time enrollment: 277
doctoral students: 7%; master's students: 93%; education specialists: 0%; men: 23%; women: 77%; minorities: 5%; international: 3%
Part-time enrollment: 352
doctoral students: 37%; master's students: 60%; education specialists: 3%; men: 29%; women: 71%; minorities: 4%; international: 1%
Acceptance rate (master's): 77%
Acceptance rate (doctoral): 50%
Entrance test required: GRE
Avg. GRE (of all entering students with scores): quantitative: 484; verbal 434
TOEFL requirement: YES
Minimum TOEFL score: 550
Fellowships: 0
Teaching assistantships: 30
Research assistantships: 31
Students reporting specialty: 98%
Students specializing in: admin.: 28%; counseling: 12%; elementary: 16%; secondary: 12%; special: 5%; instructional media design: 4%; other: 23%

Tennessee State University[1]

3500 John A. Merritt Boulevard
Nashville, TN 37209
Public
NCATE accredited: YES
Admissions: (615) 963-5901
E-mail: gradschool@tnstate.edu
Web site: http://www.tnstate.edu
Financial aid: (615) 963-5701
Tuition: N/A
Room/board/expenses: N/A
Enrollment: N/A

University of Memphis

215 Ball Hall
Memphis, TN 38152-6015
Public
NCATE accredited: YES
Admissions: (901) 678-2911
E-mail: gradsch@memphis.edu
Web site: http://www.people.memphis.edu/~gradsch/
Internet application: http://www.enrollment.memphis.edu/admissions/applications/graduate
Financial aid: (901) 678-4825
Application deadline: rolling
In-state tuition: full time: $250/credit hour; part time: $250/credit hour
Out-of-state tuition: full time: $548/credit hour
Room/board/expenses: $3,723
Full-time enrollment: 317
doctoral students: 20%; master's students: 79%; education specialists: 1%; men: 22%; women: 78%; minorities: 34%; international: 6%
Part-time enrollment: 692
doctoral students: 23%; master's students: 74%; education specialists: 2%; men: 27%; women: 73%; minorities: 37%; international: 1%
Acceptance rate (master's): 90%
Acceptance rate (doctoral): 97%
Entrance test required: GRE or MAT
Avg. GRE (of all entering students with scores): quantitative: 509; verbal 465
TOEFL requirement: YES
Minimum TOEFL score: 550
Fellowships: 0
Teaching assistantships: 24
Research assistantships: 45
Students reporting specialty: 100%
Students specializing in: admin.: 7%; counseling: 16%; curriculum/instr.: 14%; evaluation/research/statistics: 1%; educational psych.: 2%; elementary: 19%; higher education admin.: 5%; secondary: 18%; special: 5%; instructional media design: 4%; other: 9%

University of Tennessee–Knoxville

335 Claxton Complex
Knoxville, TN 37996-3400
Public
NCATE accredited: YES
Admissions: (865) 974-4118
E-mail: nfox@utk.edu
Web site: http://cehhs.utk.edu
Financial aid: (865) 974-3131
Application deadline: rolling
In-state tuition: full time: $6,360; part time: $208/credit hour
Out-of-state tuition: full time: $17,664
Room/board/expenses: $10,350
Full-time enrollment: 519
doctoral students: 25%; master's students: 74%; education specialists: 1%; men: 25%; women: 75%; minorities: 12%; international: 4%

Part-time enrollment: 409
doctoral students: 39%; master's
students: 48%; education
specialists: 13%; men: 26%;
women: 74%; minorities: 11%;
international: 2%
Acceptance rate (master's): 92%
Acceptance rate (doctoral): 56%
Entrance test required: GRE
Avg. GRE (of all entering students
with scores): quantitative: 515;
verbal 482
TOEFL requirement: YES
Minimum TOEFL score: N/A
Fellowships: 69
Teaching assistantships: 62
Research assistantships: 16
Students reporting specialty: 100%
Students specializing in: admin.:
2%; counseling: 10%; educational
psych.: 2%; other: 86%

Vanderbilt University (Peabody)

PO Box 327
Nashville, TN 37203
Private
NCATE accredited: YES
Admissions: (615) 322-8410
E-mail: peabody.admissions@
vanderbilt.edu
Web site:
http://peabody.vanderbilt.edu
Internet application:
http://peabody.vanderbilt.edu/
admissions/apply_online.htm
Financial aid: (615) 322-8410
Application deadline: 01/15
Tuition: full time: $1,100/credit
hour; part time: $1,100/credit hour
Room/board/expenses: $13,075
Full-time enrollment: 447
doctoral students: 53%; master's
students: 47%; education special-
ists: N/A; men: 28%; women: 72%;
minorities: 13%; international: 8%
Part-time enrollment: 114
doctoral students: 43%; master's
students: 57%; education special-
ists: N/A; men: 28%; women: 72%;
minorities: 10%; international: 2%
Acceptance rate (master's): 74%
Acceptance rate (doctoral): 41%
Entrance test required: GRE or
MAT
Avg. GRE (of all entering students
with scores): quantitative: 637;
verbal 548
TOEFL requirement: YES
Minimum TOEFL score: 550
Fellowships: 77
Teaching assistantships: 87
Research assistantships: 108
Students reporting specialty: 100%
Students specializing in: admin.:
8%; counseling: 6%; curriculum/
instr.: 2%; policy: 8%; educational
psych.: 11%; elementary: 6%;
higher education admin.: 14%;
secondary: 8%; special: 17%; in-
structional media design: 5%;
other: 14%

Baylor University

PO Box 97304
Waco, TX 76798-7304
Private
NCATE accredited: YES
Admissions: (254) 710-3584
E-mail:
maranda_knox@baylor.edu
Web site:
http://www.baylor.edu/SOE/
Internet application: https://www.
baylor.edu/Graduate_School/
prospective_students/admission/
Application/online_step1.htm
Financial aid: (254) 710-2611

Application deadline: 08/01
Tuition: full time: $654/credit hour;
part time: $654/credit hour
Room/board/expenses: $6,476
Full-time enrollment: 140
doctoral students: 56%; master's
students: 39%; education special-
ists: 5%; men: 41%; women: 59%;
minorities: 19%; international: 9%
Part-time enrollment: 159
doctoral students: 45%; master's
students: 52%; education special-
ists: 3%; men: 37%; women: 63%;
minorities: 18%; international: 1%
Acceptance rate (master's): 69%
Acceptance rate (doctoral): 56%
Entrance test required: GRE
Avg. GRE (of all entering students
with scores): quantitative: 562;
verbal 474
TOEFL requirement: YES
Minimum TOEFL score: 550
Fellowships: 14
Teaching assistantships: 32
Research assistantships: 37
Students reporting specialty: 100%
Students specializing in: admin.:
41%; curriculum/instr.: 41%;
educational psych.: 18%

Texas A&M University– College Station

College of Education
4222 TAMUS
College Station, TX 77843-4222
Public
NCATE accredited: YES
Admissions: (979) 845-5311
E-mail: admissions@tamu.edu
Web site:
http://www.coe.tamu.edu/
Internet application:
http://www.tamu.edu/
admissions/grad
Financial aid: (979) 845-3236
Application deadline: N/A
In-state tuition: full time:
$132/credit hour; part time:
$132/credit hour
Out-of-state tuition: full time:
$350/credit hour
Room/board/expenses: $11,262
Full-time enrollment: 465
doctoral students: 53%; master's
students: 47%; education special-
ists: N/A; men: 31%; women: 69%;
minorities: 16%; international: 14%
Part-time enrollment: 578
doctoral students: 66%; master's
students: 34%; education special-
ists: N/A; men: 29%; women: 71%;
minorities: 23%; international: 2%
Acceptance rate (master's): 65%
Acceptance rate (doctoral): 59%
Entrance test required: GRE
Avg. GRE (of all entering students
with scores): quantitative: 544;
verbal 472
TOEFL requirement: YES
Minimum TOEFL score: 550
Fellowships: 54
Teaching assistantships: 51
Research assistantships: 5
Students reporting specialty: 100%
Students specializing in: admin.:
20%; curriculum/instr.: 17%; edu-
cational psych.: 28%; higher edu-
cation admin.: 5%; instructional
media design: 4%; other: 26%

Texas A&M University–Commerce

PO Box 3011
Commerce, TX 75429-3011
Public
NCATE accredited: NO
Admissions: (903) 886-5159
E-mail: graduate_school@
tamu-commerce.edu

Web site:
http://www.tamu-commerce.edu
Internet application: http://www7.
tamu-commerce.edu/
admissions/application.htm
Financial aid: (903) 886-5096
Application deadline: 08/01
In-state tuition: full time: $2,472;
part time: $1,836
Out-of-state tuition: full time:
$5,712
Room/board/expenses: $8,500
Full-time enrollment: 368
doctoral students: 17%; master's
students: 83%; education special-
ists: N/A; men: 30%; women: 70%;
minorities: 23%; international: 5%
Part-time enrollment: 1,610
doctoral students: 12%; master's
students: 88%; education special-
ists: N/A; men: 25%; women: 75%;
minorities: 26%; international: 2%
Acceptance rate (master's): N/A
Acceptance rate (doctoral): N/A
Entrance test required: GRE
Avg. GRE (of all entering students
with scores): quantitative: N/A;
verbal N/A
TOEFL requirement: YES
Minimum TOEFL score: 500
Teaching assistantships: 25
Research assistantships: 25
Students reporting specialty: 99%
Students specializing in: admin.:
26%; counseling: 13%; educational psych.: 7%; elementary: 12%;
higher education admin.: 11%;
secondary: 9%; special: 6%; in-
structional media design: 4%;
other: 13%

Texas Southern University[1]

College of Education
Houston, TX 77004
Public
NCATE accredited: NO
Admissions: (713) 313-7435
E-mail: admissions@tsu.edu
Web site:
http://www.tsu.edu/education
Financial aid: (713) 313-7530
Tuition: N/A
Room/board/expenses: N/A
Enrollment: N/A

Texas Tech University

Box 41071
Broadway and University
Lubbock, TX 79409-1071
Public
NCATE accredited: YES
Admissions: (806) 742-2787
E-mail: gradschool@ttu.edu
Web site: http://www.educ.ttu.edu/
Internet application:
http://www.ttu.edu/gradschool/
Financial aid: (806) 742-3681
Application deadline: 03/01
In-state tuition: full time:
$126/credit hour; part time:
$126/credit hour
Out-of-state tuition: full time:
$344/credit hour
Room/board/expenses: $6,597
Full-time enrollment: 142
doctoral students: 44%; master's
students: 56%; education special-
ists: 0%; men: 29%; women: 71%;
minorities: 15%; international: 19%
Part-time enrollment: 382
doctoral students: 37%; master's
students: 63%; education special-
ists: 0%; men: 27%; women: 73%;
minorities: 12%; international: 1%
Acceptance rate (master's): 61%
Acceptance rate (doctoral): 64%
Entrance test required: GRE

Avg. GRE (of all entering students
with scores): quantitative: 507;
verbal 441
TOEFL requirement: YES
Minimum TOEFL score: 550
Fellowships: 0
Teaching assistantships: 0
Research assistantships: 36
Students reporting specialty: 100%
Students specializing in: admin.:
17%; counseling: 20%;
curriculum/instr.: 10%; evaluation/
research/statistics: 19%; elementary: 4%; secondary: 2%; special:
10%; instructional media design:
7%; other: 12%

University of Houston–Main Campus

4800 Calhoun
Farish Hall
Houston, TX 77204-5872
Public
NCATE accredited: YES
Admissions: (713) 743-1010
E-mail: admissions@uh.edu
Web site: http://www.uh.edu/
grad_catalog/edu/
Financial aid: (713) 743-9090
Application deadline: 07/02
In-state tuition: full time: $88/credit
hour; part time: $88/credit hour
Out-of-state tuition: full time:
$306/credit hour
Room/board/expenses: $10,212
Full-time enrollment: 263
doctoral students: 35%; master's
students: 65%; education special-
ists: N/A; men: 27%; women: 73%;
minorities: 30%; international: 10%
Part-time enrollment: 912
doctoral students: 29%; master's
students: 71%; education special-
ists: N/A; men: 23%; women: 77%;
minorities: 31%; international: 1%
Acceptance rate (master's): 59%
Acceptance rate (doctoral): 44%
Entrance test required: GRE or
MAT
Avg. GRE (of all entering students
with scores): quantitative: 582;
verbal 503
TOEFL requirement: YES
Minimum TOEFL score: 550
Fellowships: 0
Teaching assistantships: 50
Research assistantships: 8
Students reporting specialty: 100%
Students specializing in: admin.:
29%; counseling: 5%; curriculum/
instr.: 34%; social/philosophical
foundations: 1%; educational
psych.: 9%; elementary: 5%; high-
er education admin.: 1%;
secondary: 2%; special: 4%; instructional media design: 4%;
other: 7%

University of North Texas

PO Box 311337
Denton, TX 76203
Public
NCATE accredited: YES
Admissions: (940) 565-2383
E-mail: gradsch@unt.edu
Web site: http://www.unt.edu
Internet application:
http://www.applytexas.org
Financial aid: (940) 565-2302
Application deadline: 07/15
In-state tuition: full time: $2,930;
part time: $114/credit hour
Out-of-state tuition: full time:
$6,854
Room/board/expenses: $9,600

Full-time enrollment: 343
doctoral students: 31%; master's
students: 69%; education specialists: N/A; men: 27%; women: 73%;
minorities: 17%; international: 13%
Part-time enrollment: 1,254
doctoral students: 27%; master's
students: 73%; education specialists: N/A; men: 25%; women: 75%;
minorities: 14%; international: 1%
Acceptance rate (master's): 96%
Acceptance rate (doctoral): 93%
Entrance test required: GRE or
MAT
Avg. GRE (of all entering students
with scores): quantitative: 505;
verbal 446
TOEFL requirement: YES
Minimum TOEFL score: 550
Fellowships: 15
Teaching assistantships: 15
Research assistantships: 2
Students reporting specialty: 100%
Students specializing in: admin.:
20%; counseling: 19%;
curriculum/instr.: 4%; evaluation/
research/statistics: 1%; elemen-
tary: 5%; higher education admin.:
6%; secondary: 8%; special: 10%;
instructional media design: 10%;
other: 17%

University of Texas–Austin

Sanchez Building
Room 210
Austin, TX 78712
Public
NCATE accredited: NO
Admissions: (512) 475-7390
E-mail:
adgrd@utxdp.dp.utexas.edu
Web site: http://www.utexas.edu/
student/giac
Internet application:
http://dpweb1.dp.utexas.edu/
adappw/apply.wb
Financial aid: (512) 471-7213
Application deadline: 02/01
In-state tuition: full time: $5,286;
part time: $4,098
Out-of-state tuition: full time:
$10,518
Room/board/expenses: $9,467
Full-time enrollment: 826
doctoral students: 60%; master's
students: 40%; education special-
ists: 0%; men: 28%; women: 72%;
minorities: 20%; international: 18%
Part-time enrollment: 471
doctoral students: 68%; master's
students: 32%; education special-
ists: 0%; men: 27%; women: 73%;
minorities: 24%; international: 6%
Acceptance rate (master's): 52%
Acceptance rate (doctoral): 42%
Entrance test required: GRE
Avg. GRE (of all entering students
with scores): quantitative: 611;
verbal 542
TOEFL requirement: YES
Minimum TOEFL score: 550
Fellowships: 177
Teaching assistantships: 296
Research assistantships: 199
Students reporting specialty: N/A
Students specializing in: N/A

University of Texas–El Paso[1]

500 W. University
414 College of Education
El Paso, TX 79968
Public
NCATE accredited: NO
Admissions: (915) 747-5572
E-mail: gradschool@utep.edu
Web site:
http://www.education.utep.edu

Internet application: http://www.utep.edu/graduate/forms/index.html
Financial aid: (915) 747-5204
Tuition: N/A
Room/board/expenses: N/A
Enrollment: N/A

UTAH

Brigham Young University–Provo
237 MCKB
Provo, UT 84602
Private
NCATE accredited: YES
Admissions: (801) 422-4091
E-mail: james_crane@byu.edu
Web site: http://www.byu.edu/gradstudies
Internet application: https://app.applyyourself.com/?id=byugrad
Financial aid: (801) 422-4104
Application deadline: 02/01
Tuition: full time: $3,860; part time: $214/credit hour
Room/board/expenses: $7,440
Full-time enrollment: 197
doctoral students: 38%; master's students: 62%; education specialists: N/A; men: 34%; women: 66%; minorities: 1%; international: 6%
Part-time enrollment: 80
doctoral students: 56%; master's students: 44%; education specialists: N/A; men: 48%; women: 53%; minorities: N/A; international: 10%
Acceptance rate (master's): 53%
Acceptance rate (doctoral): 31%
Entrance test required: GRE or MAT
Avg. GRE (of all entering students with scores): quantitative: 590; verbal 491
TOEFL requirement: YES
Minimum TOEFL score: 550
Fellowships: 4
Teaching assistantships: 34
Research assistantships: 47
Students reporting specialty: N/A
Students specializing in: N/A

University of Utah
1705 Campus Center Drive
Room 225
Salt Lake City, UT 84112-9251
Public
NCATE accredited: APPLYING
Admissions: (801) 581-7452
E-mail: uadmiss@saff.utah.edu
Web site: http://www.saff.utah.edu/admiss
Financial aid: (801) 581-6211
Application deadline: 05/01
In-state tuition: full time: $2,569; part time: $2,063
Out-of-state tuition: full time: $7,780
Room/board/expenses: $9,507
Full-time enrollment: 208
doctoral students: 36%; master's students: 64%; education specialists: 0%; men: 27%; women: 73%; minorities: 20%; international: 4%
Part-time enrollment: 384
doctoral students: 30%; master's students: 70%; education specialists: 0%; men: 33%; women: 67%; minorities: 8%; international: 1%
Acceptance rate (master's): 63%
Acceptance rate (doctoral): 27%
Entrance test required: GRE or MAT
Avg. GRE (of all entering students with scores): quantitative: 527; verbal 502
TOEFL requirement: YES
Minimum TOEFL score: 500
Fellowships: 32
Teaching assistantships: 29
Research assistantships: 12
Students reporting specialty: N/A
Students specializing in: N/A

Utah State University
College of Education
2800 Old Main Hill
Logan, UT 84322-2800
Public
NCATE accredited: YES
Admissions: (435) 797-1189
E-mail: dmt@grad.usu.edu
Web site: http://www.usu.edu/gradsch/home.html
Internet application: http://www.usu.edu/gradsch/approcdr.html
Financial aid: (435) 797-0173
Application deadline: rolling
In-state tuition: full time: $2,592; part time: $1,998
Out-of-state tuition: full time: $7,820
Room/board/expenses: $9,811
Full-time enrollment: 300
doctoral students: 30%; master's students: 70%; education specialists: 0%; men: 38%; women: 62%; minorities: 12%; international: 9%
Part-time enrollment: 486
doctoral students: 18%; master's students: 82%; education specialists: 0%; men: 42%; women: 58%; minorities: N/A; international: N/A
Acceptance rate (master's): 51%
Acceptance rate (doctoral): 44%
Entrance test required: GRE or MAT
Avg. GRE (of all entering students with scores): quantitative: 580; verbal 502
TOEFL requirement: YES
Minimum TOEFL score: 550
Fellowships: 5
Teaching assistantships: 22
Research assistantships: 59
Students reporting specialty: 100%
Students specializing in: counseling: 17%; curriculum/instr.: 10%; evaluation/research/statistics: 3%; elementary: 12%; secondary: 4%; special: 16%; instructional media design: 22%; other: 16%

VERMONT

University of Vermont
309 Waterman Building
Burlington, VT 05405-0160
Public
NCATE accredited: YES
Admissions: (802) 656-2699
E-mail: graduate.admissions@uvm.edu
Web site: http://www.uvm.edu/~gradcoll
Internet application: http://www.applyweb.com/apply/uvmg/menu.html
Financial aid: (802) 656-3156
Application deadline: N/A
In-state tuition: full time: $8,874; part time: $347/credit hour
Out-of-state tuition: full time: $21,364
Room/board/expenses: $6,270
Full-time enrollment: 154
doctoral students: 4%; master's students: 96%; education specialists: N/A; men: 25%; women: 75%; minorities: 10%; international: 2%
Part-time enrollment: 158
doctoral students: 35%; master's students: 65%; education specialists: N/A; men: 27%; women: 73%; minorities: 5%; international: 1%
Acceptance rate (master's): 74%
Acceptance rate (doctoral): 43%
Entrance test required: GRE
Avg. GRE (of all entering students with scores): quantitative: 559; verbal 514
TOEFL requirement: YES
Minimum TOEFL score: 550
Fellowships: 15
Teaching assistantships: 18
Research assistantships: 11
Students reporting specialty: 100%
Students specializing in: admin.: 26%; counseling: 16%; curriculum/instr.: 17%; higher education admin.: 10%; special: 4%; other: 27%

VIRGINIA

College of William and Mary
PO Box 8795
Williamsburg, VA 23187-8795
Public
NCATE accredited: YES
Admissions: (757) 221-2317
E-mail: GradEd@wm.edu
Web site: http://www.wm.edu/education/index.html
Financial aid: (757) 221-2317
Application deadline: 02/01
In-state tuition: full time: $6,138; part time: $191/credit hour
Out-of-state tuition: full time: $17,940
Room/board/expenses: $7,688
Full-time enrollment: 181
doctoral students: 27%; master's students: 67%; education specialists: 6%; men: 25%; women: 75%; minorities: 24%; international: 4%
Part-time enrollment: 167
doctoral students: 40%; master's students: 54%; education specialists: 6%; men: 22%; women: 78%; minorities: 14%; international: 1%
Acceptance rate (master's): 30%
Acceptance rate (doctoral): 49%
Entrance test required: GRE or MAT
Avg. GRE (of all entering students with scores): quantitative: 599; verbal 520
TOEFL requirement: YES
Minimum TOEFL score: N/A
Fellowships: 0
Teaching assistantships: 93
Research assistantships: 0
Students reporting specialty: N/A
Students specializing in: N/A

George Mason University
4400 University Drive
MSN 2F1
Fairfax, VA 22030-4444
Public
NCATE accredited: YES
Admissions: (703) 993-2010
E-mail: gseadmit@gmu.edu
Web site: http://gse.gmu.edu
Internet application: http://www.admissions.gmu.edu
Financial aid: (703) 993-2353
Application deadline: 03/01
In-state tuition: full time: $225/credit hour; part time: $225/credit hour
Out-of-state tuition: full time: $588/credit hour
Room/board/expenses: $13,010
Full-time enrollment: 307
doctoral students: 4%; master's students: 96%; education specialists: N/A; men: 16%; women: 84%; minorities: 23%; international: 2%
Part-time enrollment: 1,596
doctoral students: 9%; master's students: 91%; education specialists: N/A; men: 18%; women: 82%; minorities: 18%; international: 1%
Acceptance rate (master's): 74%
Acceptance rate (doctoral): 43%
Entrance test required: GRE
Avg. GRE (of all entering students with scores): quantitative: 540; verbal 529
TOEFL requirement: YES
Minimum TOEFL score: 600
Fellowships: 78
Teaching assistantships: 0
Research assistantships: 87
Students reporting specialty: 100%
Students specializing in: admin.: 12%; counseling: 9%; curriculum/instr.: 19%; evaluation/research/statistics: 0%; social/philosophical foundations: 12%; elementary: 10%; higher education admin.: 0%; junior high: 0%; secondary: 6%; special: 13%; instructional media design: 14%; other: 4%

Old Dominion University
Hampton Boulevard
Norfolk, VA 23529
Public
NCATE accredited: YES
Admissions: (757) 683-3685
E-mail: admit@odu.edu
Web site: http://www.odu.edu/educ/education/index.html
Internet application: http://www.odu.edu/ao/admissions/docs/applications.html
Financial aid: (757) 683-3683
Application deadline: 06/15
In-state tuition: full time: $216/credit hour; part time: $216/credit hour
Out-of-state tuition: full time: $574/credit hour
Room/board/expenses: $9,136
Full-time enrollment: 326
doctoral students: 4%; master's students: 95%; education specialists: 1%; men: 23%; women: 77%; minorities: 21%; international: 4%
Part-time enrollment: 952
doctoral students: 5%; master's students: 92%; education specialists: 3%; men: 29%; women: 71%; minorities: 21%; international: 1%
Acceptance rate (master's): 58%
Acceptance rate (doctoral): 45%
Entrance test required: GRE or MAT
Avg. GRE (of all entering students with scores): quantitative: 501; verbal 456
TOEFL requirement: YES
Minimum TOEFL score: 550
Fellowships: 0
Teaching assistantships: 5
Research assistantships: 65
Students reporting specialty: 100%
Students specializing in: admin.: 8%; counseling: 9%; elementary: 24%; secondary: 14%; special: 17%; other: 28%

University of Virginia (Curry)
405 Emmet Street S
Charlottesville, VA 22903-2495
Public
NCATE accredited: YES
Admissions: (434) 924-3334
E-mail: curry@virginia.edu
Web site: http://curry.edschool.virginia.edu/
Internet application: https://www.applyweb.com/aw?uvaed
Financial aid: (434) 982-6000
Application deadline: rolling
In-state tuition: full time: $5,671; part time: $3,471
Out-of-state tuition: full time: $18,761
Room/board/expenses: $12,650
Full-time enrollment: 656
doctoral students: 47%; master's students: 52%; education specialists: 1%; men: 26%; women: 74%; minorities: 10%; international: 5%
Part-time enrollment: 190
doctoral students: 59%; master's students: 39%; education specialists: 2%; men: 35%; women: 65%; minorities: 11%; international: 1%
Acceptance rate (master's): 69%
Acceptance rate (doctoral): 56%
Entrance test required: GRE
Avg. GRE (of all entering students with scores): quantitative: 575; verbal 530
TOEFL requirement: YES
Minimum TOEFL score: 600
Fellowships: 266
Teaching assistantships: 55
Research assistantships: 341
Students reporting specialty: 100%
Students specializing in: admin.: 12%; counseling: 8%; curriculum/instr.: 3%; evaluation/research/statistics: 3%; social/philosophical foundations: 6%; policy: 4%; educational psych.: 4%; elementary: 8%; higher education admin.: 4%; secondary: 15%; special: 7%; instructional media design: 3%; other: 23%

Virginia Commonwealth University
1015 W. Main Street
PO Box 842020
Richmond, VA 23284-2020
Public
NCATE accredited: YES
Admissions: (804) 828-3382
E-mail: mddavis@vcu.edu
Web site: http://www.soe.vcu.edu
Financial aid: (804) 828-6181
Application deadline: 05/15
In-state tuition: full time: $5,804; part time: $514/credit hour
Out-of-state tuition: full time: $14,872
Room/board/expenses: $10,600
Full-time enrollment: 272
doctoral students: 5%; master's students: 95%; education specialists: N/A; men: 25%; women: 75%; minorities: 18%; international: 2%
Part-time enrollment: 460
doctoral students: 17%; master's students: 83%; education specialists: N/A; men: 22%; women: 78%; minorities: 18%; international: 1%
Acceptance rate (master's): 74%
Acceptance rate (doctoral): 55%
Entrance test required: GRE or MAT
Avg. GRE (of all entering students with scores): quantitative: 503; verbal 456
TOEFL requirement: YES
Minimum TOEFL score: 600
Fellowships: 4
Teaching assistantships: 3
Research assistantships: 7
Students reporting specialty: 83%
Students specializing in: admin.: 11%; counseling: 17%; curriculum/instr.: 6%; elementary: 14%; junior high: 1%; secondary: 8%; special: 9%; other: 34%

Virginia Tech
260 Wallace Hall
Blacksburg, VA 24061-0426
Public
NCATE accredited: YES
Admissions: (540) 231-6691
E-mail: awwebb@vt.edu
Web site: http://www.grads.vt.edu/

KEY TO TERMINOLOGY ON PAGE 126

Financial aid: (540) 231-4558
Application deadline: rolling
In-state tuition: full time: $5,631;
part time: $263/credit hour
Out-of-state tuition: full time:
$8,866
Room/board/expenses: $6,896
Full-time enrollment: 450
doctoral students: 34%; master's
students: 66%; education special-
ists: N/A; men: 32%; women: 68%;
minorities: 18%; international: 8%
Part-time enrollment: 795
doctoral students: 34%; master's
students: 66%; education special-
ists: N/A; men: 31%; women: 69%;
minorities: 17%; international: 1%
Acceptance rate (master's): 73%
Acceptance rate (doctoral): 54%
Entrance test required: GRE
**Avg. GRE (of all entering students
with scores):** quantitative: 560;
verbal 446
TOEFL requirement: YES
Minimum TOEFL score: 550
Fellowships: 0
Teaching assistantships: 22
Research assistantships: 6
Students reporting specialty: 100%
Students specializing in: admin.:
31%; counseling: 11%;
curriculum/instr.: 57%;
evaluation/research/statistics: 1%

WASHINGTON

Gonzaga University[1]
502 E. Boone Avenue
Spokane, WA 99258-0025
Private
NCATE accredited: YES
Admissions: (509) 323-6572
E-mail: soriet@soe.gonzaga.edu
Web site: http://www.
gonzaga.edu/Academics/
Graduate/default.htm
Financial aid: (509) 323-6582
Tuition: N/A
Room/board/expenses: N/A
Enrollment: N/A

Seattle Pacific University
3307 Third Avenue W
Seattle, WA 98119-1997
Private
NCATE accredited: YES
Admissions: (206) 281-2378
E-mail: blomqa@spu.edu
Web site: http://www.spu.edu
Financial aid: (206) 281-2469
Application deadline: rolling
Tuition: full time: N/A; part time:
$325/credit hour
Room/board/expenses: N/A
Full-time enrollment: N/A
doctoral students: N/A; master's
students: N/A; education special-
ists: N/A; men: N/A; women: N/A;
minorities: N/A; international: N/A
Part-time enrollment: 327
doctoral students: 25%; master's
students: 75%; education special-
ists: N/A; men: 65%; women: 35%;
minorities: 8%; international: 1%
Acceptance rate (master's): N/A
Acceptance rate (doctoral): N/A
Entrance test required: GRE or
MAT
**Avg. GRE (of all entering students
with scores):** quantitative: N/A;
verbal N/A

TOEFL requirement: YES
Minimum TOEFL score: 550
Teaching assistantships: 4
Students reporting specialty: 100%
Students specializing in: admin.:
48%; counseling: 13%;
curriculum/instr.: 21%; educational
psych.: 1%; secondary: 18%

University of Washington
206 Miller
Box 353600
Seattle, WA 98195-3600
Public
NCATE accredited: YES
Admissions: (206) 543-7834
E-mail: edinfo@u.washington.edu
Web site: http://www.
educ.washington.edu/
COEWebSite/
Internet application: http://www.
educ.washington.edu/
COEWebSite/students/
prospective/admissions.html
Financial aid: (206) 543-7834
Application deadline: N/A
In-state tuition: full time: $6,508;
part time: $310/credit hour
Out-of-state tuition: full time:
$15,595
Room/board/expenses: $13,386
Full-time enrollment: 461
doctoral students: 17%; master's
students: 83%; education special-
ists: N/A; men: 23%; women: 77%;
minorities: 15%; international: 5%
Part-time enrollment: 319
doctoral students: 64%; master's
students: 36%; education special-
ists: N/A; men: 26%; women: 74%;
minorities: 17%; international: 5%
Acceptance rate (master's): 59%
Acceptance rate (doctoral): 36%
Entrance test required: GRE
**Avg. GRE (of all entering students
with scores):** quantitative: 607;
verbal 547
TOEFL requirement: YES
Minimum TOEFL score: 580
Fellowships: 2
Teaching assistantships: 66
Research assistantships: 48
Students reporting specialty: 96%
Students specializing in: admin.:
4%; counseling: 2%; curriculum/
instr.: 23%; policy: 10%; educa-
tional psych.: 12%; elementary:
9%; higher education admin.: 8%;
secondary: 17%; special: 14%

Washington State University
College of Education
PO Box 642114
Pullman, WA 99164-2114
Public
NCATE accredited: YES
Admissions: (509) 335-1446
E-mail: gradsch@wsu.edu
Web site:
http://www.wsu.edu/~gradsch/
Financial aid: (509) 335-9711
Application deadline: N/A
In-state tuition: full time: $6,288;
part time: $288/credit hour
Out-of-state tuition: full time:
$15,118
Room/board/expenses: $12,239

Full-time enrollment: 485
doctoral students: 40%; master's
students: 60%; education specialists: N/A; men: 37%; women: 63%;
minorities: 16%; international: 5%
Part-time enrollment: 412
doctoral students: 28%; master's
students: 72%; education special-
ists: N/A; men: 28%; women: 72%;
minorities: 11%; international: 1%
Acceptance rate (master's): 49%
Acceptance rate (doctoral): 19%
Entrance test required: GRE
**Avg. GRE (of all entering students
with scores):** quantitative: 584;
verbal 516
TOEFL requirement: YES
Minimum TOEFL score: 550
Fellowships: 3
Teaching assistantships: 24
Research assistantships: 14
Students reporting specialty: 27%
Students specializing in: N/A

WEST VIRGINIA

West Virginia University
802 Allen Hall
PO Box 6122
Morgantown, WV 26506-6122
Public
NCATE accredited: YES
Admissions: (304) 293-2124
E-mail: go2wvu@wvu.edu
Web site: http://www.wvu.edu
Internet application: http://www.
applyweb.com/apply/wvu/
Financial aid: (304) 293-5242
Application deadline: rolling
In-state tuition: full time: $3,564;
part time: $201/credit hour
Out-of-state tuition: full time:
$10,016
Room/board/expenses: $10,347
Full-time enrollment: 569
doctoral students: 18%; master's
students: 82%; education special-
ists: N/A; men: 25%; women: 75%;
minorities: 6%; international: 6%
Part-time enrollment: 865
doctoral students: 20%; master's
students: 80%; education special-
ists: N/A; men: 25%; women: 75%;
minorities: 3%; international: 1%
Acceptance rate (master's): 90%
Acceptance rate (doctoral): 64%
Entrance test required: GRE or
MAT
**Avg. GRE (of all entering students
with scores):** quantitative: 535;
verbal 448
TOEFL requirement: YES
Minimum TOEFL score: 550
Fellowships: 3
Teaching assistantships: 25
Research assistantships: 29
Students reporting specialty: 100%
Students specializing in: admin.:
14%; counseling: 13%;
curriculum/instr.: 5%; educational
psych.: 2%; elementary: 13%; sec-
ondary: 12%; special: 25%; techni-
cal (vocational): 6%; other: 12%

WISCONSIN

Marquette University
Schroeder Complex
Box 1881
Milwaukee, WI 53201
Private
NCATE accredited: YES
Admissions: (414) 288-7137
E-mail: mugs@marquette.edu
Web site:
http://www.grad.marquette.edu
Financial aid: (414) 288-5325
Application deadline: rolling
Tuition: full time: $445/credit hour;
part time: $445/credit hour
Room/board/expenses: $10,150
Full-time enrollment: 65
doctoral students: 48%; master's
students: 52%; education special-
ists: 0%; men: 28%; women: 72%;
minorities: 17%; international: 17%
Part-time enrollment: 159
doctoral students: 34%; master's
students: 66%; education special-
ists: 0%; men: 34%; women: 66%;
minorities: 29%; international: 2%
Acceptance rate (master's): 73%
Acceptance rate (doctoral): 43%
Entrance test required: GRE or
MAT
**Avg. GRE (of all entering students
with scores):** quantitative: 551;
verbal 484
TOEFL requirement: YES
Minimum TOEFL score: 550
Fellowships: 2
Teaching assistantships: 4
Research assistantships: 3
Students reporting specialty: 100%
Students specializing in: admin.:
12%; counseling: 30%;
curriculum/instr.: 53%; social/
philosophical foundations: 0%;
policy: 1%; educational psych.:
4%

University of Wisconsin–Madison
123 Education Building
Madison, WI 53706-1398
Public
NCATE accredited: NO
Admissions: (608) 262-2433
E-mail:
gradadmiss@bascom.wisc.edu
Web site:
http://www.wisc.edu/grad
Internet application: http://www.
wisc.edu/grad/eapp/index.html
Financial aid: (608) 262-3060
Application deadline: rolling
In-state tuition: full time: $6,880;
part time: $431/credit hour
Out-of-state tuition: full time:
$22,150
Room/board/expenses: $5,500
Full-time enrollment: 667
doctoral students: 57%; master's
students: 43%; education special-
ists: N/A; men: 35%; women: 65%;
minorities: 5%; international: 5%
Part-time enrollment: 438
doctoral students: 57%; master's
students: 43%; education specialists: N/A; men: 35%; women: 65%;
minorities: 5%; international: 5%
Acceptance rate (master's): 41%
Acceptance rate (doctoral): 42%
Entrance test required: GRE
**Avg. GRE (of all entering students
with scores):** quantitative: 591;
verbal 479

TOEFL requirement: YES
Minimum TOEFL score: 550
Fellowships: 72
Teaching assistantships: 143
Research assistantships: 10
Students reporting specialty: 100%
Students specializing in: admin.:
23%; counseling: 9%; curriculum/
instr.: 27%; policy: 6%; education-
al psych.: 10%; special: 3%; other:
22%

University of Wisconsin–Milwaukee
PO Box 413
Milwaukee, WI 53201
Public
NCATE accredited: APPLYING
Admissions: (414) 229-4729
E-mail: randall@uwm.edu
Web site: http://www.uwm.edu
Internet application: http://www.
uwm.edu/Dept/Grad_Sch/
Prospective/onlineapp.html
Financial aid: (414) 229-5840
Application deadline: rolling
In-state tuition: full time: $6,762;
part time: $570/credit hour
Out-of-state tuition: full time:
$21,394
Room/board/expenses: $7,076
Full-time enrollment: 263
doctoral students: 25%; master's
students: 75%; education special-
ists: N/A; men: 19%; women: 81%;
minorities: 29%; international: 2%
Part-time enrollment: 505
doctoral students: 21%; master's
students: 79%; education special-
ists: N/A; men: 25%; women: 75%;
minorities: 22%; international: 1%
Acceptance rate (master's): 56%
Acceptance rate (doctoral): 59%
Entrance test required: GRE
**Avg. GRE (of all entering students
with scores):** quantitative: 513;
verbal 459
TOEFL requirement: YES
Minimum TOEFL score: 550
Fellowships: 17
Teaching assistantships: 4
Students reporting specialty: 100%
Students specializing in: admin.:
15%; curriculum/instr.: 21%;
social/philosophical foundations:
2%; educational psych.: 34%;
special: 6%; other: 22%

WYOMING

University of Wyoming[1]
Box 3374
University Station
Laramie, WY 82071
Public
NCATE accredited: YES
Admissions: (307) 766-2287
E-mail: uwgrad@uwyo.edu
Web site: http://uwadmnweb.
uwyo.edu/uwgrad/
Internet application:
http://uwadmnweb.uwyo.edu/
uwgrad/app_index.htm
Financial aid: (307) 766-2118
Tuition: N/A
Room/board/expenses: N/A
Enrollment: N/A

ENGINEERING

The engineering school directory lists the 185 schools in the country that offer doctoral programs. One hundred sixty-nine schools responded to the *U.S. News* survey, which was conducted in the fall of 2002. Information about entrance requirements, enrollment, the cost of attendance, assistantships and fellowships, and student areas of specialization is reported in the following pages. Institutions that did not respond to the survey have abbreviated entries.

TERMINOLOGY

1 A school whose name is footnoted with the numeral 1 did not return the *U.S. News* statistical survey; limited data appear in its entry.

N/A. Not available from the school or not applicable.

Admissions. The admissions office phone number.

E-mail. The electronic address of the admissions office. If, instead of an E-mail address, a Web site address is listed, the Web site will automatically present an E-mail screen programmed to reach the admissions office.

Internet application. The electronic address for online applications.

Financial aid. The financial aid office phone number.

Application deadline. For fall 2004 enrollment. "Rolling" means there is no application deadline; the school acts on applications as they are received. "Varies" means deadlines vary according to department or whether applicants are U.S. citizens or foreign nationals.

Tuition. For the 2002–2003 academic year. Includes fees.

Room/board/expenses. For the 2002–2003 academic year.

Credit hour. The cost per credit hour for the 2002–2003 academic year.

Enrollment. Full and part time for fall 2002. The total is the combination of master's and doctoral students, if the school offers both degrees. Where available, the breakdown for men, women, minorities, and international students is provided. Percentages for men and women may not add to 100 because of rounding.

Minorities. For the fall of 2002, the percentage of students who are Asian-American, African-American, Hispanic, or American Indian. (When the U.S. Department of Education calculates minority enrollment percentages, these are the demo-graphic groupings it uses.)

Acceptance rate. Percent of applicants who were accepted for fall 2002 master's and doctoral programs.

TOEFL requirement. A "yes" means that students from non-English-speaking countries must submit scores for the Test of English as a Foreign Language.

Minimum TOEFL score. The lowest score accepted for admission. The score listed is the minimum acceptable score for the paper TOEFL. (The computer-administered TOEFL is graded on a different scale.)

GRE requirement. A "yes" means Graduate Record Examinations scores are required by some or all departments.

Average GRE scores. For students who entered in fall 2002.

Total fellowships, teaching assistant-ships, and research assistantships. For the 2002–2003 academic year. These are the number of student appointments. Students may hold multiple appointments and would therefore be counted more than once.

Students reporting specialty. The percent of master's and doctoral students, both full and part time, reporting a program specialization in fall 2002. If this figure is less than 50 percent, this entry and the following do not appear for the school.

Student specialties. Proportion of students in the specialty-reporting population (not necessarily the entire student body) who are enrolled in a particular specialty. Specialty fields listed in engineering are aerospace/aeronautical/astronautical, agriculture, bioengineering/biomedical, chemical, civil, computer engineering, electrical/electronic/communications, environmental/environmental health, industrial/manufacturing, materials, mechanical, mining, nuclear, petroleum, and other. Numbers may not add to 100 because of rounding.

ALABAMA

Auburn University
108 Ramsay Hall
Auburn, AL 36849-5330
Public
Admissions: (334) 844-4700
E-mail: gradadm@mail.auburn.edu
Web site: http://www.grad.auburn.edu
Financial aid: (334) 844-4723
Application deadline: rolling
In-state tuition: full time: $3,784; part time: $151/credit hour
Out-of-state tuition: full time: $11,084
Room/board/expenses: $8,126
Full-time enrollment: 439
men: 74%; women: 26%; minorities: 6%; international: 67%
Part-time enrollment: 194
men: 79%; women: 21%; minorities: 10%; international: 21%
Acceptance rate: 56%
GRE requirement: YES
Avg. GRE: quantitative: 710; analytical 628
TOEFL requirement: YES
Minimum TOEFL score: 550
Fellowships: 191
Teaching assistantships: 154
Research assistantships: 305
Students reporting specialty: 100%
Students specializing in: aerospace: 3%; chemical: 9%; civil: 11%; computer: 20%; electrical: 21%; industrial: 10%; mechanical: 19%; other: 6%

University of Alabama–Birmingham
1530 Third Avenue S
HOEN 100
Birmingham, AL 35294-4440
Public
Admissions: (205) 934-8232
E-mail: mnorwood@uab.edu
Web site: http://www.eng.uab.edu
Internet application: http://main.uab.edu/show.asp?durki=24740
Financial aid: (205) 934-8123
Application deadline: 07/01
In-state tuition: full time: $123/credit hour; part time: $123/credit hour
Out-of-state tuition: full time: $277/credit hour
Room/board/expenses: $8,592
Full-time enrollment: 141
men: 79%; women: 21%; minorities: 11%; international: 64%
Part-time enrollment: 122
men: 86%; women: 14%; minorities: 13%; international: 28%
Acceptance rate: 44%
GRE requirement: YES
Avg. GRE: quantitative: 692; analytical 642
TOEFL requirement: YES
Minimum TOEFL score: 550
Fellowships: 39
Teaching assistantships: 1
Research assistantships: 92
Students reporting specialty: 100%
Students specializing in: biomedical: 20%; civil: 21%; electrical: 38%; environmental: 0%; materials: 11%; mechanical: 9%

University of Alabama–Huntsville
College of Engineering
Huntsville, AL 35899
Public
Admissions: (256) 824-6070
E-mail: admitme@email.uah.edu
Web site: http://www.uah.edu
Financial aid: (256) 824-6241
Application deadline: rolling
In-state tuition: full time: $4,714; part time: $2,662
Out-of-state tuition: full time: $9,678
Room/board/expenses: $8,200
Full-time enrollment: 311
men: 77%; women: 23%; minorities: 6%; international: 74%
Part-time enrollment: 400
men: 81%; women: 20%; minorities: 9%; international: 9%
Acceptance rate: 50%
GRE requirement: YES
Avg. GRE: quantitative: 699; analytical 605
TOEFL requirement: YES
Minimum TOEFL score: 600
Fellowships: 3
Teaching assistantships: 60
Research assistantships: 93
Students reporting specialty: 100%
Students specializing in: aerospace: 4%; biomedical: 2%; chemical: 1%; civil: 3%; computer: 6%; electrical: 21%; industrial: 22%; mechanical: 10%; other: 31%

University of Alabama–Tuscaloosa
Box 870200
Tuscaloosa, AL 35487-0200
Public
Admissions: (205) 348-5921
E-mail: cwilliam@aalan.ua.edu
Web site: http://www.ua.edu/academic/colleges/graduate
Internet application: http://www.ua.edu/academic/colleges/graduate/application/index.html
Financial aid: (205) 348-2976
Application deadline: 07/01
In-state tuition: full time: $3,556; part time: N/A
Out-of-state tuition: full time: $9,624
Room/board/expenses: $6,938
Full-time enrollment: 257
men: 80%; women: 20%; minorities: 5%; international: 75%
Part-time enrollment: 110
men: 91%; women: 9%; minorities: 11%; international: 40%
Acceptance rate: 24%
GRE requirement: YES
Avg. GRE: quantitative: 748; analytical 680
TOEFL requirement: YES
Minimum TOEFL score: 550
Fellowships: 0
Teaching assistantships: 68
Research assistantships: 112
Students reporting specialty: 100%
Students specializing in: aerospace: 14%; chemical: 7%; civil: 13%; computer: 15%; electrical: 16%; industrial: 10%; materials: 9%; mechanical: 13%; other: 4%

ALASKA

University of Alaska–Fairbanks

PO Box 755940
Fairbanks, AK 99775-5940
Public
Admissions: (800) 478-1823
E-mail: fyapply@uaf.edu
Web site: http://www.uaf.edu/csem
Internet application:
http://www.uaf.edu/admrec/
Financial aid: (907) 474-7256
Application deadline: 08/01
In-state tuition: full time:
$184/credit hour; part time:
$184/credit hour
Out-of-state tuition: full time:
$358/credit hour
Room/board/expenses: $6,010
Full-time enrollment: 72
men: 81%; women: 19%;
minorities: 8%; international: 63%
Part-time enrollment: 25
men: 64%; women: 36%;
minorities: 12%; international: 4%
Acceptance rate: 49%
GRE requirement: YES
Avg. GRE: quantitative: 708;
analytical 623
TOEFL requirement: YES
Minimum TOEFL score: 550
Teaching assistantships: 21
Research assistantships: 26
Students reporting specialty: 100%
Students specializing in: civil: 10%;
computer: 12%; electrical: 20%;
environmental: 7%; mechanical:
11%; mining: 6%; petroleum: 11%;
other: 22%

ARIZONA

Arizona State University

College of Engineering &
Applied Science
Tempe, AZ 85287-5506
Public
Admissions: (480) 965-6113
E-mail: asuengr@asu.edu
Web site: http://www.eas.asu.edu/
Internet application:
http://www.asu.edu/graduate/
Financial aid: (480) 965-3355
Application deadline: rolling
In-state tuition: full time: $2,584;
part time: $131/credit hour
Out-of-state tuition: full time:
$6,516
Room/board/expenses: $11,740
Full-time enrollment: 1,168
men: 79%; women: 21%;
minorities: 4%; international: 82%
Part-time enrollment: 496
men: 82%; women: 18%;
minorities: 12%; international: 37%
Acceptance rate: 34%
GRE requirement: YES
Avg. GRE: quantitative: 749;
analytical 671
TOEFL requirement: YES
Minimum TOEFL score: 550
Teaching assistantships: 144
Research assistantships: 616
Students reporting specialty: 100%
Students specializing in: aero-
space: 2%; biomedical: 4%; chemical: 3%; civil: 7%; computer: 25%;
electrical: 38%; industrial: 12%;
materials: 1%; mechanical: 5%;
other: 3%

University of Arizona

Civil Engineering Building
Room 100
Tucson, AZ 85721
Public
Admissions: (520) 621-3471
E-mail: gradadm@
lorax.admin.arizona.edu
Web site:
http://grad.admin.arizona.edu
Internet application:
http://grad.admin.arizona.edu/
gradadm/gradadm.htm
Financial aid: (520) 621-1585
Application deadline: 06/02
In-state tuition: full time: $2,594;
part time: $142/credit hour
Out-of-state tuition: full time:
$11,114
Room/board/expenses: $9,581
Full-time enrollment: 946
men: 56%; women: 44%;
minorities: 8%; international: 62%
Part-time enrollment: N/A
men: N/A; women: N/A;
minorities: N/A; international: N/A
Acceptance rate: 36%
GRE requirement: YES
Avg. GRE: quantitative: 731;
analytical 650
TOEFL requirement: YES
Minimum TOEFL score: 550
Fellowships: 62
Teaching assistantships: 109
Research assistantships: 294
Students reporting specialty: 100%
Students specializing in: aero-
space: 3%; agriculture: 3%; chemical: 4%; civil: 6%; electrical: 37%;
environmental: 3%; industrial:
13%; materials: 5%; mechanical:
10%; mining: 3%; nuclear: 0%;
other: 12%

ARKANSAS

University of Arkansas–Fayetteville

Bell Engineering Center
Room 4183
Fayetteville, AR 72701
Public
Admissions: (501) 575-4401
E-mail: gradinfo@cavern.uark.edu
Web site:
http://www.engr.uark.edu
Financial aid: (501) 575-3806
Application deadline: 05/01
In-state tuition: full time:
$200/credit hour; part time:
$200/credit hour
Out-of-state tuition: full time:
$500/credit hour
Room/board/expenses: $7,000
Full-time enrollment: 313
men: 78%; women: 22%;
minorities: 12%; international: 50%
Part-time enrollment: 155
men: 77%; women: 23%;
minorities: 23%; international: 13%
Acceptance rate: 61%
GRE requirement: YES
Avg. GRE: quantitative: 689;
analytical 602
TOEFL requirement: YES
Minimum TOEFL score: 550
Fellowships: 9
Teaching assistantships: 111
Research assistantships: 75
Students reporting specialty: 100%
Students specializing in: agricul-
ture: 4%; chemical: 5%; civil: 11%;
computer: 11%; electrical: 17%;
industrial: 44%; mechanical: 7%

CALIFORNIA

California Institute of Technology

1200 E. California Boulevard
Pasadena, CA 91125-4400
Private
Admissions: (626) 395-6346
E-mail: gradofc@its.caltech.edu
Web site:
http://www.gradoffice.caltech.edu
Internet application:
http://www.gradoffice.caltech.edu/
admissions/application.htm
Financial aid: (626) 395-6346
Application deadline: 01/15
Tuition: full time: $21,927; part
time: N/A
Room/board/expenses: $13,658
Full-time enrollment: 524
men: 77%; women: 23%;
minorities: 5%; international: 55%
Part-time enrollment: 2
men: 0%; women: 100%;
minorities: 0%; international: 0%
Acceptance rate: 9%
GRE requirement: YES
Avg. GRE: quantitative: 762;
analytical 722
TOEFL requirement: YES
Minimum TOEFL score: 600
Fellowships: 215
Teaching assistantships: 175
Research assistantships: 444
Students reporting specialty: 100%
Students specializing in: aero-
space: 10%; biomedical: 4%;
chemical: 11%; civil: 2%; comput-
er: 5%; electrical: 19%; environ-
mental: 5%; materials: 8%;
mechanical: 10%; other: 27%

Naval Postgraduate School[1]

1 University Circle
Monterey, CA 93943-5001
Public
Admissions: (831) 656-3093
E-mail: grad-ed@nps.navy.mil
Web site: http://www.
nps.navy.mil/inps/GSEAS.htm
Internet application: http://www.
nps.navy.mil/ofcinst/admissn.htm
Financial aid: N/A
Tuition: N/A
Room/board/expenses: N/A
Enrollment: N/A

Santa Clara University

School of Engineering
Santa Clara, CA 95053-0583
Private
Admissions: (408) 554-4313
E-mail:
engr-grad@sunrise.scu.edu
Web site: http://www.engr.scu.edu
Internet application: https://www.
scu.edu/apply/engineering/
Financial aid: (408) 554-4505
Application deadline: 06/01
Tuition: full time: $568/credit hour;
part time: $568/credit hour
Room/board/expenses: $11,160
Full-time enrollment: 176
men: 58%; women: 42%;
minorities: 24%; international: 57%
Part-time enrollment: 384
men: 70%; women: 30%;
minorities: 39%; international: 30%
Acceptance rate: 48%
GRE requirement: YES
Avg. GRE: quantitative: 739;
analytical 653
TOEFL requirement: YES
Minimum TOEFL score: N/A
Fellowships: 5
Teaching assistantships: 23
Research assistantships: 11
Students reporting specialty: 100%
Students specializing in: civil: 0%;
computer: 39%; electrical: 26%;
mechanical: 7%; other: 28%

Stanford University

Terman Engineering Center
Room 214
Stanford, CA 94305-4027
Private
Admissions: (650) 723-4291
E-mail:
ck.gaa@forsythe.stanford.edu
Web site: http://soe.stanford.edu/
Internet application:
https://apply.embark.com/
grad/stanford
Financial aid: (650) 723-3058
Application deadline: N/A
Tuition: full time: $29,004; part
time: N/A
Room/board/expenses: $22,803
Full-time enrollment: 2,216
men: 79%; women: 21%;
minorities: 17%; international: 53%
Part-time enrollment: 669
men: 81%; women: 19%;
minorities: 21%; international: 40%
Acceptance rate: 29%
GRE requirement: YES
Avg. GRE: quantitative: 781;
analytical 725
TOEFL requirement: YES
Minimum TOEFL score: 575
Fellowships: 713
Teaching assistantships: 313
Research assistantships: 1053
Students reporting specialty: 100%
Students specializing in: aero-
space: 7%; biomedical: 3%; chemical: 3%; civil: 5%; computer: 15%;
electrical: 31%; environmental:
4%; industrial: 10%; materials: 4%;
mechanical: 11%; petroleum: 2%;
other: 5%

University of California–Berkeley

320 McLaughlin Hall
Berkeley, CA 94720-1700
Public
Admissions: (510) 642-7405
E-mail: gradadm@
uclink4.berkeley.edu
Web site: http://www.berkeley.edu
Internet application:
http://www.grad.berkeley.edu/
admissions/grad_app.shtml
Financial aid: (510) 642-0485
Application deadline: N/A
In-state tuition: full time: $4,430;
part time: N/A
Out-of-state tuition: full time:
$15,562
Room/board/expenses: $16,160
Full-time enrollment: 1,652
men: 78%; women: 22%;
minorities: 18%; international: 41%
Part-time enrollment: N/A
men: N/A; women: N/A;
minorities: N/A; international: N/A
Acceptance rate: 16%
GRE requirement: YES
Avg. GRE: quantitative: 785;
analytical 744
TOEFL requirement: YES
Minimum TOEFL score: 570
Fellowships: 406
Teaching assistantships: 281
Research assistantships: 1065
Students reporting specialty: 100%
Students specializing in: biomed-
ical: 3%; chemical: 7%; civil: 22%;
electrical: 34%; industrial: 5%;
materials: 5%; mechanical: 19%;
nuclear: 3%; other: 2%

University of California–Davis

1050 Engineering II
1 Shields Avenue
Davis, CA 95616-5294
Public
Admissions: (530) 752-0592
E-mail:
gradapps@engr.ucdavis.edu
Web site:
http://engineering.ucdavis.edu
Financial aid: (530) 752-0592
Application deadline: 01/15
In-state tuition: full time: $4,902;
part time: $3,456
Out-of-state tuition: full time:
$16,224
Room/board/expenses: $12,538
Full-time enrollment: 880
men: 74%; women: 26%;
minorities: 21%; international: 38%
Part-time enrollment: 40
men: 78%; women: 23%;
minorities: 15%; international: 13%
Acceptance rate: 34%
GRE requirement: YES
Avg. GRE: quantitative: 753;
analytical 670
TOEFL requirement: YES
Minimum TOEFL score: 550
Fellowships: 129
Teaching assistantships: 178
Research assistantships: 409
Students reporting specialty: N/A
Students specializing in: aero-
space: 10%; agricultural: 4%;
biomedical: 5%; chemical: 3%;
civil: 13%; computer: 14%;
electrical: 16%; environ-
mental 13%; materials: 3%;
mechanical: 10%; other: 9%

University of California–Irvine

305 REC
Irvine, CA 92697-2700
Public
Admissions: (949) 824-6475
E-mail: jdsommer@uci.edu
Web site: http://www.eng.uci.edu
Internet application:
http://www.rgs.uci.edu/
grad/prospective/app_how.htm
Financial aid: (949) 824-6261
Application deadline: 01/15
In-state tuition: full time: $5,294;
part time: $5,294
Out-of-state tuition: full time:
$16,426
Room/board/expenses: $10,600
Full-time enrollment: 722
men: 78%; women: 22%;
minorities: 16%; international: 62%
Part-time enrollment: 86
men: 84%; women: 16%;
minorities: 42%; international: 12%
Acceptance rate: 25%
GRE requirement: YES
Avg. GRE: quantitative: 760;
analytical 678
TOEFL requirement: YES
Minimum TOEFL score: 550
Fellowships: 291
Teaching assistantships: 219
Research assistantships: 580
Students reporting specialty: 100%
Students specializing in: biomed-
ical: 4%; chemical: 6%;
civil: 7%; computer: 44%;
electrical: 21%; environ-
mental: 0%; materials: 6%;
mechanical: 11%; other: 1%

University of California–Los Angeles

6426 Boelter Hall
Box 951601
Los Angeles, CA 90095-1601
Public
Admissions: (310) 825-1711
E-mail: gradadm@ea.ucla.edu
Web site:
http://www.engineer.ucla.edu
Internet application:
http://www.gdnet.ucla.edu/gasaa/
admissions/applicat.htm

Financial aid: (310) 206-0400
Application deadline: 01/15
In-state tuition: full time: $4,549;
part time: N/A
Out-of-state tuition: full time:
$15,871
Room/board/expenses: $16,428
Full-time enrollment: 1,347
men: 82%; women: 18%;
minorities: 30%; international: 45%
Part-time enrollment: N/A
men: N/A; women: N/A;
minorities: N/A; international: N/A
Acceptance rate: 25%
GRE requirement: YES
Avg. GRE: quantitative: 760;
analytical 680
TOEFL requirement: YES
Minimum TOEFL score: 560
Fellowships: 144
Teaching assistantships: 346
Research assistantships: 801
Students reporting specialty: 100%
Students specializing in: aero-
space: 2%; biomedical: 8%; chem-
ical: 5%; civil: 7%; computer: 26%;
electrical: 33%; materials: 5%; me-
chanical: 14%

University of California–Riverside (Bourns)
University Office Building
Riverside, CA 92521-0208
Public
Admissions: (909) 787-3313
E-mail: grdadmis@pop.ucr.edu
Web site:
http://www.graddiv.ucr.edu
Internet application: http://www.
graddiv.ucr.edu/howapply.html
Financial aid: (909) 787-4302
Application deadline: 05/01
In-state tuition: full time: $5,175;
part time: $3,729
Out-of-state tuition: full time:
$16,497
Room/board/expenses: $11,850
Full-time enrollment: 199
men: 73%; women: 27%;
minorities: 2%; international: 80%
Part-time enrollment: 20
men: 80%; women: 20%;
minorities: 5%; international: 55%
Acceptance rate: 23%
GRE requirement: YES
Avg. GRE: quantitative: 770;
analytical 695
TOEFL requirement: YES
Minimum TOEFL score: 550
Fellowships: 105
Teaching assistantships: 79
Research assistantships: 97
Students reporting specialty: 100%
Students specializing in: chemical:
17%; computer: 49%; electrical:
25%; mechanical: 8%

University of California–San Diego
9500 Gilman Drive
La Jolla, CA 92093-0405
Public
Admissions: (858) 534-3554
E-mail: gradadmissions@ucsd.edu
Web site:
http://www.ogsr.ucsd.edu
Internet application: http://www.
ogsr.ucsd.edu/admissions/
application/
Financial aid: (858) 534-1173
Application deadline: N/A
In-state tuition: full time: $4,979;
part time: $4,979
Out-of-state tuition: full time:
$16,112
Room/board/expenses: $10,834

Full-time enrollment: 980
men: 79%; women: 21%;
minorities: 21%; international: 39%
Part-time enrollment: N/A
men: N/A; women: N/A;
minorities: N/A; international: N/A
Acceptance rate: 17%
GRE requirement: YES
Avg. GRE: quantitative: 767;
analytical 707
TOEFL requirement: YES
Minimum TOEFL score: 550
Fellowships: 150
Teaching assistantships: 280
Research assistantships: 700
Students reporting specialty: 100%
Students specializing in: aero-
space: 2%; biomedical: 10%;
chemical: 1%; civil: 8%; computer:
26%; electrical: 40%; materials:
4%; mechanical: 10%

University of California–San Francisco[1]
4 Koret Way
Box 0775
San Francisco, CA 94143-0775
Public
Admissions: (510) 642-7405
E-mail: gradadm@
uclink4.berkeley.edu
Web site: http://grad.berkeley.edu
Internet application:
http://grad.berkeley.edu/
admissions/grad_app.shtml
Financial aid: (510) 642-0485
Tuition: N/A
Room/board/expenses: N/A
Enrollment: N/A

University of California–Santa Barbara
College of Engineering
Santa Barbara, CA 93106-5130
Public
Admissions: (805) 893-3207
Web site:
http://www.engineering.ucsb.edu
Internet application: http://www.
engineering.ucsb.edu/
graduatepreapp.php
Financial aid: (805) 893-3207
Application deadline: 01/15
In-state tuition: full time: $5,165;
part time: $5,165
Out-of-state tuition: full time:
$16,487
Room/board/expenses: $9,817
Full-time enrollment: 696
men: 79%; women: 21%;
minorities: 7%; international: 53%
Part-time enrollment: N/A
men: N/A; women: N/A;
minorities: N/A; international: N/A
Acceptance rate: 19%
GRE requirement: YES
Avg. GRE: quantitative: 769;
analytical 726
TOEFL requirement: YES
Minimum TOEFL score: 600
Fellowships: 103
Teaching assistantships: 141
Research assistantships: 396
Students reporting specialty: 100%
Students specializing in: chemical:
12%; computer: 24%; electrical:
36%; materials: 17%; mechanical:
11%

University of California–Santa Cruz
Jack Baskin Engineering
Santa Cruz, CA 95064
Public
Admissions: (831) 459-2301
E-mail:
soegradadm@soe.ucsc.edu
Web site: http://www.cse.ucsc.edu
Internet application:
http://apply.embark.com/
grad/ucsantacruz/73/
Financial aid: (831) 459-2963
Application deadline: 01/15
In-state tuition: full time: $5,634;
part time: $5,634
Out-of-state tuition: full time:
$16,747
Room/board/expenses: $13,890
Full-time enrollment: 202
men: 72%; women: 28%;
minorities: 12%; international: 57%
Part-time enrollment: 12
men: 67%; women: 33%;
minorities: 17%; international: 17%
Acceptance rate: 36%
GRE requirement: YES
Avg. GRE: quantitative: 770;
analytical 700
TOEFL requirement: YES
Minimum TOEFL score: 570
Fellowships: 40
Teaching assistantships: 131
Research assistantships: 263
Students reporting specialty: 100%
Students specializing in: computer:
88%; electrical: 12%

University of Southern California
University Park
Olin Hall 200
Los Angeles, CA 90089-1450
Private
Admissions: (213) 740-4832
E-mail: engrgrad@usc.edu
Web site: http://www.usc.edu/
dept/engineering
Internet application: http://www.
usc.edu/dept/admissions/grad
Financial aid: (213) 740-6241
Application deadline: 03/15
Tuition: full time: $17,783; part
time: $915/credit hour
Room/board/expenses: $11,998
Full-time enrollment: 2,259
men: 82%; women: 18%;
minorities: 7%; international: 85%
Part-time enrollment: 728
men: 78%; women: 22%;
minorities: 41%; international: 21%
Acceptance rate: 36%
GRE requirement: YES
Avg. GRE: quantitative: 761;
analytical 673
TOEFL requirement: NO
Minimum TOEFL score: N/A
Fellowships: 96
Teaching assistantships: 336
Research assistantships: 907
Students reporting specialty: 97%
Students specializing in: aero-
space: 3%; biomedical: 3%; chem-
ical: 2%; civil: 6%; computer: 30%;
electrical: 44%; environmental:
1%; industrial: 5%; materials: 2%;
mechanical: 3%; petroleum: 0%

COLORADO

Colorado School of Mines
1500 Illinois Street
Golden, CO 80401
Public
Admissions: (303) 273-3348
E-mail: grad-school@mines.edu
Web site: http://www.mines.edu

Internet application: http://www.
mines.edu/admiss/grad/
Financial aid: (303) 273-3207
Application deadline: rolling
In-state tuition: full time: $5,952;
part time: $261/credit hour
Out-of-state tuition: full time:
$18,222
Room/board/expenses: $14,058
Full-time enrollment: 433
men: 69%; women: 31%;
minorities: 7%; international: 33%
Part-time enrollment: 324
men: 69%; women: 31%;
minorities: 6%; international: 35%
Acceptance rate: 74%
GRE requirement: YES
Avg. GRE: quantitative: 696;
analytical 643
TOEFL requirement: YES
Minimum TOEFL score: 550
Fellowships: 51
Teaching assistantships: 119
Research assistantships: 251
Students reporting specialty: 100%
Students specializing in: chemical:
7%; computer: 5%; environmental:
11%; materials: 5%; mining: 4%;
petroleum: 6%; other: 62%

Colorado State University
202 Engineering Building
Fort Collins, CO 80523-1301
Public
Admissions: (970) 491-8657
E-mail: sabt@engr.colostate.edu
Web site:
http://www.engr.colostate.edu
Financial aid: (970) 491-8657
Application deadline: 04/01
In-state tuition: full time: $4,133;
part time: $170/credit hour
Out-of-state tuition: full time:
$13,513
Room/board/expenses: $12,830
Full-time enrollment: 259
men: 83%; women: 17%;
minorities: 5%; international: 40%
Part-time enrollment: 279
men: 82%; women: 18%;
minorities: 5%; international: 57%
Acceptance rate: 34%
GRE requirement: YES
Avg. GRE: quantitative: 733;
analytical 676
TOEFL requirement: YES
Minimum TOEFL score: 550
Fellowships: 7
Teaching assistantships: 54
Research assistantships: 153
Students reporting specialty: 100%
Students specializing in: biomed-
ical: 2%; chemical: 6%; civil: 30%;
electrical: 30%; mechanical: 15%;
other: 17%

University of Colorado–Boulder
422 UCB
Boulder, CO 80309
Public
Admissions: (303) 492-5071
Web site: http://www.
colorado.edu/engineering
Financial aid: (303) 492-5091
Application deadline: rolling
In-state tuition: full time: $5,051;
part time: $2,703
Out-of-state tuition: full time:
$19,779
Room/board/expenses: $10,708
Full-time enrollment: 878
men: 77%; women: 23%;
minorities: 9%; international: 41%
Part-time enrollment: 198
men: 76%; women: 24%;
minorities: 6%; international: 39%
Acceptance rate: 55%
GRE requirement: YES

Avg. GRE: quantitative: 753;
analytical 691
TOEFL requirement: YES
Minimum TOEFL score: 560
Fellowships: 116
Teaching assistantships: 203
Research assistantships: 298
Students reporting specialty: 100%
Students specializing in: aero-
space: 14%; chemical: 7%; civil:
19%; computer: 13%; electrical:
22%; mechanical: 8%; other: 17%

University of Colorado–Colorado Springs
PO Box 7150
Colorado Springs, CO 80933
Public
Admissions: (719) 262-3383
E-mail: admrec@mail.uccs.edu
Web site: http://www.uccs.edu
Internet application: http://www.
uccs.edu/admin/adminb.htm
Financial aid: (719) 262-3460
Application deadline: 07/05
In-state tuition: full time:
$220/credit hour; part time: N/A
Out-of-state tuition: full time:
$803/credit hour
Room/board/expenses: $6,893
Full-time enrollment: 120
men: 73%; women: 27%;
minorities: 8%; international: 12%
Part-time enrollment: 115
men: 83%; women: 17%;
minorities: 17%; international: 8%
Acceptance rate: 91%
GRE requirement: YES
Avg. GRE: quantitative: N/A;
analytical N/A
TOEFL requirement: YES
Minimum TOEFL score: 550
Fellowships: 4
Teaching assistantships: 18
Research assistantships: 6
Students reporting specialty: 100%
Students specializing in: computer:
38%; electrical: 34%; mechanical:
9%; other: 19%

University of Colorado–Denver
PO Box 173364
Campus Box 104
Denver, CO 80217-3364
Public
Admissions: (303) 556-2704
E-mail: admissions@cudenver.edu
Web site:
http://www.cudenver.edu/
Financial aid: (303) 556-2886
Application deadline: 05/01
In-state tuition: full time: $4,596;
part time: $247/credit hour
Out-of-state tuition: full time:
$16,012
Room/board/expenses: $12,130
Full-time enrollment: 73
men: 78%; women: 22%;
minorities: 18%; international: 45%
Part-time enrollment: 246
men: 77%; women: 23%;
minorities: 20%; international: 15%
Acceptance rate: 79%
GRE requirement: NO
Avg. GRE: quantitative: N/A;
analytical N/A
TOEFL requirement: YES
Minimum TOEFL score: 500
Fellowships: 0
Teaching assistantships: 16
Research assistantships: 25
Students reporting specialty: 100%
Students specializing in: civil: 24%;
computer: 47%; electrical: 12%;
mechanical: 8%; other: 8%

University of Denver

2390 York Street
Denver, CO 80208
Private
Admissions: (303) 871-3119
E-mail: grad_adm@du.edu
Web site:
http://www.du.edu/NSME
Internet application:
http://www.du.edu/grad/
onlineapp.html
Financial aid: (303) 871-4900
Application deadline: 08/01
Tuition: full time: $630/credit hour;
part time: $630/credit hour
Room/board/expenses: $11,261
Full-time enrollment: 29
men: 72%; women: 28%;
minorities: 3%; international: 52%
Part-time enrollment: N/A
men: N/A; women: N/A;
minorities: N/A; international: N/A
Acceptance rate: 40%
GRE requirement: YES
Avg. GRE: quantitative: N/A;
analytical N/A
TOEFL requirement: YES
Minimum TOEFL score: 570
Fellowships: 0
Teaching assistantships: 8
Research assistantships: 9
Students reporting specialty: 100%
Students specializing in: computer:
17%; electrical: 48%; materials:
10%; mechanical: 24%

CONNECTICUT

University of Connecticut

261 Glenbrook Road
Unit 2237
Storrs, CT 06269-2237
Public
Admissions: (860) 486-3617
E-mail: gradschool@uconn.edu
Web site: http://www.uconn.edu
Internet application:
http://www.grad.uconn.edu
Financial aid: (860) 486-2819
Application deadline: rolling
In-state tuition: full time: $6,836;
part time: $316/credit hour
Out-of-state tuition: full time:
$15,928
Room/board/expenses: $10,864
Full-time enrollment: 361
men: 71%; women: 29%;
minorities: 3%; international: 73%
Part-time enrollment: 157
men: 82%; women: 18%;
minorities: 6%; international: 27%
Acceptance rate: 21%
GRE requirement: YES
Avg. GRE: quantitative: 747;
analytical 684
TOEFL requirement: YES
Minimum TOEFL score: 550
Fellowships: 38
Teaching assistantships: 66
Research assistantships: 373
Students reporting specialty: 99%
Students specializing in: biomedical: 8%; chemical: 14%; civil: 8%; computer: 15%; electrical: 19%; environmental: 5%; materials: 7%; mechanical: 16%; other: 8%

Yale University

226 Dunham Lab
10 Hillhouse Avenue
New Haven, CT 06520
Private
Admissions: (203) 432-2771
E-mail:
graduate.admissions@yale.edu
Web site: http://www.eng.yale.edu
Internet application:
http://www.yale.edu/
graduateschool/
Financial aid: (203) 432-2739
Application deadline: 01/02
Tuition: full time: $24,480; part
time: $3,060/credit hour
Room/board/expenses: $18,177
Full-time enrollment: 172
men: 81%; women: 19%;
minorities: 3%; international: 65%
Part-time enrollment: 4
men: 50%; women: 50%;
minorities: 0%; international: 0%
Acceptance rate: 14%
GRE requirement: YES
Avg. GRE: quantitative: 782;
analytical 727
TOEFL requirement: YES
Minimum TOEFL score: 590
Fellowships: 46
Teaching assistantships: 90
Research assistantships: 102
Students reporting specialty: 100%
Students specializing in: biomedical: 11%; chemical: 15%; computer: 30%; electrical: 19%; environmental: 8%; mechanical: 9%; other: 8%

DELAWARE

University of Delaware

102 DuPont Hall
Newark, DE 19716
Public
Admissions: (302) 831-8697
Web site:
http://www.udel.edu/engg
Internet application:
http://www.udel.edu/gradoffice/
Financial aid: (302) 831-8761
Application deadline: 07/01
In-state tuition: full time: $5,520;
part time: $282/credit hour
Out-of-state tuition: full time:
$15,050
Room/board/expenses: $10,257
Full-time enrollment: 535
men: 73%; women: 27%;
minorities: 4%; international: 65%
Part-time enrollment: 49
men: 78%; women: 22%;
minorities: 12%; international: 14%
Acceptance rate: 15%
GRE requirement: YES
Avg. GRE: quantitative: 751;
analytical 683
TOEFL requirement: YES
Minimum TOEFL score: 550
Fellowships: 49
Teaching assistantships: 62
Research assistantships: 304
Students reporting specialty: 100%
Students specializing in: chemical:
20%; civil: 15%; computer: 19%;
electrical: 23%; materials: 11%;
mechanical: 12%

DISTRICT OF COLUMBIA

Catholic University of America

Cardinal Station
Washington, DC 20064
Private
Admissions: (202) 319-5057
E-mail: cua-engineer@cua.edu
Web site: http://www.cua.edu
Internet application:
http://admissions.cua.edu/
graduate/
Financial aid: (202) 319-5307
Application deadline: rolling
Tuition: full time: $22,070; part
time: $810/credit hour
Room/board/expenses: $13,508
Full-time enrollment: 32
men: 72%; women: 28%;
minorities: 19%; international: 66%

Part-time enrollment: 82
men: 84%; women: 16%;
minorities: 27%; international: 23%
Acceptance rate: 61%
GRE requirement: NO
Avg. GRE: quantitative: 660;
analytical 590
TOEFL requirement: YES
Minimum TOEFL score: 580
Fellowships: 1
Teaching assistantships: 8
Research assistantships: 13
Students reporting specialty: 100%
Students specializing in: biomedical: 11%; civil: 22%; electrical: 40%; mechanical: 15%; other: 12%

George Washington University

725 23rd Street NW
Tompkins Hall
Washington, DC 20052
Private
Admissions: (202) 994-6158
E-mail: seasadm@gwu.edu
Web site:
http://www.seas.gwu.edu/
Internet application:
http://www.gwu.edu/~gradinfo/
index2.htm
Financial aid: (202) 994-6620
Application deadline: 02/01
Tuition: full time: $810/credit hour;
part time: $810/credit hour
Room/board/expenses: $16,680
Full-time enrollment: 453
men: 80%; women: 20%;
minorities: 12%; international: 62%
Part-time enrollment: 935
men: 78%; women: 22%;
minorities: 26%; international: 23%
Acceptance rate: 47%
GRE requirement: YES
Avg. GRE: quantitative: 722;
analytical 634
TOEFL requirement: YES
Minimum TOEFL score: 550
Fellowships: 62
Teaching assistantships: 95
Research assistantships: 10
Students reporting specialty: 100%
Students specializing in: aerospace: 6%; biomedical: 0%; civil: 6%; computer: 21%; electrical: 20%; mechanical: 4%; other: 43%

Howard University

2366 Sixth Street NW
Suite 100
Washington, DC 20059
Private
Admissions: (202) 806-6800
E-mail: admission@howard.edu
Web site: http://www.howard.edu
Internet application:
http://www.gs.howard.edu/
Financial aid: (202) 806-2820
Application deadline: 02/15
Tuition: full time: $13,100; part
time: $644/credit hour
Room/board/expenses: $16,332
Full-time enrollment: 70
men: 74%; women: 26%;
minorities: 24%; international: 76%
Part-time enrollment: 34
men: 59%; women: 41%;
minorities: 59%; international: 41%
Acceptance rate: 52%
GRE requirement: YES
Avg. GRE: quantitative: 653;
analytical 511
TOEFL requirement: YES
Minimum TOEFL score: 550
Fellowships: 9
Teaching assistantships: 18
Research assistantships: 45
Students reporting specialty: 100%

Students specializing in: chemical:
11%; civil: 13%; computer: 31%;
electrical: 36%; mechanical: 11%

FLORIDA

Florida Atlantic University[1]

College of Engineering
Boca Raton, FL 33431
Public
Admissions: (561) 297-3040
E-mail: gradadm@fau.edu
Web site: http://www.fau.edu/
Internet application:
http://www.fau.edu/academic/
gradstud/grad.htm
Financial aid: (561) 297-3530
Tuition: N/A
Room/board/expenses: N/A
Enrollment: N/A

Florida Institute of Technology

150 W. University Boulevard
Melbourne, FL 32901-6975
Private
Admissions: (800) 944-4348
E-mail: admissions@fit.edu
Web site: http://www.fit.edu
Financial aid: (321) 674-8070
Application deadline: rolling
Tuition: full time: $690/credit hour;
part time: $690/credit hour
Room/board/expenses: $9,800
Full-time enrollment: 216
men: 76%; women: 24%;
minorities: 7%; international: 58%
Part-time enrollment: 395
men: 78%; women: 22%;
minorities: 14%; international: 20%
Acceptance rate: 50%
GRE requirement: YES
Avg. GRE: quantitative: 690;
analytical 611
TOEFL requirement: YES
Minimum TOEFL score: 550
Fellowships: 42
Teaching assistantships: 60
Research assistantships: 56
Students reporting specialty: 100%
Students specializing in: aerospace: 3%; chemical: 2%; civil: 3%; computer: 6%; electrical: 18%; mechanical: 4%; other: 64%

Florida International University

10555 W. Flagler Street
Miami, FL 33174
Public
Admissions: (305) 348-2363
E-mail: brownc@servms.fiu.edu
Web site: http://www.fiu.edu
Financial aid: (305) 348-2489
Application deadline: rolling
In-state tuition: full time:
$162/credit hour; part time:
$162/credit hour
Out-of-state tuition: full time:
$569/credit hour
Room/board/expenses: $16,467
Full-time enrollment: 272
men: 76%; women: 24%;
minorities: 23%; international: 71%
Part-time enrollment: 298
men: 75%; women: 25%;
minorities: 53%; international: 29%
Acceptance rate: 47%
GRE requirement: YES
Avg. GRE: quantitative: N/A;
analytical N/A
TOEFL requirement: YES
Minimum TOEFL score: 500
Fellowships: 6
Teaching assistantships: 85
Research assistantships: 83
Students reporting specialty: 82%

Students specializing in: biomedical: 5%; civil: 19%; electrical: 25%; industrial: 29%; mechanical: 9%; other: 13%

Florida State University/Florida A&M University[1]

2525 Pottsdamer Street
Tallahassee, FL 32310
Public
Admissions: (850) 644-3420
E-mail: gradadms@admin.fsu.edu
Web site: http://www.eng.fsu.edu
Financial aid: (850) 644-5871
Tuition: N/A
Room/board/expenses: N/A
Enrollment: N/A

University of Central Florida

4000 Central Florida Boulevard
Orlando, FL 32816-2993
Public
Admissions: (407) 823-5775
E-mail: gradengr@mail.ucf.edu
Web site:
http://www.engr.ucf.edu/graduate
Internet application:
http://www.graduate.ucf.edu/
gradonlineapp
Financial aid: (407) 823-6074
Application deadline: 07/15
In-state tuition: full time:
$181/credit hour; part time:
$181/credit hour
Out-of-state tuition: full time:
$667/credit hour
Room/board/expenses: $11,780
Full-time enrollment: 745
men: 80%; women: 20%;
minorities: 10%; international: 70%
Part-time enrollment: 363
men: 77%; women: 23%;
minorities: 30%; international: 0%
Acceptance rate: 62%
GRE requirement: YES
Avg. GRE: quantitative: 715;
analytical 628
TOEFL requirement: YES
Minimum TOEFL score: 550
Fellowships: 117
Teaching assistantships: 150
Research assistantships: 274
Students reporting specialty: 100%
Students specializing in: aerospace: 1%; civil: 6%; computer: 33%; electrical: 19%; environmental: 5%; industrial: 24%; materials: 4%; mechanical: 7%

University of Florida

300 Weil Hall
Gainesville, FL 32611-6550
Public
Admissions: (352) 392-0943
E-mail: admissions@eng.ufl.edu
Web site: http://www.eng.ufl.edu
Internet application:
http://www.reg.ufl.edu/
regadmi.htm
Financial aid: (352) 392-0943
Application deadline: 06/01
In-state tuition: full time: $4,304;
part time: $179/credit hour
Out-of-state tuition: full time:
$16,030
Room/board/expenses: $9,685
Full-time enrollment: 1,992
men: 81%; women: 19%;
minorities: 13%; international: 53%
Part-time enrollment: N/A
men: N/A; women: N/A;
minorities: N/A; international: N/A
Acceptance rate: 11%
GRE requirement: YES
Avg. GRE: quantitative: 750;
analytical 664

TOEFL requirement: YES
Minimum TOEFL score: 550
Fellowships: 112
Teaching assistantships: 278
Research assistantships: 845
Students reporting specialty: 100%
Students specializing in: aerospace: 5%; agriculture: 2%; biomedical: 2%; chemical: 5%; civil: 10%; computer: 14%; electrical: 24%; environmental: 5%; industrial: 9%; materials: 13%; mechanical: 8%; nuclear: 3%

University of Miami[1]

1251 Memorial Drive
Coral Gables, FL 33146
Private
Admissions: (305) 284-2942
E-mail: grad.eng@miami.edu
Web site:
http://www.miami.edu/engineering
Financial aid: (305) 284-5212
Tuition: N/A
Room/board/expenses: N/A
Enrollment: N/A

University of South Florida

4202 Fowler Avenue
ENB118
Tampa, FL 33620
Public
Admissions: (813) 974-8800
E-mail: admissions@grad.usf.edu
Web site:
http://admissions.grad.usf.edu/
Internet application:
http://admissions.grad.usf.edu/
materials.html
Financial aid: (813) 974-4700
Application deadline: 06/01
In-state tuition: full time: $3,306;
part time: N/A
Out-of-state tuition: full time:
$12,174
Room/board/expenses: $10,410
Full-time enrollment: 458
men: 74%; women: 26%;
minorities: 15%; international: 67%
Part-time enrollment: 279
men: 77%; women: 23%;
minorities: 19%; international: 37%
Acceptance rate: 44%
GRE requirement: YES
Avg. GRE: quantitative: 757;
analytical 668
TOEFL requirement: YES
Minimum TOEFL score: 550
Fellowships: 12
Teaching assistantships: 143
Research assistantships: 228
Students reporting specialty: N/A
Students specializing in: N/A

Georgia Institute of Technology

225 North Avenue
Atlanta, GA 30332-0321
Public
Admissions: (404) 894-1610
E-mail: gradstudies@gatech.edu
Web site:
http://www.grad.gatech.edu
Internet application:
http://www.grad.gatech.edu/
admissions
Financial aid: (404) 894-4582
Application deadline: rolling
In-state tuition: full time: $4,174;
part time: $179/credit hour
Out-of-state tuition: full time:
$15,218
Room/board/expenses: $8,300
Full-time enrollment: 2,835
men: 80%; women: 20%;
minorities: 11%; international: 58%

Part-time enrollment: 750
men: 81%; women: 19%;
minorities: 13%; international: 15%
Acceptance rate: 32%
GRE requirement: YES
Avg. GRE: quantitative: 755;
analytical 683
TOEFL requirement: YES
Minimum TOEFL score: 550
Fellowships: 506
Teaching assistantships: 291
Research assistantships: 2839
Students reporting specialty: 100%
Students specializing in: aerospace: 8%; biomedical: 4%; chemical: 4%; civil: 6%; computer: 12%; electrical: 28%; environmental: 3%; industrial: 14%; materials: 2%; mechanical: 18%; nuclear: 1%; other: 1%

University of Georgia[1]

Driftmier Engineering Center
Athens, GA 30602
Public
Admissions: (706) 542-1739
E-mail: gradadm@arches.uga.edu
Web site: http://www.engr.uga.edu
Internet application:
https://app.applyyourself.
com/?id=uga-g
Financial aid: (706) 542-6147
Tuition: N/A
Room/board/expenses: N/A
Enrollment: N/A

University of Hawaii–Manoa

2540 Dole Street
Holmes Hall 240
Honolulu, HI 96822
Public
Admissions: (808) 956-8544
E-mail:
admissions@grad.hawaii.edu
Web site:
http://www.hawaii.edu/graduate/
Financial aid: (808) 956-7251
Application deadline: N/A
In-state tuition: full time: $4,454;
part time: $180/credit hour
Out-of-state tuition: full time:
$10,526
Room/board/expenses: $12,000
Full-time enrollment: 130
men: 79%; women: 21%;
minorities: 32%; international: 58%
Part-time enrollment: 16
men: 69%; women: 31%;
minorities: 31%; international: 0%
Acceptance rate: 62%
GRE requirement: YES
Avg. GRE: quantitative: 758;
analytical 711
TOEFL requirement: YES
Minimum TOEFL score: 500
Fellowships: 7
Teaching assistantships: 25
Research assistantships: 48
Students reporting specialty: N/A
Students specializing in: N/A

Idaho State University

PO Box 8060
Pocatello, ID 83209
Public
Admissions: (208) 282-2150
E-mail: graddean@isu.edu
Web site:
http://www.coe.isu.edu/engrg
Internet application: http://www.
isu.edu/departments/graduate/
Financial aid: (208) 282-2756
Application deadline: 07/01

In-state tuition: full time: N/A; part
time: N/A
Out-of-state tuition: full time: N/A
Room/board/expenses: N/A
Full-time enrollment: 36
men: 72%; women: 28%;
minorities: 33%; international: 61%
Part-time enrollment: 38
men: 74%; women: 26%;
minorities: 29%; international: 13%
GRE requirement: YES
Avg. GRE: quantitative: N/A;
analytical N/A
TOEFL requirement: YES
Minimum TOEFL score: 550
Students reporting specialty: 100%
Students specializing in: electrical:
14%; environmental: 20%;
nuclear: 18%; other: 49%

University of Idaho

College of Engineering
Moscow, ID 83844-1011
Public
Admissions: (208) 885-4001
E-mail: admappl@uidaho.edu
Web site:
http://www.engr.uidaho.edu/
Internet application: http://www.
uidaho.edu/cogs/application/
index.html
Financial aid: (208) 885-6312
Application deadline: rolling
In-state tuition: full time: $3,584;
part time: $181/credit hour
Out-of-state tuition: full time:
$10,304
Room/board/expenses: $6,160
Full-time enrollment: 176
men: 85%; women: 15%;
minorities: 10%; international: 66%
Part-time enrollment: 294
men: 88%; women: 12%;
minorities: 12%; international: 11%
Acceptance rate: 47%
GRE requirement: YES
Avg. GRE: quantitative: 734;
analytical 635
TOEFL requirement: YES
Minimum TOEFL score: 550
Fellowships: 1
Teaching assistantships: 21
Research assistantships: 75
Students reporting specialty: 100%
Students specializing in: agriculture: 4%; chemical: 3%; civil: 16%; computer: 19%; electrical: 31%; environmental: 0%; materials: 3%; mechanical: 16%; mining: 3%; other: 5%

Illinois Institute of Technology

3301 S. Dearborn
Siegel Hall, Room 103
Chicago, IL 60616
Private
Admissions: (312) 567-3020
E-mail: gradstu@iit.edu
Web site: http://www.iit.edu
Internet application: http://www.
grad.iit.edu/graduatecollege/
app/appfront.html
Financial aid: (312) 567-3647
Application deadline: rolling
Tuition: full time: $610/credit hour;
part time: $610/credit hour
Room/board/expenses: $10,244
Full-time enrollment: 968
men: 81%; women: 19%;
minorities: 3%; international: 93%
Part-time enrollment: 668
men: 81%; women: 19%;
minorities: 16%; international: 50%
Acceptance rate: 57%
GRE requirement: YES
Avg. GRE: quantitative: 739;
analytical 649

TOEFL requirement: YES
Minimum TOEFL score: 550
Fellowships: 15
Teaching assistantships: 142
Research assistantships: 150
Students reporting specialty: 91%
Students specializing in: biomedical: 1%; chemical: 10%; civil: 6%; computer: 45%; electrical: 25%; environmental: 3%; industrial: 1%; materials: 1%; mechanical: 8%

Northwestern University

2145 Sheridan Road
Evanston, IL 60208
Private
Admissions: (847) 491-7264
E-mail:
gradapp@northwestern.edu
Web site:
http://www.northwestern.edu
Internet application: http://www.
northwestern.edu/graduate/
admission/adindex.html
Financial aid: (847) 491-7266
Application deadline: 01/15
Tuition: full time: $26,526; part
time: $8,842
Room/board/expenses: $12,138
Full-time enrollment: 913
men: 76%; women: 24%;
minorities: 16%; international: 38%
Part-time enrollment: 170
men: 82%; women: 18%;
minorities: 26%; international: 21%
Acceptance rate: 20%
GRE requirement: YES
Avg. GRE: quantitative: 762;
analytical 721
TOEFL requirement: YES
Minimum TOEFL score: 560
Fellowships: 150
Teaching assistantships: 54
Research assistantships: 363
Students reporting specialty: 100%
Students specializing in: biomedical: 7%; chemical: 8%; civil: 9%; computer: 5%; electrical: 11%; industrial: 4%; materials: 11%; mechanical: 10%; other: 35%

Southern Illinois University–Carbondale

College of Engineering
SIUC
Carbondale, IL 62901-6603
Public
Admissions: (618) 536-7791
E-mail: gradsch@siu.edu
Web site:
http://www.siu.edu/gradschl/
Financial aid: (618) 453-4334
Application deadline: rolling
In-state tuition: full time:
$154/credit hour; part time:
$154/credit hour
Out-of-state tuition: full time:
$308/credit hour
Room/board/expenses: $9,187
Full-time enrollment: 224
men: 80%; women: 20%;
minorities: 4%; international: 85%
Part-time enrollment: 86
men: 81%; women: 19%;
minorities: 7%; international: 58%
Acceptance rate: 56%
GRE requirement: YES
Avg. GRE: quantitative: 756;
analytical 646
TOEFL requirement: YES
Minimum TOEFL score: 550
Fellowships: 2
Teaching assistantships: 60
Research assistantships: 63
Students reporting specialty: 100%
Students specializing in: civil: 9%;
electrical: 58%; mechanical: 14%;
mining: 4%; other: 15%

University of Illinois–Chicago

851 S. Morgan Street
Chicago, IL 60607-7043
Public
Admissions: (312) 996-5133
E-mail: uicadmit@uic.edu
Web site: http://www.uic.edu/
Internet application: http://www.
uic.edu/depts/oar/index.html
Financial aid: (312) 996-5563
Application deadline: 05/15
In-state tuition: full time: $8,463;
part time: $6,535
Out-of-state tuition: full time:
$16,445
Room/board/expenses: $15,850
Full-time enrollment: 632
men: 72%; women: 28%;
minorities: 11%; international: 73%
Part-time enrollment: 409
men: 80%; women: 20%;
minorities: 19%; international: 44%
Acceptance rate: 22%
GRE requirement: YES
Avg. GRE: quantitative: 755;
analytical 691
TOEFL requirement: YES
Minimum TOEFL score: 550
Fellowships: 31
Teaching assistantships: 126
Research assistantships: 287
Students reporting specialty: 100%
Students specializing in: biomedical: 16%; chemical: 5%; civil: 7%; computer: 21%; electrical: 27%; industrial: 4%; materials: 2%; mechanical: 13%; other: 5%

University of Illinois– Urbana-Champaign

1308 W. Green
Urbana, IL 61801
Public
Admissions: (217) 333-0035
Web site:
http://www.engr.uiuc.edu
Internet application:
http://www.oar.uiuc.edu/
prospective/grad/applygr.html
Financial aid: (217) 333-0100
Application deadline: 02/15
In-state tuition: full time: $8,040;
part time: $5,882
Out-of-state tuition: full time:
$16,714
Room/board/expenses: $10,768
Full-time enrollment: 2,379
men: 84%; women: 16%;
minorities: 10%; international: 55%
Part-time enrollment: 112
men: 86%; women: 14%;
minorities: 13%; international: 41%
Acceptance rate: 13%
GRE requirement: YES
Avg. GRE: quantitative: 773;
analytical 722
TOEFL requirement: YES
Minimum TOEFL score: 550
Fellowships: 257
Teaching assistantships: 468
Research assistantships: 1513
Students reporting specialty: 100%
Students specializing in: aerospace: 3%; agriculture: 2%; chemical: 4%; civil: 13%; computer: 21%; electrical: 22%; environmental: 3%; industrial: 1%; materials: 6%; mechanical: 10%; nuclear: 2%; other: 13%

INDIANA

Purdue University–West Lafayette

400 Centennial Mall Drive
Room 101
West Lafayette, IN 47907-2016
Public
Admissions: (765) 494-5340
E-mail: graduate@ecn.purdue.edu
Web site:
http://engineering.purdue.edu
Financial aid: (765) 494-5340
Application deadline: rolling
In-state tuition: full time: $7,263;
part time: $200/credit hour
Out-of-state tuition: full time:
$17,943
Room/board/expenses: $8,510
Full-time enrollment: 1,902
men: 83%; women: 17%;
minorities: 6%; international: 68%
Part-time enrollment: 537
men: 79%; women: 21%;
minorities: 13%; international: 18%
Acceptance rate: 23%
GRE requirement: YES
Avg. GRE: quantitative: 756;
analytical 688
TOEFL requirement: YES
Minimum TOEFL score: 550
Fellowships: 205
Teaching assistantships: 401
Research assistantships: 869
Students reporting specialty: 100%
Students specializing in: aero-
space: 6%; agriculture: 2%; biomedical: 1%; chemical: 4%; civil:
10%; computer: 13%; electrical:
16%; environmental: 3%; industri-
al: 8%; materials: 2%; mechanical:
15%; nuclear: 1%; other: 18%

University of Notre Dame

257 Fitzpatrick Hall of Engineering
Notre Dame, IN 46556
Private
Admissions: (574) 631-7706
E-mail: gradad.1@nd.edu
Web site: http://www.nd.edu
Internet application:
http://www.nd.edu/~gradsch/
applying/appintro.html
Financial aid: (574) 631-6436
Application deadline: 02/01
Tuition: full time: $25,615; part
time: $1,412/credit hour
Room/board/expenses: $12,095
Full-time enrollment: 377
men: 76%; women: 24%;
minorities: 5%; international: 59%
Part-time enrollment: 13
men: 77%; women: 23%;
minorities: 8%; international: 38%
Acceptance rate: 19%
GRE requirement: YES
Avg. GRE: quantitative: 758;
analytical 723
TOEFL requirement: YES
Minimum TOEFL score: 600
Fellowships: 64
Teaching assistantships: 88
Research assistantships: 174
Students reporting specialty: 100%
Students specializing in: aero-
space: 10%; chemical: 18%; civil:
16%; computer: 14%; electrical:
28%; mechanical: 14%

IOWA

Iowa State University

104 Marston Hall
College of Engineering
Ames, IA 50011
Public
Admissions: (800) 262-3810
E-mail:
grad_admissions@iastate.edu
Web site: http://www.iastate.edu
Internet application:
http://www.iastate.edu/~
adm_info/homepage.html
Financial aid: (515) 294-2223
Application deadline: rolling
In-state tuition: full time: $4,976;
part time: $244/credit hour
Out-of-state tuition: full time:
$13,502
Room/board/expenses: $6,311
Full-time enrollment: 881
men: 84%; women: 16%;
minorities: 13%; international: 59%
Part-time enrollment: N/A
men: N/A; women: N/A;
minorities: N/A; international: N/A
Acceptance rate: 17%
GRE requirement: YES
Avg. GRE: quantitative: 767;
analytical 703
TOEFL requirement: YES
Minimum TOEFL score: 550
Fellowships: 29
Teaching assistantships: 150
Research assistantships: 469
Students reporting specialty: 100%
Students specializing in: aero-
space: 7%; agriculture: 4%; bio-
medical: 0%; chemical: 5%; civil:
13%; computer: 14%; electrical:
15%; industrial: 15%; materials:
8%; mechanical: 19%

University of Iowa

3100 Seamans Center
Iowa City, IA 52242
Public
Admissions: (319) 335-1525
E-mail: admissions@uiowa.edu
Web site: http://www.
uiowa.edu/admissions/graduate/
Internet application: http://www.
uiowa.edu/admissions/
applications/graduate_
college.html
Financial aid: (319) 335-1450
Application deadline: 07/15
In-state tuition: full time: $5,115;
part time: N/A
Out-of-state tuition: full time:
$14,493
Room/board/expenses: $9,730
Full-time enrollment: 358
men: 74%; women: 26%;
minorities: 7%; international: 61%
Part-time enrollment: N/A
men: N/A; women: N/A;
minorities: N/A; international: N/A
Acceptance rate: 23%
GRE requirement: YES
Avg. GRE: quantitative: 750;
analytical 694
TOEFL requirement: YES
Minimum TOEFL score: 550
Fellowships: 6
Teaching assistantships: 90
Research assistantships: 220
Students reporting specialty: 100%
Students specializing in: biomed-
ical: 13%; chemical: 11%; civil:
25%; electrical: 22%; industrial:
10%; mechanical: 19%

KANSAS

Kansas State University

146 Rathbone Hall
Manhattan, KS 66506-5201
Public
Admissions: (785) 532-6191
E-mail: gradschool@ksu.edu
Web site:
http://www.engg.ksu.edu/
Internet application:
http://www.ksu.edu/grad/
application/index.htm
Financial aid: (785) 532-6420
Application deadline: rolling
In-state tuition: full time:
$138/credit hour; part time:
$138/credit hour
Out-of-state tuition: full time:
$392/credit hour
Room/board/expenses: $6,500
Full-time enrollment: 327
men: 76%; women: 24%;
minorities: 2%; international: 78%
Part-time enrollment: 171
men: 85%; women: 15%;
minorities: 9%; international: 39%
Acceptance rate: 24%
GRE requirement: YES
Avg. GRE: quantitative: N/A;
analytical N/A
TOEFL requirement: YES
Minimum TOEFL score: 550
Teaching assistantships: 51
Research assistantships: 174
Students reporting specialty: 100%
Students specializing in: agricul-
ture: 6%; chemical: 4%; civil: 11%;
computer: 38%; electrical: 11%;
industrial: 15%; mechanical: 10%;
nuclear: 1%; other: 3%

University of Kansas

4010 Learned Hall
1530 W. 15th Street
Lawrence, KS 66045-7609
Public
Admissions: (785) 864-2983
E-mail: KUengr@ku.edu
Web site: http://www.engr.ku.edu
Financial aid: (785) 864-4700
Application deadline: 05/01
In-state tuition: full time:
$134/credit hour; part time:
$134/credit hour
Out-of-state tuition: full time:
$389/credit hour
Room/board/expenses: $10,253
Full-time enrollment: 261
men: 79%; women: 21%;
minorities: 1%; international: 69%
Part-time enrollment: 446
men: 84%; women: 16%;
minorities: 4%; international: 29%
Acceptance rate: 28%
GRE requirement: YES
Avg. GRE: quantitative: N/A;
analytical N/A
TOEFL requirement: YES
Minimum TOEFL score: 570
Fellowships: 59
Teaching assistantships: 56
Research assistantships: 134
Students reporting specialty: 100%
Students specializing in: aero-
space: 4%; chemical: 5%; civil:
16%; computer: 27%; electrical:
10%; environmental: 5%;
mechanical: 7%; petroleum: 1%;
other: 26%

Wichita State University

1845 N. Fairmount
Wichita, KS 67260-0044
Public
Admissions: (316) 978-3095
E-mail: gradinqu@wichita.edu
Web site:
http://webs.wichita.edu/gradsch/
Financial aid: (316) 978-3430
Application deadline: 06/01
In-state tuition: full time: $3,782;
part time: $118/credit hour
Out-of-state tuition: full time:
$9,542
Room/board/expenses: $5,280
Full-time enrollment: 349
men: 91%; women: 9%;
minorities: 1%; international: 95%
Part-time enrollment: 342
men: 87%; women: 13%;
minorities: 17%; international: 55%
Acceptance rate: 53%
GRE requirement: YES
Avg. GRE: quantitative: 710;
analytical 600
TOEFL requirement: YES
Minimum TOEFL score: 550
Fellowships: 0
Teaching assistantships: 12
Research assistantships: 85
Students reporting specialty: 100%
Students specializing in: aero-
space: 12%; electrical: 43%;
industrial: 23%; mechanical: 22%

KENTUCKY

University of Kentucky

351 Ralph G. Anderson Building
Lexington, KY 40506-0503
Public
Admissions: (859) 257-4905
E-mail: gradapps@pop.uky.edu
Web site: http://www.engr.uky.edu
Internet application:
http://www.rgs.uky.edu/
gs/gsapplication.html
Financial aid: (859) 257-3172
Application deadline: 07/25
In-state tuition: full time: $4,347;
part time: $227/credit hour
Out-of-state tuition: full time:
$11,565
Room/board/expenses: $8,500
Full-time enrollment: 606
men: 79%; women: 21%;
minorities: 2%; international: 71%
Part-time enrollment: 99
men: 82%; women: 18%;
minorities: 7%; international: 31%
GRE requirement: YES
Avg. GRE: quantitative: N/A;
analytical N/A
TOEFL requirement: YES
Minimum TOEFL score: 550
Fellowships: 51
Teaching assistantships: 68
Research assistantships: 193
Students reporting specialty: 100%
Students specializing in: agricul-
ture: 4%; biomedical: 4%; chemi-
cal: 7%; civil: 10%; computer:
30%; electrical: 17%; industrial:
4%; materials: 4%; mechanical:
19%; mining: 2%

University of Louisville

2301 S. Third Street
Louisville, KY 40292
Public
Admissions: (502) 852-6531
E-mail:
admitme@gwise.louisville.edu
Web site:
http://www.louisville.edu/speed
Internet application:
http://www.louisville.edu/student/
services/admissions/gapp/
index.html
Financial aid: (502) 852-5511
Application deadline: rolling
In-state tuition: full time: $4,442;
part time: $247/credit hour
Out-of-state tuition: full time:
$12,236
Room/board/expenses: N/A
Full-time enrollment: 309
men: 79%; women: 21%;
minorities: 17%; international: 46%
Part-time enrollment: 336
men: 79%; women: 21%;
minorities: 20%; international: 12%
GRE requirement: YES
Avg. GRE: quantitative: N/A;
analytical N/A
TOEFL requirement: YES
Minimum TOEFL score: 550
Fellowships: 20
Teaching assistantships: 29
Research assistantships: 61
Students reporting specialty: 100%
Students specializing in: chemical:
10%; civil: 10%; computer: 17%;
electrical: 20%; industrial: 13%;
mechanical: 13%; other: 17%

LOUISIANA

Louisiana State University–Baton Rouge

3304 CEBA Building
Baton Rouge, LA 70803
Public
Admissions: (225) 578-1641
E-mail: gradadm@lsu.edu
Web site: http://www.eng.lsu.edu
Internet application:
http://gradlsu.gs.lsu.edu/
admiss.htm
Financial aid: (225) 578-3113
Application deadline: rolling
In-state tuition: full time: $3,485;
part time: $2,026
Out-of-state tuition: full time:
$8,785
Room/board/expenses: $8,920
Full-time enrollment: 430
men: 80%; women: 20%;
minorities: 3%; international: 85%
Part-time enrollment: 82
men: 79%; women: 21%;
minorities: 12%; international: 39%
Acceptance rate: 34%
GRE requirement: YES
Avg. GRE: quantitative: 741;
analytical 633
TOEFL requirement: YES
Minimum TOEFL score: 550
Fellowships: 22
Teaching assistantships: 94
Research assistantships: 236
Students reporting specialty: 100%
Students specializing in: agricul-
ture: 3%; chemical: 9%; civil: 22%;
electrical: 21%; industrial: 6%;
mechanical: 18%; petroleum: 5%;
other: 15%

Louisiana Tech University

PO Box 10348
Ruston, LA 71272
Public
Admissions: (318) 257-3229
E-mail: gmail@gschool.latech.edu
Web site:
http://www.latech.edu/tech/engr
Financial aid: (318) 257-4314
Application deadline: 08/01
In-state tuition: full time: $3,020;
part time: $807/credit hour
Out-of-state tuition: full time:
$2,439
Room/board/expenses: $5,520
Full-time enrollment: 286
men: 79%; women: 21%;
minorities: 0%; international: 88%
Part-time enrollment: 81
men: 69%; women: 31%;
minorities: 1%; international: 56%
Acceptance rate: 47%
GRE requirement: YES
Avg. GRE: quantitative: 749;
analytical 634

TOEFL requirement: YES
Minimum TOEFL score: 550
Fellowships: 4
Teaching assistantships: 152
Research assistantships: 85
Students reporting specialty: 100%
Students specializing in: biomedical: 14%; chemical: 5%; civil: 1%; computer: 19%; electrical: 13%; industrial: 6%; mechanical: 7%; other: 35%

Tulane University

201 Lindy Boggs
Building–Engineering
New Orleans, LA 70118
Private
Admissions: (504) 865-5764
E-mail: emichael@tulane.edu
Web site: http://www2.tulane.edu/
Internet application:
http://www2.tulane.edu/
Financial aid: (504) 865-5764
Application deadline: 02/01
Tuition: full time: $27,600; part time: $1,502/credit hour
Room/board/expenses: N/A
Full-time enrollment: 167
men: 65%; women: 35%;
minorities: 9%; international: 42%
Part-time enrollment: 38
men: 63%; women: 37%;
minorities: 11%; international: 0%
Acceptance rate: 26%
GRE requirement: YES
Avg. GRE: quantitative: 720;
analytical N/A
TOEFL requirement: YES
Minimum TOEFL score: 550
Fellowships: 31
Teaching assistantships: 38
Research assistantships: 50
Students reporting specialty: 100%
Students specializing in: biomedical: 25%; chemical: 20%; civil: 12%; electrical: 19%; environmental: 6%; mechanical: 17%

University of Louisiana–Lafayette

PO Box 42251
Lafayette, LA 70504
Public
Admissions: (337) 482-6467
E-mail: gradschool@louisiana.edu
Web site: http://www.louisiana.edu
Financial aid: (337) 482-6506
Application deadline: rolling
In-state tuition: full time: $2,440;
part time: N/A
Out-of-state tuition: full time:
$8,620
Room/board/expenses: $3,896
Full-time enrollment: 305
men: 78%; women: 22%;
minorities: 2%; international: 92%
Part-time enrollment: 78
men: 86%; women: 14%;
minorities: 10%; international: 54%
Acceptance rate: 63%
GRE requirement: YES
Avg. GRE: quantitative: 728;
analytical 650
TOEFL requirement: YES
Minimum TOEFL score: 550
Fellowships: 6
Teaching assistantships: 54
Research assistantships: 59
Students reporting specialty: 100%
Students specializing in: chemical: 10%; civil: 4%; computer: 48%; electrical: 27%; mechanical: 4%; other: 7%

University of New Orleans[1]

Lake Front
New Orleans, LA 70148
Public
Admissions: (504) 280-6595
E-mail: admissions@uno.edu
Web site: http://www.uno.edu
Internet application: http://www.uno.edu/~admi/app.html
Financial aid: (504) 280-6603
Tuition: N/A
Room/board/expenses: N/A
Enrollment: N/A

MAINE

University of Maine

Barrows Hall
Orono, ME 04469
Public
Admissions: (207) 581-3218
E-mail:
graduate@maine.maine.edu
Web site:
http://www.umaine.edu/graduate
Internet application: http://www.umaine.edu/graduate/onlineap.htm
Financial aid: (207) 581-1324
Application deadline: 01/15
In-state tuition: full time:
$218/credit hour; part time:
$218/credit hour
Out-of-state tuition: full time:
$623/credit hour
Room/board/expenses: $7,372
Full-time enrollment: 99
men: 79%; women: 21%;
minorities: 3%; international: 45%
Part-time enrollment: 43
men: 88%; women: 12%;
minorities: 2%; international: 23%
Acceptance rate: 49%
GRE requirement: YES
Avg. GRE: quantitative: 705;
analytical 638
TOEFL requirement: YES
Minimum TOEFL score: 550
Fellowships: 1
Teaching assistantships: 10
Research assistantships: 89
Students reporting specialty: 100%
Students specializing in: biomedical: 1%; chemical: 15%; civil: 19%; computer: 4%; electrical: 14%; mechanical: 11%; other: 35%

MARYLAND

Johns Hopkins University

3400 N. Charles Street
Baltimore, MD 21218
Private
Admissions: (410) 516-8174
E-mail: grad_adm@jhu.edu
Web site: http://wse.jhu.edu
Internet application: http://www.jhu.edu/~admis/grad.html
Financial aid: (410) 516-8028
Application deadline: N/A
Tuition: full time: $27,390; part time: $483/credit hour
Room/board/expenses: $11,950
Full-time enrollment: 572
men: 73%; women: 27%;
minorities: 9%; international: 56%
Part-time enrollment: 1,531
men: 77%; women: 23%;
minorities: 23%; international: 8%
Acceptance rate: 14%
GRE requirement: YES
Avg. GRE: quantitative: 766;
analytical 715
TOEFL requirement: YES
Minimum TOEFL score: 600
Fellowships: 100

Teaching assistantships: 108
Research assistantships: 277
Students reporting specialty: 100%
Students specializing in: biomedical: 7%; chemical: 3%; civil: 2%; computer: 33%; electrical: 19%; environmental: 5%; materials: 1%; mechanical: 4%; other: 26%

University of Maryland–Baltimore County

College of Engineering
1000 Hilltop Circle
Baltimore, MD 21250
Public
Admissions: (410) 455-2537
E-mail: umbcgrad@umbc.edu
Web site:
http://www.umbc.edu/gradschool
Internet application: http://www.umbc.edu/gradschool/admissions.html
Financial aid: (410) 455-2387
Application deadline: rolling
In-state tuition: full time:
$303/credit hour; part time:
$303/credit hour
Out-of-state tuition: full time:
$486/credit hour
Room/board/expenses: $8,390
Full-time enrollment: 249
men: 73%; women: 27%;
minorities: 6%; international: 81%
Part-time enrollment: 174
men: 76%; women: 24%;
minorities: 16%; international: 40%
Acceptance rate: 27%
GRE requirement: YES
Avg. GRE: quantitative: 765;
analytical 706
TOEFL requirement: YES
Minimum TOEFL score: 550
Fellowships: 5
Teaching assistantships: 78
Research assistantships: 121
Students reporting specialty: 100%
Students specializing in: chemical: 8%; computer: 54%; electrical: 21%; mechanical: 15%; other: 2%

University of Maryland–College Park

1137 Glenn L. Martin Hall
College Park, MD 20742
Public
Admissions: (301) 405-4198
E-mail: grschool@deans.umd.edu
Web site: http://www.eng.umd.edu
Internet application: http://www.admit.umd.edu/grd/login.html
Financial aid: (301) 314-9000
Application deadline: 05/01
In-state tuition: full time: $6,224;
part time: $305/credit hour
Out-of-state tuition: full time:
$9,410
Room/board/expenses: $13,834
Full-time enrollment: 1,391
men: 80%; women: 20%;
minorities: 9%; international: 69%
Part-time enrollment: 479
men: 80%; women: 20%;
minorities: 23%; international: 20%
Acceptance rate: 18%
GRE requirement: YES
Avg. GRE: quantitative: 770;
analytical 720
TOEFL requirement: YES
Minimum TOEFL score: 575
Fellowships: 131
Teaching assistantships: 222
Research assistantships: 937
Students reporting specialty: 100%

Students specializing in: aerospace: 7%; chemical: 3%; civil: 10%; computer: 13%; electrical: 25%; materials: 4%; mechanical: 12%; nuclear: 1%; other: 26%

MASSACHUSETTS

Boston University

44 Cummington Street
Boston, MA 02215
Private
Admissions: (617) 353-9760
E-mail: enggrad@bu.edu
Web site: http://www.bu.edu/eng
Internet application:
https://app.applyyourself.com/?id=bu-e
Financial aid: (617) 353-9760
Application deadline: 04/01
Tuition: full time: $27,314; part time: $845/credit hour
Room/board/expenses: $12,194
Full-time enrollment: 463
men: 73%; women: 27%;
minorities: 6%; international: 56%
Part-time enrollment: 65
men: 74%; women: 26%;
minorities: 15%; international: 9%
Acceptance rate: 27%
GRE requirement: YES
Avg. GRE: quantitative: 746;
analytical 697
TOEFL requirement: YES
Minimum TOEFL score: 550
Fellowships: 56
Teaching assistantships: 76
Research assistantships: 241
Students reporting specialty: 95%
Students specializing in: aerospace: 2%; biomedical: 21%; computer: 18%; electrical: 30%; industrial: 16%; mechanical: 8%; other: 5%

Harvard University

29 Oxford Street
Room 217A Pierce Hall
Cambridge, MA 02138
Private
Admissions: (617) 495-5315
E-mail: admiss@fas.harvard.edu
Web site:
http://www.gsas.harvard.edu
Financial aid: (617) 495-5396
Application deadline: 01/02
Tuition: full time: $26,400; part time: $3,079/credit hour
Room/board/expenses: $16,100
Full-time enrollment: 225
men: 79%; women: 21%;
minorities: 11%; international: 47%
Part-time enrollment: 7
men: 100%; women: 0%;
minorities: 14%; international: 0%
Acceptance rate: 13%
GRE requirement: YES
Avg. GRE: quantitative: 787;
analytical 734
TOEFL requirement: YES
Minimum TOEFL score: 550
Fellowships: 82
Teaching assistantships: 40
Research assistantships: 106
Students reporting specialty: 100%
Students specializing in: biomedical: 6%; computer: 28%; electrical: 22%; environmental: 7%; materials: 19%; mechanical: 9%; other: 8%

Massachusetts Institute of Technology

77 Massachusetts Avenue
Cambridge, MA 02139
Private
Admissions: (617) 253-2917
E-mail: mitgrad@mit.edu

Web site: http://web.mit.edu/engineering/
Internet application:
http://web.mit.edu/admissions/www/graduate/applications/index.html
Financial aid: (617) 253-4971
Application deadline: 12/15
Tuition: full time: $29,130; part time: N/A
Room/board/expenses: $18,880
Full-time enrollment: 2,689
men: 76%; women: 24%;
minorities: 16%; international: 40%
Part-time enrollment: 20
men: 80%; women: 20%;
minorities: 25%; international: 15%
Acceptance rate: 24%
GRE requirement: YES
Avg. GRE: quantitative: 774;
analytical 716
TOEFL requirement: YES
Minimum TOEFL score: 577
Fellowships: 508
Teaching assistantships: 252
Research assistantships: 1,765
Students reporting specialty: 100%
Students specializing in: aerospace: 9%; biomedical: 3%; chemical: 8%; civil: 8%; computer: 13%; electrical: 19%; environmental: 3%; materials: 8%; mechanical: 13%; nuclear: 4%; other: 11%

Northeastern University

130 Snell Engineering Center
Boston, MA 02115-5096
Private
Admissions: (617) 373-2711
E-mail: grad-eng@coe.neu.edu
Web site: http://www.coe.neu.edu
Internet application:
http://www.coe.neu.edu
Financial aid: (617) 373-4099
Application deadline: 02/15
Tuition: full time: $575/credit hour; part time: $575/credit hour
Room/board/expenses: $12,750
Full-time enrollment: 520
men: 70%; women: 30%;
minorities: 4%; international: 77%
Part-time enrollment: 387
men: 85%; women: 15%;
minorities: 18%; international: 16%
Acceptance rate: 42%
GRE requirement: YES
Avg. GRE: quantitative: 754;
analytical 682
TOEFL requirement: YES
Minimum TOEFL score: 550
Fellowships: 7
Teaching assistantships: 103
Research assistantships: 121
Students reporting specialty: 100%
Students specializing in: chemical: 3%; civil: 13%; electrical: 36%; industrial: 20%; mechanical: 9%; other: 20%

Tufts University

Anderson Hall
Medford, MA 02155
Private
Admissions: (617) 627-3395
E-mail: gradschool@tufts.edu
Web site:
http://ase.tufts.edu/gradstudy
Financial aid: (617) 627-2000
Application deadline: 02/15
Tuition: full time: $29,728; part time: $2,826/credit hour
Room/board/expenses: $10,975
Full-time enrollment: 250
men: 64%; women: 36%;
minorities: 8%; international: 34%
Part-time enrollment: 116
men: 73%; women: 27%;
minorities: 14%; international: 9%
Acceptance rate: 54%

GRE requirement: YES
Avg. GRE: quantitative: 710; analytical 700
TOEFL requirement: YES
Minimum TOEFL score: 550
Fellowships: 1
Teaching assistantships: 72
Research assistantships: 58
Students reporting specialty: 100%
Students specializing in: biomedical: 2%; chemical: 16%; civil: 19%; computer: 23%; electrical: 17%; mechanical: 20%; other: 3%

University of Massachusetts–Amherst

Room 125, Marston Hall
Amherst, MA 01003
Public
Admissions: (413) 545-0721
E-mail: gradinfo@resgs.umass.edu
Web site: http://www.ecs.umass.edu
Internet application: http://www.umass.edu/gradschool/
Financial aid: (413) 545-0801
Application deadline: 02/01
In-state tuition: full time: $7,978; part time: $110/credit hour
Out-of-state tuition: full time: $15,275
Room/board/expenses: $7,473
Full-time enrollment: 688
men: 75%; women: 25%; minorities: 5%; international: 58%
Part-time enrollment: 93
men: 88%; women: 12%; minorities: 9%; international: 26%
Acceptance rate: 12%
GRE requirement: YES
Avg. GRE: quantitative: 742; analytical 676
TOEFL requirement: YES
Minimum TOEFL score: 550
Fellowships: 37
Teaching assistantships: 147
Research assistantships: 582
Students reporting specialty: 100%
Students specializing in: chemical: 8%; civil: 6%; computer: 28%; electrical: 27%; environmental: 4%; industrial: 8%; materials: 11%; mechanical: 8%

University of Massachusetts–Dartmouth

285 Old Westport Road
North Dartmouth, MA 02747-2300
Public
Admissions: (508) 999-8604
E-mail: graduate@umassd.edu
Web site: http://www.umassd.edu/graduate
Financial aid: (508) 999-8632
Application deadline: 06/01
In-state tuition: full time: $6,266; part time: $261/credit hour
Out-of-state tuition: full time: $13,629
Room/board/expenses: $8,988
Full-time enrollment: 135
men: 78%; women: 22%; minorities: 1%; international: 90%
Part-time enrollment: 111
men: 80%; women: 20%; minorities: 4%; international: 69%
Acceptance rate: 65%
GRE requirement: YES
Avg. GRE: quantitative: 745; analytical 651
TOEFL requirement: YES
Minimum TOEFL score: 550
Fellowships: 0
Teaching assistantships: 26
Research assistantships: 71
Students reporting specialty: 100%

Students specializing in: computer: 46%; electrical: 39%; industrial: 9%; mechanical: 6%

University of Massachusetts–Lowell[1]

1 University Avenue
Lowell, MA 01854
Public
Admissions: (978) 934-2381
E-mail: graduate_school@uml.edu
Web site: http://www.uml.edu/grad
Internet application: http://www.uml.edu/grad/req_app.htm
Financial aid: (978) 934-4232
Tuition: N/A
Room/board/expenses: N/A
Enrollment: N/A

Worcester Polytechnic Institute

100 Institute Road
Worcester, MA 01609-2280
Private
Admissions: (508) 831-5301
E-mail: gao@wpi.edu
Web site: http://www.wpi.edu/
Internet application: http://www.wpi.edu/Admin/GAO/apply.html
Financial aid: (508) 831-5469
Application deadline: 02/01
Tuition: full time: $14,378; part time: $796/credit hour
Room/board/expenses: $11,576
Full-time enrollment: 274
men: 74%; women: 26%; minorities: 4%; international: 59%
Part-time enrollment: 300
men: 79%; women: 21%; minorities: 9%; international: 37%
Acceptance rate: 53%
GRE requirement: YES
Avg. GRE: quantitative: 739; analytical 649
TOEFL requirement: YES
Minimum TOEFL score: 550
Fellowships: 31
Teaching assistantships: 135
Research assistantships: 94
Students reporting specialty: 100%
Students specializing in: biomedical: 3%; chemical: 5%; civil: 9%; computer: 30%; electrical: 18%; industrial: 4%; materials: 2%; mechanical: 13%; other: 14%

Michigan State University

3410 ENG Building
East Lansing, MI 48824
Public
Admissions: (517) 353-5221
E-mail: egrgrad@egr.msu.edu
Web site: http://www.egr.msu.edu
Internet application: http://www.msu.edu/user/gradschl/apply.htm
Financial aid: (517) 353-3220
Application deadline: 12/31
In-state tuition: full time: $265/credit hour; part time: $265/credit hour
Out-of-state tuition: full time: $536/credit hour
Room/board/expenses: $11,162
Full-time enrollment: 683
men: 81%; women: 19%; minorities: 11%; international: 61%
Part-time enrollment: N/A
men: N/A; women: N/A; minorities: N/A; international: N/A
Acceptance rate: 13%
GRE requirement: YES
Avg. GRE: quantitative: 738; analytical 689
TOEFL requirement: YES

Minimum TOEFL score: 550
Fellowships: 84
Teaching assistantships: 158
Research assistantships: 268
Students reporting specialty: 100%
Students specializing in: agriculture: 3%; chemical: 8%; civil: 8%; computer: 25%; electrical: 28%; environmental: 6%; materials: 5%; mechanical: 18%

Michigan Technological University

1400 Townsend Drive
Houghton, MI 49931-1295
Public
Admissions: (906) 487-2327
E-mail: gradadms@mtu.edu
Web site: http://www.mtu.edu/grad/
Internet application: http://www.mtu.edu/apply
Financial aid: (906) 487-2622
Application deadline: rolling
In-state tuition: full time: $7,185; part time: $531/credit hour
Out-of-state tuition: full time: $13,901
Room/board/expenses: $8,265
Full-time enrollment: 367
men: 76%; women: 24%; minorities: 2%; international: 54%
Part-time enrollment: 75
men: 88%; women: 12%; minorities: 5%; international: 41%
Acceptance rate: 55%
GRE requirement: YES
Avg. GRE: quantitative: 743; analytical 691
TOEFL requirement: YES
Minimum TOEFL score: 550
Fellowships: 39
Teaching assistantships: 100
Research assistantships: 170
Students reporting specialty: 100%
Students specializing in: chemical: 7%; civil: 9%; computer: 11%; electrical: 12%; environmental: 11%; materials: 6%; mechanical: 32%; mining: 2%; other: 9%

Oakland University

School of Engineering and Computer Science
Rochester, MI 48309
Public
Admissions: (248) 370-3167
E-mail: applygrad@oakland.edu
Web site: http://www.oakland.edu/
Financial aid: (248) 370-2550
Application deadline: 08/01
In-state tuition: full time: $268/credit hour; part time: $268/credit hour
Out-of-state tuition: full time: $508/credit hour
Room/board/expenses: $6,652
Full-time enrollment: 315
men: 75%; women: 25%; minorities: 17%; international: 49%
Part-time enrollment: 374
men: 79%; women: 21%; minorities: 15%; international: 11%
Acceptance rate: 87%
GRE requirement: YES
Avg. GRE: quantitative: N/A; analytical N/A
TOEFL requirement: YES
Minimum TOEFL score: 550
Students reporting specialty: 100%
Students specializing in: computer: 28%; electrical: 13%; mechanical: 25%; other: 33%

University of Detroit Mercy[1]

PO Box 19900
Detroit, MI 48219-0900
Private
Admissions: (313) 993-3335
E-mail: engineering@udmercy.edu
Web site: http://www.udmercy.edu
Internet application: http://jackson.udmercy.edu/apply/programs.jsp
Financial aid: (313) 993-3350
Tuition: N/A
Room/board/expenses: N/A
Enrollment: N/A

University of Michigan–Ann Arbor

Robert H. Lurie Engineering Center
Ann Arbor, MI 48109-2102
Public
Admissions: (734) 647-7090
E-mail: grad-ed@engin.umich.edu
Web site: http://www.engin.umich.edu/students/prospective/graduate/admissions/
Internet application: http://apply.embark.com/Grad/umich/Rackham/
Financial aid: (734) 647-7090
Application deadline: 02/01
In-state tuition: full time: $13,875; part time: $1,036/credit hour
Out-of-state tuition: full time: $25,991
Room/board/expenses: $11,646
Full-time enrollment: 2,183
men: 80%; women: 20%; minorities: 13%; international: 53%
Part-time enrollment: 391
men: 81%; women: 19%; minorities: 13%; international: 22%
Acceptance rate: 33%
GRE requirement: YES
Avg. GRE: quantitative: 772; analytical 714
TOEFL requirement: YES
Minimum TOEFL score: 560
Fellowships: 254
Teaching assistantships: 209
Research assistantships: 791
Students reporting specialty: 100%
Students specializing in: aerospace: 4%; biomedical: 7%; chemical: 4%; civil: 5%; computer: 10%; electrical: 17%; industrial: 7%; materials: 3%; mechanical: 18%; nuclear: 2%; other: 22%

Wayne State University

5050 Anthony Wayne Drive
Detroit, MI 48202
Public
Admissions: (313) 577-3577
E-mail: admissions@wayne.edu
Web site: http://www.eng.wayne.edu
Internet application: http://www.admissions.wayne.edu/grad/appl/index.html
Financial aid: (313) 577-3378
Application deadline: rolling
In-state tuition: full time: $239/credit hour; part time: $239/credit hour
Out-of-state tuition: full time: $528/credit hour
Room/board/expenses: $11,113
Full-time enrollment: 832
men: 85%; women: 15%; minorities: 0%; international: 0%
Part-time enrollment: 568
men: 85%; women: 15%; minorities: 0%; international: 0%
Acceptance rate: 36%
GRE requirement: NO

Avg. GRE: quantitative: N/A; analytical N/A
TOEFL requirement: YES
Minimum TOEFL score: 550
Students reporting specialty: N/A
Students specializing in: N/A

Western Michigan University

1903 W. Michigan Avenue
Kalamazoo, MI 49008
Public
Admissions: (269) 387-2000
Web site: http://www.wmich.edu/engineer/
Internet application: http://www.wmich.edu/grad/
Financial aid: (269) 387-6000
Application deadline: 07/01
In-state tuition: full time: $205/credit hour; part time: $205/credit hour
Out-of-state tuition: full time: $503/credit hour
Room/board/expenses: $12,358
Full-time enrollment: 478
men: 82%; women: 18%; minorities: 3%; international: 89%
Part-time enrollment: 155
men: 88%; women: 12%; minorities: 8%; international: 41%
Acceptance rate: 68%
GRE requirement: YES
Avg. GRE: quantitative: 699; analytical 617
TOEFL requirement: YES
Minimum TOEFL score: 550
Fellowships: 5
Teaching assistantships: 70
Research assistantships: 28
Students reporting specialty: 100%
Students specializing in: computer: 21%; electrical: 29%; industrial: 16%; materials: 2%; mechanical: 11%; other: 20%

University of Minnesota–Twin Cities

117 Pleasant Street SE
Minneapolis, MN 55455
Public
Admissions: (612) 625-3014
E-mail: gsadmit@tc.umn.edu
Web site: http://www.it.umn.edu
Internet application: http://www.grad.umn.edu/application.html
Financial aid: (612) 624-1665
Application deadline: 06/15
In-state tuition: full time: $7,992; part time: $567/credit hour
Out-of-state tuition: full time: $14,550
Room/board/expenses: $13,000
Full-time enrollment: 1,309
men: 80%; women: 20%; minorities: 2%; international: 64%
Part-time enrollment: 283
men: 84%; women: 16%; minorities: 11%; international: 16%
Acceptance rate: 27%
GRE requirement: YES
Avg. GRE: quantitative: 762; analytical 703
TOEFL requirement: YES
Minimum TOEFL score: 550
Fellowships: 136
Teaching assistantships: 318
Research assistantships: 605
Students reporting specialty: 100%
Students specializing in: aerospace: 4%; agriculture: 1%; biomedical: 4%; chemical: 7%; civil: 11%; computer: 28%; electrical: 24%; industrial: 2%; materials: 5%; mechanical: 14%

MISSISSIPPI

Mississippi State University

Box 9544
Mississippi State, MS 39762
Public
Admissions: (662) 325-7393
E-mail: grad@grad.msstate.edu
Web site: http://www.msstate.edu
Internet application: http://www.msstate.edu/dept/admissions
Financial aid: (662) 325-2450
Application deadline: 07/01
In-state tuition: full time: $5,070; part time: $199/credit hour
Out-of-state tuition: full time: $11,491
Room/board/expenses: $8,627
Full-time enrollment: 363
men: 79%; women: 21%; minorities: 5%; international: 74%
Part-time enrollment: 174
men: 79%; women: 21%; minorities: 11%; international: 50%
Acceptance rate: 32%
GRE requirement: YES
Avg. GRE: quantitative: 730; analytical 638
TOEFL requirement: YES
Minimum TOEFL score: 550
Fellowships: 13
Teaching assistantships: 40
Research assistantships: 229
Students reporting specialty: 100%
Students specializing in: aerospace: 3%; biomedical: 3%; chemical: 7%; civil: 8%; computer: 24%; electrical: 33%; industrial: 7%; mechanical: 5%; other: 17%

University of Mississippi

Carrier Hall
University, MS 38677
Public
Admissions: (662) 915-7474
E-mail: gschool@olemiss.edu
Web site: http://www.olemiss.edu/depts/engineering_school
Internet application: http://www.olemiss.edu/depts/graduate_school
Financial aid: (662) 915-7175
Application deadline: 04/01
In-state tuition: full time: $25,912; part time: $25,510
Out-of-state tuition: full time: $30,458
Room/board/expenses: $6,219
Full-time enrollment: 170
men: 76%; women: 24%; minorities: 4%; international: 75%
Part-time enrollment: 46
men: 72%; women: 28%; minorities: 15%; international: 35%
Acceptance rate: 43%
GRE requirement: YES
Avg. GRE: quantitative: 698; analytical N/A
TOEFL requirement: YES
Minimum TOEFL score: 523
Fellowships: 5
Teaching assistantships: 55
Research assistantships: 76
Students reporting specialty: 81%
Students specializing in: chemical: 11%; civil: 10%; computer: 35%; electrical: 20%; mechanical: 13%; other: 12%

MISSOURI

University of Missouri–Columbia

W 1025 Engineering Building East
Columbia, MO 65211
Public
Admissions: (573) 882-7786
E-mail: mu4u@missouri.edu
Web site: http://www.missouri.edu/
Internet application: http://www.missouri.edu/~regwww/admission/us/application_form/application.index
Financial aid: (573) 882-7506
Application deadline: N/A
In-state tuition: full time: $246/credit hour; part time: $246/credit hour
Out-of-state tuition: full time: $636/credit hour
Room/board/expenses: $12,705
Full-time enrollment: 248
men: 79%; women: 21%; minorities: N/A; international: N/A
Part-time enrollment: 176
men: 81%; women: 19%; minorities: N/A; international: N/A
Acceptance rate: 60%
GRE requirement: YES
Avg. GRE: quantitative: 739; analytical 641
TOEFL requirement: YES
Minimum TOEFL score: 550
Fellowships: 34
Teaching assistantships: 56
Research assistantships: 180
Students reporting specialty: 100%
Students specializing in: agriculture: 0%; chemical: 5%; civil: 13%; computer: 23%; electrical: 25%; industrial: 4%; mechanical: 16%; nuclear: 9%; other: 4%

University of Missouri–Kansas City[1]

352 R.H. Flarsheim Hall
5100 Rockhill Rd
Kansas City, MO 64110-2499
Public
Admissions: (816) 235-1161
E-mail: graduate@umkc.edu
Web site: http://www.sice.umkc.edu
Financial aid: (816) 235-1154
Tuition: N/A
Room/board/expenses: N/A
Enrollment: N/A

University of Missouri–Rolla

1870 Miner Circle
101 ERL
Rolla, MO 65409-0840
Public
Admissions: (800) 522-0938
E-mail: admissions@umr.edu
Web site: http://www.umr.edu
Internet application: http://www.umr.edu/enrol
Financial aid: (573) 341-4282
Application deadline: 07/15
In-state tuition: full time: $5,041; part time: $3,567
Out-of-state tuition: full time: $12,060
Room/board/expenses: $7,955
Full-time enrollment: 783
men: 84%; women: 16%; minorities: 3%; international: 67%
Part-time enrollment: 377
men: 85%; women: 15%; minorities: 8%; international: 21%
Acceptance rate: 65%
GRE requirement: YES
Avg. GRE: quantitative: 731; analytical 655
TOEFL requirement: YES

Minimum TOEFL score: 600
Fellowships: 123
Teaching assistantships: 101
Research assistantships: 369
Students reporting specialty: 100%
Students specializing in: aerospace: 2%; chemical: 3%; civil: 12%; computer: 14%; electrical: 16%; environmental: 1%; industrial: 31%; materials: 5%; mechanical: 11%; mining: 2%; nuclear: 1%; petroleum: 1%; other: 2%

Washington University in St. Louis

1 Brookings Drive
Campus Box 1163
St. Louis, MO 63130
Private
Admissions: (314) 935-6166
E-mail: gradengineering@seas.wustl.edu
Web site: http://www.seas.wustl.edu
Internet application: http://www.sever.wustl.edu/apply
Financial aid: (314) 935-5900
Application deadline: rolling
Tuition: full time: $27,330; part time: $950/credit hour
Room/board/expenses: $11,528
Full-time enrollment: 400
men: 79%; women: 21%; minorities: 7%; international: 51%
Part-time enrollment: 293
men: 80%; women: 20%; minorities: 12%; international: 8%
Acceptance rate: 28%
GRE requirement: YES
Avg. GRE: quantitative: 770; analytical 710
TOEFL requirement: YES
Minimum TOEFL score: 550
Fellowships: 19
Teaching assistantships: 7
Research assistantships: 199
Students reporting specialty: 100%
Students specializing in: biomedical: 8%; chemical: 7%; civil: 7%; computer: 26%; electrical: 11%; environmental: 3%; materials: 1%; mechanical: 10%; other: 29%

MONTANA

Montana State University

212 Roberts Hall
PO Box 173820
Bozeman, MT 59717-3820
Public
Admissions: (406) 994-4145
E-mail: engrinfo@coe.montana.edu
Web site: http://www.coe.montana.edu
Internet application: http://www.montana.edu/wwwdg/apply.shtml
Financial aid: (406) 994-2845
Application deadline: 07/15
In-state tuition: full time: $5,407; part time: $218/credit hour
Out-of-state tuition: full time: $11,135
Room/board/expenses: $8,320
Full-time enrollment: 94
men: 84%; women: 16%; minorities: 0%; international: 35%
Part-time enrollment: 61
men: 72%; women: 28%; minorities: 2%; international: 25%
Acceptance rate: 54%
GRE requirement: YES
Avg. GRE: quantitative: 703; analytical 617
TOEFL requirement: YES
Minimum TOEFL score: 550
Fellowships: 8
Teaching assistantships: 37
Research assistantships: 72

Students reporting specialty: 100%
Students specializing in: chemical: 10%; civil: 14%; computer: 24%; electrical: 17%; environmental: 5%; industrial: 14%; materials: 2%; mechanical: 9%; other: 5%

NEBRASKA

University of Nebraska–Lincoln

114 Othmer Hall
Lincoln, NE 68588-0642
Public
Admissions: (402) 472-2878
E-mail: grad_admissions@unl.edu
Web site: http://www.nuengr.unl.edu/
Internet application: http://www.unl.edu/gradstud/
Financial aid: (402) 472-2030
Application deadline: 01/07
In-state tuition: full time: $148/credit hour; part time: $148/credit hour
Out-of-state tuition: full time: $398/credit hour
Room/board/expenses: $8,231
Full-time enrollment: 386
men: 78%; women: 22%; minorities: 1%; international: 83%
Part-time enrollment: 120
men: 82%; women: 18%; minorities: 7%; international: 48%
Acceptance rate: 21%
GRE requirement: YES
Avg. GRE: quantitative: N/A; analytical N/A
TOEFL requirement: YES
Minimum TOEFL score: 550
Fellowships: 27
Teaching assistantships: 65
Research assistantships: 231
Students reporting specialty: 97%
Students specializing in: agriculture: 1%; chemical: 4%; civil: 5%; computer: 30%; electrical: 12%; environmental: 2%; industrial: 14%; materials: 7%; mechanical: 26%

NEVADA

University of Nevada–Las Vegas

4505 Maryland Parkway
Box 544005
Las Vegas, NV 89154-4005
Public
Admissions: (702) 895-4391
Web site: http://www.unlv.edu
Financial aid: (702) 895-3697
Application deadline: rolling
In-state tuition: full time: $799/credit hour; part time: $361/credit hour
Out-of-state tuition: full time: $4,100/credit hour
Room/board/expenses: $3,413
Full-time enrollment: N/A
men: N/A; women: N/A; minorities: N/A; international: N/A
Part-time enrollment: N/A
men: N/A; women: N/A; minorities: N/A; international: N/A
GRE requirement: YES
Avg. GRE: quantitative: N/A; analytical N/A
TOEFL requirement: YES
Minimum TOEFL score: 550
Teaching assistantships: 46
Research assistantships: 52
Students reporting specialty: 76%
Students specializing in: civil: 47%; computer: 31%; electrical: 22%

University of Nevada–Reno

College of Engineering & School of Mines
Reno, NV 89557-0030
Public
Admissions: (775) 784-4700
E-mail: asknevada@unr.edu
Web site: http://www.unr.edu
Internet application: http://coeweb.engr.unr.edu
Financial aid: (775) 784-4666
Application deadline: 02/01
In-state tuition: full time: $111/credit hour; part time: $111/credit hour
Out-of-state tuition: full time: $9,136
Room/board/expenses: $9,050
Full-time enrollment: 171
men: 77%; women: 23%; minorities: 0%; international: 0%
Part-time enrollment: 172
men: 74%; women: 26%; minorities: 0%; international: 0%
GRE requirement: YES
Avg. GRE: quantitative: N/A; analytical N/A
TOEFL requirement: YES
Minimum TOEFL score: 600
Fellowships: 10
Teaching assistantships: 62
Research assistantships: 108
Students reporting specialty: 100%
Students specializing in: chemical: 5%; civil: 17%; computer: 25%; electrical: 9%; environmental: 0%; materials: 6%; mechanical: 11%; mining: 1%; other: 27%

NEW HAMPSHIRE

Dartmouth College (Thayer)

8000 Cummings Hall
Hanover, NH 03755
Private
Admissions: (603) 646-2606
E-mail: thayer.admissions@dartmouth.edu
Web site: http://engineering.dartmouth.edu
Internet application: http://engineering.dartmouth.edu/thayer/academicsadmissions/graduate-application.html
Financial aid: (603) 646-3844
Application deadline: 01/01
Tuition: full time: $27,600; part time: $3,680/credit hour
Room/board/expenses: $17,731
Full-time enrollment: 201
men: 78%; women: 22%; minorities: 4%; international: 52%
Part-time enrollment: 1
men: 100%; women: 0%; minorities: 0%; international: 0%
Acceptance rate: 18%
GRE requirement: YES
Avg. GRE: quantitative: 767; analytical 709
TOEFL requirement: YES
Minimum TOEFL score: 600
Fellowships: 44
Teaching assistantships: 52
Research assistantships: 111
Students reporting specialty: 100%
Students specializing in: computer: 36%; other: 64%

University of New Hampshire[1]

Kingsbury Hall
33 College Road
Durham, NH 03824
Public
Admissions: (603) 862-3000
E-mail: grad.school@unh.edu
Web site:
http://www.gradschool.unh.edu/
Internet application:
http://webcat.unh.edu/
index_adm.html
Financial aid: (603) 862-3600
Tuition: N/A
Room/board/expenses: N/A
Enrollment: N/A

NEW JERSEY

New Jersey Institute of Technology

University Heights
Newark, NJ 07102-1982
Public
Admissions: (973) 596-3300
E-mail: admissions@njit.edu
Web site: http://www.njit.edu
Financial aid: (973) 596-3479
Application deadline: rolling
In-state tuition: full time: $11,134;
part time: $479/credit hour
Out-of-state tuition: full time:
$14,742
Room/board/expenses: $9,864
Full-time enrollment: 528
men: 79%; women: 21%;
minorities: 10%; international: 77%
Part-time enrollment: 515
men: 81%; women: 19%;
minorities: 36%; international: 16%
Acceptance rate: 54%
GRE requirement: YES
Avg. GRE: quantitative: 729;
analytical 629
TOEFL requirement: YES
Minimum TOEFL score: 550
Fellowships: 14
Teaching assistantships: 92
Research assistantships: 111
Students reporting specialty: 100%
Students specializing in: biomedical: 6%; chemical: 5%; civil: 13%;
computer: 10%; electrical: 32%;
environmental: 3%; industrial: 5%;
mechanical: 8%; other: 19%

Princeton University

C230 Engineering Quadrangle
Princeton, NJ 08544-5263
Private
Admissions: (609) 258-3034
Web site:
http://www.princeton.edu/egrad
Internet application:
http://webware.princeton.edu/
GSO
Financial aid: (609) 258-3037
Application deadline: 01/02
Tuition: full time: $27,830; part
time: N/A
Room/board/expenses: $11,441
Full-time enrollment: 487
men: 77%; women: 23%;
minorities: 10%; international: 56%
Part-time enrollment: N/A
men: N/A; women: N/A;
minorities: N/A; international: N/A
Acceptance rate: 15%
GRE requirement: YES
Avg. GRE: quantitative: 710;
analytical 674
TOEFL requirement: YES
Minimum TOEFL score: 600
Fellowships: 164
Teaching assistantships: 53
Research assistantships: 232
Students reporting specialty: 100%

Students specializing in: chemical:
14%; civil: 7%; computer: 19%;
electrical: 36%; mechanical: 16%;
other: 6%

Rutgers State University– New Brunswick

98 Brett Road
Piscataway, NJ 08854-8058
Public
Admissions: (732) 932-7711
Web site:
http://gradstudy.rutgers.edu
Financial aid: (732) 932-7755
Application deadline: rolling
In-state tuition: full time: $9,194;
part time: $338/credit hour
Out-of-state tuition: full time:
$13,022
Room/board/expenses: $9,173
Full-time enrollment: 395
men: 75%; women: 25%;
minorities: 9%; international: 77%
Part-time enrollment: 432
men: 76%; women: 24%;
minorities: 11%; international: 51%
Acceptance rate: 18%
GRE requirement: YES
Avg. GRE: quantitative: 756;
analytical 676
TOEFL requirement: YES
Minimum TOEFL score: 550
Fellowships: 65
Teaching assistantships: 157
Research assistantships: 230
Students reporting specialty: 100%
Students specializing in: agriculture: 1%; biomedical: 9%; chemical: 8%; civil: 12%; computer:
18%; electrical: 27%; industrial:
6%; materials: 8%; mechanical:
10%

Stevens Institute of Technology

Castle Point on Hudson
Hoboken, NJ 07030
Private
Admissions: (201) 216-8031
E-mail:
gradschool@stevens-tech.edu
Web site:
http://www.stevens-tech.edu
Internet application:
http://gradschool.stevens-tech.
edu/admissions/index.html
Financial aid: (201) 216-5555
Application deadline: rolling
Tuition: full time: $775/credit hour;
part time: $775/credit hour
Room/board/expenses: $11,375
Full-time enrollment: 244
men: 80%; women: 20%;
minorities: 18%; international: 78%
Part-time enrollment: 505
men: 80%; women: 20%;
minorities: 71%; international: 0%
Acceptance rate: 55%
GRE requirement: YES
Avg. GRE: quantitative: N/A;
analytical N/A
TOEFL requirement: YES
Minimum TOEFL score: 550
Students reporting specialty: N/A
Students specializing in: N/A

NEW MEXICO

New Mexico Institute of Mining and Technology

801 Leroy Place
Socorro, NM 87801
Public
Admissions: (505) 835-5513
E-mail: mwatson@admin.nmt.edu
Web site: http://www.nmt.edu

Internet application: http://www.
nmt.edu/mainpage/prospective.
html#Graduate
Financial aid: (505) 835-5333
Application deadline: 08/01
In-state tuition: full time: $3,026;
part time: $120/credit hour
Out-of-state tuition: full time:
$9,532
Room/board/expenses: $8,900
Full-time enrollment: 121
men: 80%; women: 20%;
minorities: 5%; international: 65%
Part-time enrollment: 47
men: 85%; women: 15%;
minorities: 15%; international: 17%
Acceptance rate: 66%
GRE requirement: YES
Avg. GRE: quantitative: 714;
analytical 618
TOEFL requirement: YES
Minimum TOEFL score: 540
Teaching assistantships: 40
Research assistantships: 66
Students reporting specialty: 100%
Students specializing in: computer:
29%; environmental: 5%; materials: 18%; mechanical: 23%; mining: 5%; petroleum: 15%; other:
4%

New Mexico State University

Box 30001
Department 3449
Las Cruces, NM 88003
Public
Admissions: (505) 646-2736
E-mail: gradinfo@nmsu.edu
Web site: http://www.nmsu.edu
Internet application:
http://www.nmsu.edu/~coe/
Financial aid: (505) 646-3121
Application deadline: rolling
In-state tuition: full time: $3,456;
part time: $144/credit hour
Out-of-state tuition: full time:
$11,076
Room/board/expenses: $6,250
Full-time enrollment: 301
men: 84%; women: 16%;
minorities: 22%; international: 47%
Part-time enrollment: N/A
men: N/A; women: N/A;
minorities: N/A; international: N/A
Acceptance rate: 47%
GRE requirement: YES
Avg. GRE: quantitative: 742;
analytical 618
TOEFL requirement: YES
Minimum TOEFL score: 530
Fellowships: 7
Teaching assistantships: 66
Research assistantships: 48
Students reporting specialty: 100%
Students specializing in: chemical:
7%; civil: 10%; electrical: 51%; environmental: 1%; industrial: 18%;
mechanical: 12%

University of New Mexico

Farris Engineering Center
Albuquerque, NM 87131-1336
Public
Admissions: (505) 277-2711
E-mail: gradstud@unm.edu
Web site:
http://www.cs.unm.edu/soe/
Financial aid: (505) 277-2711
Application deadline: 07/30
In-state tuition: full time: $3,485;
part time: $145/credit hour
Out-of-state tuition: full time:
$11,436
Room/board/expenses: $7,080
Full-time enrollment: 644
men: 81%; women: 19%;
minorities: 14%; international: 50%

Part-time enrollment: N/A
men: N/A; women: N/A;
minorities: N/A; international: N/A
Acceptance rate: 45%
GRE requirement: YES
Avg. GRE: quantitative: 738;
analytical 647
TOEFL requirement: YES
Minimum TOEFL score: 550
Fellowships: 27
Teaching assistantships: 41
Research assistantships: 267
Students reporting specialty: 100%
Students specializing in: chemical:
8%; civil: 10%; computer: 27%;
electrical: 32%; industrial: 3%; mechanical: 14%; nuclear: 4%; other:
2%

NEW YORK

Alfred University– New York State College of Ceramics

School of Ceramic Engineering &
Materials Sciences
Alfred, NY 14802
Public
Admissions: (800) 541-9229
E-mail: admwww@alfred.edu
Web site: http://nyscc.alfred.edu
Internet application: http://www.
alfred.edu/admissions/graduate/
graduate_application_form.html
Financial aid: (607) 871-2159
Application deadline: rolling
In-state tuition: full time: $15,324;
part time: $572/credit hour
Out-of-state tuition: full time:
$15,324
Room/board/expenses: $9,686
Full-time enrollment: 50
men: 78%; women: 22%;
minorities: 2%; international: 30%
Part-time enrollment: 12
men: 67%; women: 33%;
minorities: 0%; international: 50%
Acceptance rate: 46%
GRE requirement: NO
Avg. GRE: quantitative: 770;
analytical 660
TOEFL requirement: YES
Minimum TOEFL score: 590
Fellowships: 2
Teaching assistantships: 15
Research assistantships: 32
Students reporting specialty: 100%
Students specializing in: materials:
100%

Clarkson University

PO Box 5625
Potsdam, NY 13699-5625
Private
Admissions: (315) 268-7929
E-mail: enggrad@clarkson.edu
Web site:
http://www.clarkson.edu/graduate/
Financial aid: (315) 268-6413
Application deadline: 05/15
Tuition: full time: $770/credit hour;
part time: $770/credit hour
Room/board/expenses: $7,300
Full-time enrollment: 145
men: 76%; women: 24%;
minorities: 2%; international: 67%
Part-time enrollment: N/A
men: N/A; women: N/A;
minorities: N/A; international: N/A
Acceptance rate: 51%
GRE requirement: YES
Avg. GRE: quantitative: N/A;
analytical N/A
TOEFL requirement: YES
Minimum TOEFL score: 550
Fellowships: 13
Teaching assistantships: 30
Research assistantships: 60
Students reporting specialty: 98%

Students specializing in: chemical:
22%; civil: 24%; electrical: 21%;
mechanical: 30%; other: 3%

Columbia University (Fu Foundation)

500 W. 120th Street
Room 510 Mudd
New York, NY 10027
Private
Admissions: (212) 854-6438
E-mail:
seasgradmit@columbia.edu
Web site: http://www.
engineering.columbia.edu
Financial aid: (212) 854-6438
Application deadline: N/A
Tuition: full time: $28,633; part
time: $906/credit hour
Room/board/expenses: $18,320
Full-time enrollment: 687
men: 77%; women: 23%;
minorities: 10%; international: 66%
Part-time enrollment: 337
men: 74%; women: 26%;
minorities: 18%; international: 33%
Acceptance rate: 26%
GRE requirement: YES
Avg. GRE: quantitative: 762;
analytical 694
TOEFL requirement: YES
Minimum TOEFL score: 550
Fellowships: 27
Teaching assistantships: 109
Research assistantships: 277
Students reporting specialty: 91%
Students specializing in: biomedical: 7%; chemical: 3%; civil: 6%;
computer: 24%; electrical: 26%;
environmental: 4%; industrial:
12%; materials: 3%; mechanical:
6%; mining: 0%; other: 8%

Cornell University

242 Carpenter Hall
Ithaca, NY 14853
Private
Admissions: (607) 255-4884
E-mail:
gradadmissions@cornell.edu
Web site: http://www.
engineering.cornell.edu
Internet application:
http://www.gradschool.cornell.edu
Financial aid: (607) 255-6521
Application deadline: 01/01
Tuition: full time: $28,361; part
time: N/A
Room/board/expenses: $13,295
Full-time enrollment: 1,160
men: 80%; women: 20%;
minorities: 17%; international: 49%
Part-time enrollment: N/A
men: N/A; women: N/A;
minorities: N/A; international: N/A
Acceptance rate: 27%
GRE requirement: YES
Avg. GRE: quantitative: 765;
analytical 700
TOEFL requirement: YES
Minimum TOEFL score: 550
Fellowships: 190
Teaching assistantships: 307
Research assistantships: 435
Students reporting specialty: 100%
Students specializing in: aerospace: 2%; agriculture: 6%; biomedical: 1%; chemical: 7%; civil:
5%; computer: 16%; electrical:
23%; environmental: 5%; industrial: 11%; materials: 4%; mechanical: 12%; nuclear: 0%; other: 8%

CUNY Graduate School and University Center

Convent Avenue at 138th Street
New York, NY 10031
Public
Admissions: (212) 650-6432
E-mail: admissions@gc.cuny.edu
Web site:
http://www.engr.ccny.cuny.edu
Internet application:
http://www.gc.cuny.edu
Financial aid: (212) 817-7460
Application deadline: 05/01
In-state tuition: full time: $4,530; part time: $245/credit hour
Out-of-state tuition: full time: $7,780
Room/board/expenses: $10,750
Full-time enrollment: 292
men: 77%; women: 23%;
minorities: 22%; international: 61%
Part-time enrollment: 368
men: 80%; women: 20%;
minorities: 36%; international: 39%
Acceptance rate: 68%
GRE requirement: YES
Avg. GRE: quantitative: 710; analytical 658
TOEFL requirement: YES
Minimum TOEFL score: 500
Fellowships: 84
Teaching assistantships: 43
Research assistantships: 57
Students reporting specialty: 100%
Students specializing in: biomedical: 3%; chemical: 8%; civil: 20%; computer: 23%; electrical: 29%; mechanical: 16%

Polytechnic University

6 MetroTech Center
Brooklyn, NY 11201
Private
Admissions: (718) 260-3200
E-mail: admitme@poly.edu
Web site: http://www.poly.edu
Financial aid: (718) 260-3300
Application deadline: N/A
Tuition: full time: $810/credit hour; part time: $810/credit hour
Room/board/expenses: $13,058
Full-time enrollment: 337
men: 82%; women: 18%;
minorities: 20%; international: 45%
Part-time enrollment: 582
men: 81%; women: 19%;
minorities: 20%; international: 12%
Acceptance rate: 72%
GRE requirement: NO
Avg. GRE: quantitative: N/A; analytical N/A
TOEFL requirement: YES
Minimum TOEFL score: 550
Fellowships: 101
Students reporting specialty: 100%
Students specializing in: biomedical: 1%; chemical: 3%; civil: 14%; computer: 46%; electrical: 30%; environmental: 1%; industrial: 2%; materials: 1%; mechanical: 3%

Rensselaer Polytechnic Institute

Jonsson Engineering Center-3004
Troy, NY 12180-3590
Private
Admissions: (518) 276-6216
E-mail: admissions@rpi.edu
Web site: http://www.rpi.edu
Financial aid: (518) 276-6813
Application deadline: 01/15
Tuition: full time: $27,837; part time: $1,320/credit hour
Room/board/expenses: $10,500
Full-time enrollment: 754
men: 78%; women: 22%;
minorities: 8%; international: 65%

Part-time enrollment: 1,033
men: 81%; women: 19%;
minorities: 16%; international: 10%
Acceptance rate: 23%
GRE requirement: YES
Avg. GRE: quantitative: 738; analytical 670
TOEFL requirement: YES
Minimum TOEFL score: 570
Fellowships: 51
Teaching assistantships: 228
Research assistantships: 300
Students reporting specialty: 100%
Students specializing in: aerospace: 1%; biomedical: 2%; chemical: 4%; civil: 2%; computer: 33%; electrical: 15%; environmental: 1%; industrial: 5%; materials: 4%; mechanical: 16%; nuclear: 2%; other: 17%

SUNY Binghamton (Watson)

Watson School of Engineering
Binghamton, NY 13902-6000
Public
Admissions: (607) 777-2151
E-mail: cbrown@binghamton.edu
Web site:
http://watson.binghamton.edu
Internet application:
http://gradschool.binghamton.edu/graduate/Gradapp.htm
Financial aid: (607) 777-2428
Application deadline: 02/15
In-state tuition: full time: $5,977; part time: $213/credit hour
Out-of-state tuition: full time: $9,283
Room/board/expenses: $9,312
Full-time enrollment: 351
men: 84%; women: 16%;
minorities: 7%; international: 80%
Part-time enrollment: 244
men: 80%; women: 20%;
minorities: 11%; international: 34%
Acceptance rate: 51%
GRE requirement: YES
Avg. GRE: quantitative: 747; analytical 681
TOEFL requirement: YES
Minimum TOEFL score: 550
Fellowships: 12
Teaching assistantships: 67
Research assistantships: 101
Students reporting specialty: 100%
Students specializing in: computer: 2%; electrical: 23%; industrial: 24%; mechanical: 13%; other: 39%

SUNY College of Environmental Science and Forestry

227 Bray Hall
Syracuse, NY 13210
Public
Admissions: (315) 470-6599
E-mail: esfgrad@esf.edu
Web site: http://www.esf.edu
Financial aid: (315) 470-6706
Application deadline: rolling
In-state tuition: full time: $5,471; part time: $213/credit hour
Out-of-state tuition: full time: $8,671
Room/board/expenses: $11,190
Full-time enrollment: 30
men: 70%; women: 30%;
minorities: 3%; international: 33%
Part-time enrollment: 62
men: 74%; women: 26%;
minorities: 2%; international: 23%
Acceptance rate: 68%
GRE requirement: YES
Avg. GRE: quantitative: 660; analytical 617
TOEFL requirement: YES
Minimum TOEFL score: 550

Fellowships: 1
Teaching assistantships: 17
Research assistantships: 19
Students reporting specialty: 100%
Students specializing in: chemical: 20%; environmental: 62%; materials: 18%

SUNY–Stony Brook

College of Engineering
and Applied Sciences
Stony Brook, NY 11794-2200
Public
Admissions: (631) 632-4723
E-mail:
graduate.school@sunysb.edu
Web site:
http://www.grad.sunysb.edu
Financial aid: (631) 632-6840
Application deadline: N/A
In-state tuition: full time: $5,592; part time: $213/credit hour
Out-of-state tuition: full time: $8,908
Room/board/expenses: $8,870
Full-time enrollment: 723
men: 72%; women: 28%;
minorities: 9%; international: 77%
Part-time enrollment: 191
men: 67%; women: 33%;
minorities: 17%; international: 40%
Acceptance rate: 34%
GRE requirement: YES
Avg. GRE: quantitative: 721; analytical 662
TOEFL requirement: YES
Minimum TOEFL score: 550
Fellowships: 93
Teaching assistantships: 175
Research assistantships: 163
Students reporting specialty: 100%
Students specializing in: biomedical: 6%; computer: 32%; electrical: 22%; materials: 7%; mechanical: 9%; other: 24%

Syracuse University

223 Link Hall
Syracuse, NY 13244-1240
Private
Admissions: (315) 443-4492
E-mail: gradinfo@syr.edu
Web site: http://www.ecs.syr.edu
Internet application:
http://apply.embarkrelease.com/grad/syracuse
Financial aid: (315) 443-2545
Application deadline: rolling
Tuition: full time: $686/credit hour; part time: $686/credit hour
Room/board/expenses: $15,014
Full-time enrollment: 735
men: 87%; women: 13%;
minorities: 9%; international: 72%
Part-time enrollment: 156
men: 87%; women: 13%;
minorities: 21%; international: 33%
Acceptance rate: 48%
GRE requirement: YES
Avg. GRE: quantitative: 746; analytical 644
TOEFL requirement: YES
Minimum TOEFL score: 550
Fellowships: 11
Teaching assistantships: 71
Research assistantships: 115
Students reporting specialty: 100%
Students specializing in: aerospace: 1%; biomedical: 4%; chemical: 2%; civil: 4%; computer: 52%; electrical: 24%; environmental: 1%; industrial: 8%; mechanical: 4%

University at Buffalo

412 Bonner Hall
Buffalo, NY 14260-1900
Public
Admissions: (716) 645-2771
E-mail: seasgrad@eng.buffalo.edu
Web site:
http://www.eng.buffalo.edu
Financial aid: (716) 645-2450
Application deadline: rolling
In-state tuition: full time: $6,118; part time: $213/credit hour
Out-of-state tuition: full time: $9,434
Room/board/expenses: $11,078
Full-time enrollment: 949
men: 83%; women: 17%;
minorities: 3%; international: 84%
Part-time enrollment: 142
men: 90%; women: 10%;
minorities: 5%; international: 7%
Acceptance rate: 42%
GRE requirement: YES
Avg. GRE: quantitative: 752; analytical 669
TOEFL requirement: YES
Minimum TOEFL score: 550
Fellowships: 21
Teaching assistantships: 172
Research assistantships: 193
Students reporting specialty: 100%
Students specializing in: aerospace: 2%; chemical: 6%; civil: 18%; computer: 26%; electrical: 15%; industrial: 14%; mechanical: 19%

University of Rochester

Lattimore Hall
Box 270076
Rochester, NY 14627-0076
Private
Admissions: (585) 275-4153
E-mail:
gradstudies@mail.rochester.edu
Web site: http://www.seas.rochester.edu:8080/
Financial aid: (585) 275-3226
Application deadline: 02/01
Tuition: full time: $25,902; part time: $795/credit hour
Room/board/expenses: $12,900
Full-time enrollment: 303
men: 77%; women: 23%;
minorities: 5%; international: 51%
Part-time enrollment: 29
men: 86%; women: 14%;
minorities: 14%; international: 14%
Acceptance rate: 10%
GRE requirement: YES
Avg. GRE: quantitative: 770; analytical 741
TOEFL requirement: YES
Minimum TOEFL score: 600
Fellowships: 87
Teaching assistantships: 79
Research assistantships: 111
Students reporting specialty: 100%
Students specializing in: biomedical: 8%; chemical: 11%; computer: 15%; electrical: 20%; materials: 6%; mechanical: 10%; other: 29%

Duke University

305 Teer Building
Durham, NC 27708-0271
Private
Admissions: (919) 684-3913
E-mail: grad-admissions@duke.edu
Web site: http://www.egr.duke.edu
Financial aid: (919) 684-5708
Application deadline: 12/31
Tuition: full time: $26,292; part time: $875/credit hour
Room/board/expenses: $12,555

Full-time enrollment: 419
men: 73%; women: 27%;
minorities: 6%; international: 55%
Part-time enrollment: 6
men: 67%; women: 33%;
minorities: 17%; international: 17%
Acceptance rate: 21%
GRE requirement: YES
Avg. GRE: quantitative: 762; analytical 719
TOEFL requirement: YES
Minimum TOEFL score: 550
Fellowships: 40
Teaching assistantships: 76
Research assistantships: 225
Students reporting specialty: 100%
Students specializing in: biomedical: 27%; civil: 8%; computer: 21%; electrical: 24%; mechanical: 13%; other: 6%

North Carolina A&T State University[1]

1601 E. Market Street
651 McNair Hall
Greensboro, NC 27411
Public
Admissions: (336) 334-7920
E-mail: gradsch@ncat.edu
Web site: http://www.eng.ncat.edu
Financial aid: (336) 334-7973
Tuition: N/A
Room/board/expenses: N/A
Enrollment: N/A

North Carolina State University

Box 7901
Raleigh, NC 27695
Public
Admissions: (919) 515-2872
Web site:
http://www.engr.ncsu.edu/
Financial aid: (919) 515-2421
Application deadline: 06/25
In-state tuition: full time: $4,126; part time: $2,620
Out-of-state tuition: full time: $15,775
Room/board/expenses: $11,436
Full-time enrollment: 1,291
men: 78%; women: 22%;
minorities: 10%; international: 53%
Part-time enrollment: 487
men: 82%; women: 18%;
minorities: 16%; international: 0%
Acceptance rate: 17%
GRE requirement: YES
Avg. GRE: quantitative: 736; analytical 672
TOEFL requirement: YES
Minimum TOEFL score: 550
Fellowships: 101
Teaching assistantships: 261
Research assistantships: 569
Students reporting specialty: 100%
Students specializing in: aerospace: 2%; agriculture: 2%; chemical: 5%; civil: 12%; computer: 12%; electrical: 17%; industrial: 4%; materials: 5%; mechanical: 6%; nuclear: 2%; other: 33%

University of North Carolina–Chapel Hill

CB# 7431
106 Rosenau Hall
Chapel Hill, NC 27599-7431
Public
Admissions: (919) 966-3844
E-mail: jack_whaley@unc.edu
Web site:
http://www.sph.unc.edu/envr
Internet application:
https://www-s2.ais.unc.edu/sis/adm/gradapp.html
Financial aid: (919) 966-3844

Application deadline: 12/01
In-state tuition: full time: $4,830;
part time: $479/credit hour
Out-of-state tuition: full time:
$15,764
Room/board/expenses: $11,310
Full-time enrollment: 142
men: 45%; women: 55%;
minorities: 7%; international: 29%
Part-time enrollment: 10
men: 60%; women: 40%;
minorities: 0%; international: 0%
Acceptance rate: 44%
GRE requirement: YES
Avg. GRE: quantitative: 686;
analytical 677
TOEFL requirement: YES
Minimum TOEFL score: 550
Fellowships: 18
Teaching assistantships: 11
Research assistantships: 72
Students reporting specialty: 100%
Students specializing in:
environmental: 100%

University of North Carolina–Charlotte

Smith Engineering Building
9201 University Boulevard
Charlotte, NC 28223-0001
Public
Admissions: (704) 687-3366
E-mail: gradadm@email.uncc.edu
Web site: http://www.uncc.edu/
gradmiss/index.asp
Financial aid: (704) 687-2461
Application deadline: 07/01
In-state tuition: full time: $3,172;
part time: $2,701
Out-of-state tuition: full time:
$12,898
Room/board/expenses: $8,134
Full-time enrollment: 182
men: 77%; women: 23%;
minorities: 6%; international: 62%
Part-time enrollment: 263
men: 77%; women: 23%;
minorities: 13%; international: 46%
Acceptance rate: 64%
GRE requirement: YES
Avg. GRE: quantitative: 708;
analytical 606
TOEFL requirement: YES
Minimum TOEFL score: 550
Fellowships: 13
Teaching assistantships: 189
Research assistantships: 196
Students reporting specialty: 100%
Students specializing in: civil: 12%;
computer: 34%; electrical: 26%;
mechanical: 21%; other: 7%

NORTH DAKOTA

North Dakota State University

University Station
PO Box 5285
Fargo, ND 58105
Public
Admissions: (701) 231-7033
E-mail: NDSU.Grad.School@
ndsu.nodak.edu
Web site:
http://www.cea.ndsu.nodak.edu
Internet application: http://www.
ndsu.nodak.edu/gradschool
Financial aid: (701) 231-7533
Application deadline: 04/01
In-state tuition: full time:
$117/credit hour; part time:
$117/credit hour
Out-of-state tuition: full time:
$313/credit hour
Room/board/expenses: $6,900
Full-time enrollment: 46
men: 87%; women: 13%;
minorities: 26%; international: 54%

Part-time enrollment: 211
men: 81%; women: 19%;
minorities: 34%; international: 35%
Acceptance rate: 47%
GRE requirement: YES
Avg. GRE: quantitative: 650;
analytical 575
TOEFL requirement: YES
Minimum TOEFL score: 550
Fellowships: 2
Teaching assistantships: 66
Research assistantships: 100
Students reporting specialty: 47%
Students specializing in: N/A

University of North Dakota[1]

PO Box 8155
University of North Dakota
Grand Forks, ND 58202
Public
Admissions: (701) 777-2945
E-mail:
gradschool@mail.und.nodak.edu
Web site: http://www.
und.nodak.edu/dept/grad
Internet application:
http://www.und.nodak.edu/
dept/grad/admissns.html
Financial aid: (701) 777-3121
Tuition: N/A
Room/board/expenses: N/A
Enrollment: N/A

OHIO

Air Force Institute of Technology[1]

AFIT/RRA
2950 P Street
WPAFB, OH 45433-7765
Public
Admissions: (800) 211-5097
E-mail: counselors@afit.edu
Web site: http://www.afit.edu/
Internet application:
http://www.afit.edu/afit.cfm?p=2
Financial aid: N/A
Tuition: N/A
Room/board/expenses: N/A
Enrollment: N/A

Case Western Reserve University

312 Glennan Building
10900 Euclid Avenue
Cleveland, OH 44106-7220
Private
Admissions: (216) 368-4390
E-mail: gradadmit@po.cwru.edu
Web site:
http://www.case.cwru.edu/
Financial aid: (216) 368-4530
Application deadline: rolling
Tuition: full time: $16,884; part
time: $938/credit hour
Room/board/expenses: N/A
Full-time enrollment: 380
men: 76%; women: 24%;
minorities: 7%; international: 61%
Part-time enrollment: 249
men: 76%; women: 24%;
minorities: 12%; international: 39%
Acceptance rate: 22%
GRE requirement: YES
Avg. GRE: quantitative: 771;
analytical 712
TOEFL requirement: YES
Minimum TOEFL score: 550
Fellowships: 253
Teaching assistantships: 133
Research assistantships: 244
Students reporting specialty: 88%

Students specializing in: aerospace: 1%; biomedical: 26%;
chemical: 8%; civil: 3%; computer:
13%; electrical: 13%; materials:
10%; mechanical: 14%; other:
11%

Cleveland State University[1]

1960 E. 24th Street
SH 104
Cleveland, OH 44115-2425
Public
Admissions: (216) 687-5599
E-mail: graduate.admissions@
csuohio.edu
Web site: http://www.csuohio.edu/
engineering/
Internet application: http://www.
csuohio.edu/gradcollege/
Financial aid: (216) 687-3764
Tuition: N/A
Room/board/expenses: N/A
Enrollment: N/A

Ohio State University

2070 Neil Avenue
Columbus, OH 43210-1278
Public
Admissions: (614) 292-9444
E-mail: admissions@osu.edu
Web site:
http://www.eng.ohio-state.edu
Internet application:
http://gradapply.osu.edu
Financial aid: (614) 292-0300
Application deadline: 08/15
In-state tuition: full time: $9,168;
part time: N/A
Out-of-state tuition: full time:
$22,596
Room/board/expenses: $15,842
Full-time enrollment: 1,064
men: 82%; women: 18%;
minorities: 5%; international: 70%
Part-time enrollment: 222
men: 79%; women: 21%;
minorities: 8%; international: 53%
Acceptance rate: 30%
GRE requirement: YES
Avg. GRE: quantitative: 769;
analytical 715
TOEFL requirement: YES
Minimum TOEFL score: 550
Fellowships: 150
Teaching assistantships: 134
Research assistantships: 625
Students reporting specialty: 100%
Students specializing in: aero-
space: 1%; agriculture: 2%; biomedical: 3%; chemical: 7%; civil:
6%; computer: 13%; electrical:
26%; industrial: 12%; materials:
7%; mechanical: 14%; nuclear:
2%; other: 7%

Ohio University

150 Stocker Center
Athens, OH 45701
Public
Admissions: (740) 593-2800
E-mail: gradstu@www.ohiou.edu
Web site:
http://www.ent.ohiou.edu
Internet application: http://www.
ohio.edu/graduate/reqform.htm
Financial aid: (740) 593-4141
Application deadline: rolling
In-state tuition: full time: $7,607;
part time: $299/credit hour
Out-of-state tuition: full time:
$14,277
Room/board/expenses: $8,599
Full-time enrollment: 277
men: 79%; women: 21%;
minorities: 2%; international: 77%
Part-time enrollment: 54
men: 80%; women: 20%;
minorities: 2%; international: 80%

Acceptance rate: 67%
GRE requirement: NO
Avg. GRE: quantitative: N/A;
analytical N/A
TOEFL requirement: YES
Minimum TOEFL score: 550
Fellowships: 30
Teaching assistantships: 74
Research assistantships: 105
Students reporting specialty: 95%
Students specializing in: chemical:
7%; civil: 7%; electrical: 37%; in-
dustrial: 13%; mechanical: 19%;
other: 16%

University of Akron

201 ASEC
Akron, OH 44325-3901
Public
Admissions: (330) 972-7663
E-mail: gradschool@uakron.edu
Web site:
http://www.ecgf.uakron.edu
Internet application:
http://www.uakron.edu/gradsch
Financial aid: (330) 972-6405
Application deadline: 07/19
In-state tuition: full time:
$253/credit hour; part time:
$253/credit hour
Out-of-state tuition: full time:
$433/credit hour
Room/board/expenses: $9,504
Full-time enrollment: 185
men: 79%; women: 21%;
minorities: 4%; international: 78%
Part-time enrollment: 105
men: 81%; women: 19%;
minorities: 7%; international: 27%
Acceptance rate: 44%
GRE requirement: YES
Avg. GRE: quantitative: 747;
analytical 680
TOEFL requirement: YES
Minimum TOEFL score: 550
Fellowships: 0
Teaching assistantships: 104
Research assistantships: 50
Students reporting specialty: 100%
Students specializing in: biomed-
ical: 6%; chemical: 9%; civil: 10%;
electrical: 10%; mechanical: 17%;
other: 49%

University of Cincinnati

PO Box 210018
Cincinnati, OH 45221-0018
Public
Admissions: (513) 556-5157
E-mail: Shirley.Freeman@uc.edu
Web site: http://www.eng.uc.edu
Internet application: http://www.
grad.uc.edu/content/gradapp.cfm
Financial aid: (513) 556-6982
Application deadline: rolling
In-state tuition: full time: $10,792;
part time: $276/credit hour
Out-of-state tuition: full time:
$19,908
Room/board/expenses: $11,919
Full-time enrollment: 919
men: 80%; women: 20%;
minorities: 2%; international: 68%
Part-time enrollment: 247
men: 80%; women: 20%;
minorities: 2%; international: 63%
Acceptance rate: 28%
GRE requirement: YES
Avg. GRE: quantitative: 762;
analytical 733
TOEFL requirement: YES
Minimum TOEFL score: 550
Fellowships: 17
Teaching assistantships: 104
Research assistantships: 523
Students reporting specialty: 90%

Students specializing in: aerospace: 8%; biomedical: 1%; chemical: 5%; civil: 7%; computer: 21%;
electrical: 21%; environmental:
8%; industrial: 11%; materials:
10%; mechanical: 7%; nuclear: 2%

University of Dayton

300 College Park
Dayton, OH 45469-0228
Private
Admissions: (937) 229-2390
E-mail: nancy.wilson@
notes.udayton.edu
Web site: http://www.udayton.
edu/~gradsch/main.htm
Financial aid: (937) 229-4311
Application deadline: rolling
Tuition: full time: N/A; part time:
N/A
Room/board/expenses: $9,100
Full-time enrollment: 276
men: 79%; women: 21%;
minorities: 0%; international: 0%
Part-time enrollment: 127
men: 80%; women: 20%;
minorities: 0%; international: 0%
Acceptance rate: 78%
GRE requirement: NO
Avg. GRE: quantitative: N/A;
analytical N/A
TOEFL requirement: YES
Minimum TOEFL score: 550
Fellowships: 4
Teaching assistantships: 10
Research assistantships: 81
Students reporting specialty: 100%
Students specializing in: aero-
space: 1%; chemical: 5%; civil:
4%; electrical: 18%; materials:
10%; mechanical: 16%; other:
46%

University of Toledo

2801 W. Bancroft
Toledo, OH 43606
Public
Admissions: (419) 530-4723
E-mail: gradoff@eng.utoledo.edu
Web site:
http://www.eng.utoledo.edu/grad
Internet application:
http://www.utoledo.edu/
grad-school/application.html
Financial aid: (419) 530-8700
Application deadline: rolling
In-state tuition: full time: $8,323;
part time: $346/credit hour
Out-of-state tuition: full time:
$15,730
Room/board/expenses: $9,919
Full-time enrollment: 389
men: 80%; women: 20%;
minorities: 2%; international: 77%
Part-time enrollment: 25
men: 92%; women: 8%;
minorities: 4%; international: 4%
Acceptance rate: 39%
GRE requirement: YES
Avg. GRE: quantitative: 768;
analytical 676
TOEFL requirement: YES
Minimum TOEFL score: 550
Fellowships: 4
Teaching assistantships: 116
Research assistantships: 96
Students reporting specialty: 100%
Students specializing in: biomed-
ical: 9%; chemical: 10%; civil:
15%; computer: 12%; electrical:
18%; industrial: 7%; mechanical:
24%; other: 5%

Wright State University

3640 Colonel Glenn Highway
Dayton, OH 45435
Public
Admissions: (937) 775-2976
E-mail: wsugrad@wright.edu
Web site:
http://www.wright.edu/sogs/
Financial aid: (937) 775-5721
Application deadline: rolling
In-state tuition: full time: $7,161;
part time: $225/credit hour
Out-of-state tuition: full time:
$12,324
Room/board/expenses: $11,508
Full-time enrollment: 478
men: 75%; women: 25%;
minorities: 4%; international: 77%
Part-time enrollment: 140
men: 84%; women: 16%;
minorities: 3%; international: 24%
Acceptance rate: 79%
GRE requirement: YES
Avg. GRE: quantitative: 719;
analytical 645
TOEFL requirement: YES
Minimum TOEFL score: 550
Fellowships: 110
Teaching assistantships: 30
Research assistantships: 93
Students reporting specialty: 100%
Students specializing in: biomed-
ical: 6%; computer: 31%; electri-
cal: 35%; industrial: 8%; materials:
1%; mechanical: 9%; other: 10%

OKLAHOMA

Oklahoma State University

111 Engineering North
Stillwater, OK 74078-0535
Public
Admissions: (405) 744-6368
E-mail: grad-i@okstate.edu
Web site: http://www.
osu-ours.okstate.edu/gradcoll
Internet application: http://www.
osu-ours.okstate.edu/
gradcoll/apply
Financial aid: (405) 744-6604
Application deadline: 03/01
In-state tuition: full time: $98/credit
hour; part time: $98/credit hour
Out-of-state tuition: full time:
$318/credit hour
Room/board/expenses: $8,940
Full-time enrollment: 1,033
men: 83%; women: 17%;
minorities: 6%; international: 67%
Part-time enrollment: N/A
men: N/A; women: N/A;
minorities: N/A; international: N/A
Acceptance rate: 52%
GRE requirement: YES
Avg. GRE: quantitative: 767;
analytical 707
TOEFL requirement: YES
Minimum TOEFL score: 550
Fellowships: 11
Teaching assistantships: 177
Research assistantships: 199
Students reporting specialty: 100%
Students specializing in: aero-
space: 2%; agriculture: 3%; chem-
ical: 4%; civil: 4%; computer: 18%;
electrical: 24%; environmental:
2%; industrial: 27%; mechanical:
15%

University of Oklahoma

202 W. Boyd
CEC 107
Norman, OK 73019
Public
Admissions: (405) 325-2252
E-mail: admrec@ou.edu
Web site: http://www.coe.ou.edu
Internet application:
http://www.ou.edu/admrec
Financial aid: (405) 325-5505
Application deadline: 06/01
In-state tuition: full time:
$118/credit hour; part time:
$118/credit hour
Out-of-state tuition: full time:
$342/credit hour
Room/board/expenses: $12,610
Full-time enrollment: 509
men: 82%; women: 18%;
minorities: N/A; international: N/A
Part-time enrollment: 156
men: 82%; women: 18%;
minorities: N/A; international: N/A
Acceptance rate: 69%
GRE requirement: YES
Avg. GRE: quantitative: 725;
analytical 637
TOEFL requirement: YES
Minimum TOEFL score: 550
Fellowships: 56
Teaching assistantships: 101
Research assistantships: 283
Students reporting specialty: 100%
Students specializing in: aero-
space: 1%; chemical: 8%; civil:
7%; computer: 28%; electrical:
18%; environmental: 3%;
industrial: 14%; mechanical: 12%;
petroleum: 9%; other: 1%

University of Tulsa

600 S. College Avenue
Tulsa, OK 74104-3189
Private
Admissions: (918) 631-2336
E-mail: grad@utulsa.edu
Web site: http://www.utulsa.edu
Internet application:
http://www.utulsa.edu/graduate
Financial aid: (918) 631-2526
Application deadline: rolling
Tuition: full time: $560/credit hour;
part time: $560/credit hour
Room/board/expenses: $7,686
Full-time enrollment: 161
men: 85%; women: 15%;
minorities: 5%; international: 60%
Part-time enrollment: 97
men: 87%; women: 13%;
minorities: 4%; international: 79%
Acceptance rate: 61%
GRE requirement: YES
Avg. GRE: quantitative: 716;
analytical 632
TOEFL requirement: YES
Minimum TOEFL score: 550
Fellowships: 13
Teaching assistantships: 35
Research assistantships: 78
Students reporting specialty: 100%
Students specializing in: chemical:
12%; computer: 40%;
electrical: 14%; mechanical: 14%;
petroleum: 21%

OREGON

OGI School of Science and Engineering– Oregon Health and Science University

20000 N.W. Walker Road
Beaverton, OR 97006-8921
Private
Admissions: (503) 748-1027
E-mail:
admissions@admin.ogi.edu
Web site: http://www.ogi.edu
Internet application: http://www.
ogi.edu/forms/application.html
Financial aid: (503) 494-5117
Application deadline: rolling
Tuition: full time: $20,196; part
time: $561/credit hour
Room/board/expenses: $13,775

Full-time enrollment: 179
men: 69%; women: 31%;
minorities: 26%; international: 36%
Part-time enrollment: 158
men: 78%; women: 22%;
minorities: 15%; international: 9%
Acceptance rate: 37%
GRE requirement: YES
Avg. GRE: quantitative: 744;
analytical 683
TOEFL requirement: YES
Minimum TOEFL score: 600
Fellowships: 0
Teaching assistantships: 24
Research assistantships: 71
Students reporting specialty: 100%
Students specializing in: biomed-
ical: 8%; computer: 38%; electri-
cal: 28%; environmental: 7%;
other: 18%

Oregon State University

101 Covell Hall
Corvallis, OR 97331-2409
Public
Admissions: (541) 737-4411
E-mail: osuadmit@orst.edu
Web site:
http://engr.oregonstate.edu/
Internet application:
http://oregonstate.edu/admissions
Financial aid: (541) 737-2241
Application deadline: 02/01
In-state tuition: full time: $9,249;
part time: $310/credit hour
Out-of-state tuition: full time:
$14,454
Room/board/expenses: $9,135
Full-time enrollment: 482
men: 82%; women: 18%;
minorities: 7%; international: 62%
Part-time enrollment: 95
men: 80%; women: 20%;
minorities: 0%; international: 63%
Acceptance rate: 33%
GRE requirement: YES
Avg. GRE: quantitative: 756;
analytical 675
TOEFL requirement: YES
Minimum TOEFL score: 550
Fellowships: 22
Teaching assistantships: 72
Research assistantships: 134
Students reporting specialty: 100%
Students specializing in: biomed-
ical: 8%; chemical: 5%; civil: 10%;
computer: 22%; electrical: 32%;
industrial: 9%; materials: 2%;
mechanical: 11%; nuclear: 3%;
other: 1%

Portland State University

PO Box 751
Portland, OR 97207
Public
Admissions: (503) 725-3511
E-mail: cecsdept@cecs.pdx.edu
Web site: http://www.cecs.pdx.edu
Internet application:
http://www.ess.pdx.edu/adm
Financial aid: (503) 725-3461
Application deadline: rolling
In-state tuition: full time: $7,212;
part time: $230/credit hour
Out-of-state tuition: full time:
$12,228
Room/board/expenses: $10,875
Full-time enrollment: 291
men: 76%; women: 24%;
minorities: 9%; international: 67%
Part-time enrollment: 200
men: 77%; women: 23%;
minorities: 20%; international: 31%
Acceptance rate: 80%
GRE requirement: YES
Avg. GRE: quantitative: 691;
analytical 590
TOEFL requirement: YES

Minimum TOEFL score: 550
Fellowships: 0
Teaching assistantships: 49
Research assistantships: 27
Students reporting specialty: 100%
Students specializing in: civil: 8%;
computer: 23%; electrical: 42%;
industrial: 0%; mechanical: 7%;
other: 20%

PENNSYLVANIA

Carnegie Mellon University

5000 Forbes Avenue
Pittsburgh, PA 15213
Private
Admissions: (412) 268-2478
E-mail: garrett@cmu.edu
Web site: http://www.cit.cmu.edu/
Internet application:
http://www.cit.cmu.edu/grad
Financial aid: (412) 268-2482
Application deadline: 12/01
Tuition: full time: $26,582; part
time: $1,099/credit hour
Room/board/expenses: $18,190
Full-time enrollment: 1,134
men: 78%; women: 22%;
minorities: 8%; international: 57%
Part-time enrollment: 250
men: 78%; women: 22%;
minorities: 3%; international: 39%
Acceptance rate: 20%
GRE requirement: YES
Avg. GRE: quantitative: 766;
analytical 718
TOEFL requirement: YES
Minimum TOEFL score: N/A
Fellowships: 87
Teaching assistantships: 65
Research assistantships: 617
Students reporting specialty: 100%
Students specializing in: biomed-
ical: 1%; chemical: 8%; civil: 5%;
computer: 42%; electrical: 23%;
materials: 5%; mechanical: 6%;
other: 10%

Drexel University

32nd and Chestnut Streets
Philadelphia, PA 19104
Private
Admissions: (215) 895-6700
E-mail: admissions@drexel.edu
Web site:
http://www.drexel.edu/coe
Internet application:
http://apply.drexel.starcomm.com
Financial aid: (215) 895-2964
Application deadline: 08/15
Tuition: full time: $20,005; part
time: $667/credit hour
Room/board/expenses: $16,400
Full-time enrollment: 259
men: 73%; women: 27%;
minorities: 7%; international: 66%
Part-time enrollment: 414
men: 82%; women: 18%;
minorities: 13%; international: 21%
Acceptance rate: 53%
GRE requirement: YES
Avg. GRE: quantitative: 760;
analytical 687
TOEFL requirement: YES
Minimum TOEFL score: 560
Fellowships: 15
Teaching assistantships: 100
Research assistantships: 162
Students reporting specialty: 100%
Students specializing in: biomed-
ical: 9%; chemical: 5%; civil: 7%;
computer: 16%; electrical: 24%;
environmental: 4%; materials: 9%;
mechanical: 12%; other: 14%

Lehigh University

19 Memorial Drive W
Bethlehem, PA 18015
Private
Admissions: (610) 758-6310
E-mail: ineas@lehigh.edu
Web site: http://www3.
lehigh.edu/engineering
Internet application:
http://www3.lehigh.edu/
engineering/admissions/
gradadmission.asp
Financial aid: (610) 758-3181
Application deadline: 01/15
Tuition: full time: $920/credit hour;
part time: $920/credit hour
Room/board/expenses: $12,335
Full-time enrollment: 407
men: 79%; women: 21%;
minorities: 5%; international: 57%
Part-time enrollment: 134
men: 72%; women: 28%;
minorities: 16%; international: 3%
Acceptance rate: 20%
GRE requirement: YES
Avg. GRE: quantitative: 764;
analytical 701
TOEFL requirement: YES
Minimum TOEFL score: 550
Fellowships: 55
Teaching assistantships: 73
Research assistantships: 230
Students reporting specialty: 100%
Students specializing in: chemical:
22%; civil: 13%; computer: 11%;
electrical: 11%; environmental:
1%; industrial: 18%; materials: 9%;
mechanical: 13%

Pennsylvania State University– University Park

College of Engineering
Hammond Building 101
University Park, PA 16802
Public
Admissions: (814) 865-1795
E-mail: gadm@psu.edu
Web site: http://www.engr.psu.edu
Financial aid: (814) 865-2514
Application deadline: rolling
In-state tuition: full time: $9,894;
part time: $378/credit hour
Out-of-state tuition: full time:
$19,272
Room/board/expenses: $6,640
Full-time enrollment: 1,390
men: 80%; women: 20%;
minorities: 3%; international: 64%
Part-time enrollment: 240
men: 83%; women: 17%;
minorities: 2%; international: 49%
Acceptance rate: 25%
GRE requirement: YES
Avg. GRE: quantitative: 755;
analytical 687
TOEFL requirement: YES
Minimum TOEFL score: 550
Fellowships: 254
Teaching assistantships: 370
Research assistantships: 583
Students reporting specialty: 100%
Students specializing in: aerospace: 4%; agriculture: 2%; biomedical: 3%; chemical: 4%; civil:
7%; computer: 11%; electrical:
16%; environmental: 3%; industri-
al: 9%; materials: 12%; mechani-
cal: 11%; mining: 0%; nuclear:
2%; petroleum: 1%; other: 14%

Temple University

1947 N. 12th Street
Philadelphia, PA 19122
Public
Admissions: (215) 204-8403
E-mail:
gradengr@blue.temple.edu

Web site:
http://www.eng.temple.edu
Internet application:
http://www.temple.edu/grad
Financial aid: (215) 204-1405
Application deadline: 07/01
In-state tuition: full time:
$402/credit hour; part time:
$402/credit hour
Out-of-state tuition: full time:
$582/credit hour
Room/board/expenses: $10,000
Full-time enrollment: 73
men: 68%; women: 32%;
minorities: 0%; international: 0%
Part-time enrollment: 34
men: 82%; women: 18%;
minorities: 0%; international: 0%
Acceptance rate: 47%
GRE requirement: YES
Avg. GRE: quantitative: N/A;
analytical N/A
TOEFL requirement: YES
Minimum TOEFL score: 575
Fellowships: 0
Teaching assistantships: 24
Research assistantships: 15
Students reporting specialty: 100%
Students specializing in: civil: 21%;
electrical: 65%; mechanical: 14%

University of Pennsylvania

107 Towne Building
Philadelphia, PA 19104
Private
Admissions: (215) 898-4542
E-mail:
engadmis@seas.upenn.edu
Web site:
http://www.seas.upenn.edu/grad
Financial aid: (215) 898-1988
Application deadline: rolling
Tuition: full time: $29,068; part
time: $3,672/credit hour
Room/board/expenses: $16,355
Full-time enrollment: 641
men: 75%; women: 25%;
minorities: 14%; international: 59%
Part-time enrollment: 438
men: 80%; women: 20%;
minorities: 20%; international: 23%
Acceptance rate: 31%
GRE requirement: YES
Avg. GRE: quantitative: 753;
analytical 696
TOEFL requirement: YES
Minimum TOEFL score: 600
Fellowships: 19
Teaching assistantships: 9
Research assistantships: 305
Students reporting specialty: 100%
Students specializing in: biomed-
ical: 18%; chemical: 6%; comput-
er: 25%; electrical: 10%; materials:
5%; mechanical: 7%; other: 28%

University of Pittsburgh

240 Benedum Hall
Pittsburgh, PA 15261
Public
Admissions: (412) 624-9800
E-mail: admin@engrng.pitt.edu
Web site: http://www.engr.pitt.edu
Financial aid: (412) 624-7488
Application deadline: 08/01
In-state tuition: full time: $12,874;
part time: $589/credit hour
Out-of-state tuition: full time:
$25,030
Room/board/expenses: $11,680
Full-time enrollment: 434
men: 76%; women: 24%;
minorities: 6%; international: 56%
Part-time enrollment: 237
men: 82%; women: 18%;
minorities: 8%; international: 9%
Acceptance rate: 31%
GRE requirement: YES

Avg. GRE: quantitative: 756;
analytical 704
TOEFL requirement: YES
Minimum TOEFL score: 550
Fellowships: 18
Teaching assistantships: 88
Research assistantships: 244
Students reporting specialty: 100%
Students specializing in: biomed-
ical: 15%; chemical: 9%; civil:
13%; computer: 13%; electrical:
20%; industrial: 12%; materials:
6%; mechanical: 12%

Brown University

Box D
Providence, RI 02912
Private
Admissions: (401) 863-2600
E-mail:
admission_graduate@brown.edu
Web site:
http://www.engin.brown.edu/
Internet application:
https://apply.embark.com/
Grad/Brown/60/
Financial aid: (401) 863-3184
Application deadline: rolling
Tuition: full time: $28,527; part
time: $7,635
Room/board/expenses: $10,663
Full-time enrollment: 175
men: 81%; women: 19%;
minorities: 6%; international: 71%
Part-time enrollment: 6
men: 100%; women: 0%;
minorities: 17%; international: 17%
Acceptance rate: 18%
GRE requirement: NO
Avg. GRE: quantitative: N/A;
analytical N/A
TOEFL requirement: YES
Minimum TOEFL score: 600
Fellowships: 28
Teaching assistantships: 20
Research assistantships: 94
Students reporting specialty: 100%
Students specializing in: computer:
42%; other: 58%

University of Rhode Island

102 Bliss Hall
Kingston, RI 02881
Public
Admissions: (401) 874-2872
E-mail: tpj101@uriacc.uri.edu
Web site:
http://www.uri.edu/gsadmis
Financial aid: (401) 874-2314
Application deadline: 07/15
In-state tuition: full time: $5,820;
part time: $225/credit hour
Out-of-state tuition: full time:
$13,390
Room/board/expenses: $8,528
Full-time enrollment: 75
men: 80%; women: 20%;
minorities: 3%; international: 61%
Part-time enrollment: 86
men: 90%; women: 10%;
minorities: 5%; international: 23%
Acceptance rate: 34%
GRE requirement: YES
Avg. GRE: quantitative: 760;
analytical 680
TOEFL requirement: YES
Minimum TOEFL score: 575
Fellowships: 0
Teaching assistantships: 29
Research assistantships: 20
Students reporting specialty: 100%
Students specializing in: chemical:
11%; civil: 19%; electrical: 30%; in-
dustrial: 9%; mechanical: 20%;
other: 10%

Clemson University

Room 109
Riggs Hall
Clemson, SC 29634
Public
Admissions: (864) 656-3195
E-mail: grdapp@clemson.edu
Web site:
http://www.ces.clemson.edu/
Internet application:
http://www.grad.clemson.edu/
Financial aid: (864) 656-2280
Application deadline: rolling
In-state tuition: full time: $6,494;
part time: $300/credit hour
Out-of-state tuition: full time:
$13,342
Room/board/expenses: $9,056
Full-time enrollment: 761
men: 77%; women: 23%;
minorities: 3%; international: 60%
Part-time enrollment: 97
men: 71%; women: 29%;
minorities: 5%; international: 34%
Acceptance rate: 44%
GRE requirement: YES
Avg. GRE: quantitative: 731;
analytical 656
TOEFL requirement: YES
Minimum TOEFL score: 500
Fellowships: 23
Teaching assistantships: 209
Research assistantships: 361
Students reporting specialty: 100%
Students specializing in: agricul-
ture: 1%; biomedical: 7%; chemi-
cal: 5%; civil: 8%; computer: 21%;
electrical: 17%; environmental:
10%; industrial: 7%; materials:
10%; mechanical: 14%

University of South Carolina

Swearingen Engineering Center
Columbia, SC 29208
Public
Admissions: (803) 777-4177
E-mail: info@engr.sc.edu
Web site: http://www.engr.sc.edu
Internet application:
http://www.gradschool.sc.edu
Financial aid: (803) 777-8134
Application deadline: rolling
In-state tuition: full time: $5,560;
part time: $266/credit hour
Out-of-state tuition: full time:
$11,848
Room/board/expenses: $8,300
Full-time enrollment: 396
men: 76%; women: 24%;
minorities: 5%; international: 79%
Part-time enrollment: 148
men: 87%; women: 13%;
minorities: 5%; international: 21%
Acceptance rate: 38%
GRE requirement: YES
Avg. GRE: quantitative: N/A;
analytical N/A
TOEFL requirement: YES
Minimum TOEFL score: 570
Fellowships: 15
Teaching assistantships: 56
Research assistantships: 234
Students reporting specialty: 100%
Students specializing in: chemical:
13%; civil: 9%; computer: 34%;
electrical: 24%; environmental:
4%; mechanical: 15%

South Dakota School of Mines and Technology

501 E. St. Joseph Street
Rapid City, SD 57701-3995
Public
Admissions: (605) 394-2493
E-mail:
graduate.admissions@sdsmt.edu
Web site: http://www.sdsmt.edu/
Financial aid: (605) 394-2400
Application deadline: 08/15
In-state tuition: full time: $99/credit
hour; part time: $99/credit hour
Out-of-state tuition: full time:
$291/credit hour
Room/board/expenses: $4,070
Full-time enrollment: 344
men: 76%; women: 24%;
minorities: 0%; international: 47%
Part-time enrollment: 9
men: 89%; women: 11%;
minorities: 0%; international: 0%
GRE requirement: YES
Avg. GRE: quantitative: N/A;
analytical N/A
TOEFL requirement: YES
Minimum TOEFL score: 520
Students reporting specialty: N/A
Students specializing in: N/A

South Dakota State University

College of Engineering
PO Box 2219
Brookings, SD 57007
Public
Admissions: (605) 688-4181
E-mail:
gradschl@adm.sdstate.edu
Web site: http://www3.sdstate.edu/
Internet application: http://www3.
sdstate.edu/Academics/
GraduateSchool/Index.cfm
Financial aid: (605) 688-4695
Application deadline: 06/16
In-state tuition: full time: $99/credit
hour; part time: $99/credit hour
Out-of-state tuition: full time:
$291/credit hour
Room/board/expenses: $4,392
Full-time enrollment: 176
men: 81%; women: 19%;
minorities: 3%; international: 61%
Part-time enrollment: 11.
men: 64%; women: 36%;
minorities: 9%; international: 0%
Acceptance rate: 75%
GRE requirement: NO
Avg. GRE: quantitative: N/A;
analytical N/A
TOEFL requirement: YES
Minimum TOEFL score: 550
Fellowships: 1
Teaching assistantships: 30
Research assistantships: 34
Students reporting specialty: 97%
Students specializing in: agricul-
ture: 3%; civil: 24%; computer:
25%; electrical: 20%; industrial:
19%; mechanical: 9%

Tennessee Tech University

N. Dixie Avenue
Cookeville, TN 38505
Public
Admissions: (931) 372-3233
E-mail: g_admissions@tntech.edu
Web site: http://www.
tntech.edu/www/acad/eng/
engineering.html

Internet application: http://www.
tntech.edu/www/academics.html
Financial aid: (931) 372-3073
Application deadline: 08/01
In-state tuition: full time: $4,852;
part time: $228/credit hour
Out-of-state tuition: full time:
$11,810
Room/board/expenses: $9,558
Full-time enrollment: 107
men: 83%; women: 17%;
minorities: 4%; international: 69%
Part-time enrollment: 56
men: 89%; women: 11%;
minorities: 0%; international: 54%
Acceptance rate: 40%
GRE requirement: YES
Avg. GRE: quantitative: 730;
analytical 640
TOEFL requirement: YES
Minimum TOEFL score: 550
Fellowships: 2
Teaching assistantships: 0
Research assistantships: 81
Students reporting specialty: 100%
Students specializing in: chemical:
12%; civil: 17%; electrical: 31%;
industrial: 1%; mechanical: 39%

University of Memphis

Herff College of Engineering
Memphis, TN 38152
Public
Admissions: (901) 678-2911
E-mail: mejanna@cc.memphis.edu
Web site:
http://www.memphis.edu/
Financial aid: (901) 678-4825
Application deadline: N/A
In-state tuition: full time: $2,251;
part time: $250/credit hour
Out-of-state tuition: full time:
$5,828
Room/board/expenses: $9,376
Full-time enrollment: 268
men: 81%; women: 19%;
minorities: 5%; international: 87%
Part-time enrollment: 59
men: 80%; women: 20%;
minorities: 2%; international: 54%
Acceptance rate: 87%
GRE requirement: YES
Avg. GRE: quantitative: 722;
analytical 589
TOEFL requirement: YES
Minimum TOEFL score: 550
Teaching assistantships: 9
Research assistantships: 63
Students reporting specialty: 100%
Students specializing in: biomed-
ical: 17%; civil: 7%; electrical:
23%; industrial: 10%; mechanical:
15%; other: 28%

University of Tennessee

124 Perkins Hall
Knoxville, TN 37996-2000
Public
Admissions: (865) 974-3251
E-mail: gsinfo@utk.edu
Web site:
http://web.utk.edu/~gsinfo/
Internet application:
http://admissions.utk.edu/
graduate/apply.shtml
Financial aid: (865) 974-3131
Application deadline: rolling
In-state tuition: full time: $5,850;
part time: $249/credit hour
Out-of-state tuition: full time:
$14,202
Room/board/expenses: $10,350
Full-time enrollment: 378
men: 79%; women: 21%;
minorities: 4%; international: 54%
Part-time enrollment: 360
men: 80%; women: 20%;
minorities: 7%; international: 25%
Acceptance rate: 34%

GRE requirement: YES
Avg. GRE: quantitative: 716;
analytical 651
TOEFL requirement: YES
Minimum TOEFL score: 550
Fellowships: 18
Teaching assistantships: 156
Research assistantships: 284
Students reporting specialty: 88%
Students specializing in: aero-
space: 1%; agriculture: 4%; chem-
ical: 5%; civil: 16%; computer:
15%; electrical: 18%; environmen-
tal: 5%; industrial: 4%; materials:
11%; mechanical: 6%; nuclear:
9%; other: 6%

Vanderbilt University
VU Station B 351826
2301 Vanderbilt Place
Nashville, TN 37235
Private
Admissions: (615) 322-2651
E-mail:
terry.owens@vanderbilt.edu
Web site: http://frontweb.vuse.
vanderbilt.edu/vuse_web
Internet application: http://www.
vanderbilt.edu/gradschool/
application_and_information.htm
Financial aid: (615) 322-3591
Application deadline: 01/15
Tuition: full time: $20,068; part
time: $1,100/credit hour
Room/board/expenses: $12,960
Full-time enrollment: 327
men: 70%; women: 30%;
minorities: 10%; international: 49%
Part-time enrollment: 21
men: 81%; women: 19%;
minorities: 5%; international: 29%
Acceptance rate: 30%
GRE requirement: YES
Avg. GRE: quantitative: 754;
analytical 698
TOEFL requirement: YES
Minimum TOEFL score: 550
Fellowships: 32
Teaching assistantships: 145
Research assistantships: 169
Students reporting specialty: 96%
Students specializing in: biomed-
ical: 14%; chemical: 8%; civil: 9%;
computer: 18%; electrical: 28%;
environmental: 6%; materials: 1%;
mechanical: 11%; other: 5%

TEXAS

Lamar University
4400 Martin Luther King Parkway
Beaumont, TX 77710
Public
Admissions: (409) 880-8888
E-mail: admissions@hal.lamar.edu
Web site: http://www.
lamar.edu/lamar/colleges/
engineering/index.html
Financial aid: (409) 880-8450
Application deadline: rolling
In-state tuition: full time: $2,468;
part time: $78/credit hour
Out-of-state tuition: full time:
$7,484
Room/board/expenses: $5,634
Full-time enrollment: 450
men: 88%; women: 12%;
minorities: 1%; international: 98%
Part-time enrollment: 82
men: 84%; women: 16%;
minorities: 4%; international: 84%
Acceptance rate: 64%
GRE requirement: YES
Avg. GRE: quantitative: 725;
analytical 587
TOEFL requirement: YES
Minimum TOEFL score: 525
Fellowships: 10
Teaching assistantships: 17
Research assistantships: 32
Students reporting specialty: 100%

Students specializing in: chemical:
15%; civil: 12%; computer: 40%;
electrical: 11%; industrial: 13%;
mechanical: 9%

Rice University
6100 Main Street, MS 364
Houston, TX 77005
Private
Admissions: (713) 348-4002
E-mail: grbsoe@rice.edu
Web site: http://engr.rice.edu
Internet application:
http://rgs.rice.edu/Grad/
Admissions/Application
Financial aid: (713) 348-4958
Application deadline: 02/01
Tuition: full time: $18,963; part
time: $1,030/credit hour
Room/board/expenses: $10,580
Full-time enrollment: 443
men: 75%; women: 25%;
minorities: 13%; international: 52%
Part-time enrollment: 31
men: 68%; women: 32%;
minorities: 23%; international: 26%
Acceptance rate: 11%
GRE requirement: YES
Avg. GRE: quantitative: 755;
analytical 698
TOEFL requirement: YES
Minimum TOEFL score: 600
Fellowships: 245
Teaching assistantships: 16
Research assistantships: 218
Students reporting specialty: 100%
Students specializing in: biomed-
ical: 15%; chemical: 11%; civil:
3%; computer: 15%; electrical:
21%; environmental: 3%; materi-
als: 0%; mechanical: 12%; other:
19%

Southern Methodist University
3145 Dyer Street
Dallas, TX 75275-0335
Private
Admissions: (214) 768-3484
E-mail: valerin@engr.smu.edu
Web site:
http://www.engr.smu.edu
Financial aid: (214) 768-3484
Application deadline: 07/04
Tuition: full time: $567/credit hour;
part time: $567/credit hour
Room/board/expenses: $12,330
Full-time enrollment: 221
men: 82%; women: 18%;
minorities: 13%; international: 73%
Part-time enrollment: 594
men: 78%; women: 22%;
minorities: 32%; international: 10%
Acceptance rate: 68%
GRE requirement: YES
Avg. GRE: quantitative: 731;
analytical N/A
TOEFL requirement: YES
Minimum TOEFL score: 550
Fellowships: 0
Teaching assistantships: 34
Research assistantships: 42
Students reporting specialty: 99%
Students specializing in: civil: 0%;
computer: 27%; electrical: 39%;
environmental: 2%; industrial: 3%;
mechanical: 4%; other: 25%

Texas A&M University– College Station
301 Wisenbaker Research
Center
3126 TAMU
College Station, TX 77843
Public
Admissions: (979) 845-7200
E-mail: eapo@tamu.edu

Web site:
http://www.tamu.edu/admissions
Financial aid: (979) 845-3236
Application deadline: rolling
In-state tuition: full time: $3,854;
part time: $2,666
Out-of-state tuition: full time:
$7,778
Room/board/expenses: $11,804
Full-time enrollment: 1,824
men: 84%; women: 16%;
minorities: 4%; international: 80%
Part-time enrollment: 319
men: 81%; women: 19%;
minorities: 10%; international: 55%
Acceptance rate: 29%
GRE requirement: YES
Avg. GRE: quantitative: 754;
analytical 661
TOEFL requirement: YES
Minimum TOEFL score: 550
Fellowships: 256
Teaching assistantships: 253
Research assistantships: 954
Students reporting specialty: 100%
Students specializing in: aero-
space: 4%; agriculture: 2%; bio-
medical: 3%; chemical: 2%; civil:
13%; computer: 14%; electrical:
15%; industrial: 12%; mechanical:
17%; nuclear: 3%; petroleum: 7%;
other: 2%

Texas Tech University
MS 43103
Lubbock, TX 79409-3103
Public
Admissions: (806) 742-2787
E-mail: gradschool@ttu.edu
Web site: http://www.coe.ttu.edu
Internet application:
http://www.ttu.edu/gradschool
Financial aid: (806) 742-3681
Application deadline: 03/01
In-state tuition: full time:
$126/credit hour; part time:
$126/credit hour
Out-of-state tuition: full time:
$344/credit hour
Room/board/expenses: $6,597
Full-time enrollment: 446
men: 84%; women: 16%;
minorities: 5%; international: 71%
Part-time enrollment: 132
men: 83%; women: 17%;
minorities: 9%; international: 42%
Acceptance rate: 31%
GRE requirement: YES
Avg. GRE: quantitative: 723;
analytical 638
TOEFL requirement: YES
Minimum TOEFL score: 550
Teaching assistantships: 33
Research assistantships: 245
Students reporting specialty: 100%
Students specializing in: chemical:
6%; civil: 16%; computer: 19%;
electrical: 24%; industrial: 13%;
mechanical: 12%; petroleum: 3%;
other: 6%

University of Houston
E421 Engineering Building 2
Houston, TX 77204-4007
Public
Admissions: (713) 743-4205
E-mail: grad-admit@egr.uh.edu
Web site: http://www.egr.uh.edu
Financial aid: (713) 743-9090
Application deadline: rolling
In-state tuition: full time: $88/credit
hour; part time: $88/credit hour
Out-of-state tuition: full time:
$306/credit hour
Room/board/expenses: $10,212
Full-time enrollment: 518
men: 79%; women: 21%;
minorities: 8%; international: 79%

Part-time enrollment: 269
men: 79%; women: 21%;
minorities: 31%; international: 14%
Acceptance rate: 55%
GRE requirement: YES
Avg. GRE: quantitative: 738;
analytical 648
TOEFL requirement: YES
Minimum TOEFL score: 550
Fellowships: 303
Teaching assistantships: 99
Research assistantships: 155
Students reporting specialty: 100%
Students specializing in: aero-
space: 1%; biomedical: 1%; chem-
ical: 13%; civil: 9%; computer: 2%;
electrical: 34%; environmental:
6%; industrial: 16%; materials: 1%;
mechanical: 10%; petroleum: 7%

University of Texas–Arlington
PO Box 19019
Arlington, TX 76019
Public
Admissions: (817) 272-3186
E-mail: graduate.school@uta.edu
Web site: http://grad.uta.edu
Financial aid: (817) 272-3561
Application deadline: 06/11
In-state tuition: full time: $3,395;
part time: N/A
Out-of-state tuition: full time:
$7,517
Room/board/expenses: $8,330
Full-time enrollment: 1,244
men: 82%; women: 18%;
minorities: 3%; international: 94%
Part-time enrollment: 588
men: 80%; women: 20%;
minorities: 21%; international: 49%
Acceptance rate: 90%
GRE requirement: YES
Avg. GRE: quantitative: 743;
analytical 637
TOEFL requirement: YES
Minimum TOEFL score: 550
Fellowships: 137
Teaching assistantships: 186
Research assistantships: 207
Students reporting specialty: 100%
Students specializing in: aero-
space: 2%; biomedical: 5%; civil:
8%; computer: 30%; electrical:
36%; industrial: 10%; materials:
3%; mechanical: 8%

University of Texas–Austin
College of Engineering
Austin, TX 78712-0284
Public
Admissions: (512) 475-7390
E-mail:
adgrd@utxdp.dp.utexas.edu
Web site: http://www.
utexas.edu/student/giac/
Internet application:
http://utdirect.utexas.edu/
adappw/apply.wb
Financial aid: (512) 475-6282
Application deadline: rolling
In-state tuition: full time: $4,186;
part time: $132/credit hour
Out-of-state tuition: full time:
$8,110
Room/board/expenses: $11,122
Full-time enrollment: 1,585
men: 81%; women: 19%;
minorities: 8%; international: 64%
Part-time enrollment: 444
men: 84%; women: 16%;
minorities: 22%; international: 25%
Acceptance rate: 26%
GRE requirement: YES
Avg. GRE: quantitative: 761;
analytical 696
TOEFL requirement: YES
Minimum TOEFL score: 550
Fellowships: 324

Teaching assistantships: 361
Research assistantships: 834
Students reporting specialty: 100%
Students specializing in: aerospace: 7%; biomedical: 3%; chemical: 8%; civil: 16%; computer:
13%; electrical: 20%; environmental: 2%; industrial: 7%; materials:
4%; mechanical: 11%; petroleum:
6%; other: 3%

University of Texas–Dallas
PO Box 830688
Mail Station EC32
Richardson, TX 75083-0688
Public
Admissions: (972) 883-2341
E-mail: enrollment@utdallas.edu
Web site: http://www.utdallas.edu/
Internet application: http://www.
utdallas.edu/student/admissions/
application.htm
Financial aid: (972) 883-2941
Application deadline: 07/01
In-state tuition: full time: $3,923;
part time: $2,588
Out-of-state tuition: full time:
$7,847
Room/board/expenses: $8,736
Full-time enrollment: 802
men: 73%; women: 27%;
minorities: 5%; international: 89%
Part-time enrollment: 493
men: 72%; women: 28%;
minorities: 28%; international: 50%
Acceptance rate: 50%
GRE requirement: YES
Avg. GRE: quantitative: 755;
analytical 662
TOEFL requirement: YES
Minimum TOEFL score: 550
Fellowships: 5
Teaching assistantships: 118
Research assistantships: 94
Students reporting specialty: 100%
Students specializing in: computer:
69%; electrical: 31%

University of Texas–El Paso
College of Engineering
El Paso, TX 79968
Public
Admissions: (915) 747-5491
E-mail: gradschool@utep.edu
Web site:
http://www.utep.edu/graduate
Financial aid: (915) 747-5204
Application deadline: rolling
In-state tuition: full time: $2,649;
part time: $114/credit hour
Out-of-state tuition: full time:
$6,429
Room/board/expenses: $7,908
Full-time enrollment: 232
men: 83%; women: 17%;
minorities: 24%; international: 69%
Part-time enrollment: 190
men: 74%; women: 26%;
minorities: 41%; international: 49%
Acceptance rate: 81%
GRE requirement: YES
Avg. GRE: quantitative: 631;
analytical 505
TOEFL requirement: YES
Minimum TOEFL score: 550
Students reporting specialty: 100%
Students specializing in: civil: 8%;
computer: 45%; electrical: 17%;
environmental: 4%; industrial:
13%; materials: 3%; mechanical:
10%

UTAH

Brigham Young University[1]

College of Engineering & Technology
270 CB
Provo, UT 84602
Private
Admissions: (801) 422-2507
E-mail: gradstudies@byu.edu
Web site: http://www.et.byu.edu
Internet application: http://www.et.byu.edu/admissions.html
Financial aid: (801) 378-4104
Tuition: N/A
Room/board/expenses: N/A
Enrollment: N/A

University of Utah

1495 E. 100 S
Salt Lake City, UT 84112-1114
Public
Admissions: (801) 581-7281
E-mail: admissions@sssbl.staff.utah.edu
Web site: http://www.utah.edu
Internet application: http://www.saff.utah.edu/admiss/
Financial aid: (801) 581-6211
Application deadline: rolling
In-state tuition: full time: $2,568; part time: N/A
Out-of-state tuition: full time: $7,780
Room/board/expenses: $5,336
Full-time enrollment: 498
men: 82%; women: 18%;
minorities: 37%; international: 23%
Part-time enrollment: 217
men: 86%; women: 14%;
minorities: 28%; international: 8%
Acceptance rate: 44%
GRE requirement: YES
Avg. GRE: quantitative: 763; analytical 699
TOEFL requirement: YES
Minimum TOEFL score: 500
Fellowships: 14
Teaching assistantships: 151
Research assistantships: 375
Students reporting specialty: 99%
Students specializing in: biomedical: 12%; chemical: 10%; civil: 12%; computer: 13%; electrical: 24%; environmental: 1%; materials: 5%; mechanical: 22%; nuclear: 1%

Utah State University

School of Graduate Studies
0900 Old Main
Logan, UT 84322-0900
Public
Admissions: (435) 797-1189
E-mail: gradsch@cc.usu.edu
Web site: http://www.engineering.usu.edu/
Internet application: http://www.usu.edu/gradsch/home.html
Financial aid: (435) 797-0173
Application deadline: 06/15
In-state tuition: full time: $2,592; part time: $1,998
Out-of-state tuition: full time: $7,820
Room/board/expenses: $9,811
Full-time enrollment: 265
men: 80%; women: 20%;
minorities: 0%; international: 0%
Part-time enrollment: 191
men: 84%; women: 16%;
minorities: 0%; international: 0%
Acceptance rate: 48%
GRE requirement: YES
Avg. GRE: quantitative: 748; analytical 670
TOEFL requirement: YES
Minimum TOEFL score: 550
Fellowships: 5
Teaching assistantships: 5
Research assistantships: 85
Students reporting specialty: N/A
Students specializing in: N/A

VERMONT

University of Vermont

College of Engineering and Mathematics
Burlington, VT 05405
Public
Admissions: (802) 656-2699
E-mail: graduate.admissions@uvm.edu
Web site: http://www.emba.uvm.edu
Financial aid: (802) 656-3156
Application deadline: 04/01
In-state tuition: full time: $347/credit hour; part time: $347/credit hour
Out-of-state tuition: full time: $867/credit hour
Room/board/expenses: $8,696
Full-time enrollment: 38
men: 71%; women: 29%;
minorities: 5%; international: 29%
Part-time enrollment: 73
men: 81%; women: 19%;
minorities: 11%; international: 15%
Acceptance rate: 69%
GRE requirement: YES
Avg. GRE: quantitative: 711; analytical 674
TOEFL requirement: YES
Minimum TOEFL score: 550
Fellowships: 21
Research assistantships: 22
Students reporting specialty: 100%
Students specializing in: civil: 14%; computer: 16%; electrical: 50%; mechanical: 19%

VIRGINIA

George Mason University

4400 University Drive–MS4A3
Fairfax, VA 22030-4444
Public
Admissions: (703) 993-1505
E-mail: itegrad@gmu.edu
Web site: http://www.ite.gmu.edu/
Financial aid: (703) 993-2353
Application deadline: 04/15
In-state tuition: full time: $5,004; part time: $209/credit hour
Out-of-state tuition: full time: $13,716
Room/board/expenses: $5,340
Full-time enrollment: 394
men: 67%; women: 33%;
minorities: 18%; international: 60%
Part-time enrollment: 1,657
men: 73%; women: 27%;
minorities: 29%; international: 22%
Acceptance rate: 66%
GRE requirement: YES
Avg. GRE: quantitative: N/A; analytical N/A
TOEFL requirement: YES
Minimum TOEFL score: 575
Fellowships: 53
Teaching assistantships: 111
Research assistantships: 90
Students reporting specialty: 100%
Students specializing in: civil: 2%; computer: 52%; electrical: 29%; industrial: 17%

Old Dominion University

102 Kaufman Hall
Norfolk, VA 23529
Public
Admissions: (757) 683-3685
E-mail: admit@odu.edu
Web site: http://www.eng.odu.edu
Financial aid: (757) 683-3689
Application deadline: rolling
In-state tuition: full time: $216/credit hour; part time: $216/credit hour
Out-of-state tuition: full time: $574/credit hour
Room/board/expenses: $5,250
Full-time enrollment: 183
men: 84%; women: 16%;
minorities: 44%; international: 44%
Part-time enrollment: 496
men: 85%; women: 15%;
minorities: 3%; international: 6%
Acceptance rate: 96%
GRE requirement: YES
Avg. GRE: quantitative: 716; analytical 628
TOEFL requirement: YES
Minimum TOEFL score: 550
Fellowships: 5
Teaching assistantships: 6
Research assistantships: 8
Students reporting specialty: 17%
Students specializing in: N/A

University of Virginia

Thornton Hall
Charlottesville, VA 22903
Public
Admissions: (434) 924-3897
E-mail: seas-grad-admission@virginia.edu
Web site: http://www.cs.virginia.edu/graduate
Financial aid: (434) 924-3897
Application deadline: 02/01
In-state tuition: full time: $5,623; part time: $294/credit hour
Out-of-state tuition: full time: $18,712
Room/board/expenses: $13,618
Full-time enrollment: 620
men: 76%; women: 24%;
minorities: 7%; international: 48%
Part-time enrollment: 70
men: 86%; women: 14%;
minorities: 17%; international: 0%
Acceptance rate: 13%
GRE requirement: YES
Avg. GRE: quantitative: 755; analytical 702
TOEFL requirement: YES
Minimum TOEFL score: 600
Fellowships: 150
Teaching assistantships: 102
Research assistantships: 441
Students reporting specialty: 100%
Students specializing in: biomedical: 8%; chemical: 8%; civil: 11%; computer: 15%; electrical: 16%; materials: 8%; mechanical: 11%; other: 23%

Virginia Commonwealth University

Box 843068
Richmond, VA 23284-3068
Public
Admissions: (804) 827-7033
E-mail: ltoverby@mail1.vcu.edu
Web site: http://www.vcu.edu/egrweb/
Internet application: http://www.vcu.edu/gradweb/admission.htm
Financial aid: (804) 828-3925
Application deadline: 02/15
In-state tuition: full time: $5,804; part time: $256/credit hour

Out-of-state tuition:

Out-of-state tuition: full time: $14,872
Room/board/expenses: $9,494
Full-time enrollment: 92
men: 72%; women: 28%;
minorities: 5%; international: 53%
Part-time enrollment: 58
men: 74%; women: 26%;
minorities: 12%; international: 26%
Acceptance rate: 80%
GRE requirement: YES
Avg. GRE: quantitative: 689; analytical 614
TOEFL requirement: YES
Minimum TOEFL score: 600
Fellowships: 2
Teaching assistantships: 33
Research assistantships: 22
Students reporting specialty: 100%
Students specializing in: biomedical: 37%; chemical: 9%; computer: 33%; electrical: 11%; mechanical: 9%

Virginia Tech

333 Norris Hall
Blacksburg, VA 24061-0217
Public
Admissions: (540) 231-6691
Web site: http://www.eng.vt.edu
Financial aid: (540) 231-5179
Application deadline: rolling
In-state tuition: full time: $5,632; part time: $263/credit hour
Out-of-state tuition: full time: $8,866
Room/board/expenses: $10,462
Full-time enrollment: 1,417
men: 81%; women: 19%;
minorities: 6%; international: 54%
Part-time enrollment: 601
men: 80%; women: 20%;
minorities: 15%; international: 25%
Acceptance rate: 25%
GRE requirement: YES
Avg. GRE: quantitative: 746; analytical 672
TOEFL requirement: YES
Minimum TOEFL score: 550
Fellowships: 151
Teaching assistantships: 294
Research assistantships: 680
Students reporting specialty: 100%
Students specializing in: aerospace: 5%; biomedical: 1%; chemical: 3%; civil: 14%; computer: 18%; electrical: 26%; environmental: 3%; industrial: 14%; materials: 2%; mechanical: 8%; mining: 1%; other: 4%

WASHINGTON

University of Washington

College of Engineering
Box 352180
Seattle, WA 98195-2180
Public
Admissions: (206) 543-5929
E-mail: uwgrad2@grad.washington.edu
Web site: http://www.engr.washington.edu
Internet application: https://www.grad.washington.edu/application
Financial aid: (206) 543-6101
Application deadline: 07/01
In-state tuition: full time: $6,508; part time: $308/credit hour
Out-of-state tuition: full time: $15,595
Room/board/expenses: $13,386
Full-time enrollment: 1,074
men: 72%; women: 28%;
minorities: 12%; international: 38%
Part-time enrollment: 354
men: 80%; women: 20%;
minorities: 8%; international: 21%
Acceptance rate: 34%

GRE requirement: YES
Avg. GRE: quantitative: 733; analytical 675
TOEFL requirement: YES
Minimum TOEFL score: 500
Fellowships: 110
Teaching assistantships: 350
Research assistantships: 745
Students reporting specialty: 100%
Students specializing in: aerospace: 5%; biomedical: 10%; chemical: 5%; civil: 11%; computer: 24%; electrical: 21%; industrial: 3%; materials: 4%; mechanical: 11%; other: 6%

Washington State University

College of Engineering and Architecture
Pullman, WA 99164-2714
Public
Admissions: (509) 335-5586
E-mail: admiss2@wsu.edu
Web site: http://www.cea.wsu.edu
Internet application: http://www.wsu.edu/future-students/admission/apply.html
Financial aid: (509) 335-9711
Application deadline: rolling
In-state tuition: full time: $6,462; part time: $304/credit hour
Out-of-state tuition: full time: $15,288
Room/board/expenses: $12,748
Full-time enrollment: 274
men: 74%; women: 26%;
minorities: 4%; international: 59%
Part-time enrollment: 165
men: 76%; women: 24%;
minorities: 10%; international: 10%
Acceptance rate: 20%
GRE requirement: YES
Avg. GRE: quantitative: N/A; analytical N/A
TOEFL requirement: YES
Minimum TOEFL score: 520
Fellowships: 53
Teaching assistantships: 84
Research assistantships: 141
Students reporting specialty: 100%
Students specializing in: agriculture: 10%; chemical: 7%; civil: 19%; electrical: 29%; mechanical: 18%; other: 17%

WEST VIRGINIA

West Virginia University

PO Box 6070
Morgantown, WV 26506-6070
Public
Admissions: (304) 293-4821
E-mail: info@cemr.wvu.edu
Web site: http://www.cemr.wvu.edu
Internet application: http://www.arc.wvu.edu
Financial aid: (304) 293-5242
Application deadline: N/A
In-state tuition: full time: $3,564; part time: $230/credit hour
Out-of-state tuition: full time: $10,016
Room/board/expenses: $10,347
Full-time enrollment: 608
men: 82%; women: 18%;
minorities: 1%; international: 72%
Part-time enrollment: 157
men: 85%; women: 15%;
minorities: 5%; international: 34%
Acceptance rate: 30%
GRE requirement: YES
Avg. GRE: quantitative: 748; analytical 645
TOEFL requirement: YES
Minimum TOEFL score: 550
Fellowships: 18
Teaching assistantships: 68

Research assistantships: 299
Students reporting specialty: 100%
Students specializing in: aerospace: 2%; chemical: 5%; civil: 9%; computer: 21%; electrical: 17%; industrial: 11%; mechanical: 18%; mining: 4%; petroleum: 1%; other: 11%

WISCONSIN

Marquette University

PO Box 1881
Milwaukee, WI 53201-1881
Private
Admissions: (414) 288-7137
E-mail: mugs@mu.edu
Web site:
http://www.grad.marquette.edu
Internet application:
http://www.grad.marquette.edu
Financial aid: (414) 288-5325
Application deadline: rolling
Tuition: full time: $600/credit hour; part time: $600/credit hour
Room/board/expenses: $11,450
Full-time enrollment: 147
men: 74%; women: 26%;
minorities: 50%; international: 52%
Part-time enrollment: 162
men: 83%; women: 17%;
minorities: 22%; international: 23%
Acceptance rate: 74%
GRE requirement: YES

Avg. GRE: quantitative: 723; analytical 648
TOEFL requirement: YES
Minimum TOEFL score: 550
Fellowships: 25
Teaching assistantships: 38
Research assistantships: 13
Students reporting specialty: 96%
Students specializing in: biomedical: 21%; civil: 16%; electrical: 29%; materials: 1%; mechanical: 17%; other: 16%

University of Wisconsin–Madison

2610 Engineering Hall
Madison, WI 53706
Public
Admissions: (608) 262-2433
Web site:
http://www.engr.wisc.edu/
Internet application:
http://www.wisc.edu/grad/eapp
Financial aid: (608) 262-3060
Application deadline: N/A
In-state tuition: full time: $7,452; part time: $431/credit hour
Out-of-state tuition: full time: $22,722
Room/board/expenses: $10,750
Full-time enrollment: 1,334
men: 83%; women: 17%;
minorities: 3%; international: 60%

Part-time enrollment: 177
men: 85%; women: 15%;
minorities: 3%; international: 42%
Acceptance rate: 27%
GRE requirement: YES
Avg. GRE: quantitative: 780; analytical 741
TOEFL requirement: YES
Minimum TOEFL score: 580
Fellowships: 101
Teaching assistantships: 207
Research assistantships: 718
Students reporting specialty: 100%
Students specializing in: biomedical: 4%; chemical: 7%; civil: 10%; computer: 14%; electrical: 24%; industrial: 13%; materials: 5%; mechanical: 12%; nuclear: 3%; other: 7%

University of Wisconsin–Milwaukee

PO Box 784
Milwaukee, WI 53201
Public
Admissions: (414) 229-6169
E-mail: paulvds@uwm.edu
Web site:
http://www.uwm.edu/CEAS
Internet application: http://www.uwm.edu/Dept/Grad_Sch/Prospective/
Financial aid: (414) 229-4541

Application deadline: rolling
In-state tuition: full time: $6,652; part time: $570/credit hour
Out-of-state tuition: full time: $21,016
Room/board/expenses: $7,076
Full-time enrollment: 113
men: 81%; women: 19%;
minorities: N/A; international: N/A
Part-time enrollment: 159
men: 80%; women: 20%;
minorities: N/A; international: N/A
Acceptance rate: 58%
GRE requirement: NO
Avg. GRE: quantitative: N/A; analytical N/A
TOEFL requirement: YES
Minimum TOEFL score: 550
Fellowships: 2
Teaching assistantships: 82
Research assistantships: 18
Students reporting specialty: N/A
Students specializing in: N/A

WYOMING

University of Wyoming

PO Box 3295
Laramie, WY 82071-3295
Public
Admissions: (307) 766-2287
E-mail: uwgrad@uwyo.edu
Web site: http://wwweng.uwyo.edu

Internet application:
http://uwadmnweb.uwyo.edu/UWGrad/
Financial aid: (307) 766-2118
Application deadline: 04/01
In-state tuition: full time: $3,585; part time: $166/credit hour
Out-of-state tuition: full time: $9,273
Room/board/expenses: $8,425
Full-time enrollment: 131
men: 81%; women: 19%;
minorities: 1%; international: 52%
Part-time enrollment: 50
men: 86%; women: 14%;
minorities: 6%; international: 40%
Acceptance rate: 36%
GRE requirement: YES
Avg. GRE: quantitative: 702; analytical 610
TOEFL requirement: YES
Minimum TOEFL score: 550
Fellowships: 0
Teaching assistantships: 47
Research assistantships: 69
Students reporting specialty: 100%
Students specializing in: chemical: 10%; civil: 14%; electrical: 27%; environmental: 4%; mechanical: 10%; petroleum: 6%; other: 29%

LAW

The law school directory lists the 185 American Bar Association-accredited law schools as published in the 2003 edition of the *Official Guide to ABA-Approved Law Schools,* produced by the Law School Admission Council and the American Bar Association. All of these schools offer the J.D. degree. There were 176 schools that responded to the *U.S. News* survey conducted in fall 2002, and their data are reported below. Schools that did not respond have abbreviated entries.

TERMINOLOGY

1 A school whose name is footnoted with the numeral 1 did not return the *U.S. News* statistical survey; limited data appear in its entry.

N/A. Not available from the school or not applicable.

Admissions. The admissions office phone number.

E-mail. The electronic address of the admissions office. If, instead of an E-mail address, a Web site address is listed, the Web site will automatically present an E-mail screen programmed to reach the admissions office.

Internet application. The electronic address for online applications.

Financial aid. The financial aid office phone number.

Application deadline. For fall 2004 enrollment. "Rolling" means there is no application deadline; the school acts on applications as they are received. "Varies" means deadlines vary according to department or whether applicants are U.S. citizens or foreign nationals.

Tuition. For the 2002–2003 academic year. Includes fees.

Room/board/expenses. For the 2002–2003 academic year.

Credit hour. The cost per credit hour for the 2002–2003 academic year.

Enrollment. Full and part time, fall 2002.

Minorities. For fall 2002, percent of students who are Asian-American, African-American, Hispanic, or American Indian. (When the U.S. Department of Education calculates minority enrollment percentages, these are the demographic groupings it uses.)

Median grant. The median value of grants to full-time students enrolled in 2002. This is calculated for all full-time students who received grants, not just first-year students.

Average indebtedness. For 2002 graduates who attended full time and incurred law-school debt.

Acceptance rate. Percent of applicants who were accepted for fall 2002 law school J.D. program.

Midrange Law School Admission Test (LSAT) score. For full-time students who entered in fall 2002. The first number is the 25th percentile test score for the class, the second the 75th percentile.

Midrange undergraduate grade-point average. For full-time students who entered in fall 2002. The first number is the 25th percentile GPA for the class, the second the 75th percentile.

Midrange of full-time private sector starting salaries. For the 2001 graduating class, the starting salary is for those employed full time in the private sector in law firms, business, industry, or other private-sector jobs. The first number is the starting salary at the 25th percentile of the graduating class; the second number is the starting salary at the 75th percentile. When a school has the same salary at the 25th and 75th percentiles, it means that the starting salaries for private sector jobs were at the same level for a large proportion of the class.

Job classifications. For the 2001 graduating class, the percentage breakdown for the following types of employment is listed: law firms, business and industry (legal), business and industry (nonlegal), government, public interest, judicial clerkship, academia, and unknown. Numbers may not add up to 100 because of rounding.

Employment locations: For the 2001 graduating class. Abbreviations: **Intl.** international; **N.E.** New England (Conn., Maine, Mass., N.H., R.I., Vt.); **M.A.** Middle Atlantic (N.J., N.Y., Pa.); **S.A.** South Atlantic (Del., D.C., Fla., Ga., Md., N.C., S.C., Va., W.Va.); **E.N.C.** East North Central (Ill., Ind., Mich., Ohio, Wis.); **W.N.C.** West North Central (Iowa, Kan., Minn., Mo., Neb., N.D., S.D.); **E.S.C.** East South Central (Ala., Ky., Miss., Tenn.); **W.S.C.** West South Central (Ark., La., Okla., Texas); **Mt.** Mountain (Ariz., Colo., Idaho, Mont., Nev., N.M., Utah, Wyo.); **Pac.** Pacific (Alaska, Calif., Hawaii, Ore., Wash.).

ALABAMA

Samford University (Cumberland)
800 Lakeshore Drive
Birmingham, AL 35229
Private
Admissions: (205) 726-2702
E-mail:
law.admissions@samford.edu
Web site:
http://cumberland.samford.edu
Financial aid: (205) 726-2905
Application deadline: 05/01
Tuition: full time: $21,350; part time: $712/credit hour
Room/board/expenses: $15,790
Students receiving grants: 34%
Median grant: $10,000
Average student indebtedness at graduation: $74,477
Enrollment: full time: 506; part time: 1
men: 59%; women: 41%;
minorities: 5%
Acceptance rate (full time): 43%
Midrange LSAT (full time): 151-155
Midrange undergraduate GPA (full time): 2.89-3.43
Midrange of full-time private sector salaries of 2001 grads: $43,000-$64,000
2000 grads employed in: law firms: 67%; business and industry (legal): 2%; business and industry (nonlegal): 4%; government: 13%; public interest: 1%; judicial clerk: 12%; academia: 1%; unknown: 0%
Employment location for 2001 class: Intl. 1%; N.E. 1%; M.A. 1%; E.N.C. 1%; W.N.C. 0%; S.A. 37%; E.S.C. 56%; W.S.C. 3%; Mt. 0%; Pac. 1%; unknown 0%

University of Alabama
Box 870382
Tuscaloosa, AL 35487
Public
Admissions: (205) 348-5440
E-mail: admissions@law.ua.edu
Web site: http://www.law.ua.edu
Financial aid: (205) 348-6756
Application deadline: 03/01
In-state tuition: full time: $6,144; part time: N/A
Out-of-state tuition: full time: $12,972
Room/board/expenses: $11,950
Students receiving grants: 31%
Median grant: $3,000
Average student indebtedness at graduation: $31,322
Enrollment: full time: 541; part time: N/A
men: 62%; women: 38%;
minorities: 9%
Acceptance rate (full time): 33%
Midrange LSAT (full time): 157-162
Midrange undergraduate GPA (full time): 3.10-3.63
Midrange of full-time private sector salaries of 2001 grads: $60,000-$80,000
2000 grads employed in: law firms: 60%; business and industry (legal): 4%; business and industry (nonlegal): 2%; government: 7%; public interest: 2%; judicial clerk: 20%; academia: 2%; unknown: 2%

Employment location for 2001 class:
Intl. N/A; N.E. N/A; M.A. N/A; E.N.C. N/A; W.N.C. 2%; S.A. 15%; E.S.C. 81%; W.S.C. N/A; Mt. N/A; Pac. 1%; unknown 1%

ARIZONA

Arizona State University
Box 877906
Tempe, AZ 85287-7906
Public
Admissions: (480) 965-7896
E-mail: law.admissions@asu.edu
Web site: http://www.law.asu.edu
Financial aid: (480) 965-7911
Application deadline: 03/01
In-state tuition: full time: $5,835; part time: N/A
Out-of-state tuition: full time: $14,355
Room/board/expenses: $12,159
Students receiving grants: 43%
Median grant: $4,222
Average student indebtedness at graduation: $46,888
Enrollment: full time: 550; part time: N/A
men: 47%; women: 53%;
minorities: 29%
Acceptance rate (full time): 17%
Midrange LSAT (full time): 154-163
Midrange undergraduate GPA (full time): 3.15-3.69
Midrange of full-time private sector salaries of 2001 grads: $70,000-$100,000
2000 grads employed in: law firms: 54%; business and industry (legal): 1%; business and industry (nonlegal): 6%; government: 20%; public interest: 3%; judicial clerk: 14%; academia: 3%; unknown: 0%
Employment location for 2001 class: Intl. 0%; N.E. 0%; M.A. 1%; E.N.C. 0%; W.N.C. 0%; S.A. 3%; E.S.C. 0%; W.S.C. 0%; Mt. 88%; Pac. 9%; unknown 0%

University of Arizona (Rogers)
James E. Rogers College of Law
PO Box 210176
Tucson, AZ 85721-0176
Public
Admissions: (520) 621-3477
E-mail:
admissions@law.arizona.edu
Web site:
http://www.law.arizona.edu
Internet application: http://www.law.arizona.edu/admissions/application.htm
Financial aid: (520) 626-8101
Application deadline: 02/15
In-state tuition: full time: $5,843; part time: N/A
Out-of-state tuition: full time: $14,363
Room/board/expenses: $12,778
Students receiving grants: 76%
Median grant: $3,250
Average student indebtedness at graduation: $40,755
Enrollment: full time: 480; part time: N/A
men: 48%; women: 52%;
minorities: 18%
Acceptance rate (full time): 18%
Midrange LSAT (full time): 157-164

Midrange undergraduate GPA (full time): 3.23-3.78
Midrange of full-time private sector salaries of 2001 grads: $55,000-$90,000
2000 grads employed in: law firms: 47%; business and industry (legal): 5%; business and industry (nonlegal): 2%; government: 22%; public interest: 3%; judicial clerk: 18%; academia: 3%; unknown: 0%
Employment location for 2001 class: Intl. 0%; N.E. 1%; M.A. 4%; E.N.C. 3%; W.N.C. 2%; S.A. 7%; E.S.C. 1%; W.S.C. 1%; Mt. 67%; Pac. 17%; unknown 0%

ARKANSAS

University of Arkansas–Fayetteville

School of Law
107 Waterman Hall
Fayetteville, AR 72701
Public
Admissions: (479) 575-3102
E-mail: jkmiller@uark.edu
Web site: http://law.uark.edu/
Financial aid: (479) 575-3277
Application deadline: 04/01
In-state tuition: full time: $7,108; part time: N/A
Out-of-state tuition: full time: $14,192
Room/board/expenses: $11,624
Students receiving grants: 29%
Median grant: $4,502
Average student indebtedness at graduation: $42,774
Enrollment: full time: 409; part time: N/A
men: 54%; women: 46%; minorities: 18%
Acceptance rate (full time): 43%
Midrange LSAT (full time): 149-156
Midrange undergraduate GPA (full time): 3.04-3.63
Midrange of full-time private sector salaries of 2001 grads: N/A-N/A
2000 grads employed in: law firms: 64%; business and industry (legal): 6%; business and industry (nonlegal): 9%; government: 12%; public interest: 1%; judicial clerk: 8%; academia: 0%; unknown: 0%
Employment location for 2001 class: Intl. 1%; N.E. 0%; M.A. 0%; E.N.C. 0%; W.N.C. 10%; S.A. 4%; E.S.C. 2%; W.S.C. 81%; Mt. 2%; Pac. 0%; unknown 0%

University of Arkansas–Little Rock (Bowen)

1201 McMath Avenue
Little Rock, AR 72202-5142
Public
Admissions: (501) 324-9439
E-mail: lawadm@ualr.edu
Web site: http://www.law.ualr.edu/
Financial aid: (501) 569-3035
Application deadline: 04/15
In-state tuition: full time: $7,641; part time: $4,929
Out-of-state tuition: full time: $14,241
Room/board/expenses: $10,000
Students receiving grants: 37%
Median grant: $6,426
Average student indebtedness at graduation: $23,284
Enrollment: full time: 258; part time: 135
men: 50%; women: 50%; minorities: 10%
Acceptance rate (full time): 53%
Midrange LSAT (full time): 149-156
Midrange undergraduate GPA (full time): 2.92-3.58

CALIFORNIA

California Western School of Law

225 Cedar Street
San Diego, CA 92101-3090
Private
Admissions: (619) 525-1401
E-mail: admissions@cwsl.edu
Web site: http://www.cwsl.edu
Financial aid: (619) 525-7060
Application deadline: 04/01
Tuition: full time: $24,850; part time: $17,750
Room/board/expenses: $13,976
Students receiving grants: 36%
Median grant: $5,855
Average student indebtedness at graduation: $87,639
Enrollment: full time: 836; part time: 137
men: 47%; women: 53%; minorities: 21%
Acceptance rate (full time): 64%
Midrange LSAT (full time): 147-154
Midrange undergraduate GPA (full time): 2.88-3.44
Midrange of full-time private sector salaries of 2001 grads: $50,000-$70,000
2000 grads employed in: law firms: 64%; business and industry (legal): 8%; business and industry (nonlegal): 3%; government: 12%; public interest: 7%; judicial clerk: 2%; academia: 2%; unknown: N/A
Employment location for 2001 class: Intl. 0%; N.E. 1%; M.A. 2%; E.N.C. 0%; W.N.C. 0%; S.A. 2%; E.S.C. 1%; W.S.C. 1%; Mt. 14%; Pac. 79%; unknown 0%

Chapman University

1 University Drive
Orange, CA 92866
Private
Admissions: (714) 628-2500
E-mail: lawadm@chapman.edu
Web site: http://www.chapman.edu/law
Financial aid: (714) 628-2510
Application deadline: rolling
Tuition: full time: $24,300; part time: $16,720
Room/board/expenses: $14,763
Students receiving grants: 38%
Median grant: $17,400
Average student indebtedness at graduation: $58,530
Enrollment: full time: 265; part time: 107
men: 52%; women: 48%; minorities: 25%
Acceptance rate (full time): 36%
Midrange LSAT (full time): 151-157
Midrange undergraduate GPA (full time): 2.93-3.47
Midrange of full-time private sector salaries of 2001 grads: $50,000-$95,000
2000 grads employed in: law firms: 59%; business and industry (legal): 3%; business and industry (nonlegal): 24%; government: 7%;

public interest: 0%; judicial clerk: 3%; academia: 3%; unknown: 0%
Employment location for 2001 class: Intl. 0%; N.E. 0%; M.A. 0%; E.N.C. 0%; W.N.C. 3%; S.A. 0%; E.S.C. 0%; W.S.C. 0%; Mt. 14%; Pac. 83%; unknown 0%

Golden Gate University

536 Mission Street
San Francisco, CA 94105
Private
Admissions: (415) 442-6630
E-mail: lawadmit@ggu.edu
Web site: http://www.ggu.edu/law/
Financial aid: (415) 442-6630
Application deadline: 04/15
Tuition: full time: $24,716; part time: $17,120
Room/board/expenses: $13,920
Students receiving grants: 35%
Median grant: $6,000
Average student indebtedness at graduation: $68,787
Enrollment: full time: 441; part time: 184
men: 39%; women: 61%; minorities: 25%
Acceptance rate (full time): 56%
Midrange LSAT (full time): 147-153
Midrange undergraduate GPA (full time): 2.77-3.37
Midrange of full-time private sector salaries of 2001 grads: $45,000-$75,000
2000 grads employed in: law firms: 52%; business and industry (legal): N/A; business and industry (nonlegal): 22%; government: 13%; public interest: 9%; judicial clerk: 2%; academia: 2%; unknown: N/A
Employment location for 2001 class: Intl. N/A; N.E. 1%; M.A. 1%; E.N.C. N/A; W.N.C. N/A; S.A. 1%; E.S.C. N/A; W.S.C. N/A; Mt. 1%; Pac. 75%; unknown 21%

Loyola Law School

919 Albany Street
Los Angeles, CA 90015-1211
Private
Admissions: (213) 736-1074
E-mail: Admissions@lls.edu
Web site: http://www.lls.edu
Internet application: http://www.lls.edu/admissions/admissionsface.htm
Financial aid: (213) 736-1140
Application deadline: 02/03
Tuition: full time: $26,806; part time: $17,990
Room/board/expenses: $15,579
Students receiving grants: 16%
Median grant: $19,000
Average student indebtedness at graduation: $83,779
Enrollment: full time: 1,007; part time: 344
men: 49%; women: 51%; minorities: 39%
Acceptance rate (full time): 31%
Midrange LSAT (full time): 157-162
Midrange undergraduate GPA (full time): 3.14-3.61
Midrange of full-time private sector salaries of 2001 grads: $60,000-$125,000
2000 grads employed in: law firms: 61%; business and industry (legal): 4%; business and industry (nonlegal): 12%; government: 10%; public interest: 5%; judicial clerk: 3%; academia: 3%; unknown: 2%
Employment location for 2001 class: Intl. 0%; N.E. 0%; M.A. 1%; E.N.C. 1%; W.N.C. 0%; S.A. 1%; E.S.C. 0%; W.S.C. 0%; Mt. 1%; Pac. 95%; unknown 1%

Pepperdine University

24255 Pacific Coast Highway
Malibu, CA 90263
Private
Admissions: (310) 506-4631
E-mail: soladmis@pepperdine.edu
Web site: http://law.pepperdine.edu
Financial aid: (310) 506-4633
Application deadline: 03/01
Tuition: full time: $27,210; part time: N/A
Room/board/expenses: $17,702
Students receiving grants: 60%
Median grant: $3,500
Average student indebtedness at graduation: $84,669
Enrollment: full time: 662; part time: N/A
men: 52%; women: 48%; minorities: 18%
Acceptance rate (full time): 35%
Midrange LSAT (full time): 155-160
Midrange undergraduate GPA (full time): 3.15-3.65
Midrange of full-time private sector salaries of 2001 grads: $60,000-$125,000
2000 grads employed in: law firms: 58%; business and industry (legal): 11%; business and industry (nonlegal): 4%; government: 13%; public interest: 4%; judicial clerk: 5%; academia: 1%; unknown: 4%
Employment location for 2001 class: Intl. N/A; N.E. N/A; M.A. 1%; E.N.C. 1%; W.N.C. N/A; S.A. 7%; E.S.C. 1%; W.S.C. 4%; Mt. 4%; Pac. 71%; unknown N/A

Santa Clara University

500 El Camino Real
Santa Clara, CA 95053-0421
Private
Admissions: (408) 554-4800
E-mail: lawadmissions@scu.edu
Web site: http://www.scu.edu/law
Internet application: http://www4.lsac.org/school/santaclara.htm
Financial aid: (408) 554-4447
Application deadline: 03/01
Tuition: full time: $912/credit hour; part time: $912/credit hour
Room/board/expenses: $19,068
Students receiving grants: 33%
Median grant: $11,396
Average student indebtedness at graduation: $76,777
Enrollment: full time: 720; part time: 210
men: 47%; women: 53%; minorities: 40%
Acceptance rate (full time): 38%
Midrange LSAT (full time): 153-159
Midrange undergraduate GPA (full time): 3.12-3.54
Midrange of full-time private sector salaries of 2001 grads: $70,000-$125,000
2000 grads employed in: law firms: 63%; business and industry (legal): 10%; business and industry (nonlegal): 8%; government: 4%; public interest: 5%; judicial clerk: 5%; academia: 1%; unknown: 4%
Employment location for 2001 class: Intl. 1%; N.E. 0%; M.A. 2%; E.N.C. 0%; W.N.C. 0%; S.A. 0%; E.S.C. 0%; W.S.C. 1%; Mt. 3%; Pac. 93%; unknown 0%

Southwestern University School of Law

675 S. Westmoreland Avenue
Los Angeles, CA 90005-3992
Private
Admissions: (213) 738-6717
E-mail: admissions@swlaw.edu
Web site: http://www.swlaw.edu
Internet application: http://www.swlaw.edu/prospective/admissions.html
Financial aid: (213) 738-6719
Application deadline: 06/30
Tuition: full time: $26,200; part time: $16,630
Room/board/expenses: $15,600
Students receiving grants: 25%
Median grant: $5,000
Average student indebtedness at graduation: $74,400
Enrollment: full time: 666; part time: 288
men: 47%; women: 53%; minorities: 34%
Acceptance rate (full time): 40%
Midrange LSAT (full time): 152-158
Midrange undergraduate GPA (full time): 3.00-3.50
Midrange of full-time private sector salaries of 2001 grads: $56,700-$98,250
2000 grads employed in: law firms: 59%; business and industry (legal): 11%; business and industry (nonlegal): 3%; government: 10%; public interest: 1%; judicial clerk: 1%; academia: 2%; unknown: 13%
Employment location for 2001 class: Intl. 0%; N.E. 1%; M.A. 1%; E.N.C. 1%; W.N.C. 0%; S.A. 1%; E.S.C. 0%; W.S.C. 1%; Mt. 1%; Pac. 88%; unknown 8%

Stanford University

Crown Quadrangle
559 Nathan Abbott Way
Stanford, CA 94305-8610
Private
Admissions: (650) 723-4985
E-mail: admissions@law.stanford.edu
Web site: http://www.law.stanford.edu
Internet application: http://www.law.stanford.edu/admissions/
Financial aid: (650) 723-9247
Application deadline: 02/01
Tuition: full time: $31,230; part time: N/A
Room/board/expenses: $15,618
Students receiving grants: 36%
Median grant: $9,114
Average student indebtedness at graduation: $86,876
Enrollment: full time: 545; part time: N/A
men: 50%; women: 50%; minorities: 31%
Acceptance rate (full time): 9%
Midrange LSAT (full time): 166-170
Midrange undergraduate GPA (full time): 3.67-3.93
Midrange of full-time private sector salaries of 2001 grads: $116,000-$125,000
2000 grads employed in: law firms: 56%; business and industry (legal): 0%; business and industry (nonlegal): 10%; government: 2%; public interest: 8%; judicial clerk: 24%; academia: 0%; unknown: 0%
Employment location for 2001 class: Intl. 1%; N.E. 2%; M.A. 9%; E.N.C. 2%; W.N.C. 1%; S.A. 12%; E.S.C. 1%; W.S.C. 3%; Mt. 2%; Pac. 66%; unknown 1%

Thomas Jefferson School of Law

2121 San Diego Avenue
San Diego, CA 92110
Private
Admissions: (619) 297-9700
E-mail: info@tjsl.edu
Web site: http://www.tjsl.edu
Financial aid: (619) 297-9700
Application deadline: rolling
Tuition: full time: $23,600; part time: $14,900
Room/board/expenses: N/A
Students receiving grants: 35%
Median grant: $10,000
Enrollment: full time: 494; part time: 191
men: 58%; women: 42%;
minorities: N/A
Acceptance rate (full time): 54%
Midrange LSAT (full time): 148-156
Midrange undergraduate GPA (full time): 2.60-3.25
Midrange of full-time private sector salaries of 2001 grads: N/A-N/A
2000 grads employed in: law firms: 64%; business and industry (legal): 7%; business and industry (nonlegal): 9%; government: 13%; public interest: N/A; judicial clerk: 5%; academia: 2%; unknown: N/A
Employment location for 2001 class: Intl. N/A; N.E. N/A; M.A. N/A; E.N.C. N/A; W.N.C. N/A; S.A. N/A; E.S.C. N/A; W.S.C. N/A; Mt. N/A; Pac. N/A; unknown N/A

University of California–Berkeley

School of Law
Boalt Hall
Berkeley, CA 94720-7200
Public
Admissions: (510) 642-2274
E-mail: admissions@law.berkeley.edu
Web site: http://www.law.berkeley.edu
Internet application: http://www.law.berkeley.edu/prospectives/admissions/jdinstructions.html#appliication
Financial aid: (510) 642-1563
Application deadline: 02/01
In-state tuition: full time: $11,027; part time: N/A
Out-of-state tuition: full time: $22,731
Room/board/expenses: $17,442
Students receiving grants: 56%
Median grant: $5,500
Average student indebtedness at graduation: $51,155
Enrollment: full time: 909; part time: N/A
men: 39%; women: 61%;
minorities: 35%
Acceptance rate (full time): 11%
Midrange LSAT (full time): 161-168
Midrange undergraduate GPA (full time): 3.68-3.90
Midrange of full-time private sector salaries of 2001 grads: $125,000-$125,000
2000 grads employed in: law firms: 70%; business and industry (legal): 3%; business and industry (nonlegal): N/A; government: 5%; public interest: 4%; judicial clerk: 16%; academia: 3%; unknown: N/A
Employment location for 2001 class: Intl. 2%; N.E. 1%; M.A. 11%; E.N.C. 1%; W.N.C. 1%; S.A. 6%; E.S.C. N/A; W.S.C. 1%; Mt. 2%; Pac. 74%; unknown 2%

University of California–Davis

School of Law
400 Mrak Hall Drive
Davis, CA 95616-5201
Public
Admissions: (530) 752-6477
E-mail: lawadmissions@ucdavis.edu
Web site: http://www.law.ucdavis.edu
Internet application: https://www4.lsac.org/school/Davis.htm
Financial aid: (530) 752-6573
Application deadline: 02/01
In-state tuition: full time: $11,502; part time: N/A
Out-of-state tuition: full time: $22,634
Room/board/expenses: $12,458
Students receiving grants: 77%
Median grant: $5,205
Average student indebtedness at graduation: $46,477
Enrollment: full time: 551; part time: N/A
men: 44%; women: 56%;
minorities: 33%
Acceptance rate (full time): 23%
Midrange LSAT (full time): 157-163
Midrange undergraduate GPA (full time): 3.28-3.68
Midrange of full-time private sector salaries of 2001 grads: $70,000-$125,000
2000 grads employed in: law firms: 61%; business and industry (legal): 1%; business and industry (nonlegal): 5%; government: 21%; public interest: 3%; judicial clerk: 4%; academia: 1%; unknown: 3%
Employment location for 2001 class: Intl. 0%; N.E. 1%; M.A. 0%; E.N.C. 1%; W.N.C. 0%; S.A. 1%; E.S.C. 0%; W.S.C. 0%; Mt. 2%; Pac. 90%; unknown 5%

University of California (Hastings)

200 McAllister Street
San Francisco, CA 94102
Public
Admissions: (415) 565-4623
E-mail: admiss@uchastings.edu
Web site: http://www.uchastings.edu
Internet application: http://www.uchastings.edu/admwelcome_01
Financial aid: (415) 565-4624
Application deadline: 03/01
In-state tuition: full time: $11,616; part time: N/A
Out-of-state tuition: full time: $21,623
Room/board/expenses: $19,689
Students receiving grants: 74%
Median grant: $4,000
Average student indebtedness at graduation: $53,198
Enrollment: full time: 1,232; part time: N/A
men: 44%; women: 56%;
minorities: 33%
Acceptance rate (full time): 23%
Midrange LSAT (full time): 159-164
Midrange undergraduate GPA (full time): 3.35-3.70
Midrange of full-time private sector salaries of 2001 grads: $75,000-$125,000
2000 grads employed in: law firms: 69%; business and industry (legal): 2%; business and industry (nonlegal): 7%; government: 10%; public interest: 6%; judicial clerk: 4%; academia: 0%; unknown: 1%
Employment location for 2001 class: Intl. 3%; N.E. 1%; M.A. 2%; E.N.C. 0%; W.N.C. 0%; S.A. 3%; E.S.C.

0%; W.S.C. 0%; Mt. 0%; Pac. 90%; unknown 2%

University of California–Los Angeles

71 Dodd Hall
PO Box 951445
Los Angeles, CA 90095-1445
Public
Admissions: (310) 825-4041
E-mail: admissions@law.ucla.edu
Web site: http://www.law.ucla.edu
Financial aid: (310) 825-2459
Application deadline: 02/02
In-state tuition: full time: $11,412; part time: N/A
Out-of-state tuition: full time: $22,544
Room/board/expenses: $16,428
Students receiving grants: 47%
Median grant: $6,470
Average student indebtedness at graduation: $56,000
Enrollment: full time: 970; part time: N/A
men: 49%; women: 51%;
minorities: 28%
Acceptance rate (full time): 15%
Midrange LSAT (full time): 162-167
Midrange undergraduate GPA (full time): 3.52-3.80
Midrange of full-time private sector salaries of 2001 grads: $115,000-$125,000
2000 grads employed in: law firms: 76%; business and industry (legal): 2%; business and industry (nonlegal): 3%; government: 6%; public interest: 5%; judicial clerk: 7%; academia: 1%; unknown: 0%
Employment location for 2001 class: Intl. 1%; N.E. 1%; M.A. 8%; E.N.C. 1%; W.N.C. 1%; S.A. 3%; E.S.C. 0%; W.S.C. 1%; Mt. 2%; Pac. 82%; unknown 0%

University of San Diego

5998 Alcala Park
San Diego, CA 92110-2492
Private
Admissions: (619) 260-4528
E-mail: jdinfo@SanDiego.edu
Web site: http://www.SanDiego.edu/usdlaw
Financial aid: (619) 260-4570
Application deadline: 02/01
Tuition: full time: $26,120; part time: $18,550
Room/board/expenses: $14,204
Students receiving grants: 37%
Median grant: $12,500
Average student indebtedness at graduation: $73,568
Enrollment: full time: 752; part time: 238
men: 52%; women: 48%;
minorities: 26%
Acceptance rate (full time): 27%
Midrange LSAT (full time): 158-162
Midrange undergraduate GPA (full time): 3.09-3.53
Midrange of full-time private sector salaries of 2001 grads: $52,000-$110,000
2000 grads employed in: law firms: 62%; business and industry (legal): 8%; business and industry (nonlegal): 10%; government: 14%; public interest: 1%; judicial clerk: 3%; academia: 1%; unknown: 1%
Employment location for 2001 class: Intl. N/A; N.E. 1%; M.A. 0%; E.N.C. 0%; W.N.C. 0%; S.A. 2%; E.S.C. 0%; W.S.C. 1%; Mt. 4%; Pac. 90%; unknown 1%

University of San Francisco

2130 Fulton Street
San Francisco, CA 94117-1080
Private
Admissions: (415) 422-6586
E-mail: lawadmissions@usfca.edu
Web site: http://www.law.usfca.edu
Financial aid: (415) 422-6210
Application deadline: 02/03
Tuition: full time: $26,362; part time: $941/credit hour
Room/board/expenses: $16,926
Students receiving grants: 44%
Median grant: $10,000
Average student indebtedness at graduation: $68,772
Enrollment: full time: 547; part time: 123
men: 44%; women: 56%;
minorities: 28%
Acceptance rate (full time): 33%
Midrange LSAT (full time): 154-159
Midrange undergraduate GPA (full time): 3.01-3.45
Midrange of full-time private sector salaries of 2001 grads: $65,000-$125,000
2000 grads employed in: law firms: 56%; business and industry (legal): 5%; business and industry (nonlegal): 5%; government: 12%; public interest: 4%; judicial clerk: 1%; academia: 1%; unknown: 16%
Employment location for 2001 class: Intl. 0%; N.E. 0%; M.A. 2%; E.N.C. 0%; W.N.C. 0%; S.A. 1%; E.S.C. 0%; W.S.C. 0%; Mt. 2%; Pac. 59%; unknown 36%

University of Southern California

Law School
Los Angeles, CA 90089-0071
Private
Admissions: (213) 740-2523
E-mail: admissions@law.usc.edu
Web site: http://www.usc.edu/law
Financial aid: (213) 740-2523
Application deadline: 02/01
Tuition: full time: $32,145; part time: N/A
Room/board/expenses: $14,006
Students receiving grants: 47%
Median grant: $7,500
Average student indebtedness at graduation: $80,985
Enrollment: full time: 636; part time: N/A
men: 53%; women: 47%;
minorities: 42%
Acceptance rate (full time): 21%
Midrange LSAT (full time): 163-166
Midrange undergraduate GPA (full time): 3.41-3.70
Midrange of full-time private sector salaries of 2001 grads: $91,000-$125,000
2000 grads employed in: law firms: 61%; business and industry (legal): 13%; business and industry (nonlegal): 0%; government: 3%; public interest: 5%; judicial clerk: 8%; academia: 5%; unknown: 5%
Employment location for 2001 class: Intl. 2%; N.E. 0%; M.A. 5%; E.N.C. 1%; W.N.C. 0%; S.A. 2%; E.S.C. 0%; W.S.C. 1%; Mt. 2%; Pac. 82%; unknown 5%

University of the Pacific (McGeorge)

3200 Fifth Avenue
Sacramento, CA 95817
Private
Admissions: (916) 739-7105
E-mail: admissionsmcgeorge@uop.edu
Web site: http://www.mcgeorge.edu
Internet application: http://www.mcgeorge.edu/admissions/apply/index.htm
Financial aid: (916) 739-7158
Application deadline: 08/01
Tuition: full time: $26,070; part time: $17,344
Room/board/expenses: $18,368
Students receiving grants: 51%
Median grant: $7,850
Average student indebtedness at graduation: $72,896
Enrollment: full time: 686; part time: 321
men: 51%; women: 49%;
minorities: 19%
Acceptance rate (full time): 49%
Midrange LSAT (full time): 150-156
Midrange undergraduate GPA (full time): 2.86-3.35
Midrange of full-time private sector salaries of 2001 grads: $50,000-$70,000
2000 grads employed in: law firms: 59%; business and industry (legal): 3%; business and industry (nonlegal): 5%; government: 26%; public interest: 2%; judicial clerk: 2%; academia: 3%; unknown: N/A
Employment location for 2001 class: Intl. 1%; N.E. 0%; M.A. 0%; E.N.C. 1%; W.N.C. 0%; S.A. 2%; E.S.C. 0%; W.S.C. 0%; Mt. 5%; Pac. 90%; unknown 1%

Western State University

1111 N. State College Boulevard
Fullerton, CA 92831
Private
Admissions: (714) 738-1000
E-mail: adm@wsulaw.edu
Web site: http://www.wsulaw.edu
Financial aid: (714) 738-1000
Application deadline: 08/01
Tuition: full time: $23,738; part time: $16,040
Room/board/expenses: $15,549
Students receiving grants: 34%
Median grant: $10,000
Enrollment: full time: 258; part time: 248
men: 46%; women: 54%;
minorities: 44%
Acceptance rate (full time): 52%
Midrange LSAT (full time): 143-149
Midrange undergraduate GPA (full time): 2.67-3.22
Midrange of full-time private sector salaries of 2001 grads: $53,615-$90,250
2000 grads employed in: law firms: 45%; business and industry (legal): 7%; business and industry (nonlegal): 21%; government: 18%; public interest: 1%; judicial clerk: 0%; academia: 4%; unknown: 4%
Employment location for 2001 class: Intl. 0%; N.E. 0%; M.A. 1%; E.N.C. 1%; W.N.C. 0%; S.A. 0%; E.S.C. 0%; W.S.C. 0%; Mt. 1%; Pac. 97%; unknown 0%

Whittier Law School

3333 Harbor Boulevard
Costa Mesa, CA 92626
Private
Admissions: (800) 808-8188
E-mail: info@law.whittier.edu
Web site: http://www.law.whittier.edu
Financial aid: (714) 444-4141
Application deadline: 03/01
Tuition: full time: $25,264; part time: $15,172
Room/board/expenses: $15,410
Students receiving grants: 36%

Median grant: $12,507
Average student indebtedness at graduation: $75,317
Enrollment: full time: 419; part time: 327
men: 45%; women: 55%; minorities: 40%
Acceptance rate (full time): 56%
Midrange LSAT (full time): 146-152
Midrange undergraduate GPA (full time): 2.74-3.35
Midrange of full-time private sector salaries of 2001 grads: $50,000-$66,000
2000 grads employed in: law firms: 64%; business and industry (legal): 16%; business and industry (nonlegal): 8%; government: 9%; public interest: 2%; judicial clerk: 0%; academia: 1%; unknown: 0%
Employment location for 2001 class: Intl. 1%; N.E. 1%; M.A. 0%; E.N.C. 1%; W.N.C. 1%; S.A. 1%; E.S.C. 0%; W.S.C. 0%; Mt. 3%; Pac. 91%; unknown 2%

COLORADO

University of Colorado–Boulder
Box 403
Boulder, CO 80309-0403
Public
Admissions: (303) 492-7203
E-mail: lawadmin@colorado.edu
Web site: http://www.colorado.edu/law/
Financial aid: (303) 492-5091
Application deadline: 02/15
In-state tuition: full time: $6,710; part time: N/A
Out-of-state tuition: full time: $21,208
Room/board/expenses: $12,311
Students receiving grants: 61%
Median grant: $1,850
Average student indebtedness at graduation: $51,668
Enrollment: full time: 479; part time: N/A
men: 47%; women: 53%; minorities: 18%
Acceptance rate (full time): 22%
Midrange LSAT (full time): 159-165
Midrange undergraduate GPA (full time): 3.44-3.80
Midrange of full-time private sector salaries of 2001 grads: $45,000-$85,000
2000 grads employed in: law firms: 52%; business and industry (legal): 2%; business and industry (nonlegal): 8%; government: 13%; public interest: 3%; judicial clerk: 16%; academia: 3%; unknown: 3%
Employment location for 2001 class: Intl. 0%; N.E. 1%; M.A. 2%; E.N.C. 1%; W.N.C. 0%; S.A. 4%; E.S.C. 1%; W.S.C. 2%; Mt. 76%; Pac. 7%; unknown 7%

University of Denver
7039 E. 18th Avenue
Denver, CO 80220
Private
Admissions: (303) 871-6135
E-mail: admissions@mail.law.du.edu
Web site: http://www.law.du.edu
Internet application: http://www.law.du.edu/ad/
Financial aid: (303) 871-6136
Application deadline: 03/01
Tuition: full time: $21,784; part time: $15,560
Room/board/expenses: $13,847
Students receiving grants: 33%
Median grant: $8,000
Average student indebtedness at graduation: $69,688
Enrollment: full time: 899; part time: 302
men: 47%; women: 53%; minorities: 19%
Acceptance rate (full time): 27%
Midrange LSAT (full time): 152-159
Midrange undergraduate GPA (full time): 2.85-3.43
Midrange of full-time private sector salaries of 2001 grads: $51,000-$90,000
2000 grads employed in: law firms: 45%; business and industry (legal): 10%; business and industry (nonlegal): 13%; government: 19%; public interest: 2%; judicial clerk: 7%; academia: 2%; unknown: 2%
Employment location for 2001 class: Intl. 1%; N.E. 1%; M.A. 1%; E.N.C. 3%; W.N.C. 1%; S.A. 3%; E.S.C. 1%; W.S.C. 3%; Mt. 82%; Pac. 2%; unknown 2%

CONNECTICUT

Quinnipiac University
275 Mount Carmel Avenue
Hamden, CT 06518
Private
Admissions: (203) 582-3400
E-mail: ladm@quinnipiac.edu
Web site: http://law.quinnipiac.edu
Financial aid: (203) 582-3405
Application deadline: rolling
Tuition: full time: $26,565; part time: $19,125
Room/board/expenses: $14,620
Students receiving grants: 48%
Median grant: $8,500
Average student indebtedness at graduation: $73,108
Enrollment: full time: 432; part time: 243
men: 53%; women: 47%; minorities: 9%
Acceptance rate (full time): 36%
Midrange LSAT (full time): 148-153
Midrange undergraduate GPA (full time): 2.66-3.32
Midrange of full-time private sector salaries of 2001 grads: $45,500-$80,000
2000 grads employed in: law firms: 41%; business and industry (legal): 16%; business and industry (nonlegal): 11%; government: 18%; public interest: 1%; judicial clerk: 12%; academia: 2%; unknown: 0%
Employment location for 2001 class: Intl. 0%; N.E. 80%; M.A. 9%; E.N.C. 1%; W.N.C. 1%; S.A. 6%; E.S.C. 1%; W.S.C. 0%; Mt. 0%; Pac. 1%; unknown 3%

University of Connecticut
55 Elizabeth Street
Hartford, CT 06105
Public
Admissions: (860) 570-5100
E-mail: admit@law.uconn.edu
Web site: http://www.law.uconn.edu
Internet application: http://www.law.uconn.edu/admissions/application/
Financial aid: (860) 570-5147
Application deadline: 03/15
In-state tuition: full time: $12,690; part time: $8,902
Out-of-state tuition: full time: $26,106
Room/board/expenses: $13,410
Students receiving grants: 59%
Median grant: $6,300
Average student indebtedness at graduation: $43,445
Enrollment: full time: 460; part time: 162
men: 47%; women: 53%; minorities: 13%
Acceptance rate (full time): 27%
Midrange LSAT (full time): 159-162
Midrange undergraduate GPA (full time): 3.22-3.66
Midrange of full-time private sector salaries of 2001 grads: $71,250-$97,500
2000 grads employed in: law firms: 47%; business and industry (legal): 5%; business and industry (nonlegal): 13%; government: 16%; public interest: 1%; judicial clerk: 15%; academia: 2%; unknown: 0%
Employment location for 2001 class: Intl. 1%; N.E. 74%; M.A. 11%; E.N.C. 1%; W.N.C. 1%; S.A. 5%; E.S.C. 2%; W.S.C. 1%; Mt. 2%; Pac. 4%; unknown 0%

Yale University
PO Box 208215
New Haven, CT 06520-8215
Private
Admissions: (203) 432-4995
E-mail: admissions.law@yale.edu
Web site: http://www.law.yale.edu
Internet application: http://www.law.yale.edu/outside/html/Admissions/admis-index.htm
Financial aid: (203) 432-1688
Application deadline: 02/15
Tuition: full time: $31,400; part time: N/A
Room/board/expenses: $12,630
Students receiving grants: 36%
Median grant: $14,011
Average student indebtedness at graduation: $69,995
Enrollment: full time: 594; part time: N/A
men: 52%; women: 48%; minorities: 29%
Acceptance rate (full time): 7%
Midrange LSAT (full time): 168-174
Midrange undergraduate GPA (full time): 3.75-3.97
Midrange of full-time private sector salaries of 2001 grads: $118,750-$125,000
2000 grads employed in: law firms: 36%; business and industry (legal): 0%; business and industry (nonlegal): 7%; government: 2%; public interest: 8%; judicial clerk: 45%; academia: 3%; unknown: 0%
Employment location for 2001 class: Intl. 3%; N.E. 12%; M.A. 29%; E.N.C. 4%; W.N.C. 2%; S.A. 17%; E.S.C. 1%; W.S.C. 7%; Mt. 4%; Pac. 22%; unknown 0%

DELAWARE

Widener University
PO Box 7474
Concord Pike
Wilmington, DE 19803-0474
Harrisonburg, PA, campus:
3800 Varten Way
PO Box 69381
Harrisonburg, PA 17106-9381
Private
Admissions: (302) 477-2162
E-mail: law.admissions@law.widener.edu
Web site: http://www.law.widener.edu
Financial aid: (302) 477-2272
Application deadline: 05/15
Tuition: full time: $23,260; part time: $17,350
Room/board/expenses: $12,350
Students receiving grants: 35%
Median grant: $2,975
Average student indebtedness at graduation: $68,890
Enrollment: full time: 978; part time: 565
men: 52%; women: 48%; minorities: 8%
Acceptance rate (full time): 57%
Midrange LSAT (full time): 147-151
Midrange undergraduate GPA (full time): 2.72-3.36
Midrange of full-time private sector salaries of 2001 grads: $40,000-$90,000
2000 grads employed in: law firms: 40%; business and industry (legal): 3%; business and industry (nonlegal): 19%; government: 17%; public interest: 1%; judicial clerk: 18%; academia: 1%; unknown: 1%
Employment location for 2001 class: Intl. 1%; N.E. 1%; M.A. 60%; E.N.C. 1%; W.N.C. 0%; S.A. 24%; E.S.C. 0%; W.S.C. 0%; Mt. 0%; Pac. 0%; unknown 13%

DISTRICT OF COLUMBIA

American University (Washington)
4801 Massachusetts Avenue NW
Washington, DC 20016-8192
Private
Admissions: (202) 274-4101
E-mail: wcladmit@wcl.american.edu
Web site: http://www.wcl.american.edu
Financial aid: (202) 274-4040
Application deadline: 03/01
Tuition: full time: $27,712; part time: $1,007/credit hour
Room/board/expenses: $15,504
Students receiving grants: 40%
Median grant: $8,000
Average student indebtedness at graduation: $74,324
Enrollment: full time: 1,119; part time: 314
men: 37%; women: 63%; minorities: 27%
Acceptance rate (full time): 30%
Midrange LSAT (full time): 156-160
Midrange undergraduate GPA (full time): 3.24-3.62
Midrange of full-time private sector salaries of 2001 grads: $64,500-$125,000
2000 grads employed in: law firms: 46%; business and industry (legal): 7%; business and industry (nonlegal): 5%; government: 16%; public interest: 8%; judicial clerk: 14%; academia: 2%; unknown: 3%
Employment location for 2001 class: Intl. 2%; N.E. 4%; M.A. 13%; E.N.C. 3%; W.N.C. 0%; S.A. 70%; E.S.C. 0%; W.S.C. 1%; Mt. 1%; Pac. 2%; unknown 4%

Catholic University of America
School of Law
Washington, DC 20064
Private
Admissions: (202) 319-5151
E-mail: admissions@law.edu
Web site: http://www.law.edu
Financial aid: (202) 319-5143
Application deadline: 03/01
Tuition: full time: $28,106; part time: $20,330
Room/board/expenses: $14,115
Students receiving grants: 31%
Median grant: $5,000
Average student indebtedness at graduation: $83,076
Enrollment: full time: 670; part time: 285
men: 47%; women: 53%; minorities: 19%
Acceptance rate (full time): 35%
Midrange LSAT (full time): 154-158
Midrange undergraduate GPA (full time): 3.01-3.50
Midrange of full-time private sector salaries of 2001 grads: $47,000-$125,000
2000 grads employed in: law firms: 47%; business and industry (legal): 14%; business and industry (nonlegal): 0%; government: 21%; public interest: 2%; judicial clerk: 16%; academia: 0%; unknown: 0%
Employment location for 2001 class: Intl. 0%; N.E. 4%; M.A. 8%; E.N.C. 1%; W.N.C. 1%; S.A. 83%; E.S.C. 0%; W.S.C. 0%; Mt. 1%; Pac. 2%; unknown 0%

Georgetown University
600 New Jersey Avenue NW
Washington, DC 20001
Private
Admissions: (202) 662-9015
E-mail: admis@law.georgetown.edu
Web site: http://www.law.georgetown.edu
Financial aid: (202) 662-9210
Application deadline: 03/01
Tuition: full time: $29,440; part time: $1,060/credit hour
Room/board/expenses: $16,560
Students receiving grants: 25%
Median grant: $9,500
Average student indebtedness at graduation: $86,033
Enrollment: full time: 1,607; part time: 276
men: 48%; women: 52%; minorities: 24%
Acceptance rate (full time): 18%
Midrange LSAT (full time): 165-169
Midrange undergraduate GPA (full time): 3.48-3.79
Midrange of full-time private sector salaries of 2001 grads: $110,000-$125,000
2000 grads employed in: law firms: 74%; business and industry (legal): 1%; business and industry (nonlegal): 5%; government: 5%; public interest: 5%; judicial clerk: 9%; academia: 1%; unknown: 0%
Employment location for 2001 class: Intl. 2%; N.E. 4%; M.A. 26%; E.N.C. 4%; W.N.C. 1%; S.A. 48%; E.S.C. 1%; W.S.C. 2%; Mt. 2%; Pac. 10%; unknown 0%

George Washington University
2000 H Street NW
Washington, DC 20052
Private
Admissions: (202) 739-0648
E-mail: jdadmit@law.gwu.edu
Web site: http://www.law.gwu.edu
Financial aid: (202) 994-7230
Application deadline: 03/01
Tuition: full time: $29,420; part time: $20,700
Room/board/expenses: $16,290
Students receiving grants: 40%
Median grant: $10,000
Average student indebtedness at graduation: $75,548
Enrollment: full time: 1,210; part time: 248
men: 51%; women: 49%; minorities: 32%
Acceptance rate (full time): 15%
Midrange LSAT (full time): 161-165
Midrange undergraduate GPA (full time): 3.31-3.68
Midrange of full-time private sector salaries of 2001 grads: $100,000-$125,000
2000 grads employed in: law firms: 60%; business and industry (legal): 8%; business and industry (nonlegal): N/A; government: 12%; public interest: 4%; judicial clerk: 11%; academia: 1%; unknown: 4%

Employment location for 2001 class: Intl. 1%; N.E. 2%; M.A. 18%; E.N.C. 5%; W.N.C. 1%; S.A. 59%; E.S.C. 0%; W.S.C. 1%; Mt. 1%; Pac. 8%; unknown 4%

Howard University
2900 Van Ness Street NW
Washington, DC 20008
Private
Admissions: (202) 806-8009
E-mail: admissions@law.howard.edu
Web site: http://www.law.howard.edu
Internet application: http://www4. lsac.org/school/howard.htm
Financial aid: (202) 806-8005
Application deadline: 03/31
Tuition: full time: $14,865; part time: N/A
Room/board/expenses: $17,447
Students receiving grants: 44%
Median grant: $6,000
Average student indebtedness at graduation: $61,112
Enrollment: full time: 504; part time: N/A
men: 37%; women: 63%; minorities: 89%
Acceptance rate (full time): 33%
Midrange LSAT (full time): 148-154
Midrange undergraduate GPA (full time): 2.90-3.34
Midrange of full-time private sector salaries of 2001 grads: $87,500-$125,000
2000 grads employed in: law firms: 40%; business and industry (legal): 19%; business and industry (nonlegal): 2%; government: 24%; public interest: 4%; judicial clerk: 11%; academia: 0%; unknown: 0%
Employment location for 2001 class: Intl. 1%; N.E. 1%; M.A. 20%; E.N.C. 14%; W.N.C. 1%; S.A. 48%; E.S.C. 3%; W.S.C. 4%; Mt. 0%; Pac. 7%; unknown 0%

University of the District of Columbia[1]
4250 Connecticut Avenue NW
Building 48
Washington, DC 20008
Public
Admissions: (202) 274-7341
E-mail: vcanty@law.udc.edu
Web site: http://www.law.udc.edu
Internet application: http://www. law.udc.edu/prospective_ students/app/udcp-o-a.htm
Financial aid: (202) 274-7337
Tuition: N/A
Room/board/expenses: N/A
Enrollment: N/A

FLORIDA

Barry University
6441 E. Colonial Drive
Orlando, FL 32746
Private
Admissions: (866) 532-2779
E-mail: lawinfo@mail.barry.edu
Web site: http://weblaw.barry.edu/
Financial aid: (407) 275-2000
Application deadline: 04/30
Tuition: full time: $22,660; part time: $16,400
Room/board/expenses: $14,600
Students receiving grants: 11%
Median grant: $8,346
Average student indebtedness at graduation: $75,340
Enrollment: full time: 131; part time: 180
men: 60%; women: 40%; minorities: 23%

Acceptance rate (full time): 57%
Midrange LSAT (full time): 145-153
Midrange undergraduate GPA (full time): 2.60-3.26
Midrange of full-time private sector salaries of 2001 grads: N/A-N/A
2000 grads employed in: law firms: 29%; business and industry (legal): 0%; business and industry (nonlegal): 57%; government: 0%; public interest: 0%; judicial clerk: 14%; academia: 0%; unknown: 0%
Employment location for 2001 class: Intl. 0%; N.E. 0%; M.A. 0%; E.N.C. 0%; W.N.C. 0%; S.A. 100%; E.S.C. 0%; W.S.C. 0%; Mt. 0%; Pac. 0%; unknown 0%

Florida Coastal School of Law
7555 Beach Boulevard
Jacksonville, FL 32216
Private
Admissions: (904) 680-7710
E-mail: admissions@fcsl.edu
Web site: http://www.fcsl.edu
Financial aid: (904) 680-7717
Application deadline: 08/01
Tuition: full time: $21,220; part time: $17,170
Room/board/expenses: $13,336
Students receiving grants: 39%
Median grant: $5,000
Average student indebtedness at graduation: $73,321
Enrollment: full time: 292; part time: 227
men: 60%; women: 40%; minorities: 14%
Acceptance rate (full time): 36%
Midrange LSAT (full time): 149-154
Midrange undergraduate GPA (full time): 2.57-3.17
Midrange of full-time private sector salaries of 2001 grads: $43,500-$67,500
2000 grads employed in: law firms: 36%; business and industry (legal): 25%; business and industry (nonlegal): N/A; government: 32%; public interest: 1%; judicial clerk: 2%; academia: 2%; unknown: 1%
Employment location for 2001 class: Intl. 1%; N.E. N/A; M.A. N/A; E.N.C. N/A; W.N.C. N/A; S.A. 95%; E.S.C. 2%; W.S.C. 1%; Mt. N/A; Pac. N/A; unknown 0%

Florida State University
425 W. Jefferson Street
Tallahassee, FL 32306-1601
Public
Admissions: (850) 644-3787
E-mail: admissions@law.fsu.edu
Web site: http://www.law.fsu.edu
Financial aid: (850) 644-5716
Application deadline: 02/15
In-state tuition: full time: $199/credit hour; part time: N/A
Out-of-state tuition: full time: $713/credit hour
Room/board/expenses: $14,000
Students receiving grants: 14%
Median grant: $1,200
Average student indebtedness at graduation: $47,201
Enrollment: full time: 766; part time: N/A
men: 55%; women: 45%; minorities: 22%
Acceptance rate (full time): 32%
Midrange LSAT (full time): 153-157
Midrange undergraduate GPA (full time): 3.16-3.66
Midrange of full-time private sector salaries of 2001 grads: $46,000-$80,000

2000 grads employed in: law firms: 60%; business and industry (legal): 0%; business and industry (nonlegal): 4%; government: 25%; public interest: 4%; judicial clerk: 3%; academia: 1%; unknown: 3%
Employment location for 2001 class: Intl. 0%; N.E. 1%; M.A. 1%; E.N.C. 0%; W.N.C. 1%; S.A. 90%; E.S.C. 1%; W.S.C. 1%; Mt. 0%; Pac. 1%; unknown 4%

Nova Southeastern University[1]
3305 College Avenue
Fort Lauderdale, FL 33314-7721
Private
Admissions: (954) 262-6117
E-mail: admission@nsu.law.nova.edu
Web site: http://www.nsulaw.nova.edu/
Financial aid: (954) 262-7412
Tuition: N/A
Room/board/expenses: N/A
Enrollment: N/A

Stetson University
1401 61st Street S
Gulfport, FL 33707
Private
Admissions: (727) 562-7802
E-mail: lawadmit@law.stetson.edu
Web site: http://www.law.stetson.edu
Internet application: http://www.law.stetson.edu/ admissions/contact.htm
Financial aid: (727) 562-7813
Application deadline: 03/01
Tuition: full time: $22,965; part time: $8,180
Room/board/expenses: $12,781
Students receiving grants: 16%
Median grant: $11,326
Average student indebtedness at graduation: $94,500
Enrollment: full time: 723; part time: 69
men: 46%; women: 54%; minorities: 15%
Acceptance rate (full time): 34%
Midrange LSAT (full time): 149-155
Midrange undergraduate GPA (full time): 2.98-3.55
Midrange of full-time private sector salaries of 2001 grads: $50,000-$75,000
2000 grads employed in: law firms: 55%; business and industry (legal): 4%; business and industry (nonlegal): 5%; government: 29%; public interest: 1%; judicial clerk: 4%; academia: 1%; unknown: 1%
Employment location for 2001 class: Intl. 0%; N.E. 1%; M.A. 2%; E.N.C. 0%; W.N.C. 0%; S.A. 94%; E.S.C. 1%; W.S.C. 1%; Mt. 1%; Pac. 2%; unknown 1%

St. Thomas University
16400 N.W. 32nd Avenue
Miami, FL 33054
Private
Admissions: (305) 623-2311
E-mail: admitme@stu.edu
Web site: http://www.stu.edu
Financial aid: (305) 628-6725
Application deadline: 04/30
Tuition: full time: $24,200; part time: N/A
Room/board/expenses: $16,005
Students receiving grants: 27%
Median grant: $12,500
Average student indebtedness at graduation: $82,233

Enrollment: full time: 487; part time: N/A
men: 50%; women: 50%; minorities: 47%
Acceptance rate (full time): 50%
Midrange LSAT (full time): 146-151
Midrange undergraduate GPA (full time): 2.64-3.22
Midrange of full-time private sector salaries of 2001 grads: $36,000-$60,000
2000 grads employed in: law firms: 58%; business and industry (legal): 14%; business and industry (nonlegal): 2%; government: 18%; public interest: 6%; judicial clerk: 2%; academia: 0%; unknown: 0%
Employment location for 2001 class: Intl. 0%; N.E. 1%; M.A. 1%; E.N.C. 1%; W.N.C. 0%; S.A. 92%; E.S.C. 2%; W.S.C. 0%; Mt. 0%; Pac. 3%; unknown 0%

University of Florida (Levin)
Levin College of Law
PO Box 117620
Gainesville, FL 32611-7622
Public
Admissions: (352) 392-2087
E-mail: patrick@law.ufl.edu
Web site: http://www.law.ufl.edu
Financial aid: (352) 392-0422
Application deadline: 02/01
In-state tuition: full time: $5,613; part time: N/A
Out-of-state tuition: full time: $19,862
Room/board/expenses: $10,820
Students receiving grants: 21%
Median grant: $1,500
Average student indebtedness at graduation: $42,421
Enrollment: full time: 1,184; part time: N/A
men: 52%; women: 48%; minorities: 27%
Acceptance rate (full time): 18%
Midrange LSAT (full time): 154-162
Midrange undergraduate GPA (full time): 3.31-3.79
Midrange of full-time private sector salaries of 2001 grads: $52,000-$85,000
2000 grads employed in: law firms: 59%; business and industry (legal): 4%; business and industry (nonlegal): 5%; government: 20%; public interest: 3%; judicial clerk: 5%; academia: 3%; unknown: 1%
Employment location for 2001 class: Intl. 0%; N.E. 0%; M.A. 3%; E.N.C. 1%; W.N.C. 0%; S.A. 83%; E.S.C. 0%; W.S.C. 1%; Mt. 1%; Pac. 1%; unknown 10%

University of Miami
PO Box 248087
Coral Gables, FL 33124-8087
Private
Admissions: (305) 284-2795
E-mail: admissions@law.miami.edu
Web site: http://www.law.miami.edu
Financial aid: (305) 284-3115
Application deadline: 07/31
Tuition: full time: $26,494; part time: $19,602
Room/board/expenses: $16,145
Students receiving grants: 27%
Median grant: $14,297
Average student indebtedness at graduation: $73,915
Enrollment: full time: 1,097; part time: 71
men: 51%; women: 49%; minorities: 26%
Acceptance rate (full time): 40%

Midrange LSAT (full time): 153-158
Midrange undergraduate GPA (full time): 3.16-3.56
Midrange of full-time private sector salaries of 2001 grads: $52,000-$105,000
2000 grads employed in: law firms: 67%; business and industry (legal): 2%; business and industry (nonlegal): 4%; government: 16%; public interest: 2%; judicial clerk: 3%; academia: 2%; unknown: 4%
Employment location for 2001 class: Intl. 0%; N.E. 1%; M.A. 6%; E.N.C. 1%; W.N.C. 1%; S.A. 88%; E.S.C. 0%; W.S.C. 1%; Mt. 0%; Pac. 2%; unknown 0%

GEORGIA

Emory University
Gambrell Hall
Atlanta, GA 30322
Private
Admissions: (404) 727-6802
E-mail: lawinfo@law.emory.edu
Web site: http://www.law.emory.edu
Financial aid: (404) 727-6039
Application deadline: 03/01
Tuition: full time: $27,906; part time: N/A
Room/board/expenses: $13,202
Students receiving grants: 28%
Median grant: $23,030
Average student indebtedness at graduation: $74,265
Enrollment: full time: 702; part time: N/A
men: 47%; women: 53%; minorities: 18%
Acceptance rate (full time): 29%
Midrange LSAT (full time): 160-165
Midrange undergraduate GPA (full time): 3.37-3.75
Midrange of full-time private sector salaries of 2001 grads: $63,000-$110,000
2000 grads employed in: law firms: 64%; business and industry (legal): 2%; business and industry (nonlegal): 7%; government: 12%; public interest: 2%; judicial clerk: 12%; academia: 1%; unknown: 1%
Employment location for 2001 class: Intl. 0%; N.E. 3%; M.A. 18%; E.N.C. 5%; W.N.C. 1%; S.A. 59%; E.S.C. 5%; W.S.C. 5%; Mt. 1%; Pac. 3%; unknown 0%

Georgia State University
PO Box 4049
Atlanta, GA 30302-4049
Public
Admissions: (404) 651-2048
E-mail: admissions@gsulaw.gsu.edu
Web site: http://law.gsu.edu
Financial aid: (404) 651-2227
Application deadline: 03/15
In-state tuition: full time: $4,470; part time: $4,162
Out-of-state tuition: full time: $15,558
Room/board/expenses: $13,730
Students receiving grants: 15%
Median grant: $3,696
Average student indebtedness at graduation: $39,125
Enrollment: full time: 479; part time: 193
men: 47%; women: 53%; minorities: 15%
Acceptance rate (full time): 22%
Midrange LSAT (full time): 154-164
Midrange undergraduate GPA (full time): 3.10-3.52

Midrange of full-time private sector salaries of 2001 grads: $55,000-$105,000
2000 grads employed in: law firms: 54%; business and industry (legal): 9%; business and industry (nonlegal): 11%; government: 9%; public interest: 5%; judicial clerk: 8%; academia: 3%; unknown: N/A
Employment location for 2001 class: Intl. 1%; N.E. 1%; M.A. N/A; E.N.C. 1%; W.N.C. N/A; S.A. 97%; E.S.C. N/A; W.S.C. N/A; Mt. N/A; Pac. N/A; unknown N/A

Mercer University

1021 Georgia Avenue
Macon, GA 31207-0001
Private
Admissions: (478) 301-2605
E-mail: martin_sv@mercer.edu
Web site: http://www.law.mercer.edu
Internet application: http://www.law.mercer.edu/prospectivestudents
Financial aid: (478) 301-2064
Application deadline: 03/15
Tuition: full time: $22,313; part time: N/A
Room/board/expenses: $12,500
Students receiving grants: 36%
Median grant: $15,000
Average student indebtedness at graduation: $68,969
Enrollment: full time: 436; part time: 2
men: 54%; women: 46%; minorities: 12%
Acceptance rate (full time): 36%
Midrange LSAT (full time): 151-156
Midrange undergraduate GPA (full time): 2.94-3.58
Midrange of full-time private sector salaries of 2001 grads: $42,250-$65,000
2000 grads employed in: law firms: 64%; business and industry (legal): 4%; business and industry (nonlegal): 0%; government: 9%; public interest: 3%; judicial clerk: 18%; academia: 1%; unknown: 1%
Employment location for 2001 class: Intl. 0%; N.E. 1%; M.A. 0%; E.N.C. 1%; W.N.C. 0%; S.A. 87%; E.S.C. 6%; W.S.C. 0%; Mt. 3%; Pac. 0%; unknown 3%

University of Georgia

Herty Drive
Athens, GA 30602
Public
Admissions: (706) 542-7060
E-mail: ugajd@uga.edu
Web site: http://www.lawsch.uga.edu
Financial aid: (706) 542-6147
Application deadline: 03/01
In-state tuition: full time: $5,832; part time: N/A
Out-of-state tuition: full time: $20,850
Room/board/expenses: $10,188
Students receiving grants: 54%
Median grant: $1,000
Average student indebtedness at graduation: $38,957
Enrollment: full time: 640; part time: N/A
men: 53%; women: 47%; minorities: 15%
Acceptance rate (full time): 21%
Midrange LSAT (full time): 158-164
Midrange undergraduate GPA (full time): 3.30-3.81
Midrange of full-time private sector salaries of 2001 grads: $75,000-$100,000

2000 grads employed in: law firms: 58%; business and industry (legal): 1%; business and industry (nonlegal): 6%; government: 11%; public interest: 4%; judicial clerk: 19%; academia: 1%; unknown: 0%
Employment location for 2001 class: Intl. 0%; N.E. 0%; M.A. 1%; E.N.C. 2%; W.N.C. 1%; S.A. 86%; E.S.C. 3%; W.S.C. 2%; Mt. 1%; Pac. 2%; unknown 2%

HAWAII

University of Hawaii

2515 Dole Street
Honolulu, HI 96822
Public
Admissions: (808) 956-3000
E-mail: lawadm@hawaii.edu
Web site: http://www.hawaii.edu/law
Internet application: http://www.hawaii.edu/law/admissions/forms
Financial aid: (808) 956-7251
Application deadline: 03/01
In-state tuition: full time: $10,322; part time: N/A
Out-of-state tuition: full time: $17,594
Room/board/expenses: $9,633
Students receiving grants: 55%
Median grant: $4,812
Average student indebtedness at graduation: $35,408
Enrollment: full time: 260; part time: N/A
men: 40%; women: 60%; minorities: 70%
Acceptance rate (full time): 33%
Midrange LSAT (full time): 153-159
Midrange undergraduate GPA (full time): 3.00-3.66
Midrange of full-time private sector salaries of 2001 grads: $50,000-$64,000
2000 grads employed in: law firms: 40%; business and industry (legal): 3%; business and industry (nonlegal): 3%; government: 10%; public interest: 7%; judicial clerk: 35%; academia: 2%; unknown: 0%
Employment location for 2001 class: Intl. N/A; N.E. 0%; M.A. 2%; E.N.C. 2%; W.N.C. 0%; S.A. 0%; E.S.C. 0%; W.S.C. 0%; Mt. 0%; Pac. 93%; unknown 0%

IDAHO

University of Idaho

College of Law
PO Box 442321
Moscow, ID 83844-2321
Public
Admissions: (208) 885-6423
E-mail: lawadmit@uidaho.edu
Web site: http://www.law.uidaho.edu
Internet application: http://www.law.uidaho.edu/admissions/Apply.asp
Financial aid: (208) 885-6312
Application deadline: 02/01
In-state tuition: full time: $5,984; part time: N/A
Out-of-state tuition: full time: $12,704
Room/board/expenses: $11,806
Enrollment: full time: 317; part time: N/A
men: 63%; women: 37%; minorities: 6%
Acceptance rate (full time): 47%
Midrange LSAT (full time): 149-156
Midrange undergraduate GPA (full time): 3.18-3.68
Midrange of full-time private sector salaries of 2001 grads: $38,000-$53,000

2000 grads employed in: law firms: 38%; business and industry (legal): 7%; business and industry (nonlegal): 0%; government: 28%; public interest: 1%; judicial clerk: 22%; academia: 1%; unknown: 2%
Employment location for 2001 class: Intl. 0%; N.E. 0%; M.A. 2%; E.N.C. 1%; W.N.C. 2%; S.A. 1%; E.S.C. 0%; W.S.C. 0%; Mt. 60%; Pac. 34%; unknown 0%

ILLINOIS

DePaul University

25 E. Jackson Boulevard
Chicago, IL 60604
Private
Admissions: (312) 362-6831
E-mail: lawinfo@depaul.edu
Web site: http://www.law.depaul.edu
Internet application: http://www.law.depaul.edu/apply
Financial aid: (312) 362-8091
Application deadline: 04/01
Tuition: full time: $25,140; part time: $16,440
Room/board/expenses: $14,082
Students receiving grants: 68%
Median grant: $2,619
Average student indebtedness at graduation: $76,500
Enrollment: full time: 710; part time: 290
men: 46%; women: 54%; minorities: 23%
Acceptance rate (full time): 32%
Midrange LSAT (full time): 153-158
Midrange undergraduate GPA (full time): 3.21-3.65
Midrange of full-time private sector salaries of 2001 grads: $47,000-$125,000
2000 grads employed in: law firms: 56%; business and industry (legal): 3%; business and industry (nonlegal): 12%; government: 14%; public interest: 4%; judicial clerk: 2%; academia: 1%; unknown: 8%
Employment location for 2001 class: Intl. 0%; N.E. 0%; M.A. 0%; E.N.C. 86%; W.N.C. 1%; S.A. 5%; E.S.C. 0%; W.S.C. 0%; Mt. 1%; Pac. 2%; unknown 3%

Illinois Institute of Technology (Chicago-Kent)

565 W. Adams Street
Chicago, IL 60661
Private
Admissions: (312) 906-5020
E-mail: admit@kentlaw.edu
Web site: http://www.kentlaw.edu/
Financial aid: (312) 906-5180
Application deadline: 03/01
Tuition: full time: $25,300; part time: $18,600
Room/board/expenses: $17,765
Students receiving grants: 51%
Median grant: $7,000
Average student indebtedness at graduation: $78,478
Enrollment: full time: 706; part time: 259
men: 49%; women: 51%; minorities: 12%
Acceptance rate (full time): 37%
Midrange LSAT (full time): 155-159
Midrange undergraduate GPA (full time): 3.09-3.52
Midrange of full-time private sector salaries of 2001 grads: $50,000-$110,000
2000 grads employed in: law firms: 56%; business and industry (legal): 7%; business and industry (nonlegal): 13%; government:

16%; public interest: 3%; judicial clerk: 4%; academia: 1%; unknown: 0%
Employment location for 2001 class: Intl. 0%; N.E. 0%; M.A. 2%; E.N.C. 88%; W.N.C. 0%; S.A. 4%; E.S.C. 0%; W.S.C. 0%; Mt. 2%; Pac. 3%; unknown N/A

John Marshall Law School

315 S. Plymouth Court
Chicago, IL 60604
Private
Admissions: (800) 537-4280
E-mail: admission@jmls.edu
Web site: http://www.jmls.edu
Financial aid: (800) 537-4280
Application deadline: 03/01
Tuition: full time: $23,900; part time: $17,100
Room/board/expenses: $16,494
Students receiving grants: 30%
Median grant: $6,000
Average student indebtedness at graduation: $81,909
Enrollment: full time: 836; part time: 426
men: 56%; women: 44%; minorities: 13%
Acceptance rate (full time): 36%
Midrange LSAT (full time): 150-154
Midrange undergraduate GPA (full time): 2.65-3.23
Midrange of full-time private sector salaries of 2001 grads: $45,250-$97,000
2000 grads employed in: law firms: 59%; business and industry (legal): 4%; business and industry (nonlegal): 11%; government: 18%; public interest: 0%; judicial clerk: 5%; academia: 1%; unknown: 2%
Employment location for 2001 class: Intl. 0%; N.E. 0%; M.A. 2%; E.N.C. 87%; W.N.C. 0%; S.A. 2%; E.S.C. 0%; W.S.C. 0%; Mt. 1%; Pac. 2%; unknown 6%

Loyola University Chicago

1 E. Pearson Street
Chicago, IL 60611
Private
Admissions: (312) 915-7170
E-mail: law-admissions@luc.edu
Web site: http://www.luc.edu/schools/law
Internet application: http://www.luc.edu/schools/law/admissions/index.html
Financial aid: (312) 915-7170
Application deadline: 04/01
Tuition: full time: $25,344; part time: $19,038
Room/board/expenses: $13,400
Students receiving grants: 64%
Median grant: $4,800
Average student indebtedness at graduation: $59,268
Enrollment: full time: 550; part time: 255
men: 41%; women: 59%; minorities: 17%
Acceptance rate (full time): 24%
Midrange LSAT (full time): 157-161
Midrange undergraduate GPA (full time): 3.04-3.53
Midrange of full-time private sector salaries of 2001 grads: $60,000-$125,000
2000 grads employed in: law firms: 55%; business and industry (legal): 4%; business and industry (nonlegal): 7%; government: 25%; public interest: 2%; judicial clerk: 6%; academia: 1%; unknown: 0%

Employment location for 2001 class: Intl. 0%; N.E. 2%; M.A. 2%; E.N.C. 87%; W.N.C. 1%; S.A. 5%; E.S.C. 1%; W.S.C. 0%; Mt. 1%; Pac. 2%; unknown 0%

Northern Illinois University

College of Law
De Kalb, IL 60115
Public
Admissions: (815) 753-9485
E-mail: lawadm@niu.edu
Web site: http://www.niu.edu/col
Internet application: http://www3.niu.edu/claw/admissions/appinfo.htm
Financial aid: (815) 753-9485
Application deadline: 05/15
In-state tuition: full time: $8,656; part time: $361/credit hour
Out-of-state tuition: full time: $15,572
Room/board/expenses: $9,284
Students receiving grants: 19%
Median grant: $3,180
Average student indebtedness at graduation: $36,702
Enrollment: full time: 314; part time: 18
men: 50%; women: 50%; minorities: 22%
Acceptance rate (full time): 34%
Midrange LSAT (full time): 151-157
Midrange undergraduate GPA (full time): 2.90-3.49
Midrange of full-time private sector salaries of 2001 grads: $36,000-$45,000
2000 grads employed in: law firms: 56%; business and industry (legal): 10%; business and industry (nonlegal): 0%; government: 25%; public interest: 2%; judicial clerk: 8%; academia: 0%; unknown: 0%
Employment location for 2001 class: Intl. 0%; N.E. 0%; M.A. 0%; E.N.C. 86%; W.N.C. 3%; S.A. 5%; E.S.C. 0%; W.S.C. 0%; Mt. 0%; Pac. 3%; unknown N/A

Northwestern University

357 E. Chicago Avenue
Chicago, IL 60611
Private
Admissions: (312) 503-8465
E-mail: nulawadm@law.northwestern.edu
Web site: http://www.law.northwestern.edu
Internet application: http://www.law.nwu.edu/depts/admissions/index.htm
Financial aid: (312) 503-8465
Application deadline: 02/15
Tuition: full time: $32,008; part time: N/A
Room/board/expenses: $18,480
Students receiving grants: 43%
Median grant: $16,000
Average student indebtedness at graduation: $86,262
Enrollment: full time: 693; part time: N/A
men: 51%; women: 49%; minorities: 29%
Acceptance rate (full time): 17%
Midrange LSAT (full time): 165-169
Midrange undergraduate GPA (full time): 3.30-3.70
Midrange of full-time private sector salaries of 2001 grads: $125,000-$125,000
2000 grads employed in: law firms: 82%; business and industry (legal): 0%; business and industry (nonlegal): 4%; government: 1%;

public interest: 2%; judicial clerk: 9%; academia: 2%; unknown: 0%
Employment location for 2001 class: Intl. 1%; N.E. 5%; M.A. 17%; E.N.C. 48%; W.N.C. 1%; S.A. 9%; E.S.C. 1%; W.S.C. 1%; Mt. 2%; Pac. 15%; unknown 0%

Southern Illinois University–Carbondale

Lesar Law Building
Carbondale, IL 62901-6804
Public
Admissions: (800) 739-9187
E-mail: lawadmit@siu.edu
Web site: http://www.law.siu.edu
Financial aid: (618) 453-4334
Application deadline: 03/01
In-state tuition: full time: $7,319; part time: N/A
Out-of-state tuition: full time: $19,559
Room/board/expenses: $9,821
Students receiving grants: 37%
Median grant: $1,500
Average student indebtedness at graduation: $42,900
Enrollment: full time: 361; part time: 2
men: 58%; women: 42%; minorities: 8%
Acceptance rate (full time): 52%
Midrange LSAT (full time): 149-154
Midrange undergraduate GPA (full time): 3.04-3.60
Midrange of full-time private sector salaries of 2001 grads: $35,000-$55,000
2000 grads employed in: law firms: 60%; business and industry (legal): 9%; business and industry (nonlegal): N/A; government: 25%; public interest: 3%; judicial clerk: 3%; academia: N/A; unknown: N/A
Employment location for 2001 class: Intl. N/A; N.E. 1%; M.A. 1%; E.N.C. 60%; W.N.C. 20%; S.A. 7%; E.S.C. 7%; W.S.C. 0%; Mt. 3%; Pac. 0%; unknown 0%

University of Chicago

1111 E. 60th Street
Chicago, IL 60637
Private
Admissions: (773) 702-9484
E-mail: admissions@law.uchicago.edu
Web site: http://www.law.uchicago.edu
Financial aid: (773) 702-9484
Application deadline: 02/01
Tuition: full time: $31,170; part time: N/A
Room/board/expenses: $18,297
Students receiving grants: 52%
Median grant: $12,300
Average student indebtedness at graduation: $80,600
Enrollment: full time: 600; part time: N/A
men: 59%; women: 41%; minorities: 28%
Acceptance rate (full time): 16%
Midrange LSAT (full time): 167-171
Midrange undergraduate GPA (full time): 3.54-3.76
Midrange of full-time private sector salaries of 2001 grads: $120,000-$125,000
2000 grads employed in: law firms: 70%; business and industry (legal): 1%; business and industry (nonlegal): 3%; government: 2%; public interest: 0%; judicial clerk: 24%; academia: 0%; unknown: 0%
Employment location for 2001 class: Intl. 1%; N.E. 4%; M.A. 15%; E.N.C. 27%; W.N.C. 2%; S.A. 21%; E.S.C. 2%; W.S.C. 11%; Mt. 1%; Pac. 16%; unknown 0%

University of Illinois–Urbana-Champaign

504 E. Pennsylvania Avenue
Champaign, IL 61820
Public
Admissions: (217) 244-6415
E-mail: admissions@law.uiuc.edu
Web site: http://www.law.uiuc.edu/
Internet application: http://www.law.uiuc.edu/admissions/apply.asp
Financial aid: (217) 244-6415
Application deadline: 03/15
In-state tuition: full time: $12,874; part time: N/A
Out-of-state tuition: full time: $25,962
Room/board/expenses: $11,590
Students receiving grants: 46%
Median grant: $4,300
Average student indebtedness at graduation: $51,591
Enrollment: full time: 676; part time: N/A
men: 58%; women: 42%; minorities: 27%
Acceptance rate (full time): 26%
Midrange LSAT (full time): 159-163
Midrange undergraduate GPA (full time): 3.15-3.60
Midrange of full-time private sector salaries of 2001 grads: $55,000-$125,000
2000 grads employed in: law firms: 68%; business and industry (legal): 5%; business and industry (nonlegal): 2%; government: 14%; public interest: 2%; judicial clerk: 8%; academia: 1%; unknown: 0%
Employment location for 2001 class: Intl. 0%; N.E. 1%; M.A. 0%; E.N.C. 79%; W.N.C. 6%; S.A. 6%; E.S.C. 0%; W.S.C. 1%; Mt. 4%; Pac. 4%; unknown 0%

Indiana University–Bloomington

211 S. Indiana Avenue
Bloomington, IN 47405-1001
Public
Admissions: (812) 855-4765
E-mail: lawadmis@indiana.edu
Web site: http://www.law.indiana.edu
Financial aid: (812) 855-7746
Application deadline: rolling
In-state tuition: full time: $10,872; part time: N/A
Out-of-state tuition: full time: $23,119
Room/board/expenses: $13,064
Students receiving grants: 64%
Median grant: $4,000
Average student indebtedness at graduation: $54,000
Enrollment: full time: 652; part time: 4
men: 56%; women: 44%; minorities: 16%
Acceptance rate (full time): 33%
Midrange LSAT (full time): 156-163
Midrange undergraduate GPA (full time): 3.03-3.73
Midrange of full-time private sector salaries of 2001 grads: $51,000-$100,000
2000 grads employed in: law firms: 63%; business and industry (legal): 5%; business and industry (nonlegal): 0%; government: 6%; public interest: 2%; judicial clerk: 8%; academia: 11%; unknown: 5%
Employment location for 2001 class: Intl. 0%; N.E. 1%; M.A. 3%; E.N.C. 75%; W.N.C. 1%; S.A. 11%; E.S.C. 2%; W.S.C. 2%; Mt. 1%; Pac. 4%; unknown 1%

Indiana University–Indianapolis

530 W. New York Street
Indianapolis, IN 46202-3225
Public
Admissions: (317) 274-2459
E-mail: amespada@iupui.edu
Web site: http://www.indylaw.indiana.edu
Financial aid: (317) 274-5915
Application deadline: 03/01
In-state tuition: full time: $9,390; part time: $6,542
Out-of-state tuition: full time: $18,741
Room/board/expenses: $17,436
Students receiving grants: 17%
Median grant: $4,000
Average student indebtedness at graduation: $50,000
Enrollment: full time: 561; part time: 297
men: 53%; women: 47%; minorities: 14%
Acceptance rate (full time): 34%
Midrange LSAT (full time): 151-159
Midrange undergraduate GPA (full time): 3.12-3.63
Midrange of full-time private sector salaries of 2001 grads: $40,000-$75,000
2000 grads employed in: law firms: 55%; business and industry (legal): 6%; business and industry (nonlegal): 10%; government: 23%; public interest: 1%; judicial clerk: 3%; academia: 2%; unknown: N/A
Employment location for 2001 class: Intl. 1%; N.E. 1%; M.A. 1%; E.N.C. 89%; W.N.C. 2%; S.A. 4%; E.S.C. N/A; W.S.C. N/A; Mt. 1%; Pac. 1%; unknown N/A

University of Notre Dame

Notre Dame Law School
PO Box R
Notre Dame, IN 46556-0780
Private
Admissions: (574) 631-6626
E-mail: lawadmit@nd.edu
Web site: http://www.lawadmissions.nd.edu
Internet application: https://www4.lsac.org/school/NotreDame.htm
Financial aid: (574) 631-6626
Application deadline: 03/01
Tuition: full time: $26,402; part time: N/A
Room/board/expenses: $10,965
Students receiving grants: 55%
Median grant: $7,500
Average student indebtedness at graduation: $65,750
Enrollment: full time: 550; part time: N/A
men: 57%; women: 43%; minorities: 19%
Acceptance rate (full time): 20%
Midrange LSAT (full time): 160-165
Midrange undergraduate GPA (full time): 3.32-3.82
Midrange of full-time private sector salaries of 2001 grads: $80,000-$125,000
2000 grads employed in: law firms: 69%; business and industry (legal): 5%; business and industry (nonlegal): N/A; government: 13%; public interest: 3%; judicial clerk: 9%; academia: 2%; unknown: 1%
Employment location for 2001 class: Intl. N/A; N.E. 6%; M.A. 13%; E.N.C. 45%; W.N.C. 4%; S.A. 9%; E.S.C. 2%; W.S.C. 2%; Mt. 4%; Pac. 8%; unknown 7%

Valparaiso University

Wesemann Hall
Valparaiso, IN 46383
Private
Admissions: (219) 548-7703
E-mail: valpolaw@valpo.edu
Web site: http://www.valpo.edu/law
Financial aid: (219) 465-7818
Application deadline: 04/15
Tuition: full time: $21,994; part time: $840/credit hour
Room/board/expenses: $9,950
Students receiving grants: 26%
Median grant: $10,725
Average student indebtedness at graduation: $60,655
Enrollment: full time: 465; part time: 43
men: 51%; women: 49%; minorities: 9%
Acceptance rate (full time): 57%
Midrange LSAT (full time): 150-156
Midrange undergraduate GPA (full time): 3.02-3.59
Midrange of full-time private sector salaries of 2001 grads: $42,500-$80,000
2000 grads employed in: law firms: 60%; business and industry (legal): 4%; business and industry (nonlegal): 2%; government: 18%; public interest: 6%; judicial clerk: 8%; academia: 2%; unknown: N/A
Employment location for 2001 class: Intl. 1%; N.E. N/A; M.A. 1%; E.N.C. 83%; W.N.C. 2%; S.A. 11%; E.S.C. 2%; W.S.C. N/A; Mt. N/A; Pac. 1%; unknown N/A

Drake University

2507 University Avenue
Des Moines, IA 50311
Private
Admissions: (515) 271-2782
E-mail: lawadmit@drake.edu
Web site: http://www.law.drake.edu/
Financial aid: (515) 271-2905
Application deadline: 04/01
Tuition: full time: $19,450; part time: $650/credit hour
Room/board/expenses: $12,700
Students receiving grants: 40%
Median grant: $8,000
Average student indebtedness at graduation: $62,530
Enrollment: full time: 415; part time: 11
men: 49%; women: 51%; minorities: 7%
Acceptance rate (full time): 47%
Midrange LSAT (full time): 151-156
Midrange undergraduate GPA (full time): 3.06-3.63
Midrange of full-time private sector salaries of 2001 grads: $36,000-$80,000
2000 grads employed in: law firms: 61%; business and industry (legal): 3%; business and industry (nonlegal): 10%; government: 12%; public interest: 1%; judicial clerk: 12%; academia: 1%; unknown: 0%
Employment location for 2001 class: Intl. N/A; N.E. 2%; M.A. N/A; E.N.C. 8%; W.N.C. 71%; S.A. 7%; E.S.C. 1%; W.S.C. 2%; Mt. 6%; Pac. 1%; unknown 3%

University of Iowa

276 Boyd Law Building
Iowa City, IA 52242
Public
Admissions: (319) 335-9095
E-mail: law-admissions@uiowa.edu
Web site: http://www.uiowa.edu/~lawcoll
Financial aid: (319) 335-9142
Application deadline: 02/01
In-state tuition: full time: $10,508; part time: N/A
Out-of-state tuition: full time: $24,266
Room/board/expenses: $9,730
Students receiving grants: 30%
Median grant: $9,910
Average student indebtedness at graduation: $51,436
Enrollment: full time: 738; part time: N/A
men: 53%; women: 47%; minorities: 15%
Acceptance rate (full time): 28%
Midrange LSAT (full time): 157-163
Midrange undergraduate GPA (full time): 3.25-3.75
Midrange of full-time private sector salaries of 2001 grads: $50,000-$105,000
2000 grads employed in: law firms: 61%; business and industry (legal): 3%; business and industry (nonlegal): 5%; government: 13%; public interest: 4%; judicial clerk: 11%; academia: 1%; unknown: 2%
Employment location for 2001 class: Intl. 1%; N.E. 1%; M.A. 3%; E.N.C. 26%; W.N.C. 42%; S.A. 8%; E.S.C. 0%; W.S.C. 1%; Mt. 6%; Pac. 9%; unknown 2%

University of Kansas

Green Hall
1535 W. 15th Street
Lawrence, KS 66045
Public
Admissions: (866) 220-3654
E-mail: admitlaw@ku.edu
Web site: http://www.law.ku.edu
Internet application: https://www.law.ku.edu/admissions/newapp
Financial aid: (785) 864-4700
Application deadline: 03/15
In-state tuition: full time: $7,239; part time: N/A
Out-of-state tuition: full time: $14,354
Room/board/expenses: $11,658
Students receiving grants: 37%
Median grant: $4,321
Average student indebtedness at graduation: $40,815
Enrollment: full time: 539; part time: N/A
men: 57%; women: 43%; minorities: 14%
Acceptance rate (full time): 37%
Midrange LSAT (full time): 154-160
Midrange undergraduate GPA (full time): 3.11-3.74
Midrange of full-time private sector salaries of 2001 grads: $42,500-$78,000
2000 grads employed in: law firms: 51%; business and industry (legal): 6%; business and industry (nonlegal): 12%; government: 15%; public interest: 4%; judicial clerk: 8%; academia: 2%; unknown: 1%
Employment location for 2001 class: Intl. 1%; N.E. 0%; M.A. 1%; E.N.C. 1%; W.N.C. 75%; S.A. 3%; E.S.C. 0%; W.S.C. 5%; Mt. 8%; Pac. 3%; unknown 3%

Washburn University

1700 College
Topeka, KS 66621
Public
Admissions: (785) 231-1185
E-mail: admissions@washburnlaw.edu

Web site: http://washburnlaw.edu
Internet application:
http://washburnlaw.edu/
applyonline/
Financial aid: (785) 231-1151
Application deadline: 04/01
In-state tuition: full time: $9,262;
part time: N/A
Out-of-state tuition: full time:
$15,170
Room/board/expenses: $11,805
Students receiving grants: 41%
Median grant: $3,000
**Average student indebtedness at
graduation:** $48,450
Enrollment: full time: 451; part
time: N/A
men: 55%; women: 45%;
minorities: 12%
Acceptance rate (full time): 59%
Midrange LSAT (full time): 145-153
**Midrange undergraduate GPA (full
time):** 2.89-3.54
**Midrange of full-time private sector
salaries of 2001 grads:** $35,250-
$50,000
2000 grads employed in: law firms:
53%; business and industry
(legal): 9%; business and industry
(nonlegal): 0%; government: 26%;
public interest: 5%; judicial clerk:
5%; academia: 2%; unknown: 0%
**Employment location for 2001
class:** Intl: 0%; N.E. 1%; M.A. N/A; E.N.C.
3%; W.N.C. 77%; S.A. 6%; E.S.C.
N/A; W.S.C. 3%; Mt. 7%; Pac. 4%;
unknown 0%

KENTUCKY

Northern Kentucky University (Chase)
Nunn Hall
Highland Heights, KY 41099-6031
Public
Admissions: (859) 572-5384
E-mail: beersk@nku.edu
Web site:
http://www.nku.edu/~chase
Financial aid: (859) 572-6437
Application deadline: 03/01
In-state tuition: full time: $7,824;
part time: $6,520
Out-of-state tuition: full time:
$17,808
Room/board/expenses: $13,700
Students receiving grants: 30%
Median grant: $4,070
**Average student indebtedness at
graduation:** $56,856
Enrollment: full time: 256; part
time: 210
men: 53%; women: 47%;
minorities: 5%
Acceptance rate (full time): 47%
Midrange LSAT (full time): 150-155
**Midrange undergraduate GPA (full
time):** 2.97-3.56
**Midrange of full-time private sector
salaries of 2001 grads:** $38,500-
$75,000
2000 grads employed in: law firms:
46%; business and industry
(legal): 21%; business and industry (nonlegal): 14%; government:
8%; public interest: 7%; judicial
clerk: 3%; academia: 1%;
unknown: 0%
Employment location for 2001 class:
Intl: N/A; N.E. N/A; M.A. N/A;
E.N.C. 54%; W.N.C. N/A; S.A. 3%;
E.S.C. 43%; W.S.C. N/A; Mt. N/A;
Pac. N/A; unknown N/A

University of Kentucky
209 Law Building
Lexington, KY 40506-0048
Public
Admissions: (859) 257-6770
E-mail: dbakert@uky.edu

Web site: http://www.uky.edu/law
Internet application: http://www.
uky.edu/law/admissions
Financial aid: (859) 257-3172
Application deadline: 03/01
In-state tuition: full time: $7,042;
part time: N/A
Out-of-state tuition: full time:
$16,542
Room/board/expenses: $11,458
Students receiving grants: 45%
Median grant: $3,000
**Average student indebtedness at
graduation:** $43,852
Enrollment: full time: 398; part
time: N/A
men: 53%; women: 47%;
minorities: 7%
Acceptance rate (full time): 34%
Midrange LSAT (full time): 156-161
**Midrange undergraduate GPA (full
time):** 3.34-3.73
**Midrange of full-time private sector
salaries of 2001 grads:** $45,000-
$71,250
2000 grads employed in: law firms:
49%; business and industry
(legal): 5%; business and industry
(nonlegal): 1%; government: 16%;
public interest: 2%; judicial clerk:
27%; academia: 0%; unknown: 0%
Employment location for 2001 class:
Intl: 0%; N.E. 0%; M.A. 2%; E.N.C.
9%; W.N.C. 1%; S.A. 8%; E.S.C.
76%; W.S.C. 1%; Mt. 1%; Pac. 0%;
unknown 2%

LOUISIANA

Louisiana State University–Baton Rouge
400 Paul M. Hebert Law Center
Baton Rougé, LA 70803
Public
Admissions: (225) 578-8646
E-mail: admissions@law.lsu.edu
Web site: http://www.law.lsu.edu
Financial aid: (225) 578-3103
Application deadline: 02/01
In-state tuition: full time: $7,926;
part time: N/A
Out-of-state tuition: full time:
$14,852
Room/board/expenses: $10,550
Students receiving grants: 26%
Median grant: $3,059
**Average student indebtedness at
graduation:** $48,393
Enrollment: full time: 626; part
time: 5
men: 52%; women: 48%;
minorities: 14%
Acceptance rate (full time): 37%
Midrange LSAT (full time): 150-156
**Midrange undergraduate GPA (full
time):** 3.15-3.67
**Midrange of full-time private sector
salaries of 2001 grads:** N/A-N/A
2000 grads employed in: law firms:
56%; business and industry
(legal): 3%; business and industry
(nonlegal): 0%; government: 12%;
public interest: 0%; judicial clerk:
28%; academia: 1%; unknown: 0%
Employment location for 2001 class:
Intl: N/A; N.E. N/A; M.A. N/A;
E.N.C. N/A; W.N.C. N/A; S.A. N/A;
E.S.C. N/A; W.S.C. N/A; Mt. N/A;
Pac. N/A; unknown N/A

Loyola University–New Orleans
7214 St. Charles Avenue
New Orleans, LA 70118
Private
Admissions: (504) 861-5575
E-mail: ladmit@loyno.edu
Web site: http://law.loyno.edu/
Internet application:
http://law.loyno.edu/admissions/
application.php
Financial aid: (504) 865-3231
Application deadline: 03/01
Tuition: full time: $764/credit hour;
part time: $764/credit hour
Room/board/expenses: $12,025
Students receiving grants: 32%
Median grant: $12,000
**Average student indebtedness at
graduation:** $66,488
Enrollment: full time: 660; part
time: 194
men: 44%; women: 56%;
minorities: 21%
Acceptance rate (full time): 42%
Midrange LSAT (full time): 150-155
**Midrange undergraduate GPA (full
time):** 2.96-3.47
**Midrange of full-time private sector
salaries of 2001 grads:** $65,000-
$80,000
2000 grads employed in: law firms:
58%; business and industry
(legal): 3%; business and industry
(nonlegal): 6%; government: 12%;
public interest: 1%; judicial clerk:
18%; academia: 1%; unknown: 2%
Employment location for 2001 class:
Intl: 0%; N.E. 0%; M.A. 2%; E.N.C.
5%; W.N.C. 0%; S.A. 15%; E.S.C.
4%; W.S.C. 71%; Mt. 1%; Pac. 2%;
unknown 0%

Southern University[1]
PO Box 9294
Baton Rouge, LA 70813
Public
Admissions: (225) 771-5340
E-mail: ESimmons@sus.edu
Web site: http://www.sus.edu/sulc
Financial aid: (225) 771-2141
Tuition: N/A
Room/board/expenses: N/A
Enrollment: N/A

Tulane University
6329 Freret Street
John G. Weinmann Hall
New Orleans, LA 70118
Private
Admissions: (504) 865-5930
E-mail:
admissions@law.tulane.edu
Web site:
http://www.law.tulane.edu
Internet application: https://www4.
lsac.org/school/Tulane.htm
Financial aid: (504) 865-5931
Application deadline: rolling
Tuition: full time: $28,310; part
time: $1,416/credit hour
Room/board/expenses: $12,678
Students receiving grants: 48%
Median grant: $10,000
**Average student indebtedness at
graduation:** $80,695
Enrollment: full time: 1,023; part
time: 1
men: 46%; women: 54%;
minorities: 20%
Acceptance rate (full time): 31%
Midrange LSAT (full time): 156-161
**Midrange undergraduate GPA (full
time):** 3.20-3.65
**Midrange of full-time private sector
salaries of 2001 grads:** $70,000-
$125,000
2000 grads employed in: law firms:
59%; business and industry
(legal): 2%; business and industry
(nonlegal): 10%; government:
15%; public interest: 3%; judicial
clerk: 11%; academia: 0%;
unknown: 1%
Employment location for 2001 class:
Intl: N/A; N.E. 2%; M.A. 13%;
E.N.C. 4%; W.N.C. 2%; S.A. 28%;
E.S.C. 7%; W.S.C. 32%; Mt. 2%;
Pac. 9%; unknown 0%

MAINE

University of Maine
246 Deering Avenue
Portland, ME 04102
Public
Admissions: (207) 780-4341
E-mail: mainelaw@usm.maine.edu
Web site:
http://www.mainelaw.maine.edu/
Financial aid: (207) 780-5250
Application deadline: 02/15
In-state tuition: full time: $11,436;
part time: $7,675
Out-of-state tuition: full time:
$19,626
Room/board/expenses: $9,578
Students receiving grants: 34%
Median grant: $3,174
**Average student indebtedness at
graduation:** $49,279
Enrollment: full time: 244; part
time: 12
men: 43%; women: 57%;
minorities: 5%
Acceptance rate (full time): 43%
Midrange LSAT (full time): 151-157
**Midrange undergraduate GPA (full
time):** 3.03-3.53
**Midrange of full-time private sector
salaries of 2001 grads:** $38,200-
$60,000

2000 grads employed in: law firms:
45%; business and industry
(legal): 17%; business and industry (nonlegal): 2%; government:
17%; public interest: 0%; judicial
clerk: 15%; academia: 0%;
unknown: 2%
Employment location for 2001 class:
Intl: 0%; N.E. 87%; M.A. 5%;
E.N.C. 0%; W.N.C. 0%; S.A. 5%;
E.S.C. 0%; W.S.C. 2%; Mt. 0%;
Pac. 2%; unknown 0%

MARYLAND

University of Baltimore
1420 N. Charles Street
Baltimore, MD 21201-5779
Public
Admissions: (410) 837-4459
E-mail:
lwadmiss@ubmail.ubalt.edu
Web site: http://www.law.ubalt.edu
Financial aid: (410) 837-4763
Application deadline: 04/01
In-state tuition: full time: $10,503;
part time: $9,587
Out-of-state tuition: full time:
$18,321
Room/board/expenses: $12,236
Students receiving grants: 9%
Median grant: $6,000
**Average student indebtedness at
graduation:** $17,262
Enrollment: full time: 637; part
time: 284
men: 49%; women: 51%;
minorities: 19%
Acceptance rate (full time): 33%
Midrange LSAT (full time): 150-155
**Midrange undergraduate GPA (full
time):** 2.87-3.45
**Midrange of full-time private sector
salaries of 2001 grads:** N/A-N/A
2000 grads employed in: law firms:
30%; business and industry
(legal): 2%; business and industry
(nonlegal): 15%; government:
15%; public interest: 4%; judicial
clerk: 32%; academia: 1%;
unknown: 2%
Employment location for 2001 class:
Intl: N/A; N.E. N/A; M.A. N/A;
E.N.C. N/A; W.N.C. N/A; S.A. N/A;
E.S.C. N/A; W.S.C. N/A; Mt. N/A;
Pac. N/A; unknown N/A

University of Maryland
500 W. Baltimore Street
Baltimore, MD 21201-1786
Public
Admissions: (410) 706-3492
E-mail: admissions@
law.umaryland.edu
Web site:
http://www.law.umaryland.edu
Financial aid: (410) 706-7347
Application deadline: 02/28
In-state tuition: full time: $12,148;
part time: $9,208
Out-of-state tuition: full time:
$22,890
Room/board/expenses: $18,716
Students receiving grants: 51%
Median grant: $3,100
**Average student indebtedness at
graduation:** $63,071
Enrollment: full time: 650; part
time: 223
men: 43%; women: 57%;
minorities: 21%
Acceptance rate (full time): 13%
Midrange LSAT (full time): 155-162
**Midrange undergraduate GPA (full
time):** 3.29-3.71
**Midrange of full-time private sector
salaries of 2001 grads:** $50,000-
$100,000
2000 grads employed in: law firms:
36%; business and industry

University of Louisville (Brandeis)
School of Law
Louisville, KY 40292
Public
Admissions: (502) 852-6365
E-mail:
lawadmissions@louisville.edu
Web site: http://www.louisville.edu/
brandeislaw/
Financial aid: (502) 852-6391
Application deadline: 03/01
In-state tuition: full time: $7,350;
part time: $6,120
Out-of-state tuition: full time:
$18,310
Room/board/expenses: $15,242
Students receiving grants: 59%
Median grant: $3,000
**Average student indebtedness at
graduation:** $38,760
Enrollment: full time: 284; part
time: 89
men: 48%; women: 52%;
minorities: 8%
Acceptance rate (full time): 27%
Midrange LSAT (full time): 154-159
**Midrange undergraduate GPA (full
time):** 3.12-3.61
**Midrange of full-time private sector
salaries of 2001 grads:** $40,000-
$70,000
2000 grads employed in: law firms:
52%; business and industry
(legal): 4%; business and industry
(nonlegal): 11%; government:
25%; public interest: 2%; judicial
clerk: 7%; academia: 0%;
unknown: 0%
Employment location for 2001 class:
Intl: 0%; N.E. 1%; M.A. 0%; E.N.C.
10%; W.N.C. 1%; S.A. 3%; E.S.C.
85%; W.S.C. 0%; Mt. 0%; Pac. 0%;
unknown 0%

(legal): 1%; business and industry (nonlegal): 13%; government: 18%; public interest: 4%; judicial clerk: 24%; academia: 4%; unknown: 0%
Employment location for 2001 class: Intl. 1%; N.E. 1%; M.A. 5%; E.N.C. 0%; W.N.C. 0%; S.A. 91%; E.S.C. 0%; W.S.C. 1%; Mt. 0%; Pac. 0%; unknown 2%

MASSACHUSETTS

Boston College
885 Centre Street
Newton, MA 02459-1154
Private
Admissions: (617) 552-4350
E-mail: bclawadm@bc.edu
Web site:
http://www.bc.edu/lawschool
Internet application: http://www.bc.edu/schools/law/admission/applying
Financial aid: (617) 552-4243
Application deadline: 03/01
Tuition: full time: $28,504; part time: N/A
Room/board/expenses: $13,825
Students receiving grants: 50%
Median grant: $12,000
Average student indebtedness at graduation: $77,670
Enrollment: full time: 806; part time: N/A
men: 46%; women: 54%; minorities: 21%
Acceptance rate (full time): 18%
Midrange LSAT (full time): 160-165
Midrange undergraduate GPA (full time): 3.39-3.74
Midrange of full-time private sector salaries of 2001 grads: $105,000-$135,000
2000 grads employed in: law firms: 71%; business and industry (legal): 0%; business and industry (nonlegal): 4%; government: 6%; public interest: 4%; judicial clerk: 14%; academia: 0%; unknown: 0%
Employment location for 2001 class: Intl. 1%; N.E. 58%; M.A. 21%; E.N.C. 2%; W.N.C. 1%; S.A. 9%; E.S.C. 0%; W.S.C. 0%; Mt. 1%; Pac. 7%; unknown 0%

Boston University
765 Commonwealth Avenue
Boston, MA 02215
Private
Admissions: (617) 353-3100
E-mail: bulawadm@bu.edu
Web site: http://www.bu.edu/law/
Internet application: http://www.bu.edu/law/admissions/apply
Financial aid: (617) 353-3160
Application deadline: 03/01
Tuition: full time: $27,600; part time: N/A
Room/board/expenses: $14,686
Students receiving grants: 48%
Median grant: $15,000
Average student indebtedness at graduation: $74,925
Enrollment: full time: 823; part time: N/A
men: 47%; women: 53%; minorities: 23%
Acceptance rate (full time): 19%
Midrange LSAT (full time): 163-166
Midrange undergraduate GPA (full time): 3.17-3.55
Midrange of full-time private sector salaries of 2001 grads: $82,500-$125,000
2000 grads employed in: law firms: 77%; business and industry (legal): N/A; business and industry (nonlegal): 5%; government: 5%;

public interest: 2%; judicial clerk: 8%; academia: 3%; unknown: N/A
Employment location for 2001 class: Intl. 2%; N.E. 45%; M.A. 29%; E.N.C. 5%; W.N.C. 0%; S.A. 8%; E.S.C. 0%; W.S.C. 1%; Mt. 2%; Pac. 9%; unknown N/A

Harvard University
Harvard Law School
Cambridge, MA 02138
Private
Admissions: (617) 495-3109
E-mail: jdadmiss@law.harvard.edu
Web site:
http://www.law.harvard.edu
Internet application: http://www.law.harvard.edu/Admissions/JD_Admissions/apply.html
Financial aid: (617) 495-4606
Application deadline: 02/01
Tuition: full time: $30,520; part time: N/A
Room/board/expenses: $17,730
Students receiving grants: 36%
Median grant: $14,760
Average student indebtedness at graduation: $73,100
Enrollment: full time: 1,670; part time: N/A
men: 56%; women: 44%; minorities: 23%
Acceptance rate (full time): 13%
Midrange LSAT (full time): 167-173
Midrange undergraduate GPA (full time): 3.76-3.94
Midrange of full-time private sector salaries of 2001 grads: $90,000-$125,000
2000 grads employed in: law firms: 66%; business and industry (legal): 0%; business and industry (nonlegal): 6%; government: 2%; public interest: 2%; judicial clerk: 23%; academia: 0%; unknown: 0%
Employment location for 2001 class: Intl. 3%; N.E. 13%; M.A. 34%; E.N.C. 7%; W.N.C. 2%; S.A. 17%; E.S.C. 1%; W.S.C. 5%; Mt. 2%; Pac. 17%; unknown 0%

New England School of Law
154 Stuart Street
Boston, MA 02116
Private
Admissions: (617) 422-7210
E-mail: admit@admin.nesl.edu
Web site: http://www.nesl.edu
Financial aid: (617) 422-7232
Application deadline: 06/01
Tuition: full time: $20,125; part time: $15,135
Room/board/expenses: $14,450
Students receiving grants: 47%
Median grant: $3,000
Average student indebtedness at graduation: $65,672
Enrollment: full time: 660; part time: 340
men: 45%; women: 55%; minorities: 17%
Acceptance rate (full time): 58%
Midrange LSAT (full time): 147-152
Midrange undergraduate GPA (full time): 2.87-3.37
Midrange of full-time private sector salaries of 2001 grads: $38,000-$65,000
2000 grads employed in: law firms: 40%; business and industry (legal): 18%; business and industry (nonlegal): 0%; government: 18%; public interest: 3%; judicial clerk: 12%; academia: 2%; unknown: 6%

Employment location for 2001 class: Intl. 0%; N.E. 69%; M.A. 16%; E.N.C. 2%; W.N.C. 0%; S.A. 9%; E.S.C. 1%; W.S.C. 1%; Mt. 2%; Pac. 2%; unknown 0%

Northeastern University
400 Huntington Avenue
Boston, MA 02115
Private
Admissions: (617) 373-2395
E-mail:
lawadmissions@nunet.neu.edu
Web site: http://www.slaw.neu.edu
Financial aid: (617) 373-4620
Application deadline: 03/01
Tuition: full time: $28,308; part time: N/A
Room/board/expenses: $14,439
Students receiving grants: 66%
Median grant: $6,500
Average student indebtedness at graduation: $80,712
Enrollment: full time: 596; part time: N/A
men: 39%; women: 61%; minorities: 23%
Acceptance rate (full time): 29%
Midrange LSAT (full time): 155-161
Midrange undergraduate GPA (full time): 3.09-3.58
Midrange of full-time private sector salaries of 2001 grads: $60,000-$125,000
2000 grads employed in: law firms: 46%; business and industry (legal): 3%; business and industry (nonlegal): 3%; government: 11%; public interest: 14%; judicial clerk: 22%; academia: 1%; unknown: 0%
Employment location for 2001 class: Intl. 1%; N.E. 66%; M.A. 11%; E.N.C. 2%; W.N.C. 1%; S.A. 10%; E.S.C. 0%; W.S.C. 1%; Mt. 2%; Pac. 6%; unknown 0%

Suffolk University
120 Tremont Street
Boston, MA 02108
Private
Admissions: (617) 573-8144
E-mail:
lawadm@admin.suffolk.edu
Web site:
http://www.law.suffolk.edu/
Financial aid: (617) 573-8147
Application deadline: 03/01
Tuition: full time: $26,620; part time: $19,964
Room/board/expenses: $13,811
Students receiving grants: 47%
Median grant: $4,200
Average student indebtedness at graduation: $72,886
Enrollment: full time: 1,052; part time: 621
men: 45%; women: 55%; minorities: 9%
Acceptance rate (full time): 48%
Midrange LSAT (full time): 151-157
Midrange undergraduate GPA (full time): 3.20-3.50
Midrange of full-time private sector salaries of 2001 grads: $40,000-$100,000
2000 grads employed in: law firms: 49%; business and industry (legal): 8%; business and industry (nonlegal): 11%; government: 13%; public interest: 2%; judicial clerk: 8%; academia: 2%; unknown: 7%
Employment location for 2001 class: Intl. 0%; N.E. 90%; M.A. 3%; E.N.C. 0%; W.N.C. 0%; S.A. 4%; E.S.C. 0%; W.S.C. 0%; Mt. 0%; Pac. 2%; unknown 0%

Western New England College
1215 Wilbraham Road
Springfield, MA 01119-2684
Private
Admissions: (413) 782-1406
E-mail: lawadmis@wnec.edu
Web site: http://www.law.wnec.edu
Internet application:
http://wneclaw.wnec.edu/inquiries.html
Financial aid: (413) 796-2080
Application deadline: 03/15
Tuition: full time: $23,178; part time: $17,382
Room/board/expenses: $14,570
Students receiving grants: 57%
Median grant: $11,000
Average student indebtedness at graduation: $64,607
Enrollment: full time: 289; part time: 220
men: 48%; women: 52%; minorities: 10%
Acceptance rate (full time): 48%
Midrange LSAT (full time): 148-154
Midrange undergraduate GPA (full time): 2.68-3.42
Midrange of full-time private sector salaries of 2001 grads: $40,000-$63,000
2000 grads employed in: law firms: 37%; business and industry (legal): 5%; business and industry (nonlegal): 19%; government: 23%; public interest: 1%; judicial clerk: 11%; academia: 4%; unknown: 0%
Employment location for 2001 class: Intl. 0%; N.E. 85%; M.A. 8%; E.N.C. 0%; W.N.C. 0%; S.A. 5%; E.S.C. 2%; W.S.C. 0%; Mt. 0%; Pac. 0%; unknown 0%

MICHIGAN

Michigan State University– DCL College of Law
368 Law College Building
East Lansing, MI 48824-1300
Private
Admissions: (517) 432-0222
E-mail: law@msu.edu
Web site: http://www.law.msu.edu
Financial aid: (517) 432-6810
Application deadline: 04/15
Tuition: full time: $20,244; part time: $14,460
Room/board/expenses: $10,923
Students receiving grants: 22%
Median grant: $19,425
Average student indebtedness at graduation: $60,974
Enrollment: full time: 656; part time: 157
men: 58%; women: 42%; minorities: 11%
Acceptance rate (full time): 53%
Midrange LSAT (full time): 150-158
Midrange undergraduate GPA (full time): 2.91-3.51
Midrange of full-time private sector salaries of 2001 grads: $36,000-$85,000
2000 grads employed in: law firms: 56%; business and industry (legal): 3%; business and industry (nonlegal): 9%; government: 17%; public interest: 4%; judicial clerk: 6%; academia: 3%; unknown: 3%
Employment location for 2001 class: Intl. N/A; N.E. 0%; M.A. 5%; E.N.C. 85%; W.N.C. 0%; S.A. 4%; E.S.C. 0%; W.S.C. 2%; Mt. 1%; Pac. 2%; unknown N/A

Thomas M. Cooley Law School
300 S. Capitol Avenue
PO Box 13038
Lansing, MI 48901
Private
Admissions: (517) 371-5140
E-mail: admissions@cooley.edu
Web site: http://www.cooley.edu
Internet application:
http://www.cooley.edu/admissions
Financial aid: (517) 371-5140
Application deadline: 08/28
Tuition: full time: $19,528; part time: $13,960
Room/board/expenses: $11,473
Students receiving grants: 33%
Median grant: $5,115
Average student indebtedness at graduation: $82,936
Enrollment: full time: 369; part time: 1,650
men: 53%; women: 47%; minorities: 26%
Acceptance rate (full time): 69%
Midrange LSAT (full time): 141-149
Midrange undergraduate GPA (full time): 2.66-3.22
Midrange of full-time private sector salaries of 2001 grads: $35,000-$50,000
2000 grads employed in: law firms: 53%; business and industry (legal): 3%; business and industry (nonlegal): 8%; government: 16%; public interest: 4%; judicial clerk: 11%; academia: 2%; unknown: 3%
Employment location for 2001 class: Intl. 3%; N.E. 1%; M.A. 8%; E.N.C. 56%; W.N.C. 2%; S.A. 11%; E.S.C. 3%; W.S.C. 3%; Mt. 2%; Pac. 2%; unknown 9%

University of Detroit Mercy
651 E. Jefferson Avenue
Detroit, MI 48226
Private
Admissions: (313) 596-0264
E-mail: udmlawao@udmercy.edu
Web site:
http://www.law.udmercy.edu
Financial aid: (313) 596-0214
Application deadline: 04/15
Tuition: full time: $715/credit hour; part time: $715/credit hour
Room/board/expenses: N/A
Students receiving grants: 20%
Median grant: $12,600
Average student indebtedness at graduation: $69,678
Enrollment: full time: 291; part time: 167
men: 53%; women: 47%; minorities: 7%
Acceptance rate (full time): 41%
Midrange LSAT (full time): 146-153
Midrange undergraduate GPA (full time): 2.96-3.40
Midrange of full-time private sector salaries of 2001 grads: $45,000-$80,000
2000 grads employed in: law firms: 54%; business and industry (legal): 10%; business and industry (nonlegal): 12%; government: 15%; public interest: 0%; judicial clerk: 6%; academia: 3%; unknown: 0%
Employment location for 2001 class: Intl. 1%; N.E. 0%; M.A. 2%; E.N.C. 95%; W.N.C. 0%; S.A. 2%; E.S.C. 0%; W.S.C. 0%; Mt. 0%; Pac. 0%; unknown 0%

University of Michigan–Ann Arbor
625 S. State Street
Ann Arbor, MI 48109
Public
Admissions: (734) 764-0537
E-mail: law.jd.admissions@umich.edu
Web site: http://www.law.umich.edu/
Financial aid: (734) 764-5289
Application deadline: 02/15
In-state tuition: full time: $24,992; part time: N/A
Out-of-state tuition: full time: $30,992
Room/board/expenses: $13,520
Students receiving grants: 42%
Median grant: $11,037
Average student indebtedness at graduation: $75,744
Enrollment: full time: 1,109; part time: N/A
men: 58%; women: 42%; minorities: 22%
Acceptance rate (full time): 21%
Midrange LSAT (full time): 163-168
Midrange undergraduate GPA (full time): 3.43-3.77
Midrange of full-time private sector salaries of 2001 grads: $110,000-$125,000
2000 grads employed in: law firms: 73%; business and industry (legal): 1%; business and industry (nonlegal): 2%; government: 3%; public interest: 1%; judicial clerk: 18%; academia: 1%; unknown: 1%
Employment location for 2001 class: Intl. 1%; N.E. 4%; M.A. 17%; E.N.C. 38%; W.N.C. 3%; S.A. 12%; E.S.C. 1%; W.S.C. 2%; Mt. 2%; Pac. 18%; unknown 2%

Wayne State University
471 W. Palmer Street
Detroit, MI 48202
Public
Admissions: (313) 577-3937
E-mail: linda.sims@wayne.edu
Web site: http://www.law.wayne.edu
Financial aid: (313) 577-5142
Application deadline: 03/15
In-state tuition: full time: $9,998; part time: $7,191
Out-of-state tuition: full time: $19,946
Room/board/expenses: $18,207
Students receiving grants: 88%
Median grant: $3,000
Average student indebtedness at graduation: $48,403
Enrollment: full time: 519; part time: 207
men: 52%; women: 48%; minorities: 15%
Acceptance rate (full time): 44%
Midrange LSAT (full time): 151-157
Midrange undergraduate GPA (full time): 3.10-3.58
Midrange of full-time private sector salaries of 2001 grads: $45,000-$90,000
2000 grads employed in: law firms: 64%; business and industry (legal): 4%; business and industry (nonlegal): 5%; government: 14%; public interest: 2%; judicial clerk: 4%; academia: 1%; unknown: 6%
Employment location for 2001 class: Intl. 0%; N.E. 0%; M.A. 1%; E.N.C. 90%; W.N.C. 0%; S.A. 3%; E.S.C. 0%; W.S.C. 0%; Mt. 0%; Pac. 0%; unknown 7%

MINNESOTA

Hamline University
1536 Hewitt Avenue
St. Paul, MN 55104
Private
Admissions: (651) 523-2461
E-mail: lawadm@gw.hamline.edu
Web site: http://www.hamline.edu/law
Internet application: http://www.hamline.edu/law/apply.htm
Financial aid: (651) 523-3000
Application deadline: 04/01
Tuition: full time: $20,710; part time: $14,940
Room/board/expenses: $9,210
Students receiving grants: 44%
Median grant: $7,000
Average student indebtedness at graduation: $69,884
Enrollment: full time: 470; part time: 113
men: 41%; women: 59%; minorities: 11%
Acceptance rate (full time): 58%
Midrange LSAT (full time): 148-156
Midrange undergraduate GPA (full time): 3.08-3.60
Midrange of full-time private sector salaries of 2001 grads: $40,000-$62,500
2000 grads employed in: law firms: 37%; business and industry (legal): 4%; business and industry (nonlegal): 12%; government: 11%; public interest: 6%; judicial clerk: 25%; academia: 1%; unknown: 4%
Employment location for 2001 class: Intl. 0%; N.E. 1%; M.A. 1%; E.N.C. 4%; W.N.C. 83%; S.A. 4%; E.S.C. 0%; W.S.C. 1%; Mt. 1%; Pac. 2%; unknown 4%

University of Minnesota–Twin Cities
229 19th Avenue S
Minneapolis, MN 55455
Public
Admissions: (612) 625-5005
E-mail: umnlsadm@tc.umn.edu
Web site: http://www.law.umn.edu
Internet application: https://www.law.umn.edu/admissions/online_application.htm
Financial aid: (612) 625-3487
Application deadline: 03/01
In-state tuition: full time: $13,886; part time: N/A
Out-of-state tuition: full time: $22,784
Room/board/expenses: $12,572
Students receiving grants: 57%
Median grant: $6,000
Average student indebtedness at graduation: $50,000
Enrollment: full time: 759; part time: N/A
men: 52%; women: 48%; minorities: 16%
Acceptance rate (full time): 32%
Midrange LSAT (full time): 160-165
Midrange undergraduate GPA (full time): 3.42-3.86
Midrange of full-time private sector salaries of 2001 grads: $55,000-$107,500
2000 grads employed in: law firms: 55%; business and industry (legal): 6%; business and industry (nonlegal): N/A; government: 11%; public interest: 4%; judicial clerk: 23%; academia: 1%; unknown: N/A
Employment location for 2001 class: Intl. 1%; N.E. 2%; M.A. 4%; E.N.C. 5%; W.N.C. 68%; S.A. 7%; E.S.C. N/A; W.S.C. 1%; Mt. 1%; Pac. 11%; unknown N/A

William Mitchell College of Law
875 Summit Avenue
St. Paul, MN 55105-3076
Private
Admissions: (651) 290-6476
E-mail: admissions@wmitchell.edu
Web site: http://www.wmitchell.edu
Internet application: http://www.wmitchell.edu/admissions/apply/online.html
Financial aid: (651) 290-6403
Application deadline: 06/30
Tuition: full time: $21,170; part time: $15,390
Room/board/expenses: $13,440
Students receiving grants: 49%
Median grant: $11,145
Average student indebtedness at graduation: $65,412
Enrollment: full time: 559; part time: 479
men: 47%; women: 53%; minorities: 9%
Acceptance rate (full time): 64%
Midrange LSAT (full time): 152-158
Midrange undergraduate GPA (full time): 3.03-3.59
Midrange of full-time private sector salaries of 2001 grads: $42,000-$83,000
2000 grads employed in: law firms: 46%; business and industry (legal): 17%; business and industry (nonlegal): 8%; government: 8%; public interest: 2%; judicial clerk: 19%; academia: N/A; unknown: N/A
Employment location for 2001 class: Intl. 0%; N.E. 0%; M.A. 0%; E.N.C. 5%; W.N.C. 90%; S.A. 1%; E.S.C. 0%; W.S.C. 0%; Mt. 1%; Pac. 1%; unknown N/A

MISSISSIPPI

Mississippi College
151 E. Griffith Street
Jackson, MS 39201
Private
Admissions: (601) 925-7151
E-mail: hweaver@mc.edu
Web site: http://www.law.mc.edu
Financial aid: (601) 925-7110
Application deadline: 05/01
Tuition: full time: $15,823; part time: N/A
Room/board/expenses: $15,100
Students receiving grants: 25%
Median grant: $7,400
Average student indebtedness at graduation: $61,109
Enrollment: full time: 400; part time: N/A
men: 62%; women: 38%; minorities: 10%
Acceptance rate (full time): 51%
Midrange LSAT (full time): 146-151
Midrange undergraduate GPA (full time): 2.80-3.40
Midrange of full-time private sector salaries of 2001 grads: $43,750-$63,000
2000 grads employed in: law firms: 70%; business and industry (legal): 6%; business and industry (nonlegal): N/A; government: 9%; public interest: 1%; judicial clerk: 12%; academia: 2%; unknown: N/A
Employment location for 2001 class: Intl. N/A; N.E. N/A; M.A. 2%; E.N.C. N/A; W.N.C. N/A; S.A. 10%; E.S.C. 76%; W.S.C. 12%; Mt. N/A; Pac. 1%; unknown N/A

University of Mississippi
Law Center, PO Box 1848
University, MS 38677
Public
Admissions: (662) 915-6910
E-mail: lawmiss@olemiss.edu
Web site: http://www.olemiss.edu/depts/law_school/
Internet application: http://www.olemiss.edu/depts/law_school/forapps.html
Financial aid: (662) 915-7175
Application deadline: 03/01
In-state tuition: full time: $6,215; part time: $310/credit hour
Out-of-state tuition: full time: $12,142
Room/board/expenses: $11,228
Students receiving grants: 33%
Median grant: $4,063
Average student indebtedness at graduation: $40,947
Enrollment: full time: 531; part time: N/A
men: 58%; women: 42%; minorities: 10%
Acceptance rate (full time): 36%
Midrange LSAT (full time): 150-156
Midrange undergraduate GPA (full time): 3.27-3.72
Midrange of full-time private sector salaries of 2001 grads: $43,500-$64,250
2000 grads employed in: law firms: 63%; business and industry (legal): 6%; business and industry (nonlegal): 6%; government: 8%; public interest: 1%; judicial clerk: 16%; academia: 1%; unknown: N/A
Employment location for 2001 class: Intl. 1%; N.E. 1%; M.A. 3%; E.N.C. 1%; W.N.C. 0%; S.A. 12%; E.S.C. 78%; W.S.C. 3%; Mt. 0%; Pac. 1%; unknown N/A

MISSOURI

St. Louis University
3700 Lindell Boulevard
St. Louis, MO 63108
Private
Admissions: (314) 977-2800
E-mail: admissions@law.slu.edu
Web site: http://law.slu.edu
Financial aid: (314) 977-3369
Application deadline: 03/01
Tuition: full time: $24,510; part time: $17,880
Room/board/expenses: $12,000
Students receiving grants: 53%
Median grant: $5,114
Average student indebtedness at graduation: $55,146
Enrollment: full time: 580; part time: 230
men: 51%; women: 49%; minorities: 10%
Acceptance rate (full time): 54%
Midrange LSAT (full time): 151-158
Midrange undergraduate GPA (full time): 3.13-3.65
Midrange of full-time private sector salaries of 2001 grads: $45,000-$81,000
2000 grads employed in: law firms: 61%; business and industry (legal): 12%; business and industry (nonlegal): 6%; government: 9%; public interest: 2%; judicial clerk: 8%; academia: 1%; unknown: 1%
Employment location for 2001 class: Intl. 0%; N.E. 0%; M.A. 1%; E.N.C. 14%; W.N.C. 75%; S.A. 3%; E.S.C. 2%; W.S.C. 2%; Mt. 3%; Pac. 1%; unknown N/A

University of Missouri–Columbia
203 Hulston Hall
Columbia, MO 65211-4300
Public
Admissions: (573) 882-6042
E-mail: umclawadmissions@missouri.edu
Web site: http://www.law.missouri.edu
Internet application: http://www.law.missouri.edu/admissions.html
Financial aid: (573) 882-6643
Application deadline: 03/01
In-state tuition: full time: $11,264; part time: N/A
Out-of-state tuition: full time: $21,845
Room/board/expenses: $13,720
Students receiving grants: 36%
Median grant: $4,000
Average student indebtedness at graduation: $49,301
Enrollment: full time: 526; part time: N/A
men: 62%; women: 38%; minorities: 10%
Acceptance rate (full time): 36%
Midrange LSAT (full time): 154-160
Midrange undergraduate GPA (full time): 3.11-3.67
Midrange of full-time private sector salaries of 2001 grads: $35,000-$72,000
2000 grads employed in: law firms: 52%; business and industry (legal): 6%; business and industry (nonlegal): 4%; government: 25%; public interest: 3%; judicial clerk: 10%; academia: 0%; unknown: 0%
Employment location for 2001 class: Intl. 0%; N.E. 0%; M.A. 1%; E.N.C. 4%; W.N.C. 84%; S.A. 4%; E.S.C. 1%; W.S.C. 2%; Mt. 4%; Pac. 0%; unknown 0%

University of Missouri–Kansas City
5100 Rockhill Road
Kansas City, MO 64110
Public
Admissions: (816) 235-1644
E-mail: law@umkc.edu
Web site: http://www.law.umkc.edu
Internet application: http://www1.law.umkc.edu/admissions/
Financial aid: (816) 235-1154
Application deadline: 04/01
In-state tuition: full time: $9,446; part time: $6,806
Out-of-state tuition: full time: $18,256
Room/board/expenses: $13,710
Students receiving grants: 35%
Median grant: $6,258
Average student indebtedness at graduation: $56,661
Enrollment: full time: 442; part time: 33
men: 57%; women: 43%; minorities: 11%
Acceptance rate (full time): 46%
Midrange LSAT (full time): 150-156
Midrange undergraduate GPA (full time): 3.03-3.62
Midrange of full-time private sector salaries of 2001 grads: $40,000-$80,000
2000 grads employed in: law firms: 67%; business and industry (legal): 6%; business and industry (nonlegal): 6%; government: 10%; public interest: 2%; judicial clerk: 8%; academia: 1%; unknown: 1%
Employment location for 2001 class: Intl. N/A; N.E. N/A; M.A. N/A; E.N.C. N/A; W.N.C. N/A; S.A. N/A; E.S.C. N/A; W.S.C. N/A; Mt. N/A; Pac. N/A; unknown N/A

Washington University in St. Louis
1 Brookings Drive
Box 1120
St. Louis, MO 63130
Private
Admissions: (314) 935-4525
E-mail: admiss@wulaw.wustl.edu
Web site: http://www.law.wustl.edu/
Internet application: http://www4.lsac.org/school/WashingtonU.htm
Financial aid: (314) 935-4605

KEY TO TERMINOLOGY ON PAGE 162

Application deadline: 03/01
Tuition: full time: $28,960; part time: N/A
Room/board/expenses: $17,000
Students receiving grants: 55%
Median grant: $10,000
Average student indebtedness at graduation: $80,000
Enrollment: full time: 742; part time: N/A
men: 56%; women: 44%; minorities: 17%
Acceptance rate (full time): 26%
Midrange LSAT (full time): 162-165
Midrange undergraduate GPA (full time): 3.20-3.70
Midrange of full-time private sector salaries of 2001 grads: $70,000-$125,000
2000 grads employed in: law firms: 62%; business and industry (legal): 7%; business and industry (nonlegal): 3%; government: 7%; public interest: 3%; judicial clerk: 8%; academia: 0%; unknown: 10%
Employment location for 2001 class: Intl. 1%; N.E. 2%; M.A. 9%; E.N.C. 13%; W.N.C. 45%; S.A. 9%; E.S.C. 2%; W.S.C. 3%; Mt. 1%; Pac. 8%; unknown 7%

MONTANA

University of Montana

School of Law
Missoula, MT 59812
Public
Admissions: (406) 243-2698
E-mail: hid314@selway.umt.edu
Web site: http://www.umt.edu/law
Financial aid: (406) 243-5373
Application deadline: 03/01
In-state tuition: full time: $7,776; part time: N/A
Out-of-state tuition: full time: $15,156
Room/board/expenses: $7,950
Students receiving grants: 41%
Median grant: $1,295
Average student indebtedness at graduation: $42,443
Enrollment: full time: 252; part time: N/A
men: 58%; women: 42%; minorities: 4%
Acceptance rate (full time): 43%
Midrange LSAT (full time): 151-157
Midrange undergraduate GPA (full time): 3.10-3.65
Midrange of full-time private sector salaries of 2001 grads: $35,000-$42,000
2000 grads employed in: law firms: 42%; business and industry (legal): 3%; business and industry (nonlegal): 0%; government: 16%; public interest: 3%; judicial clerk: 33%; academia: 3%; unknown: 0%
Employment location for 2001 class: Intl. 0%; N.E. 0%; M.A. 0%; E.N.C. 4%; W.N.C. 1%; S.A. 4%; E.S.C. 0%; W.S.C. 4%; Mt. 80%; Pac. 6%; unknown 0%

NEBRASKA

Creighton University

2500 California Plaza
Omaha, NE 68178
Private
Admissions: (800) 282-5835
E-mail: lawadmit@creighton.edu
Web site: http://culaw2.creighton.edu/
Financial aid: (402) 280-2731
Application deadline: rolling
Tuition: full time: $20,134; part time: $13,134
Room/board/expenses: $13,720
Students receiving grants: 43%
Median grant: $8,000
Average student indebtedness at graduation: $63,388
Enrollment: full time: 464; part time: 23
men: 59%; women: 41%; minorities: 11%
Acceptance rate (full time): 52%
Midrange LSAT (full time): 149-157
Midrange undergraduate GPA (full time): 3.03-3.53
Midrange of full-time private sector salaries of 2001 grads: $36,500-$67,500
2000 grads employed in: law firms: 38%; business and industry (legal): 5%; business and industry (nonlegal): 17%; government: 22%; public interest: 5%; judicial clerk: 8%; academia: 3%; unknown: 0%
Employment location for 2001 class: Intl. 0%; N.E. 0%; M.A. 1%; E.N.C. 4%; W.N.C. 70%; S.A. 5%; E.S.C. 1%; W.S.C. 2%; Mt. 12%; Pac. 5%; unknown 0%

University of Nebraska–Lincoln

College of Law
PO Box 830902
Lincoln, NE 68583-0902
Public
Admissions: (402) 472-2161
E-mail: lawadm@unl.edu
Web site: http://www.unl.edu/lawcoll/
Financial aid: (402) 472-2161
Application deadline: 03/01
In-state tuition: full time: $5,760; part time: N/A
Out-of-state tuition: full time: $13,075
Room/board/expenses: $10,230
Students receiving grants: 44%
Median grant: $6,553
Average student indebtedness at graduation: $37,146
Enrollment: full time: 415; part time: N/A
men: 52%; women: 48%; minorities: 7%
Acceptance rate (full time): 47%
Midrange LSAT (full time): 153-158
Midrange undergraduate GPA (full time): 3.29-3.88
Midrange of full-time private sector salaries of 2001 grads: $33,567-$70,367
2000 grads employed in: law firms: 56%; business and industry (legal): 6%; business and industry (nonlegal): 13%; government: 8%; public interest: 2%; judicial clerk: 9%; academia: 7%; unknown: N/A
Employment location for 2001 class: Intl. 1%; N.E. 0%; M.A. 1%; E.N.C. 4%; W.N.C. 71%; S.A. 8%; E.S.C. 1%; W.S.C. 2%; Mt. 10%; Pac. 3%; unknown 0%

NEVADA

University of Nevada–Las Vegas (William S. Boyd)

4505 Maryland Parkway
Box 451003
Las Vegas, NV 89154-1003
Public
Admissions: (702) 895-2440
E-mail: request@law.unlv.edu
Web site: http://www.law.unlv.edu/
Internet application: http://www.law.unlv.edu/admissions_application.html
Financial aid: (702) 895-4112
Application deadline: 03/15
In-state tuition: full time: $7,294; part time: $5,262
Out-of-state tuition: full time: $14,294
Room/board/expenses: $11,910
Students receiving grants: 50%
Median grant: $2,000
Average student indebtedness at graduation: $28,909
Enrollment: full time: 266; part time: 188
men: 51%; women: 49%; minorities: 20%
Acceptance rate (full time): 24%
Midrange LSAT (full time): 151-157
Midrange undergraduate GPA (full time): 3.06-3.64
Midrange of full-time private sector salaries of 2001 grads: $42,000-$52,000
2000 grads employed in: law firms: 65%; business and industry (legal): 2%; business and industry (nonlegal): 2%; government: 10%; public interest: 2%; judicial clerk: 19%; academia: N/A; unknown: N/A
Employment location for 2001 class: Intl. N/A; N.E. N/A; M.A. N/A; E.N.C. 2%; W.N.C. N/A; S.A. 1%; E.S.C. N/A; W.S.C. N/A; Mt. 93%; Pac. 3%; unknown N/A

NEW HAMPSHIRE

Franklin Pierce Law Center

2 White Street
Concord, NH 03301
Private
Admissions: (603) 228-9217
E-mail: admissions@piercelaw.edu
Web site: http://www.piercelaw.edu
Financial aid: (603) 228-1541
Application deadline: 05/01
Tuition: full time: $21,475; part time: N/A
Room/board/expenses: $13,558
Students receiving grants: 62%
Median grant: $1,300
Average student indebtedness at graduation: $77,124
Enrollment: full time: 368; part time: 11
men: 57%; women: 43%; minorities: 9%
Acceptance rate (full time): 39%
Midrange LSAT (full time): 148-156
Midrange undergraduate GPA (full time): 2.89-3.43
Midrange of full-time private sector salaries of 2001 grads: $60,000-$125,000
2000 grads employed in: law firms: 61%; business and industry (legal): 13%; business and industry (nonlegal): 0%; government: 11%; public interest: 6%; judicial clerk: 6%; academia: 3%; unknown: 0%
Employment location for 2001 class: Intl. 3%; N.E. 45%; M.A. 7%; E.N.C. 11%; W.N.C. 2%; S.A. 19%; E.S.C. 1%; W.S.C. 1%; Mt. 2%; Pac. 9%; unknown 0%

NEW JERSEY

Rutgers State University–Camden

217 N. Fifth Street
Camden, NJ 08102-1203
Public
Admissions: (800) 466-7561
E-mail: admissions@camlaw.rutgers.edu
Web site: http://www-camlaw.rutgers.edu
Financial aid: (856) 225-6039
Application deadline: 04/01
In-state tuition: full time: $13,889; part time: $10,958
Out-of-state tuition: full time: $19,611
Room/board/expenses: $11,367
Students receiving grants: 37%
Median grant: $4,000
Average student indebtedness at graduation: $53,585
Enrollment: full time: 566; part time: 191
men: 57%; women: 43%; minorities: 18%
Acceptance rate (full time): 23%
Midrange LSAT (full time): 158-163
Midrange undergraduate GPA (full time): 3.00-3.50
Midrange of full-time private sector salaries of 2001 grads: $45,000-$100,000
2000 grads employed in: law firms: 33%; business and industry (legal): 9%; business and industry (nonlegal): 0%; government: 7%; public interest: 1%; judicial clerk: 49%; academia: 1%; unknown: 0%
Employment location for 2001 class: Intl. 0%; N.E. 0%; M.A. 90%; E.N.C. 0%; W.N.C. 0%; S.A. 5%; E.S.C. 1%; W.S.C. 1%; Mt. 1%; Pac. 2%; unknown 0%

Rutgers State University–Newark

Rutgers Law School
123 Washington Street
Newark, NJ 07102
Public
Admissions: (973) 353-5554
E-mail: awalton@andromeda.rutgers.edu
Web site: http://law.newark.rutgers.edu
Financial aid: (973) 353-1702
Application deadline: 03/15
In-state tuition: full time: $13,775; part time: $10,856
Out-of-state tuition: full time: $19,497
Room/board/expenses: $13,575
Students receiving grants: 30%
Median grant: $2,700
Average student indebtedness at graduation: $52,585
Enrollment: full time: 551; part time: 201
men: 49%; women: 51%; minorities: 37%
Acceptance rate (full time): 22%
Midrange LSAT (full time): 154-161
Midrange undergraduate GPA (full time): 3.05-3.55
Midrange of full-time private sector salaries of 2001 grads: $85,000-$125,000
2000 grads employed in: law firms: 50%; business and industry (legal): 3%; business and industry (nonlegal): 9%; government: 9%; public interest: 1%; judicial clerk: 26%; academia: 2%; unknown: 0%
Employment location for 2001 class: Intl. N/A; N.E. N/A; M.A. N/A; E.N.C. N/A; W.N.C. N/A; S.A. N/A; E.S.C. N/A; W.S.C. N/A; Mt. N/A; Pac. N/A; unknown N/A

Seton Hall University

1 Newark Center
Newark, NJ 07102-5210
Private
Admissions: (973) 642-8747
E-mail: admitme@shu.edu
Web site: http://law.shu.edu
Financial aid: (973) 642-8744
Application deadline: 04/01
Tuition: full time: $887/credit hour; part time: $887/credit hour
Room/board/expenses: $12,500
Students receiving grants: 63%
Median grant: $5,000
Average student indebtedness at graduation: $66,673
Enrollment: full time: 893; part time: 363
men: 55%; women: 45%; minorities: 17%
Acceptance rate (full time): 39%
Midrange LSAT (full time): 154-158
Midrange undergraduate GPA (full time): 2.90-3.44
Midrange of full-time private sector salaries of 2001 grads: $55,000-$95,000
2000 grads employed in: law firms: 42%; business and industry (legal): 8%; business and industry (nonlegal): 3%; government: 7%; public interest: 0%; judicial clerk: 40%; academia: 0%; unknown: 0%
Employment location for 2001 class: Intl. 0%; N.E. 1%; M.A. 97%; E.N.C. 0%; W.N.C. 0%; S.A. 1%; E.S.C. 0%; W.S.C. 0%; Mt. 0%; Pac. 1%; unknown 0%

NEW MEXICO

University of New Mexico

1117 Stanford Drive NE
Albuquerque, NM 87131-1431
Public
Admissions: (505) 277-0572
E-mail: admissions@law.unm.edu
Web site: http://lawschool.unm.edu
Financial aid: (505) 277-0572
Application deadline: 02/15
In-state tuition: full time: $6,098; part time: N/A
Out-of-state tuition: full time: $18,559
Room/board/expenses: $11,764
Students receiving grants: 20%
Median grant: $5,544
Average student indebtedness at graduation: $39,500
Enrollment: full time: 324; part time: N/A
men: 40%; women: 60%; minorities: 35%
Acceptance rate (full time): 32%
Midrange LSAT (full time): 151-160
Midrange undergraduate GPA (full time): 3.01-3.69
Midrange of full-time private sector salaries of 2001 grads: $40,000-$49,000
2000 grads employed in: law firms: 52%; business and industry (legal): 1%; business and industry (nonlegal): 0%; government: 29%; public interest: 1%; judicial clerk: 17%; academia: 0%; unknown: 0%
Employment location for 2001 class: Intl. 1%; N.E. 0%; M.A. 2%; E.N.C. 2%; W.N.C. 0%; S.A. 5%; E.S.C. 1%; W.S.C. 0%; Mt. 89%; Pac. 1%; unknown 0%

NEW YORK

Albany Law School-Union University

80 New Scotland Avenue
Albany, NY 12208
Private
Admissions: (518) 445-2326
E-mail: admissions@mail.als.edu
Web site: http://www.als.edu
Financial aid: (518) 445-2357
Application deadline: 03/15
Tuition: full time: $24,255; part time: $18,224
Room/board/expenses: $11,700
Students receiving grants: 50%
Median grant: $4,800
Average student indebtedness at graduation: $62,400
Enrollment: full time: 742; part time: 66
men: 48%; women: 52%; minorities: 15%
Acceptance rate (full time): 51%
Midrange LSAT (full time): 148-154
Midrange undergraduate GPA (full time): 2.98-3.50
Midrange of full-time private sector salaries of 2001 grads: $40,000-$64,500
2000 grads employed in: law firms: 52%; business and industry (legal): 4%; business and industry (nonlegal): 4%; government: 24%; public interest: 0%; judicial clerk: 9%; academia: 2%; unknown: 6%

Employment location for 2001 class: Intl. 0%; N.E. 3%; M.A. 82%; E.N.C. 0%; W.N.C. 1%; S.A. 6%; E.S.C. 0%; W.S.C. 2%; Mt. 0%; Pac. 1%; unknown 6%

Brooklyn Law School

250 Joralemon Street
Brooklyn, NY 11201
Private
Admissions: (718) 780-7906
E-mail: admitq@brooklaw.edu
Web site: http://www.brooklaw.edu
Financial aid: (718) 780-7915
Application deadline: rolling
Tuition: full time: $29,030; part time: $21,805
Room/board/expenses: $15,755
Students receiving grants: 46%
Median grant: $6,000
Average student indebtedness at graduation: $65,224
Enrollment: full time: 1,185; part time: 345
men: 48%; women: 52%; minorities: 18%
Acceptance rate (full time): 29%
Midrange LSAT (full time): 158-162
Midrange undergraduate GPA (full time): 3.10-3.60
Midrange of full-time private sector salaries of 2001 grads: $60,000-$125,000
2000 grads employed in: law firms: 56%; business and industry (legal): 11%; business and industry (nonlegal): 7%; government: 14%; public interest: 2%; judicial clerk: 8%; academia: 0%; unknown: 1%
Employment location for 2001 class: Intl. 1%; N.E. 1%; M.A. 92%; E.N.C. 1%; W.N.C. 0%; S.A. 1%; E.S.C. 0%; W.S.C. 1%; Mt. N/A; Pac. 1%; unknown 3%

Cardozo-Yeshiva University

55 Fifth Avenue
10th Floor
New York, NY 10003
Private
Admissions: (212) 790-0274
E-mail: lawinfo@ymail.yu.edu
Web site: http://www.cardozo.yu.edu
Internet application: http://www.cardozo.yu.edu/admissions/appinfo.html
Financial aid: (212) 790-0395
Application deadline: 04/01
Tuition: full time: $29,200; part time: $1,300/credit hour
Room/board/expenses: $21,716
Students receiving grants: 68%
Median grant: $6,000
Average student indebtedness at graduation: $80,788
Enrollment: full time: 918; part time: 69
men: 49%; women: 51%; minorities: 19%
Acceptance rate (full time): 27%
Midrange LSAT (full time): 158-163
Midrange undergraduate GPA (full time): 3.20-3.67
Midrange of full-time private sector salaries of 2001 grads: $80,000-$125,000
2000 grads employed in: law firms: 55%; business and industry (legal): 8%; business and industry (nonlegal): 8%; government: 16%; public interest: 8%; judicial clerk: 4%; academia: 1%; unknown: 0%
Employment location for 2001 class: Intl. 1%; N.E. 1%; M.A. 89%; E.N.C. 0%; W.N.C. 1%; S.A. 2%; E.S.C. 1%; W.S.C. 0%; Mt. 1%; Pac. 4%; unknown 0%

Columbia University

435 W. 116th Street
New York, NY 10027
Private
Admissions: (212) 854-2670
E-mail: admissions@law.columbia.edu
Web site: http://www.law.columbia.edu
Financial aid: (212) 854-7730
Application deadline: 02/15
Tuition: full time: $32,700; part time: N/A
Room/board/expenses: $16,130
Students receiving grants: 41%
Median grant: $15,000
Average student indebtedness at graduation: $86,980
Enrollment: full time: 1,176; part time: N/A
men: 51%; women: 49%; minorities: 31%
Acceptance rate (full time): 15%
Midrange LSAT (full time): 166-173
Midrange undergraduate GPA (full time): 3.51-3.85
Midrange of full-time private sector salaries of 2001 grads: $125,000-$125,000
2000 grads employed in: law firms: 80%; business and industry (legal): 1%; business and industry (nonlegal): 0%; government: 1%; public interest: 1%; judicial clerk: 17%; academia: 0%; unknown: 0%
Employment location for 2001 class: Intl. N/A; N.E. 3%; M.A. 75%; E.N.C. 1%; W.N.C. 0%; S.A. 7%; E.S.C. 0%; W.S.C. 3%; Mt. 1%; Pac. 9%; unknown N/A

Cornell University

Myron Taylor Hall
Ithaca, NY 14853-4901
Private
Admissions: (607) 255-5141
E-mail: lawadmit@postoffice.law.cornell.edu
Web site: http://www.lawschool.cornell.edu
Internet application: http://www.lawschool.cornell.edu/admissions
Financial aid: (607) 255-5141
Application deadline: 02/01
Tuition: full time: $31,250; part time: N/A
Room/board/expenses: $13,700
Students receiving grants: 46%
Median grant: $9,000
Enrollment: full time: 570; part time: N/A
men: 51%; women: 49%; minorities: 26%
Acceptance rate (full time): 19%
Midrange LSAT (full time): 164-166
Midrange undergraduate GPA (full time): 3.50-3.79
Midrange of full-time private sector salaries of 2001 grads: $125,000-$125,000
2000 grads employed in: law firms: 75%; business and industry (legal): 0%; business and industry (nonlegal): 0%; government: 4%; public interest: 2%; judicial clerk: 16%; academia: 2%; unknown: 2%
Employment location for 2001 class: Intl. 2%; N.E. 10%; M.A. 44%; E.N.C. 5%; W.N.C. 1%; S.A. 11%; E.S.C. 0%; W.S.C. 5%; Mt. 2%; Pac. 17%; unknown 4%

CUNY–Queens College

65-21 Main Street
Flushing, NY 11367
Public
Admissions: (718) 340-4210
E-mail: admissions@mail.law.cuny.edu
Web site: http://www.law.cuny.edu/
Financial aid: (718) 340-4284
Application deadline: 03/15
In-state tuition: full time: $6,901; part time: N/A
Out-of-state tuition: full time: $10,131
Room/board/expenses: $13,952
Students receiving grants: 69%
Median grant: $1,200
Average student indebtedness at graduation: $49,585
Enrollment: full time: 462; part time: N/A
men: 37%; women: 63%; minorities: 38%
Acceptance rate (full time): 26%
Midrange LSAT (full time): 145-153
Midrange undergraduate GPA (full time): 2.82-3.38
Midrange of full-time private sector salaries of 2001 grads: $35,000-$45,000
2000 grads employed in: law firms: 25%; business and industry (legal): 6%; business and industry (nonlegal): 5%; government: 25%; public interest: 25%; judicial clerk: 9%; academia: 2%; unknown: 3%
Employment location for 2001 class: Intl. 0%; N.E. 2%; M.A. 88%; E.N.C. 2%; W.N.C. 0%; S.A. 3%; E.S.C. 0%; W.S.C. 0%; Mt. 0%; Pac. 0%; unknown 5%

Fordham University

140 W. 62nd Street
New York, NY 10023
Private
Admissions: (212) 636-6810
E-mail: lawadmissions@law.fordham.edu
Web site: http://law.fordham.edu/index.htm
Internet application: http://law.fordham.edu/admissions.htm
Financial aid: (212) 636-6815
Application deadline: 03/01
Tuition: full time: $29,946; part time: $22,490
Room/board/expenses: $19,224
Students receiving grants: 36%
Median grant: $7,000
Average student indebtedness at graduation: $73,109
Enrollment: full time: 1,156; part time: 357
men: 48%; women: 52%; minorities: 23%
Acceptance rate (full time): 21%
Midrange LSAT (full time): 162-166
Midrange undergraduate GPA (full time): 3.32-3.76
Midrange of full-time private sector salaries of 2001 grads: $95,000-$125,000
2000 grads employed in: law firms: 80%; business and industry (legal): 4%; business and industry (nonlegal): 4%; government: 9%; public interest: 1%; judicial clerk: 3%; academia: 0%; unknown: 0%
Employment location for 2001 class: Intl. 0%; N.E. 3%; M.A. 92%; E.N.C. 1%; W.N.C. 0%; S.A. 3%; E.S.C. 0%; W.S.C. 0%; Mt. 0%; Pac. 1%; unknown 0%

Hofstra University

121 Hofstra University
Hempstead, NY 11549
Private
Admissions: (516) 463-5916
E-mail: lawadmissions@hofstra.edu
Web site: http://www.hofstra.edu/law
Internet application: https://www4.lsac.org/school/Hofstra.htm
Financial aid: (516) 463-5929
Application deadline: 04/15
Tuition: full time: $27,426; part time: $20,880
Room/board/expenses: $12,652
Students receiving grants: 48%
Median grant: $7,000
Average student indebtedness at graduation: $67,972
Enrollment: full time: 810; part time: 82
men: 52%; women: 48%; minorities: 23%
Acceptance rate (full time): 36%
Midrange LSAT (full time): 151-157
Midrange undergraduate GPA (full time): 2.83-3.50
Midrange of full-time private sector salaries of 2001 grads: $50,000-$125,000
2000 grads employed in: law firms: 66%; business and industry (legal): 7%; business and industry (nonlegal): 4%; government: 14%; public interest: 3%; judicial clerk: 4%; academia: 0%; unknown: 2%
Employment location for 2001 class: Intl. N/A; N.E. 1%; M.A. 96%; E.N.C. N/A; W.N.C. 1%; S.A. 2%; E.S.C. N/A; W.S.C. N/A; Mt. N/A; Pac. N/A; unknown N/A

New York Law School

57 Worth Street
New York, NY 10013-2960
Private
Admissions: (212) 431-2888
E-mail: admissions@nyls.edu
Web site: http://www.nyls.edu
Financial aid: (212) 431-2827
Application deadline: 04/01
Tuition: full time: $28,860; part time: $21,600
Room/board/expenses: $13,945
Students receiving grants: 35%
Median grant: $6,500
Average student indebtedness at graduation: $65,193
Enrollment: full time: 1,093; part time: 417
men: 44%; women: 56%; minorities: 16%
Acceptance rate (full time): 41%
Midrange LSAT (full time): 150-154
Midrange undergraduate GPA (full time): 3.00-3.40
Midrange of full-time private sector salaries of 2001 grads: $50,000-$125,000
2000 grads employed in: law firms: 48%; business and industry (legal): 2%; business and industry (nonlegal): 16%; government: 16%; public interest: 2%; judicial clerk: 5%; academia: 3%; unknown: 8%
Employment location for 2001 class: Intl. 1%; N.E. 1%; M.A. 86%; E.N.C. 1%; W.N.C. 0%; S.A. 5%; E.S.C. 0%; W.S.C. 0%; Mt. 0%; Pac. 1%; unknown 6%

New York University

40 Washington Square S
New York, NY 10012
Private
Admissions: (212) 998-6060
E-mail: law.moreinfo@nyu.edu
Web site: http://www.law.nyu.edu
Internet application: http://www.law.nyu.edu/depts/admissions/applications/online/jd.html
Financial aid: (212) 998-6050
Application deadline: 02/01
Tuition: full time: $33,503; part time: N/A
Room/board/expenses: $21,452
Students receiving grants: 38%
Median grant: $10,000
Average student indebtedness at graduation: $103,867
Enrollment: full time: 1,310; part time: N/A
men: 51%; women: 49%; minorities: 22%
Acceptance rate (full time): 18%
Midrange LSAT (full time): 168-172
Midrange undergraduate GPA (full time): 3.50-3.81
Midrange of full-time private sector salaries of 2001 grads: $125,000-$125,000
2000 grads employed in: law firms: 70%; business and industry (legal): 0%; business and industry (nonlegal): 3%; government: 3%; public interest: 8%; judicial clerk: 16%; academia: 0%; unknown: 0%
Employment location for 2001 class: Intl. 2%; N.E. 4%; M.A. 67%; E.N.C. 2%; W.N.C. 1%; S.A. 10%; E.S.C. 2%; W.S.C. 2%; Mt. 1%; Pac. 11%; unknown 0%

Pace University

78 N. Broadway
White Plains, NY 10603
Private
Admissions: (914) 422-4210
E-mail: admissions@law.pace.edu
Web site: http://www.law.pace.edu
Internet application: http://www.law.pace.edu/adm/apply/jd.html
Financial aid: (914) 422-4048
Application deadline: 02/01
Tuition: full time: $27,174; part time: $20,416
Room/board/expenses: $13,314
Students receiving grants: 45%
Median grant: $12,000
Average student indebtedness at graduation: $71,941
Enrollment: full time: 443; part time: 273
men: 40%; women: 60%; minorities: 16%
Acceptance rate (full time): 35%
Midrange LSAT (full time): 151-156
Midrange undergraduate GPA (full time): 3.01-3.52
Midrange of full-time private sector salaries of 2001 grads: $46,000-$77,000
2000 grads employed in: law firms: 50%; business and industry (legal): 5%; business and industry (nonlegal): 6%; government: 21%; public interest: 3%; judicial clerk: 6%; academia: 1%; unknown: 8%
Employment location for 2001 class: Intl. 0%; N.E. 10%; M.A. 85%; E.N.C. 1%; W.N.C. 0%; S.A. 1%; E.S.C. 0%; W.S.C. 0%; Mt. 0%; Pac. 1%; unknown 4%

St. John's University

8000 Utopia Parkway
Jamaica, NY 11439
Private
Admissions: (718) 990-6611
E-mail: rsvp@sjulaw.stjohns.edu
Web site: http://www.law.stjohns.edu/
Financial aid: (718) 990-1485
Application deadline: 04/01
Tuition: full time: $26,300; part time: $19,730
Room/board/expenses: $15,055
Students receiving grants: 49%
Median grant: $9,000
Average student indebtedness at graduation: $51,085
Enrollment: full time: 718; part time: 201
men: 52%; women: 48%; minorities: 19%
Acceptance rate (full time): 28%
Midrange LSAT (full time): 155-160
Midrange undergraduate GPA (full time): 3.14-3.58
Midrange of full-time private sector salaries of 2001 grads: $50,000-$125,000
2000 grads employed in: law firms: 51%; business and industry (legal): 8%; business and industry (nonlegal): 6%; government: 20%; public interest: 0%; judicial clerk: 6%; academia: 2%; unknown: 6%
Employment location for 2001 class: Intl. 0%; N.E. 2%; M.A. 95%; E.N.C. 0%; W.N.C. 0%; S.A. 3%; E.S.C. N/A; W.S.C. 0%; Mt. 0%; Pac. 0%; unknown 0%

KEY TO TERMINOLOGY ON PAGE 162

Syracuse University
College of Law
Syracuse, NY 13244-1030
Private
Admissions: (315) 443-1962
E-mail: admissions@law.syr.edu
Web site: http://www.law.syr.edu
Financial aid: (315) 443-1963
Application deadline: 04/01
Tuition: full time: $27,500; part time: $24,060
Room/board/expenses: $15,130
Students receiving grants: 72%
Median grant: $7,640
Average student indebtedness at graduation: $66,998
Enrollment: full time: 771; part time: 11
men: 50%; women: 50%; minorities: 19%
Acceptance rate (full time): 42%
Midrange LSAT (full time): 148-154
Midrange undergraduate GPA (full time): 3.02-3.55
Midrange of full-time private sector salaries of 2001 grads: $45,000-$98,000
2000 grads employed in: law firms: 56%; business and industry (legal): 10%; business and industry (nonlegal): 3%; government: 16%; public interest: 1%; judicial clerk: 11%; academia: 1%; unknown: 2%
Employment location for 2001 class: Intl. 0%; N.E. 7%; M.A. 57%; E.N.C. 3%; W.N.C. 1%; S.A. 21%; E.S.C. 0%; W.S.C. 4%; Mt. 2%; Pac. 6%; unknown 0%

Touro College (Jacob D. Fuchsberg)
300 Nassau Road
Huntington, NY 11743
Private
Admissions: (631) 421-2244
E-mail: admissions@tourolaw.edu
Web site: http://www.tourolaw.edu
Internet application: http://www.tourolaw.edu/admissions/app.asp
Financial aid: (631) 421-2244
Application deadline: rolling
Tuition: full time: $23,760; part time: $18,530
Room/board/expenses: $20,124
Students receiving grants: 43%
Median grant: $5,000
Average student indebtedness at graduation: $69,560
Enrollment: full time: 393; part time: 279
men: 53%; women: 47%; minorities: 25%
Acceptance rate (full time): 45%
Midrange LSAT (full time): 145-151
Midrange undergraduate GPA (full time): 2.62-3.29
Midrange of full-time private sector salaries of 2001 grads: $40,000-$65,000
2000 grads employed in: law firms: 54%; business and industry (legal): 0%; business and industry (nonlegal): 7%; government: 25%; public interest: 2%; judicial clerk: 2%; academia: 2%; unknown: 1%
Employment location for 2001 class: Intl. 1%; N.E. N/A; M.A. 98%; E.N.C. N/A; W.N.C. N/A; S.A. 2%; E.S.C. N/A; W.S.C. N/A; Mt. N/A; Pac. N/A; unknown 0%

University at Buffalo
John Lord O'Brian Hall
Buffalo, NY 14260
Public
Admissions: (716) 645-2907
E-mail: law-admissions@buffalo.edu
Web site: http://www.law.buffalo.edu
Financial aid: (716) 645-7324
Application deadline: 03/15
In-state tuition: full time: $11,540; part time: N/A
Out-of-state tuition: full time: $17,090
Room/board/expenses: $11,950
Students receiving grants: 52%
Median grant: $4,350
Average student indebtedness at graduation: $42,591
Enrollment: full time: 720; part time: N/A
men: 47%; women: 53%; minorities: 17%
Acceptance rate (full time): 36%
Midrange LSAT (full time): 152-158
Midrange undergraduate GPA (full time): 3.06-3.65
Midrange of full-time private sector salaries of 2001 grads: $35,000-$70,000
2000 grads employed in: law firms: 59%; business and industry (legal): 8%; business and industry (nonlegal): 10%; government: 12%; public interest: 6%; judicial clerk: 4%; academia: 1%; unknown: N/A
Employment location for 2001 class: Intl. 1%; N.E. 4%; M.A. 82%; E.N.C. 2%; W.N.C. 0%; S.A. 7%; E.S.C. 0%; W.S.C. 0%; Mt. 1%; Pac. 2%; unknown 1%

NORTH CAROLINA

Campbell University
Box 158
Buies Creek, NC 27506
Private
Admissions: (910) 893-1754
E-mail: culaw@webster.campbell.edu
Web site: http://law.campbell.edu
Financial aid: (910) 893-1310
Application deadline: 03/30
Tuition: full time: $20,191; part time: N/A
Room/board/expenses: $9,075
Students receiving grants: 34%
Median grant: $3,250
Average student indebtedness at graduation: $59,563
Enrollment: full time: 336; part time: N/A
men: 54%; women: 46%; minorities: 7%
Acceptance rate (full time): 27%
Midrange LSAT (full time): 151-156
Midrange undergraduate GPA (full time): 2.99-3.51
Midrange of full-time private sector salaries of 2001 grads: $34,000-$50,000
2000 grads employed in: law firms: 72%; business and industry (legal): 4%; business and industry (nonlegal): 1%; government: 10%; public interest: 2%; judicial clerk: 10%; academia: 1%; unknown: N/A
Employment location for 2001 class: Intl. N/A; N.E. N/A; M.A. N/A; E.N.C. N/A; W.N.C. N/A; S.A. 100%; E.S.C. N/A; W.S.C. N/A; Mt. N/A; Pac. N/A; unknown N/A

Duke University
Towerview and Science Drive
Box 90362
Durham, NC 27708-0362
Private
Admissions: (919) 613-7200
E-mail: admissions@law.duke.edu
Web site: http://www.law.duke.edu
Internet application: http://admissions.law.duke.edu/admis/appform.html
Financial aid: (919) 613-7026
Application deadline: 01/01
Tuition: full time: $30,556; part time: N/A
Room/board/expenses: $13,192
Students receiving grants: 61%
Median grant: $6,000
Average student indebtedness at graduation: $77,000
Enrollment: full time: 651; part time: N/A
men: 53%; women: 47%; minorities: 21%
Acceptance rate (full time): 20%
Midrange LSAT (full time): 164-169
Midrange undergraduate GPA (full time): 3.34-3.76
Midrange of full-time private sector salaries of 2001 grads: $120,000-$125,000
2000 grads employed in: law firms: 77%; business and industry (legal): 1%; business and industry (nonlegal): 6%; government: 2%; public interest: 1%; judicial clerk: 14%; academia: 1%; unknown: 0%
Employment location for 2001 class: Intl. 1%; N.E. 5%; M.A. 27%; E.N.C. 6%; W.N.C. 1%; S.A. 35%; E.S.C. 1%; W.S.C. 6%; Mt. 2%; Pac. 17%; unknown 1%

North Carolina Central University[1]
1512 S. Alston Avenue
Durham, NC 27707
Public
Admissions: (919) 560-5243
Web site: http://www.acc.nccu.edu/law
Financial aid: (919) 560-6409
Tuition: N/A
Room/board/expenses: N/A
Enrollment: N/A

University of North Carolina–Chapel Hill
Van Hecke-Wettach Hall
CB No. 3380
Chapel Hill, NC 27599-3380
Public
Admissions: (919) 962-5109
E-mail: law_admission@unc.edu
Web site: http://www.law.unc.edu
Financial aid: (919) 962-8396
Application deadline: 02/01
In-state tuition: full time: $9,966; part time: N/A
Out-of-state tuition: full time: $21,822
Room/board/expenses: $12,778
Students receiving grants: 59%
Median grant: $1,000
Average student indebtedness at graduation: $46,691
Enrollment: full time: 794; part time: N/A
men: 47%; women: 53%; minorities: 20%
Acceptance rate (full time): 18%
Midrange LSAT (full time): 157-163
Midrange undergraduate GPA (full time): 3.39-3.79
Midrange of full-time private sector salaries of 2001 grads: $70,000-$100,000
2000 grads employed in: law firms: 60%; business and industry (legal): 1%; business and industry (nonlegal): 7%; government: 11%; public interest: 5%; judicial clerk: 14%; academia: 2%; unknown: 0%
Employment location for 2001 class: Intl. 1%; N.E. 5%; M.A. 4%; E.N.C. 3%; W.N.C. 1%; S.A. 76%; E.S.C. 5%; W.S.C. 1%; Mt. 2%; Pac. 2%; unknown 1%

Wake Forest University
Reynolds Station
PO Box 7206
Winston-Salem, NC 27109
Private
Admissions: (336) 758-5437
E-mail: admissions@law.wfu.edu
Web site: http://www.law.wfu.edu
Financial aid: (336) 758-5437
Application deadline: 03/01
Tuition: full time: $23,950; part time: N/A
Room/board/expenses: $12,800
Students receiving grants: 33%
Median grant: $17,212
Average student indebtedness at graduation: $69,049
Enrollment: full time: 452; part time: 22
men: 53%; women: 47%; minorities: 9%
Acceptance rate (full time): 28%
Midrange LSAT (full time): 158-163
Midrange undergraduate GPA (full time): 3.14-3.69
Midrange of full-time private sector salaries of 2001 grads: $50,000-$100,000
2000 grads employed in: law firms: 68%; business and industry (legal): 1%; business and industry (nonlegal): 5%; government: 13%; public interest: 2%; judicial clerk: 8%; academia: N/A; unknown: 4%
Employment location for 2001 class: Intl. 1%; N.E. 4%; M.A. 6%; E.N.C. 1%; W.N.C. N/A; S.A. 80%; E.S.C. 2%; W.S.C. 4%; Mt. N/A; Pac. 2%; unknown 2%

NORTH DAKOTA

University of North Dakota
PO Box 9003
Grand Forks, ND 58202
Public
Admissions: (701) 777-2104
E-mail: mark.brickson@thor.law.und.nodak.edu
Web site: http://www.law.und.nodak.edu
Financial aid: (701) 777-6265
Application deadline: 04/01
In-state tuition: full time: $4,826; part time: N/A
Out-of-state tuition: full time: $10,624
Room/board/expenses: N/A
Students receiving grants: 72%
Median grant: $500
Average student indebtedness at graduation: N/A
Enrollment: full time: 211; part time: N/A
men: 49%; women: 51%; minorities: 8%
Acceptance rate (full time): 55%
Midrange LSAT (full time): 148-155
Midrange undergraduate GPA (full time): 3.13-3.69
Midrange of full-time private sector salaries of 2001 grads: N/A-N/A
2000 grads employed in: law firms: 39%; business and industry (legal): 2%; business and industry (nonlegal): N/A; government: 9%; public interest: 6%; judicial clerk: 44%; academia: N/A; unknown: N/A
Employment location for 2001 class: Intl. 2%; N.E. 0%; M.A. 0%; E.N.C. 4%; W.N.C. 83%; S.A. 2%; E.S.C. 0%; W.S.C. 0%; Mt. 7%; Pac. 2%; unknown 0%

OHIO

Capital University
303 E. Broad Street
Columbus, OH 43215-3200
Private
Admissions: (614) 236-6310
E-mail: admissions@law.capital.edu
Web site: http://www.law.capital.edu
Financial aid: (614) 236-6350
Application deadline: 05/01
Tuition: full time: $655/credit hour; part time: $655/credit hour
Room/board/expenses: $10,358
Students receiving grants: 48%
Median grant: $6,000
Average student indebtedness at graduation: $54,405
Enrollment: full time: 454; part time: 332
men: 47%; women: 53%; minorities: 11%
Acceptance rate (full time): 49%
Midrange LSAT (full time): 148-154
Midrange undergraduate GPA (full time): 2.96-3.44
Midrange of full-time private sector salaries of 2001 grads: $40,000-$80,000
2000 grads employed in: law firms: 47%; business and industry (legal): 13%; business and industry (nonlegal): 16%; government: 12%; public interest: 3%; judicial clerk: 8%; academia: 2%; unknown: 0%
Employment location for 2001 class: Intl. 1%; N.E. 0%; M.A. 3%; E.N.C. 88%; W.N.C. 1%; S.A. 4%; E.S.C. 2%; W.S.C. 1%; Mt. 2%; Pac. 1%; unknown 0%

Case Western Reserve University
11075 East Boulevard
Cleveland, OH 44106-7148
Private
Admissions: (800) 756-0036
E-mail: lawadmissions@cwru.edu
Web site: http://www.law.cwru.edu
Internet application: http://www.law.cwru.edu/admissions/
Financial aid: (877) 889-4279
Application deadline: 04/01
Tuition: full time: $25,900; part time: $1,079/credit hour
Room/board/expenses: $13,350
Students receiving grants: 41%
Median grant: $10,000
Average student indebtedness at graduation: $55,900
Enrollment: full time: 658; part time: 6
men: 55%; women: 45%; minorities: 15%
Acceptance rate (full time): 32%
Midrange LSAT (full time): 155-160
Midrange undergraduate GPA (full time): 3.01-3.49
Midrange of full-time private sector salaries of 2001 grads: $56,000-$110,000
2000 grads employed in: law firms: 61%; business and industry (legal): 2%; business and industry (nonlegal): 6%; government: 14%; public interest: 5%; judicial clerk: 5%; academia: 6%; unknown: 1%
Employment location for 2001 class: Intl. 1%; N.E. 4%; M.A. 8%; E.N.C. 69%; W.N.C. 0%; S.A. 11%; E.S.C. 1%; W.S.C. 1%; Mt. 2%; Pac. 4%; unknown 0%

Cleveland State University (Marshall)
2121 Euclid Avenue
LB 138
Cleveland, OH 44115
Public
Admissions: (216) 687-2304
E-mail: admissions@law.csuohio.edu
Web site: http://www.law.csuohio.edu
Internet application: http://www.law.csuohio.edu/admissions/apply.html
Financial aid: (216) 687-2317
Application deadline: 04/01
In-state tuition: full time: $10,543; part time: $8,110
Out-of-state tuition: full time: $20,924
Room/board/expenses: $11,050
Students receiving grants: 32%
Median grant: $3,529
Average student indebtedness at graduation: $44,915

Enrollment: full time: 535; part time: 293
men: 59%; women: 41%; minorities: 10%
Acceptance rate (full time): 45%
Midrange LSAT (full time): 147-154
Midrange undergraduate GPA (full time): 2.62-3.46
Midrange of full-time private sector salaries of 2001 grads: $45,000-$90,000
2000 grads employed in: law firms: 48%; business and industry (legal): 3%; business and industry (nonlegal): 13%; government: 25%; public interest: 3%; judicial clerk: 5%; academia: 3%; unknown: N/A
Employment location for 2001 class: Intl. N/A; N.E. N/A; M.A. 2%; E.N.C. 86%; W.N.C. 1%; S.A. 8%; E.S.C. N/A; W.S.C. 1%; Mt. 1%; Pac. 2%; unknown N/A

Ohio Northern University

525 S. Main Street
Ada, OH 45810-1599
Private
Admissions: (877) 452-9668
E-mail: admissions@eugene.onu.edu
Web site: http://www.law.onu.edu
Financial aid: (419) 772-2272
Application deadline: 07/01
Tuition: full time: $20,650; part time: N/A
Room/board/expenses: $8,050
Students receiving grants: 39%
Median grant: $10,000
Average student indebtedness at graduation: $67,877
Enrollment: full time: 272; part time: N/A
men: 62%; women: 38%; minorities: 8%
Acceptance rate (full time): 43%
Midrange LSAT (full time): 145-153
Midrange undergraduate GPA (full time): 2.76-3.45
Midrange of full-time private sector salaries of 2001 grads: $40,000-$95,000
2000 grads employed in: law firms: 49%; business and industry (legal): 10%; business and industry (nonlegal): 3%; government: 14%; public interest: 4%; judicial clerk: 14%; academia: 0%; unknown: 6%
Employment location for 2001 class: Intl. 1%; N.E. 1%; M.A. 10%; E.N.C. 47%; W.N.C. 1%; S.A. 23%; E.S.C. 10%; W.S.C. 1%; Mt. 3%; Pac. 3%; unknown 0%

Ohio State University (Moritz)

55 W. 12th Avenue
Columbus, OH 43210
Public
Admissions: (614) 292-8810
E-mail: lawadmit@osu.edu
Web site: http://www.osu.edu/units/law
Financial aid: (614) 292-8807
Application deadline: 03/15
In-state tuition: full time: $11,880; part time: N/A
Out-of-state tuition: full time: $23,300
Room/board/expenses: $12,634
Students receiving grants: 70%
Median grant: $2,500
Average student indebtedness at graduation: $49,360
Enrollment: full time: 684; part time: N/A
men: 53%; women: 47%; minorities: 17%
Acceptance rate (full time): 28%
Midrange LSAT (full time): 156-163
Midrange undergraduate GPA (full time): 3.36-3.78
Midrange of full-time private sector salaries of 2001 grads: $50,000-$90,000
2000 grads employed in: law firms: 50%; business and industry (legal): 2%; business and industry (nonlegal): 13%; government: 13%; public interest: 5%; judicial clerk: 12%; academia: 1%; unknown: 4%
Employment location for 2001 class: Intl. 1%; N.E. 1%; M.A. 7%; E.N.C. 75%; W.N.C. 2%; S.A. 6%; E.S.C. 1%; W.S.C. 2%; Mt. 2%; Pac. 4%; unknown 0%

University of Akron

C. Blake McDowell Law Center
Akron, OH 44325-2901
Public
Admissions: (800) 425-7668
E-mail: lawadmissions@uakron.edu
Web site: http://www.uakron.edu/law
Internet application: http://www.uakron.edu/law/email.html
Financial aid: (800) 621-3847
Application deadline: 03/01
In-state tuition: full time: $9,935; part time: $8,032
Out-of-state tuition: full time: $15,621
Room/board/expenses: $12,262
Students receiving grants: 54%
Median grant: $8,068
Enrollment: full time: 382; part time: 229
men: 56%; women: 44%; minorities: 9%
Acceptance rate (full time): 30%
Midrange LSAT (full time): 153-157
Midrange undergraduate GPA (full time): 2.84-3.60
Midrange of full-time private sector salaries of 2001 grads: $38,051-$57,627
2000 grads employed in: law firms: 46%; business and industry (legal): 5%; business and industry (nonlegal): 12%; government: 22%; public interest: 1%; judicial clerk: 12%; academia: 2%; unknown: 0%
Employment location for 2001 class: Intl. 0%; N.E. 0%; M.A. 6%; E.N.C. 84%; W.N.C. 1%; S.A. 6%; E.S.C. 1%; W.S.C. 2%; Mt. 0%; Pac. 2%; unknown 0%

University of Cincinnati

PO Box 210040
Cincinnati, OH 45221-0040
Public
Admissions: (513) 556-6805
E-mail: admissions@law.uc.edu
Web site: http://www.law.uc.edu
Internet application: http://www.law.uc.edu/admissions
Financial aid: (513) 556-6805
Application deadline: 04/01
In-state tuition: full time: $11,020; part time: N/A
Out-of-state tuition: full time: $20,838
Room/board/expenses: $11,450
Students receiving grants: 60%
Median grant: $5,000
Average student indebtedness at graduation: $38,800
Enrollment: full time: 364; part time: N/A
men: 47%; women: 53%; minorities: 18%
Acceptance rate (full time): 32%
Midrange LSAT (full time): 156-162
Midrange undergraduate GPA (full time): 3.20-3.72
Midrange of full-time private sector salaries of 2001 grads: $47,500-$84,500
2000 grads employed in: law firms: 62%; business and industry (legal): 3%; business and industry (nonlegal): 9%; government: 11%; public interest: 3%; judicial clerk: 7%; academia: 1%; unknown: 4%
Employment location for 2001 class: Intl. 0%; N.E. 1%; M.A. 0%; E.N.C. 78%; W.N.C. 1%; S.A. 6%; E.S.C. 7%; W.S.C. 1%; Mt. 2%; Pac. 0%; unknown 4%

University of Dayton

300 College Park
Dayton, OH 45469-2772
Private
Admissions: (937) 229-3555
E-mail: lawinfo@udayton.edu
Web site: http://www.law.udayton.edu
Financial aid: (937) 229-3555
Application deadline: 05/01
Tuition: full time: $22,550; part time: N/A
Room/board/expenses: $9,900
Students receiving grants: 52%
Median grant: $10,000
Average student indebtedness at graduation: $66,856
Enrollment: full time: 462; part time: N/A
men: 60%; women: 40%; minorities: 14%
Acceptance rate (full time): 57%
Midrange LSAT (full time): 147-154
Midrange undergraduate GPA (full time): 2.84-3.43
Midrange of full-time private sector salaries of 2001 grads: $36,000-$70,000
2000 grads employed in: law firms: 50%; business and industry (legal): 1%; business and industry (nonlegal): 20%; government: 19%; public interest: 2%; judicial clerk: 6%; academia: 1%; unknown: 1%
Employment location for 2001 class: Intl. 0%; N.E. 3%; M.A. 7%; E.N.C. 59%; W.N.C. 2%; S.A. 21%; E.S.C. 5%; W.S.C. 2%; Mt. 0%; Pac. 2%; unknown 0%

University of Toledo

2801 W. Bancroft
Toledo, OH 43606
Public
Admissions: (419) 530-4131
E-mail: law.admissions@utoledo.edu
Web site: http://www.utlaw.edu
Financial aid: (419) 530-7929
Application deadline: 07/01
In-state tuition: full time: $10,350; part time: $8,196
Out-of-state tuition: full time: $20,081
Room/board/expenses: $11,733
Students receiving grants: 67%
Median grant: $7,860
Average student indebtedness at graduation: $44,088
Enrollment: full time: 293; part time: 192
men: 55%; women: 45%; minorities: 8%
Acceptance rate (full time): 33%
Midrange LSAT (full time): 153-158
Midrange undergraduate GPA (full time): 2.84-3.53
Midrange of full-time private sector salaries of 2001 grads: $40,000-$72,000
2000 grads employed in: law firms: 52%; business and industry (legal): 9%; business and industry (nonlegal): 10%; government: 11%; public interest: 2%; judicial clerk: 9%; academia: 2%; unknown: 5%
Employment location for 2001 class: Intl. N/A; N.E. 1%; M.A. N/A; E.N.C. 76%; W.N.C. 2%; S.A. 11%; E.S.C. 1%; W.S.C. 2%; Mt. 4%; Pac. N/A; unknown 3%

OKLAHOMA

Oklahoma City University

2501 N. Blackwelder
Oklahoma City, OK 73106-1493
Private
Admissions: (800) 633-7242
E-mail: lawadmit@okcu.edu
Web site: http://www.okcu.edu/law
Internet application: http://www.okcu.edu/law/prospective/admappl.asp
Financial aid: (800) 633-7242
Application deadline: 08/01
Tuition: full time: $650/credit hour; part time: $650/credit hour
Room/board/expenses: $12,940
Students receiving grants: 15%
Median grant: $9,000
Average student indebtedness at graduation: $50,449
Enrollment: full time: 422; part time: 161
men: 59%; women: 41%; minorities: 18%
Acceptance rate (full time): 56%
Midrange LSAT (full time): 144-150
Midrange undergraduate GPA (full time): 2.77-3.40
Midrange of full-time private sector salaries of 2001 grads: $36,000-$60,000
2000 grads employed in: law firms: 61%; business and industry (legal): 5%; business and industry (nonlegal): 4%; government: 20%; public interest: 3%; judicial clerk: 4%; academia: 3%; unknown: 1%
Employment location for 2001 class: Intl. 1%; N.E. 0%; M.A. 1%; E.N.C. 1%; W.N.C. 3%; S.A. 8%; E.S.C. 0%; W.S.C. 78%; Mt. 5%; Pac. 2%; unknown 2%

University of Oklahoma

300 Timberdell Road
Norman, OK 73019-5081
Public
Admissions: (405) 325-4728
E-mail: kmadden@ou.edu
Web site: http://www.law.ou.edu
Financial aid: (405) 325-4521
Application deadline: 03/15
In-state tuition: full time: $6,376; part time: N/A
Out-of-state tuition: full time: $15,643
Room/board/expenses: $13,176
Students receiving grants: 65%
Median grant: $2,000
Average student indebtedness at graduation: $49,697
Enrollment: full time: 524; part time: N/A
men: 52%; women: 48%; minorities: 13%
Acceptance rate (full time): 28%
Midrange LSAT (full time): 153-160
Midrange undergraduate GPA (full time): 3.25-3.81
Midrange of full-time private sector salaries of 2001 grads: $39,000-$70,000
2000 grads employed in: law firms: 62%; business and industry (legal): 8%; business and industry (nonlegal): 5%; government: 19%; public interest: 4%; judicial clerk: 0%; academia: 2%; unknown: 0%
Employment location for 2001 class: Intl. 1%; N.E. 0%; M.A. 0%; E.N.C. 0%; W.N.C. 1%; S.A. 7%; E.S.C. 1%; W.S.C. 84%; Mt. 5%; Pac. 0%; unknown 1%

University of Tulsa

3120 E. Fourth Place
Tulsa, OK 74104
Private
Admissions: (918) 631-2406
E-mail: lawadmissions@utulsa.edu
Web site: http://www.law.utulsa.edu
Financial aid: (918) 631-2526
Application deadline: rolling
Tuition: full time: $19,492; part time: $13,242
Room/board/expenses: $10,522
Students receiving grants: 41%
Median grant: $5,000
Average student indebtedness at graduation: $80,970
Enrollment: full time: 452; part time: 106
men: 58%; women: 42%; minorities: 17%
Acceptance rate (full time): 52%
Midrange LSAT (full time): 145-153
Midrange undergraduate GPA (full time): 2.83-3.46
Midrange of full-time private sector salaries of 2001 grads: $40,500-$69,000
2000 grads employed in: law firms: 66%; business and industry (legal): 7%; business and industry (nonlegal): 8%; government: 12%; public interest: 1%; judicial clerk: 0%; academia: 6%; unknown: N/A
Employment location for 2001 class: Intl. 0%; N.E. 0%; M.A. 1%; E.N.C. 5%; W.N.C. 6%; S.A. 10%; E.S.C. 2%; W.S.C. 68%; Mt. 6%; Pac. 2%; unknown 0%

OREGON

Lewis and Clark College (Northwestern)

10015 S.W. Terwilliger Boulevard
Portland, OR 97219
Private
Admissions: (503) 768-6613
E-mail: lawadmss@lclark.edu
Web site: http://law.lclark.edu
Internet application: http://www.lclark.edu/dept/lawadmss/process.html
Financial aid: (503) 768-7090
Application deadline: 03/01
Tuition: full time: $23,196; part time: $17,400
Room/board/expenses: $13,205
Students receiving grants: 46%
Median grant: $6,000
Average student indebtedness at graduation: $66,020
Enrollment: full time: 509; part time: 202
men: 49%; women: 51%; minorities: 15%
Acceptance rate (full time): 37%
Midrange LSAT (full time): 156-163
Midrange undergraduate GPA (full time): 3.20-3.65
Midrange of full-time private sector salaries of 2001 grads: $42,000-$80,000
2000 grads employed in: law firms: 56%; business and industry (legal): 10%; business and industry (nonlegal): 0%; government: 13%; public interest: 10%; judicial clerk: 11%; academia: 0%; unknown: 0%
Employment location for 2001 class: Intl. 0%; N.E. 0%; M.A. 2%; E.N.C. 2%; W.N.C. 0%; S.A. 7%; E.S.C. 1%; W.S.C. 1%; Mt. 5%; Pac. 82%; unknown 0%

University of Oregon

1221 University of Oregon
Eugene, OR 97403-1221
Public
Admissions: (541) 346-3846
E-mail: admissions@law.uoregon.edu
Web site: http://www.law.uoregon.edu
Financial aid: (800) 760-6953
Application deadline: 02/15
In-state tuition: full time: $13,294; part time: N/A

KEY TO TERMINOLOGY ON PAGE 162

Out-of-state tuition: full time: $17,872
Room/board/expenses: $12,058
Students receiving grants: 46%
Median grant: $2,800
Average student indebtedness at graduation: $52,821
Enrollment: full time: 516; part time: N/A
men: 59%; women: 41%; minorities: 12%
Acceptance rate (full time): 38%
Midrange LSAT (full time): 157-161
Midrange undergraduate GPA (full time): 3.10-3.60
Midrange of full-time private sector salaries of 2001 grads: $40,000-$75,000
2000 grads employed in: law firms: 40%; business and industry (legal): 2%; business and industry (nonlegal): 5%; government: 21%; public interest: 4%; judicial clerk: 26%; academia: 3%; unknown: 0%
Employment location for 2001 class: Intl. 0%; N.E. 2%; M.A. 0%; E.N.C. 3%; W.N.C. 0%; S.A. 8%; E.S.C. 0%; W.S.C. 1%; Mt. 8%; Pac. 77%; unknown 1%

Willamette University

245 Winter Street SE
Salem, OR 97301-3922
Private
Admissions: (503) 370-6282
E-mail: law-admission@willamette.edu
Web site: http://www.willamette.edu/wucl
Internet application: http://apply.embark.com/grad/willamette/default.asp
Financial aid: (503) 370-6273
Application deadline: 04/01
Tuition: full time: $21,880; part time: N/A
Room/board/expenses: $12,650
Students receiving grants: 56%
Median grant: $10,000
Average student indebtedness at graduation: $64,315
Enrollment: full time: 424; part time: 5
men: 55%; women: 45%; minorities: 9%
Acceptance rate (full time): 63%
Midrange LSAT (full time): 151-157
Midrange undergraduate GPA (full time): 2.94-3.49
Midrange of full-time private sector salaries of 2001 grads: $43,500-$80,000
2000 grads employed in: law firms: 59%; business and industry (legal): 4%; business and industry (nonlegal): 6%; government: 19%; public interest: N/A; judicial clerk: 10%; academia: 2%; unknown: N/A
Employment location for 2001 class: Intl. 1%; N.E. 0%; M.A. 1%; E.N.C. 1%; W.N.C. 0%; S.A. 1%; E.S.C. 0%; W.S.C. 0%; Mt. 11%; Pac. 85%; unknown N/A

Duquesne University

600 Forbes Avenue
Pittsburgh, PA 15282
Private
Admissions: (412) 396-6296
E-mail: ricci@duq.edu
Web site: http://www.duq.edu/law
Financial aid: (412) 396-6607
Application deadline: 04/01
Tuition: full time: $20,054; part time: $15,564
Room/board/expenses: $12,406
Students receiving grants: 19%

Median grant: $6,564
Average student indebtedness at graduation: $74,000
Enrollment: full time: 372; part time: 279
men: 50%; women: 50%; minorities: 6%
Acceptance rate (full time): 47%
Midrange LSAT (full time): 152-155
Midrange undergraduate GPA (full time): 3.08-3.63
Midrange of full-time private sector salaries of 2001 grads: $45,000-$80,000
2000 grads employed in: law firms: 61%; business and industry (legal): 3%; business and industry (nonlegal): 14%; government: 8%; public interest: 1%; judicial clerk: 10%; academia: 2%; unknown: 1%
Employment location for 2001 class: Intl. 0%; N.E. 2%; M.A. 86%; E.N.C. 4%; W.N.C. 2%; S.A. 2%; E.S.C. 0%; W.S.C. 0%; Mt. 1%; Pac. 1%; unknown 2%

Penn State University (Dickinson School of Law)

150 S. College Street
Carlisle, PA 17013
Private
Admissions: (717) 240-5207
E-mail: dsladmit@psu.edu
Web site: http://www.dsl.psu.edu
Financial aid: (800) 840-1122
Application deadline: 03/01
Tuition: full time: $22,640; part time: N/A
Room/board/expenses: $13,000
Students receiving grants: 33%
Median grant: $3,400
Average student indebtedness at graduation: $63,632
Enrollment: full time: 594; part time: N/A
men: 52%; women: 48%; minorities: 11%
Acceptance rate (full time): 43%
Midrange LSAT (full time): 151-157
Midrange undergraduate GPA (full time): 3.05-3.53
Midrange of full-time private sector salaries of 2001 grads: $36,000-$80,000
2000 grads employed in: law firms: 55%; business and industry (legal): 4%; business and industry (nonlegal): 4%; government: 10%; public interest: 1%; judicial clerk: 23%; academia: 0%; unknown: 3%
Employment location for 2001 class: Intl. 1%; N.E. 1%; M.A. 73%; E.N.C. 0%; W.N.C. 1%; S.A. 14%; E.S.C. 0%; W.S.C. 0%; Mt. 0%; Pac. 0%; unknown 9%

Temple University (Beasley)

1719 N. Broad Street
Philadelphia, PA 19122
Public
Admissions: (800) 560-1428
E-mail: lawadmis@blue.temple.edu
Web site: http://www.temple.edu/lawschool
Financial aid: (800) 560-1428
Application deadline: 03/01
In-state tuition: full time: $11,778; part time: $9,520
Out-of-state tuition: full time: $20,052
Room/board/expenses: $16,847
Students receiving grants: 45%
Median grant: $5,154
Average student indebtedness at graduation: $61,209

Enrollment: full time: 772; part time: 293
men: 50%; women: 50%; minorities: 19%
Acceptance rate (full time): 31%
Midrange LSAT (full time): 158-162
Midrange undergraduate GPA (full time): 3.20-3.62
Midrange of full-time private sector salaries of 2001 grads: $60,000-$105,000
2000 grads employed in: law firms: 47%; business and industry (legal): 5%; business and industry (nonlegal): 17%; government: 14%; public interest: 5%; judicial clerk: 10%; academia: 2%; unknown: N/A
Employment location for 2001 class: Intl. 0%; N.E. 1%; M.A. 87%; E.N.C. 1%; W.N.C. N/A; S.A. 7%; E.S.C. N/A; W.S.C. 0%; Mt. N/A; Pac. 4%; unknown N/A

University of Pennsylvania

3400 Chestnut Street
Philadelphia, PA 19104
Private
Admissions: (215) 898-7400
E-mail: admissions@law.upenn.edu
Web site: http://www.law.upenn.edu
Financial aid: (215) 898-7400
Application deadline: 03/01
Tuition: full time: $31,138; part time: N/A
Room/board/expenses: $14,412
Students receiving grants: 33%
Median grant: $10,650
Average student indebtedness at graduation: $80,165
Enrollment: full time: 830; part time: N/A
men: 52%; women: 48%; minorities: 26%
Acceptance rate (full time): 16%
Midrange LSAT (full time): 165-168
Midrange undergraduate GPA (full time): 3.37-3.76
Midrange of full-time private sector salaries of 2001 grads: $107,000-$125,000
2000 grads employed in: law firms: 78%; business and industry (legal): N/A; business and industry (nonlegal): 1%; government: 3%; public interest: 2%; judicial clerk: 15%; academia: 1%; unknown: N/A
Employment location for 2001 class: Intl. 2%; N.E. 5%; M.A. 63%; E.N.C. 2%; W.N.C. 1%; S.A. 15%; E.S.C. 1%; W.S.C. 0%; Mt. 1%; Pac. 10%; unknown 0%

University of Pittsburgh

3900 Forbes Avenue
Pittsburgh, PA 15260
Public
Admissions: (412) 648-1415
E-mail: admissions@law.pitt.edu
Web site: http://www.law.pitt.edu
Financial aid: (412) 648-1415
Application deadline: 03/01
In-state tuition: full time: $16,496; part time: N/A
Out-of-state tuition: full time: $24,598
Room/board/expenses: $13,320
Students receiving grants: 46%
Median grant: $8,000
Average student indebtedness at graduation: $65,000
Enrollment: full time: 729; part time: N/A
men: 55%; women: 45%; minorities: 10%

Acceptance rate (full time): 35%
Midrange LSAT (full time): 155-161
Midrange undergraduate GPA (full time): 3.05-3.60
Midrange of full-time private sector salaries of 2001 grads: $58,800-$147,000
2000 grads employed in: law firms: 56%; business and industry (legal): 16%; business and industry (nonlegal): N/A; government: 11%; public interest: 2%; judicial clerk: 13%; academia: 1%; unknown: 2%
Employment location for 2001 class: Intl. 1%; N.E. 1%; M.A. 75%; E.N.C. 4%; W.N.C. 0%; S.A. 14%; E.S.C. 1%; W.S.C. 2%; Mt. 1%; Pac. 1%; unknown 3%

Villanova University

299 N. Spring Mill Road
Villanova, PA 19085
Private
Admissions: (610) 519-7010
E-mail: admissions@law.villanova.edu
Web site: http://www.law.villanova.edu/
Financial aid: (610) 519-7015
Application deadline: 03/01
Tuition: full time: $23,770; part time: N/A
Room/board/expenses: $14,110
Students receiving grants: 10%
Median grant: $4,000
Average student indebtedness at graduation: $78,364
Enrollment: full time: 752; part time: N/A
men: 52%; women: 48%; minorities: 12%
Acceptance rate (full time): 37%
Midrange LSAT (full time): 155-159
Midrange undergraduate GPA (full time): 3.10-3.56
Midrange of full-time private sector salaries of 2001 grads: $58,000-$105,000
2000 grads employed in: law firms: 69%; business and industry (legal): 1%; business and industry (nonlegal): 5%; government: 9%; public interest: 1%; judicial clerk: 16%; academia: 0%; unknown: N/A
Employment location for 2001 class: Intl. N/A; N.E. 3%; M.A. 80%; E.N.C. 1%; W.N.C. 0%; S.A. 12%; E.S.C. 0%; W.S.C. 1%; Mt. 2%; Pac. 2%; unknown 1%

Catholic University[1]

2250 Avenida Las Americas
Suite 584
Ponce, PR 00717-0777
Private
Admissions: (787) 841-2000
E-mail: admisiones@pucpr.edu
Web site: http://www.pucpr.edu
Financial aid: (787) 841-2000
Tuition: N/A
Room/board/expenses: N/A
Enrollment: N/A

Inter-American University[1]

PO Box 70351
San Juan, PR 00936-8351
Private
Admissions: (787) 765-1270
E-mail: edmendez@inter.edu
Web site: http://www.metro.inter.edu
Financial aid: (787) 250-1912
Tuition: N/A
Room/board/expenses: N/A
Enrollment: N/A

University of Puerto Rico[1]

PO Box 23303
Estacion Universidad
Rio Piedras, PR 00931-3302
Public
Admissions: (787) 764-0000
E-mail: admisiones@upr.edu
Web site: http://www.upr.edu
Internet application: http://www.upr.edu/admisiones/
Financial aid: (787) 764-0000
Tuition: N/A
Room/board/expenses: N/A
Enrollment: N/A

Roger Williams University

10 Metacom Avenue
Bristol, RI 02809-5171
Private
Admissions: (401) 254-4555
E-mail: admissions@law.rwu.edu
Web site: http://law.rwu.edu
Internet application: http://law.rwu.edu/Admissions/OnApp.htm
Financial aid: (401) 254-4510
Application deadline: 05/01
Tuition: full time: $21,990; part time: $15,750
Room/board/expenses: $14,720
Students receiving grants: 49%
Median grant: $10,000
Average student indebtedness at graduation: $62,612
Enrollment: full time: 397; part time: 128
men: 47%; women: 53%; minorities: 11%
Acceptance rate (full time): 58%
Midrange LSAT (full time): 146-154
Midrange undergraduate GPA (full time): 2.83-3.36
Midrange of full-time private sector salaries of 2001 grads: $33,333-$52,322
2000 grads employed in: law firms: 25%; business and industry (legal): 8%; business and industry (nonlegal): 18%; government: 20%; public interest: 5%; judicial clerk: 12%; academia: 7%; unknown: 7%
Employment location for 2001 class: Intl. 0%; N.E. 77%; M.A. 5%; E.N.C. 3%; W.N.C. 2%; S.A. 5%; E.S.C. 0%; W.S.C. 0%; Mt. 2%; Pac. 2%; unknown 5%

University of South Carolina

701 S. Main Street
Columbia, SC 29208
Public
Admissions: (803) 777-6605
E-mail: usclaw@law.law.sc.edu
Web site: http://www.law.sc.edu
Financial aid: (803) 777-6605
Application deadline: 02/15
In-state tuition: full time: $11,120; part time: N/A
Out-of-state tuition: full time: $22,516
Room/board/expenses: $11,519
Students receiving grants: 26%
Median grant: $5,066
Average student indebtedness at graduation: $50,000
Enrollment: full time: 720; part time: N/A
men: 57%; women: 43%; minorities: 7%
Acceptance rate (full time): 30%
Midrange LSAT (full time): 154-159

Midrange undergraduate GPA (full time): 3.33-3.65
Midrange of full-time private sector salaries of 2001 grads: $50,000-$75,000
2000 grads employed in: law firms: 51%; business and industry (legal): 0%; business and industry (nonlegal): 5%; government: 12%; public interest: 1%; judicial clerk: 31%; academia: 0%; unknown: 0%
Employment location for 2001 class: Intl. 1%; N.E. 0%; M.A. 2%; E.N.C. 0%; W.N.C. 0%; S.A. 94%; E.S.C. 0%; W.S.C. 2%; Mt. 0%; Pac. 0%; unknown 1%

SOUTH DAKOTA

University of South Dakota
414 E. Clark Street
Vermillion, SD 57069-2390
Public
Admissions: (605) 677-5443
E-mail: lawreq@usd.edu
Web site: http://www.usd.edu/law/
Financial aid: (605) 677-5446
Application deadline: 03/01
In-state tuition: full time: $6,160; part time: $4,508
Out-of-state tuition: full time: $12,491
Room/board/expenses: $11,181
Students receiving grants: 54%
Median grant: $1,000
Average student indebtedness at graduation: $26,605
Enrollment: full time: 227; part time: 6
men: 55%; women: 45%; minorities: 11%
Acceptance rate (full time): 50%
Midrange LSAT (full time): 146-154
Midrange undergraduate GPA (full time): 2.79-3.48
Midrange of full-time private sector salaries of 2001 grads: $40,000-$62,000
2000 grads employed in: law firms: 31%; business and industry (legal): 0%; business and industry (nonlegal): 12%; government: 10%; public interest: 10%; judicial clerk: 37%; academia: 2%; unknown: 0%
Employment location for 2001 class: Intl. 0%; N.E. 0%; M.A. 2%; E.N.C. 0%; W.N.C. 89%; S.A. 4%; E.S.C. 0%; W.S.C. 2%; Mt. 2%; Pac. 2%; unknown 0%

TENNESSEE

University of Memphis
207 Humphreys Law School
Memphis, TN 38152-3140
Public
Admissions: (901) 678-5403
E-mail: lawadmissions@mail.law.memphis.edu
Web site: http://www.law.memphis.edu
Internet application: http://www.law.memphis.edu/admissions
Financial aid: (901) 678-3687
Application deadline: 02/15
In-state tuition: full time: $6,828; part time: $5,888
Out-of-state tuition: full time: $18,928
Room/board/expenses: $10,950
Students receiving grants: 24%
Median grant: $6,069
Average student indebtedness at graduation: $47,797
Enrollment: full time: 449; part time: 31
men: 56%; women: 44%; minorities: 10%

Acceptance rate (full time): 36%
Midrange LSAT (full time): 151-155
Midrange undergraduate GPA (full time): 2.95-3.61
Midrange of full-time private sector salaries of 2001 grads: $44,000-$70,000
2000 grads employed in: law firms: 77%; business and industry (legal): 0%; business and industry (nonlegal): 5%; government: 10%; public interest: 0%; judicial clerk: 8%; academia: 0%; unknown: 0%
Employment location for 2001 class: Intl. 0%; N.E. 0%; M.A. 2%; E.N.C. 0%; W.N.C. 1%; S.A. 4%; E.S.C. 92%; W.S.C. 2%; Mt. 0%; Pac. 0%; unknown 0%

University of Tennessee–Knoxville
1505 W. Cumberland Avenue
Knoxville, TN 37996-1810
Public
Admissions: (865) 974-4131
E-mail: lawadmit@libra.law.utk.edu
Web site: http://www.law.utk.edu
Internet application: http://appserv.law.utk.edu/apply/personal.asp
Financial aid: (865) 974-4131
Application deadline: 02/15
In-state tuition: full time: $7,156; part time: N/A
Out-of-state tuition: full time: $19,212
Room/board/expenses: $12,400
Students receiving grants: 34%
Median grant: $6,200
Average student indebtedness at graduation: $43,224
Enrollment: full time: 475; part time: N/A
men: 53%; women: 47%; minorities: 14%
Acceptance rate (full time): 28%
Midrange LSAT (full time): 155-160
Midrange undergraduate GPA (full time): 3.25-3.76
Midrange of full-time private sector salaries of 2001 grads: $50,000-$80,000
2000 grads employed in: law firms: 71%; business and industry (legal): 1%; business and industry (nonlegal): 5%; government: 13%; public interest: 2%; judicial clerk: 7%; academia: 1%; unknown: 0%
Employment location for 2001 class: Intl. 0%; N.E. 0%; M.A. 0%; E.N.C. 2%; W.N.C. 0%; S.A. 19%; E.S.C. 71%; W.S.C. 2%; Mt. 1%; Pac. 2%; unknown 4%

Vanderbilt University
131 21st Avenue S
Nashville, TN 37203
Private
Admissions: (615) 322-6452
E-mail: admissions@law.vanderbilt.edu
Web site: http://www.vanderbilt.edu/law/
Financial aid: (615) 322-6452
Application deadline: 03/01
Tuition: full time: $28,617; part time: N/A
Room/board/expenses: $15,574
Students receiving grants: 56%
Median grant: $10,000
Average student indebtedness at graduation: $82,077
Enrollment: full time: 572; part time: N/A
men: 52%; women: 48%; minorities: 23%
Acceptance rate (full time): 22%
Midrange LSAT (full time): 161-165
Midrange undergraduate GPA (full time): 3.45-3.81

Midrange of full-time private sector salaries of 2001 grads: $80,000-$125,000
2000 grads employed in: law firms: 66%; business and industry (legal): N/A; business and industry (nonlegal): 5%; government: 5%; public interest: 1%; judicial clerk: 22%; academia: N/A; unknown: N/A
Employment location for 2001 class: Intl. 1%; N.E. 3%; M.A. 11%; E.N.C. 3%; W.N.C. 3%; S.A. 30%; E.S.C. 28%; W.S.C. 9%; Mt. 2%; Pac. 10%; unknown N/A

TEXAS

Baylor University
PO Box 97288
Waco, TX 76798-7288
Private
Admissions: (254) 710-4842
E-mail: becky_beck@baylor.edu
Web site: http://law.baylor.edu
Financial aid: (254) 710-2611
Application deadline: 03/01
Tuition: full time: $19,296; part time: N/A
Room/board/expenses: $11,331
Students receiving grants: 83%
Median grant: $3,300
Average student indebtedness at graduation: $58,157
Enrollment: full time: 438; part time: N/A
men: 58%; women: 42%; minorities: 13%
Acceptance rate (full time): 35%
Midrange LSAT (full time): 157-162
Midrange undergraduate GPA (full time): 3.45-3.84
Midrange of full-time private sector salaries of 2001 grads: $55,000-$100,000
2000 grads employed in: law firms: 68%; business and industry (legal): 4%; business and industry (nonlegal): 3%; government: 12%; public interest: 1%; judicial clerk: 11%; academia: 1%; unknown: N/A
Employment location for 2001 class: Intl. 0%; N.E. 0%; M.A. 0%; E.N.C. 1%; W.N.C. 1%; S.A. 1%; E.S.C. 2%; W.S.C. 92%; Mt. 2%; Pac. 2%; unknown N/A

Southern Methodist University
PO Box 750110
Dallas, TX 75275-0110
Private
Admissions: (214) 768-2550
E-mail: lawadmit@mail.smu.edu
Web site: http://www.law.smu.edu
Financial aid: (214) 768-3417
Application deadline: 02/01
Tuition: full time: $26,046; part time: $16,604
Room/board/expenses: $13,890
Students receiving grants: 63%
Median grant: $8,000
Average student indebtedness at graduation: $65,563
Enrollment: full time: 789; part time: 58
men: 51%; women: 49%; minorities: 15%
Acceptance rate (full time): 27%
Midrange LSAT (full time): 155-162
Midrange undergraduate GPA (full time): 3.17-3.70
Midrange of full-time private sector salaries of 2001 grads: $55,000-$110,000
2000 grads employed in: law firms: 74%; business and industry (legal): 5%; business and industry (nonlegal): 5%; government: 10%;

---

public interest: 1%; judicial clerk: 4%; academia: 1%; unknown: 0%
Employment location for 2001 class: Intl. 0%; N.E. 0%; M.A. 1%; E.N.C. 1%; W.N.C. 0%; S.A. 4%; E.S.C. 1%; W.S.C. 80%; Mt. 1%; Pac. 1%; unknown N/A

South Texas College of Law
1303 San Jacinto Street
Houston, TX 77002-7000
Private
Admissions: (713) 646-1810
E-mail: admissions@stcl.edu
Web site: http://www.stcl.edu
Financial aid: (713) 646-1820
Application deadline: 02/25
Tuition: full time: $18,750; part time: $18,750
Room/board/expenses: $13,884
Students receiving grants: 29%
Median grant: $1,172
Average student indebtedness at graduation: $61,653
Enrollment: full time: 888; part time: 352
men: 53%; women: 47%; minorities: 22%
Acceptance rate (full time): 49%
Midrange LSAT (full time): 148-154
Midrange undergraduate GPA (full time): 2.80-3.29
Midrange of full-time private sector salaries of 2001 grads: $55,000-$105,000
2000 grads employed in: law firms: 67%; business and industry (legal): 7%; business and industry (nonlegal): 6%; government: 10%; public interest: 0%; judicial clerk: 2%; academia: 2%; unknown: 6%
Employment location for 2001 class: Intl. 0%; N.E. 0%; M.A. 0%; E.N.C. 0%; W.N.C. 0%; S.A. 0%; E.S.C. 0%; W.S.C. 94%; Mt. 0%; Pac. 0%; unknown 5%

St. Mary's University
1 Camino Santa Maria
San Antonio, TX 78228-8602
Private
Admissions: (210) 436-3523
E-mail: lawadmissions@stmarytx.edu
Web site: http://www.stmarytx.edu/law
Financial aid: (210) 431-6743
Application deadline: 03/01
Tuition: full time: $19,440; part time: N/A
Room/board/expenses: $13,632
Students receiving grants: 30%
Median grant: $2,724
Average student indebtedness at graduation: $79,548
Enrollment: full time: 699; part time: N/A
men: 53%; women: 47%; minorities: 37%
Acceptance rate (full time): 49%
Midrange LSAT (full time): 148-153
Midrange undergraduate GPA (full time): 2.72-3.20
Midrange of full-time private sector salaries of 2001 grads: $45,000-$55,000
2000 grads employed in: law firms: 63%; business and industry (legal): 5%; business and industry (nonlegal): 0%; government: 18%; public interest: 6%; judicial clerk: 6%; academia: 0%; unknown: 2%
Employment location for 2001 class: Intl. 0%; N.E. N/A; M.A. N/A; E.N.C. N/A; W.N.C. N/A; S.A. N/A; E.S.C. 1%; W.S.C. 96%; Mt. 1%; Pac. N/A; unknown 2%

Texas Southern University (Thurgood Marshall)[1]
3100 Cleburne Street
Houston, TX 77004
Public
Admissions: (713) 313-7114
E-mail: lawadmit@tsulaw.edu
Web site: http://www.tsulaw.edu
Financial aid: (713) 313-7243
Tuition: N/A
Room/board/expenses: N/A
Enrollment: N/A

Texas Tech University
1802 Hartford Avenue
Lubbock, TX 79409
Public
Admissions: (806) 742-3791
E-mail: donna.williams@ttu.edu
Web site: http://www.law.ttu.edu
Financial aid: (806) 742-3681
Application deadline: 02/03
In-state tuition: full time: $8,587; part time: N/A
Out-of-state tuition: full time: $13,319
Room/board/expenses: $11,303
Students receiving grants: 47%
Median grant: $2,600
Average student indebtedness at graduation: $40,481
Enrollment: full time: 698; part time: N/A
men: 52%; women: 48%; minorities: 14%
Acceptance rate (full time): 38%
Midrange LSAT (full time): 150-157
Midrange undergraduate GPA (full time): 3.17-3.67
Midrange of full-time private sector salaries of 2001 grads: $44,000-$99,000
2000 grads employed in: law firms: 79%; business and industry (legal): 1%; business and industry (nonlegal): 0%; government: 15%; public interest: 1%; judicial clerk: 4%; academia: 0%; unknown: 0%
Employment location for 2001 class: Intl. N/A; N.E. N/A; M.A. 1%; E.N.C. N/A; W.N.C. N/A; S.A. N/A; E.S.C. 1%; W.S.C. 96%; Mt. 2%; Pac. N/A; unknown 0%

Texas Wesleyan University
1515 Commerce Street
Fort Worth, TX 76102
Private
Admissions: (817) 212-4045
E-mail: lculver@law.txwes.edu
Web site: http://www.law.txwes.edu/
Internet application: http://www.law.txwes.edu/application.htm
Financial aid: (817) 212-4090
Application deadline: 03/31
Tuition: full time: $16,000; part time: $600/credit hour
Room/board/expenses: $9,848
Students receiving grants: 12%
Median grant: $2,500
Average student indebtedness at graduation: $54,627
Enrollment: full time: 388; part time: 302
men: 48%; women: 52%; minorities: 21%
Acceptance rate (full time): 45%
Midrange LSAT (full time): 148-154
Midrange undergraduate GPA (full time): 2.80-3.40
Midrange of full-time private sector salaries of 2001 grads: $42,000-$65,000
2000 grads employed in: law firms: 64%; business and industry (legal): 24%; business and indus-

try (nonlegal): N/A; government: 9%; public interest: 1%; judicial clerk: 1%; academia: 1%; unknown: N/A
Employment location for 2001 class: Intl. N/A; N.E. N/A; M.A. N/A; E.N.C. N/A; W.N.C. N/A; S.A. N/A; E.S.C. N/A; W.S.C. N/A; Mt. N/A; Pac. N/A; unknown N/A

University of Houston
100 Law Center
Houston, TX 77204-6060
Public
Admissions: (713) 743-2280
E-mail: admissions@www.law.uh.edu
Web site: http://www.law.uh.edu
Internet application: http://www.law.uh.edu/admissions/
Financial aid: (713) 743-2269
Application deadline: 02/15
In-state tuition: full time: $9,438; part time: $7,118
Out-of-state tuition: full time: $12,238
Room/board/expenses: $10,668
Students receiving grants: 41%
Median grant: $2,500
Average student indebtedness at graduation: $43,481
Enrollment: full time: 849; part time: 179
men: 49%; women: 51%; minorities: 18%
Acceptance rate (full time): 33%
Midrange LSAT (full time): 154-160
Midrange undergraduate GPA (full time): 3.29-3.74
Midrange of full-time private sector salaries of 2001 grads: $62,000-$110,000
2000 grads employed in: law firms: 70%; business and industry (legal): 11%; business and industry (nonlegal): 1%; government: 8%; public interest: 2%; judicial clerk: 4%; academia: 1%; unknown: 3%
Employment location for 2001 class: Intl. 2%; N.E. 0%; M.A. 0%; E.N.C. 1%; W.N.C. 1%; S.A. 3%; E.S.C. 0%; W.S.C. 90%; Mt. 1%; Pac. 1%; unknown 1%

University of Texas–Austin
727 E. Dean Keeton Street
Austin, TX 78705-3299
Public
Admissions: (512) 232-1200
E-mail: admissions@mail.law.utexas.edu
Web site: http://www.utexas.edu/law
Internet application: http://www.utexas.edu/law/depts/admissions/
Financial aid: (512) 232-1130
Application deadline: 02/01
In-state tuition: full time: $11,634; part time: N/A
Out-of-state tuition: full time: $19,794
Room/board/expenses: $12,078
Students receiving grants: 70%
Median grant: $1,000
Average student indebtedness at graduation: $47,596
Enrollment: full time: 1,525; part time: N/A
men: 53%; women: 47%; minorities: 20%
Acceptance rate (full time): 21%
Midrange LSAT (full time): 160-165
Midrange undergraduate GPA (full time): 3.39-3.81
Midrange of full-time private sector salaries of 2001 grads: $85,000-$115,000

2000 grads employed in: law firms: 64%; business and industry (legal): 2%; business and industry (nonlegal): 5%; government: 11%; public interest: 2%; judicial clerk: 14%; academia: 1%; unknown: 1%
Employment location for 2001 class: Intl. 1%; N.E. 1%; M.A. 4%; E.N.C. 1%; W.N.C. 0%; S.A. 8%; E.S.C. 1%; W.S.C. 77%; Mt. 2%; Pac. 5%; unknown 0%

Brigham Young University (J. Reuben Clark)
340 JRCB
Provo, UT 84602
Private
Admissions: (801) 422-4277
E-mail: montanoa@lawgate.byu.edu
Web site: http://www.law.byu.edu
Internet application: http://www.law2.byu.edu/Admissions/application_form.htm
Financial aid: (801) 378-4104
Application deadline: 02/01
Tuition: full time: $6,140; part time: $342/credit hour
Room/board/expenses: $11,710
Students receiving grants: 54%
Median grant: $2,278
Average student indebtedness at graduation: $38,000
Enrollment: full time: 485; part time: N/A
men: 67%; women: 33%; minorities: 11%
Acceptance rate (full time): 27%
Midrange LSAT (full time): 160-166
Midrange undergraduate GPA (full time): 3.48-3.82
Midrange of full-time private sector salaries of 2001 grads: $65,000-$115,000
2000 grads employed in: law firms: 60%; business and industry (legal): 1%; business and industry (nonlegal): 10%; government: 10%; public interest: 2%; judicial clerk: 13%; academia: 4%; unknown: 0%
Employment location for 2001 class: Intl. 1%; N.E. 1%; M.A. 4%; E.N.C. 4%; W.N.C. 1%; S.A. 9%; E.S.C. 1%; W.S.C. 4%; Mt. 63%; Pac. 13%; unknown 0%

University of Utah (S.J. Quinney)
332 S. 1400 E
Room 101
Salt Lake City, UT 84112
Public
Admissions: (801) 581-7479
E-mail: admissions@law.utah.edu
Web site: http://www.law.utah.edu
Internet application: http://www.law.utah.edu/prospective/admissions.html
Financial aid: (801) 581-6211
Application deadline: 02/01
In-state tuition: full time: $7,687; part time: N/A
Out-of-state tuition: full time: $16,263
Room/board/expenses: $11,680
Students receiving grants: 37%
Median grant: $2,763
Average student indebtedness at graduation: $35,295
Enrollment: full time: 405; part time: N/A
men: 63%; women: 37%; minorities: 10%
Acceptance rate (full time): 32%
Midrange LSAT (full time): 156-161

Midrange undergraduate GPA (full time): 3.32-3.77
Midrange of full-time private sector salaries of 2001 grads: $50,000-$80,000
2000 grads employed in: law firms: 56%; business and industry (legal): 8%; business and industry (nonlegal): 4%; government: 17%; public interest: 5%; judicial clerk: 9%; academia: 1%; unknown: 0%
Employment location for 2001 class: Intl. 1%; N.E. 0%; M.A. 1%; E.N.C. 0%; W.N.C. 0%; S.A. 1%; E.S.C. 0%; W.S.C. 3%; Mt. 88%; Pac. 6%; unknown 0%

Vermont Law School
Chelsea Street
South Royalton, VT 05068-0096
Private
Admissions: (888) 277-5985
E-mail: admiss@vermontlaw.edu
Web site: http://www.vermontlaw.edu
Financial aid: (888) 277-5985
Application deadline: 03/01
Tuition: full time: $23,494; part time: N/A
Room/board/expenses: $15,871
Students receiving grants: 52%
Median grant: $5,000
Average student indebtedness at graduation: $69,000
Enrollment: full time: 511; part time: 1
men: 51%; women: 49%; minorities: 11%
Acceptance rate (full time): 61%
Midrange LSAT (full time): 149-156
Midrange undergraduate GPA (full time): 2.83-3.37
Midrange of full-time private sector salaries of 2001 grads: $35,000-$60,000
2000 grads employed in: law firms: 39%; business and industry (legal): 17%; business and industry (nonlegal): N/A; government: 18%; public interest: 9%; judicial clerk: 15%; academia: 0%; unknown: 0%
Employment location for 2001 class: Intl. 1%; N.E. 36%; M.A. 15%; E.N.C. 6%; W.N.C. 2%; S.A. 20%; E.S.C. 1%; W.S.C. 2%; Mt. 9%; Pac. 9%; unknown 0%

Appalachian School of Law[1]
PO Box 2825
Grundy, VA 24614
Private
Admissions: (276) 935-4349
E-mail: aslinfo@asl.edu
Web site: http://www.asl.edu
Internet application: http://www.asl.edu/admissions/applictn.htm
Financial aid: (800) 895-7411
Tuition: N/A
Room/board/expenses: N/A
Enrollment: N/A

College of William and Mary
PO Box 8795
Williamsburg, VA 23187-8795
Public
Admissions: (757) 221-3785
E-mail: lawadm@wm.edu
Web site: http://www.wm.edu/law
Internet application: http://www.wm.edu/law/prospective/admissions/jdprogram-forms.shtml

Financial aid: (757) 221-2420
Application deadline: 03/01
In-state tuition: full time: $11,500; part time: $374/credit hour
Out-of-state tuition: full time: $21,690
Room/board/expenses: $8,150
Students receiving grants: 29%
Median grant: $3,500
Average student indebtedness at graduation: $59,010
Enrollment: full time: 557; part time: N/A
men: 58%; women: 42%; minorities: 16%
Acceptance rate (full time): 20%
Midrange LSAT (full time): 160-165
Midrange undergraduate GPA (full time): 3.26-3.75
Midrange of full-time private sector salaries of 2001 grads: $67,500-$115,800
2000 grads employed in: law firms: 56%; business and industry (legal): 3%; business and industry (nonlegal): 3%; government: 12%; public interest: 5%; judicial clerk: 19%; academia: 1%; unknown: 1%
Employment location for 2001 class: Intl. 1%; N.E. 3%; M.A. 13%; E.N.C. 5%; W.N.C. 1%; S.A. 66%; E.S.C. 3%; W.S.C. 2%; Mt. 3%; Pac. 3%; unknown 1%

George Mason University
3301 N. Fairfax Drive
Arlington, VA 22201-4426
Public
Admissions: (703) 993-8010
E-mail: arichar5@gmu.edu
Web site: http://www.law.gmu.edu
Financial aid: (703) 993-4350
Application deadline: 03/01
In-state tuition: full time: $9,123; part time: $326/credit hour
Out-of-state tuition: full time: $19,232
Room/board/expenses: $15,574
Students receiving grants: 6%
Median grant: $7,500
Average student indebtedness at graduation: $45,058
Enrollment: full time: 388; part time: 399
men: 59%; women: 41%; minorities: 9%
Acceptance rate (full time): 13%
Midrange LSAT (full time): 159-164
Midrange undergraduate GPA (full time): 3.21-3.72
Midrange of full-time private sector salaries of 2001 grads: $50,000-$125,000
2000 grads employed in: law firms: 42%; business and industry (legal): 15%; business and industry (nonlegal): 7%; government: 16%; public interest: 3%; judicial clerk: 13%; academia: 4%; unknown: N/A
Employment location for 2001 class: Intl. 2%; N.E. 2%; M.A. 4%; E.N.C. 2%; W.N.C. 0%; S.A. 87%; E.S.C. 0%; W.S.C. 2%; Mt. 0%; Pac. 3%; unknown 0%

Regent University
1000 Regent University Drive
Virginia Beach, VA 23464-9880
Private
Admissions: (757) 226-4584
E-mail: lawschool@regent.edu
Web site: http://www.regent.edu/law/admissions
Financial aid: (757) 226-4559
Application deadline: 06/01
Tuition: full time: $18,631; part time: $13,871
Room/board/expenses: $14,348

Students receiving grants: 67%
Median grant: $3,000
Average student indebtedness at graduation: $56,397
Enrollment: full time: 387; part time: 117
men: 49%; women: 51%; minorities: 18%
Acceptance rate (full time): 53%
Midrange LSAT (full time): 148-155
Midrange undergraduate GPA (full time): 2.86-3.60
Midrange of full-time private sector salaries of 2001 grads: $30,000-$45,000
2000 grads employed in: law firms: 33%; business and industry (legal): 1%; business and industry (nonlegal): 12%; government: 24%; public interest: 10%; judicial clerk: 9%; academia: 6%; unknown: 5%
Employment location for 2001 class: Intl. 0%; N.E. 0%; M.A. 3%; E.N.C. 5%; W.N.C. 0%; S.A. 79%; E.S.C. 5%; W.S.C. 4%; Mt. 1%; Pac. 2%; unknown 0%

University of Richmond
T.C. Williams School of Law
Richmond, VA 23173
Private
Admissions: (804) 289-8189
E-mail: mrahman@richmond.edu
Web site: http://law.richmond.edu
Internet application: http://law.richmond.edu/application/application.htm
Financial aid: (804) 289-8438
Application deadline: 01/15
Tuition: full time: $22,860; part time: $1,145/credit hour
Room/board/expenses: $10,460
Students receiving grants: 56%
Median grant: $2,130
Average student indebtedness at graduation: $63,753
Enrollment: full time: 484; part time: N/A
men: 51%; women: 49%; minorities: 7%
Acceptance rate (full time): 31%
Midrange LSAT (full time): 157-160
Midrange undergraduate GPA (full time): 3.01-3.53
Midrange of full-time private sector salaries of 2001 grads: $44,000-$80,000
2000 grads employed in: law firms: 56%; business and industry (legal): 4%; business and industry (nonlegal): 5%; government: 17%; public interest: 1%; judicial clerk: 17%; academia: 1%; unknown: 0%
Employment location for 2001 class: Intl. 0%; N.E. 0%; M.A. 6%; E.N.C. 2%; W.N.C. 1%; S.A. 88%; E.S.C. 1%; W.S.C. 1%; Mt. 1%; Pac. 1%; unknown 0%

University of Virginia
580 Massie Road
Charlottesville, VA 22903-1789
Public
Admissions: (434) 924-7351
E-mail: lawadmit@virginia.edu
Web site: http://www.law.virginia.edu
Internet application: http://www.law.virginia.edu/Main/Application+Forms
Financial aid: (434) 924-7805
Application deadline: 01/15
In-state tuition: full time: $20,627; part time: N/A
Out-of-state tuition: full time: $26,967
Room/board/expenses: $12,860
Students receiving grants: 34%
Median grant: $7,500

Average student indebtedness at graduation: $61,830
Enrollment: full time: 1,066; part time: N/A
men: 58%; women: 42%; minorities: 16%
Acceptance rate (full time): 22%
Midrange LSAT (full time): 164-168
Midrange undergraduate GPA (full time): 3.49-3.78
Midrange of full-time private sector salaries of 2001 grads: $100,000-$125,000
2000 grads employed in: law firms: 76%; business and industry (legal): 1%; business and industry (nonlegal): N/A; government: 4%; public interest: 3%; judicial clerk: 13%; academia: N/A; unknown: 3%
Employment location for 2001 class: Intl. 1%; N.E. 5%; M.A. 17%; E.N.C. 6%; W.N.C. 1%; S.A. 45%; E.S.C. 6%; W.S.C. 5%; Mt. 2%; Pac. 11%; unknown 1%

Washington and Lee University

Sydney Lewis Hall
Lexington, VA 24450-0303
Private
Admissions: (540) 458-8504
E-mail: lawadm@wlu.edu
Web site: http://law.wlu.edu/admissions/
Financial aid: (540) 458-8729
Application deadline: 02/01
Tuition: full time: $21,541; part time: N/A
Room/board/expenses: $11,619
Students receiving grants: 75%
Median grant: $10,500
Average student indebtedness at graduation: $51,719
Enrollment: full time: 378; part time: N/A
men: 57%; women: 43%; minorities: 18%
Acceptance rate (full time): 21%
Midrange LSAT (full time): 163-166
Midrange undergraduate GPA (full time): 3.28-3.78
Midrange of full-time private sector salaries of 2001 grads: $50,000-$110,000
2000 grads employed in: law firms: 66%; business and industry (nonlegal): 1%; government: 6%; public interest: 4%; judicial clerk: 21%; academia: 1%; unknown: 0%
Employment location for 2001 class: Intl. 1%; N.E. 4%; M.A. 8%; E.N.C. 3%; W.N.C. 1%; S.A. 64%; E.S.C. 8%; W.S.C. 5%; Mt. 3%; Pac. 2%; unknown 1%

Gonzaga University

PO Box 3528
Spokane, WA 99220-3528
Private
Admissions: (800) 793-1710
E-mail: admissions@lawschool.gonzaga.edu
Web site: http://law.gonzaga.edu
Financial aid: (800) 448-2138
Application deadline: 07/01
Tuition: full time: $21,728; part time: $13,058
Room/board/expenses: $10,875
Students receiving grants: 60%
Median grant: $8,000
Average student indebtedness at graduation: $48,409
Enrollment: full time: 548; part time: 27
men: 54%; women: 46%; minorities: 15%
Acceptance rate (full time): 49%
Midrange LSAT (full time): 149-155
Midrange undergraduate GPA (full time): 2.93-3.49
Midrange of full-time private sector salaries of 2001 grads: $36,000-$48,000
2000 grads employed in: law firms: 51%; business and industry (legal): 0%; business and industry (nonlegal): 11%; government: 22%; public interest: 3%; judicial clerk: 11%; academia: 2%; unknown: 0%
Employment location for 2001 class: Intl. 1%; N.E. 1%; M.A. 0%; E.N.C. 0%; W.N.C. 2%; S.A. 1%; E.S.C. 0%; W.S.C. 1%; Mt. 24%; Pac. 70%; unknown 0%

Seattle University

900 Broadway
Seattle, WA 98122-4340
Private
Admissions: (206) 398-4200
E-mail: lawadmin@seattleu.edu
Web site: http://www.law.seattleu.edu
Internet application: http://www.law.seattleu.edu/admission/admissionapp.asp
Financial aid: (206) 398-4250
Application deadline: 04/01
Tuition: full time: $22,306; part time: $14,872
Room/board/expenses: $14,497
Students receiving grants: 42%
Median grant: $6,000
Average student indebtedness at graduation: $71,516
Enrollment: full time: 812; part time: 229
men: 45%; women: 55%; minorities: 20%
Acceptance rate (full time): 44%
Midrange LSAT (full time): 151-158
Midrange undergraduate GPA (full time): 3.08-3.55
Midrange of full-time private sector salaries of 2001 grads: $35,000-$85,000
2000 grads employed in: law firms: 42%; business and industry (legal): 31%; business and industry (nonlegal): 4%; government: 15%; public interest: 1%; judicial clerk: 5%; academia: 2%; unknown: 0%
Employment location for 2001 class: Intl. 0%; N.E. 3%; M.A. 0%; E.N.C. 0%; W.N.C. 0%; S.A. 3%; E.S.C. 0%; W.S.C. 0%; Mt. 3%; Pac. 91%; unknown 0%

University of Washington

1100 N.E. Campus Parkway
Seattle, WA 98105-6617
Public
Admissions: (206) 543-4078
E-mail: admissions@law.washington.edu
Web site: http://www.law.washington.edu
Financial aid: (206) 543-4552
Application deadline: 01/15
In-state tuition: full time: $10,230; part time: N/A
Out-of-state tuition: full time: $17,969
Room/board/expenses: $13,000
Students receiving grants: 46%
Median grant: $5,600
Average student indebtedness at graduation: $46,521
Enrollment: full time: 513; part time: N/A
men: 42%; women: 58%; minorities: 24%
Acceptance rate (full time): 20%
Midrange LSAT (full time): 160-165
Midrange undergraduate GPA (full time): 3.46-3.79
Midrange of full-time private sector salaries of 2001 grads: $78,000-$125,000
2000 grads employed in: law firms: 49%; business and industry (legal): 1%; business and industry (nonlegal): 2%; government: 16%; public interest: 8%; judicial clerk: 18%; academia: 1%; unknown: 5%
Employment location for 2001 class: Intl. 2%; N.E. 2%; M.A. 2%; E.N.C. 1%; W.N.C. 0%; S.A. 2%; E.S.C. 0%; W.S.C. 2%; Mt. 1%; Pac. 90%; unknown 0%

West Virginia University

PO Box 6130
Morgantown, WV 26506-6130
Public
Admissions: (304) 293-5304
E-mail: lawaply@wvu.edu
Web site: http://www.wvu.edu/~law
Financial aid: (304) 293-5302
Application deadline: 03/01
In-state tuition: full time: $6,742; part time: N/A
Out-of-state tuition: full time: $15,624
Room/board/expenses: $10,821
Students receiving grants: 28%
Median grant: $1,500
Average student indebtedness at graduation: $41,926
Enrollment: full time: 443; part time: 13
men: 57%; women: 43%; minorities: 9%
Acceptance rate (full time): 46%
Midrange LSAT (full time): 148-154
Midrange undergraduate GPA (full time): 3.10-3.68

Midrange of full-time private sector salaries of 2001 grads: $35,000-$52,000
2000 grads employed in: law firms: 54%; business and industry (legal): 6%; business and industry (nonlegal): 0%; government: 8%; public interest: 9%; judicial clerk: 20%; academia: 2%; unknown: 1%
Employment location for 2001 class: Intl. 0%; N.E. 0%; M.A. 4%; E.N.C. 3%; W.N.C. 0%; S.A. 90%; E.S.C. 0%; W.S.C. 1%; Mt. 1%; Pac. 2%; unknown 0%

Marquette University

Sensenbrenner Hall
PO Box 1881
Milwaukee, WI 53201-1881
Private
Admissions: (414) 288-6767
E-mail: law.admission@marquette.edu
Web site: http://www.mu.edu/law
Financial aid: (414) 288-7390
Application deadline: 04/01
Tuition: full time: $22,630; part time: $14,100
Room/board/expenses: $13,581
Students receiving grants: 36%
Median grant: $8,000
Average student indebtedness at graduation: $68,296
Enrollment: full time: 492; part time: 150
men: 57%; women: 43%; minorities: 6%
Acceptance rate (full time): 42%
Midrange LSAT (full time): 153-158
Midrange undergraduate GPA (full time): 3.03-3.54
Midrange of full-time private sector salaries of 2001 grads: $43,000-$80,000
2000 grads employed in: law firms: 69%; business and industry (legal): 6%; business and industry (nonlegal): 2%; government: 12%; public interest: 4%; judicial clerk: 4%; academia: 4%; unknown: 0%
Employment location for 2001 class: Intl. 1%; N.E. 2%; M.A. 2%; E.N.C. 80%; W.N.C. 2%; S.A. 6%; E.S.C. 1%; W.S.C. 1%; Mt. 4%; Pac. 2%; unknown 0%

University of Wisconsin-Madison

975 Bascom Mall
Madison, WI 53706
Public
Admissions: (608) 262-5914
E-mail: admissions@law.wisc.edu
Web site: http://www.law.wisc.edu
Financial aid: (608) 262-1815
Application deadline: 02/01
In-state tuition: full time: $9,416; part time: $370/credit hour
Out-of-state tuition: full time: $24,864
Room/board/expenses: $12,402
Students receiving grants: 12%
Median grant: $9,200

Average student indebtedness at graduation: $47,796
Enrollment: full time: 772; part time: 45
men: 52%; women: 48%; minorities: 24%
Acceptance rate (full time): 32%
Midrange LSAT (full time): 155-162
Midrange undergraduate GPA (full time): 3.04-3.58
Midrange of full-time private sector salaries of 2001 grads: $48,000-$115,000
2000 grads employed in: law firms: 59%; business and industry (legal): 4%; business and industry (nonlegal): 8%; government: 13%; public interest: 6%; judicial clerk: 8%; academia: 2%; unknown: 0%
Employment location for 2001 class: Intl. 1%; N.E. 1%; M.A. 8%; E.N.C. 63%; W.N.C. 8%; S.A. 7%; E.S.C. 0%; W.S.C. 2%; Mt. 2%; Pac. 9%; unknown 0%

University of Wyoming

PO Box 3035
Laramie, WY 82071
Public
Admissions: (307) 766-6416
E-mail: lawadmis@uwyo.edu
Web site: http://www.uwyo.edu/law
Financial aid: (307) 766-2116
Application deadline: 03/15
In-state tuition: full time: $5,199; part time: N/A
Out-of-state tuition: full time: $10,863
Room/board/expenses: $8,420
Students receiving grants: 64%
Median grant: $1,500
Average student indebtedness at graduation: $37,905
Enrollment: full time: 227; part time: N/A
men: 56%; women: 44%; minorities: 7%
Acceptance rate (full time): 30%
Midrange LSAT (full time): 149-156
Midrange undergraduate GPA (full time): 3.06-3.60
Midrange of full-time private sector salaries of 2001 grads: $33,000-$44,352
2000 grads employed in: law firms: 47%; business and industry (legal): 0%; business and industry (nonlegal): 12%; government: 14%; public interest: 2%; judicial clerk: 22%; academia: 3%; unknown: 0%
Employment location for 2001 class: Intl. 0%; N.E. 1%; M.A. 0%; E.N.C. 3%; W.N.C. 7%; S.A. 8%; E.S.C. 0%; W.S.C. 3%; Mt. 77%; Pac. 1%; unknown 0%

MEDICINE

The medical school directory lists the 125 schools offering M.D. degrees that are fully accredited by the Liaison Committee on Medical Education, plus the 19 schools that offer the D.O. degree and are fully accredited by the American Osteopathic Association. Of those, 100 M.D.-granting schools and 17 D.O.-granting schools responded to the *U.S. News* survey, which was conducted in fall 2002. Their data are reported below. Schools that did not respond have abbreviated entries.

TERMINOLOGY

1 A school whose name is footnoted with the numeral 1 did not return the *U.S. News* statistical survey; limited data appear in its entry.

N/A. Not available from the school or not applicable.

Admissions. The admissions office phone number.

E-mail. The electronic address of the admissions office. If, instead of an E-mail address, a Web site address is listed, the Web site will automatically present an E-mail screen programmed to reach the admissions office.

Internet application. The electronic address for online applications.

Financial aid. The financial aid office phone number.

Application deadline. For fall 2004 enrollment. "Rolling" means there is no application deadline; the school acts on applications as they are received.

Tuition. For the 2002–2003 academic year. Includes fees.

Room/board/expenses. For the 2002–2003 academic year.

Percent receiving grants: The percentage of the entire student body during the 2002–2003 academic year that received grants or scholarships.

Average indebtedness. For 2001 graduates who incurred medical-school-related debt.

Enrollment. Total Doctor of Medicine (M.D.) or Doctor of Osteopathy (D.O.) degree program enrollment for fall 2002.

Minorities. For fall 2002, percent of students who are Asian-American, African-American, Hispanic, or American Indian. (When the U.S. Department of Education calculates minority enrollment percentages, these are the demographic groupings it uses.)

Underrepresented minorities. For fall 2002, percent of students who are African-American, Hispanic, or American Indian. (This category is used only for medical schools.)

Acceptance rate. Percentage of applicants who were accepted for fall 2002 to an M.D. or D.O. degree program.

Average Medical College Admission Test (MCAT) score. For students who entered in fall 2002. The average of verbal and physical and biological sciences scores. (MCAT scores are on a scale of 1 to 15.)

Average undergraduate grade-point average (GPA). For students who entered in fall 2002.

Most popular undergraduate majors. For students who entered in fall 2002. The main areas are biological sciences, which includes microbiology; physical sciences, which includes chemistry; nonsciences, which includes the humanities; other health professions, which includes nursing and pharmacy; and other, which includes double majors and mixed disciplines.

Percent of graduates entering primary-care specialties. This is the three-year average percentage of the total medical school graduates entering primary-care specialties (family practice, general pediatrics, or general internal medicine) during the 2000–2002 period.

INSTITUTIONS THAT GRANT THE DOCTOR OF MEDICINE (M.D.) DEGREE

ALABAMA

University of Alabama–Birmingham
Medical Student Services
VH Suite 100
Birmingham, AL 35294-0019
Public
Admissions: (205) 934-2330
E-mail: admissions@uasom.meis.uab.edu
Web site: http://www.uab.edu/uasom/admissions
Financial aid: (205) 934-8223
Application deadline: 11/01
In-state tuition: $11,681
Out-of-state tuition: $27,339
Room/board/expenses: $9,843
Students receiving grants: 13%
Average student indebtedness at graduation: $80,029
Enrollment: 694
men: 59%; women: 41%; minorities: 24%; underrepresented minorities: 10%; in state: 86%
Acceptance rate: 17%
Average MCAT: 10.0
Average GPA: 3.67
Most popular undergraduate majors: biological sciences: 47%; physical sciences: 24%; nonsciences: 23%; other: 6%
Graduates entering primary-care specialties: 45.0%

University of South Alabama[1]
307 University Boulevard
170 CSAB
Mobile, AL 36688
Public
Admissions: (251) 460-7176
E-mail: mscott@usouthal.edu
Web site: http://southmed.usouthal.edu/
Financial aid: (251) 460-7918
Tuition: N/A
Room/board/expenses: N/A
Enrollment: N/A

ARIZONA

University of Arizona[1]
1501 N. Campbell Avenue
Tucson, AZ 85724
Public
Admissions: (520) 626-6214
E-mail: admissions@medicine.arizona.edu
Web site: http://www.medicine.arizona.edu
Financial aid: (520) 626-7145
Tuition: N/A
Room/board/expenses: N/A
Enrollment: N/A

ARKANSAS

University of Arkansas for Medical Sciences[1]
4301 W. Markham
Slot 551
Little Rock, AR 72205
Public
Admissions: (501) 686-5354
E-mail: southtomg@uams.edu
Web site: http://www.uams.edu
Financial aid: (501) 686-5813
Tuition: N/A
Room/board/expenses: N/A
Enrollment: N/A

CALIFORNIA

Loma Linda University[1]
School of Medicine
Loma Linda, CA 92350
Private
Admissions: (909) 558-4467
E-mail: edwards@som.llu.edu
Web site: http://www.llu.edu/index.htm
Internet application: http://www.llu.edu/apply
Financial aid: (909) 558-4509
Tuition: N/A
Room/board/expenses: N/A
Enrollment: N/A

Stanford University
300 Pasteur Drive
Suite M121
Stanford, CA 94305
Private
Admissions: (650) 723-6861
E-mail: admissions@med.stanford.edu
Web site: http://www.med.stanford.edu
Internet application: http://www.aamc.org
Financial aid: (650) 723-6958
Application deadline: 11/01
Tuition: $33,919
Room/board/expenses: $15,675
Students receiving grants: 59%
Average student indebtedness at graduation: $66,381
Enrollment: 465
men: 49%; women: 51%; minorities: 55%; underrepresented minorities: 21%; in state: 46%
Acceptance rate: 4%
Average MCAT: 11.0
Average GPA: 3.74
Most popular undergraduate majors: biological sciences: 43%; physical sciences: 36%; nonsciences: 19%; other: 2%
Graduates entering primary-care specialties: 41.6%

University of California–Davis

1 Shields Avenue
Davis, CA 95616
Public
Admissions: (530) 752-2717
E-mail: medadmisinfo@ucdavis.edu
Web site: http://medome.ucdavis.edu
Financial aid: (530) 752-6618
Application deadline: 11/01
In-state tuition: $10,509
Out-of-state tuition: $21,641
Room/board/expenses: $10,488
Students receiving grants: 83%
Average student indebtedness at graduation: $69,441
Enrollment: 401
men: 47%; women: 53%; minorities: 54%; underrepresented minorities: 12%; in state: 100%
Acceptance rate: 6%
Average MCAT: 10.4
Average GPA: 3.52
Most popular undergraduate majors: biological sciences: 57%; physical sciences: 15%; nonsciences: 16%; other: 11%
Graduates entering primary-care specialties: 53.9%

University of California–Irvine

Irvine Hall
Irvine, CA 92697-3950
Public
Admissions: (949) 824-5388
E-mail: epeterso@uci.edu
Web site: http://www.com.uci.edu
Financial aid: (949) 824-6476
Application deadline: 11/01
In-state tuition: $11,100
Out-of-state tuition: $22,232
Room/board/expenses: $8,790
Students receiving grants: 74%
Average student indebtedness at graduation: $69,152
Enrollment: 378
men: 54%; women: 46%; minorities: 43%; underrepresented minorities: 8%; in state: 100%
Acceptance rate: 7%
Average MCAT: 10.7
Average GPA: 3.69
Most popular undergraduate majors: biological sciences: 69%; physical sciences: 4%; nonsciences: 13%; other: 6%
Graduates entering primary-care specialties: 41.0%

University of California–Los Angeles (Geffen)

12-138 CHS
10833 Le Conte Avenue
Los Angeles, CA 90095
Public
Admissions: (310) 825-6081
E-mail: admissions@ deans.medsch.ucla.edu
Web site: http://www.medsch.ucla.edu
Internet application: http://www.medstudent.ucla.edu/admiss
Financial aid: (310) 825-4181
Application deadline: 11/01
In-state tuition: $10,173
Out-of-state tuition: $21,305
Room/board/expenses: $11,691
Students receiving grants: 77%
Average student indebtedness at graduation: $63,565
Enrollment: 693
men: 48%; women: 52%; minorities: 60%; underrepresented minorities: 30%; in state: 92%

University of California–San Diego

9500 Gilman Drive
La Jolla, CA 92093-0602
Public
Admissions: (858) 534-3880
E-mail: somadmissions@ucsd.edu
Web site: http://meded.ucsd.edu/admissions/
Financial aid: (858) 534-4664
Application deadline: 11/03
In-state tuition: $10,642
Out-of-state tuition: $21,774
Room/board/expenses: $10,555
Students receiving grants: 70%
Average student indebtedness at graduation: $66,574
Enrollment: 513
men: 54%; women: 46%; minorities: 42%; underrepresented minorities: 9%; in state: 99%
Acceptance rate: 7%
Average MCAT: 10.9
Average GPA: 3.78
Most popular undergraduate majors: biological sciences: 49%; physical sciences: 21%; nonsciences: 8%; other: 22%
Graduates entering primary-care specialties: 66.0%

University of California–San Francisco

513 Parnassus Avenue
Room S224
San Francisco, CA 94143-0410
Public
Admissions: (415) 476-4044
E-mail: admissions@medsch.ucsf.edu
Web site: http://www.som.ucsf.edu/admissions/
Internet application: http://www.aamc.org/stuapps/start.htm
Financial aid: (415) 476-4181
Application deadline: 11/03
In-state tuition: $10,445
Out-of-state tuition: $21,577
Room/board/expenses: $14,877
Students receiving grants: 79%
Average student indebtedness at graduation: $55,106
Enrollment: 623
men: 45%; women: 55%; minorities: 43%; underrepresented minorities: 15%; in state: 95%
Acceptance rate: 6%
Average MCAT: 11.2
Average GPA: 3.75
Most popular undergraduate majors: biological sciences: N/A; physical sciences: N/A; nonsciences: N/A; other: N/A
Graduates entering primary-care specialties: 47.3%

University of Southern California

1975 Zonal Avenue
KAM 500
Los Angeles, CA 90033
Private
Admissions: (323) 442-2552
E-mail: medadmit@hsc.usc.edu
Web site: http://www.usc.edu/schools/medicine
Financial aid: (323) 442-1016

Application deadline: 11/01
Tuition: $36,157
Room/board/expenses: $9,802
Students receiving grants: 38%
Average student indebtedness at graduation: $109,000
Enrollment: 655
men: 57%; women: 43%; minorities: 51%; underrepresented minorities: 15%; in state: 86%
Acceptance rate: 7%
Average MCAT: 10.8
Average GPA: 3.61
Most popular undergraduate majors: biological sciences: 50%; physical sciences: 25%; nonsciences: 17%; other: 8%
Graduates entering primary-care specialties: 53.0%

COLORADO

University of Colorado Health Sciences Center

4200 E. Ninth Avenue
Box C290
Denver, CO 80262
Public
Admissions: (303) 315-7361
E-mail: somadmin@uchsc.edu
Web site: http://www.uchsc.edu/sm/sm/mddgree.htm
Internet application: http://www.aamc.org
Financial aid: (303) 315-8364
Application deadline: 11/01
In-state tuition: $15,290
Out-of-state tuition: $66,073
Room/board/expenses: $11,160
Students receiving grants: 64%
Average student indebtedness at graduation: $86,625
Enrollment: 534
men: 51%; women: 49%; minorities: 20%; underrepresented minorities: 11%; in state: 94%
Acceptance rate: 10%
Average MCAT: 10.0
Average GPA: 3.69
Most popular undergraduate majors: biological sciences: 18%; physical sciences: 15%; nonsciences: 12%; other: 55%
Graduates entering primary-care specialties: 46.0%

CONNECTICUT

University of Connecticut

263 Farmington Avenue
Farmington, CT 06030
Public
Admissions: (860) 679-3874
E-mail: sanford@nso1.uchc.edu
Web site: http://medicine.uchc.edu
Financial aid: (860) 679-3574
Application deadline: 12/15
In-state tuition: $14,870
Out-of-state tuition: $28,180
Room/board/expenses: N/A
Students receiving grants: 45%
Average student indebtedness at graduation: $64,000
Enrollment: 311
men: 44%; women: 56%; minorities: 27%; underrepresented minorities: 15%; in state: 92%
Acceptance rate: 9%
Average MCAT: 9.9
Average GPA: 3.60
Most popular undergraduate majors: biological sciences: 60%; physical sciences: 11%; nonsciences: 24%; other: 5%
Graduates entering primary-care specialties: 54.0%

Yale University

333 Cedar Street
PO Box 208055
New Haven, CT 06520-8055
Private
Admissions: (203) 785-2643
E-mail: medical.admissions@yale.edu
Web site: http://info.med.yale.edu/education/
Financial aid: (203) 785-2645
Application deadline: 10/15
Tuition: $32,675
Room/board/expenses: $9,450
Students receiving grants: 51%
Average student indebtedness at graduation: $92,346
Enrollment: 507
men: 53%; women: 47%; minorities: 43%; underrepresented minorities: 15%; in state: 11%
Acceptance rate: 7%
Average MCAT: 11.4
Average GPA: 3.72
Most popular undergraduate majors: biological sciences: 38%; physical sciences: 24%; nonsciences: 23%; other: 15%
Graduates entering primary-care specialties: 45.0%

DISTRICT OF COLUMBIA

Georgetown University

3900 Reservoir Road NW
Med-Dent Building
Washington, DC 20057
Private
Admissions: (202) 687-1154
E-mail: medicaladmissions@ georgetown.edu
Web site: http://www.dml.georgetown.edu/schmed
Financial aid: (202) 687-1693
Application deadline: 11/03
Tuition: $31,817
Room/board/expenses: N/A
Students receiving grants: 43%
Average student indebtedness at graduation: $130,367
Enrollment: 709
men: 51%; women: 49%; minorities: 29%; underrepresented minorities: 12%; in state: 1%
Acceptance rate: 5%
Average MCAT: 10.2
Average GPA: 3.63
Most popular undergraduate majors: biological sciences: 65%; physical sciences: 13%; nonsciences: 16%; other: 6%
Graduates entering primary-care specialties: 50.0%

George Washington University

2300 Eye Street NW
Room 713W
Washington, DC 20037
Private
Admissions: (202) 994-3506
E-mail: medadmit@gwu.edu
Web site: http://www.gwumc.edu/edu/
Internet application: http://www.gwumc.edu/edu/admis/index.htm
Financial aid: (202) 994-2960
Application deadline: 12/03
Tuition: $37,784
Room/board/expenses: $16,806
Students receiving grants: 29%
Average student indebtedness at graduation: $117,734
Enrollment: 676
men: 48%; women: 52%; minorities: 40%; underrepresented minorities: 13%; in state: 3%
Acceptance rate: 6%
Average MCAT: 9.6
Average GPA: 3.52

Most popular undergraduate majors: biological sciences: 39%; physical sciences: 15%; nonsciences: 31%; other: 16%
Graduates entering primary-care specialties: 44.5%

Howard University[1]

520 W Street NW
Washington, DC 20059
Private
Admissions: (202) 806-6279
E-mail: afinney@howard.edu
Web site: http://www.med.howard.edu/
Financial aid: (202) 806-6388
Tuition: N/A
Room/board/expenses: N/A
Enrollment: N/A

FLORIDA

University of Florida

Box 100215 UFHSC
Gainesville, FL 32610-0215
Public
Admissions: (352) 392-4569
E-mail: robyn@dean.med.ufl.edu
Web site: http://www.med.ufl.edu/oea/admiss/
Financial aid: (352) 392-7800
Application deadline: 12/01
In-state tuition: $13,612
Out-of-state tuition: $36,524
Room/board/expenses: $7,438
Students receiving grants: 86%
Average student indebtedness at graduation: $81,030
Enrollment: 450
men: 48%; women: 52%; minorities: 40%; underrepresented minorities: 19%; in state: 99%
Acceptance rate: 9%
Average MCAT: 10.3
Average GPA: 3.68
Most popular undergraduate majors: biological sciences: 26%; physical sciences: 36%; nonsciences: 14%; other: 20%
Graduates entering primary-care specialties: 42.0%

University of Miami

1600 N.W. 10th Avenue
Miami, FL 33136
Private
Admissions: (305) 243-6791
E-mail: med.admissions@miami.edu
Web site: http://www.miami.edu/medical-admissions
Financial aid: (305) 243-6211
Application deadline: 12/15
Tuition: $28,180
Room/board/expenses: $21,180
Students receiving grants: 26%
Average student indebtedness at graduation: $132,000
Enrollment: 600
men: 47%; women: 53%; minorities: 42%; underrepresented minorities: 26%; in state: 95%
Acceptance rate: 25%
Average MCAT: 9.3
Average GPA: 3.66
Most popular undergraduate majors: biological sciences: 52%; physical sciences: 19%; nonsciences: 14%; other: 14%
Graduates entering primary-care specialties: 50.0%

University of South Florida

12901 Bruce B. Downs Boulevard
Box 3
Tampa, FL 33612
Public
Admissions: (813) 974-2229
E-mail: md-admissions@
lyris.hsc.usf.edu
Web site: http://www.
med.usf.edu/MD/start.htm
Financial aid: (813) 974-4700
Application deadline: 12/01
In-state tuition: $13,643
Out-of-state tuition: $37,751
Room/board/expenses: $8,660
Students receiving grants: 40%
Average student indebtedness at graduation: $82,585
Enrollment: 398
men: 52%; women: 48%; minorities: 27%; underrepresented minorities: 10%; in state: 100%
Acceptance rate: 7%
Average MCAT: 9.8
Average GPA: 3.70
Most popular undergraduate majors: biological sciences: 49%; physical sciences: 15%; non-sciences: 14%; other: 22%
Graduates entering primary-care specialties: 41.3%

GEORGIA

Emory University

1440 Clifton Road NE
Atlanta, GA 30322-4510
Private
Admissions: (404) 727-5660
E-mail: medadmiss@emory.edu
Web site:
http://www.emory.edu/WHSC
Financial aid: (800) 727-6039
Application deadline: 10/15
Tuition: $31,497
Room/board/expenses: $15,504
Students receiving grants: 57%
Average student indebtedness at graduation: $99,696
Enrollment: 450
men: 52%; women: 48%; minorities: 27%; underrepresented minorities: 12%; in state: 40%
Acceptance rate: 9%
Average MCAT: 10.7
Average GPA: 3.75
Most popular undergraduate majors: biological sciences: 45%; physical sciences: 23%; non-sciences: 21%; other: 12%
Graduates entering primary-care specialties: 48.3%

Medical College of Georgia

1120 15th Street
Augusta, GA 30912
Public
Admissions: (706) 721-3186
E-mail: stdadmin@mail.mcg.edu
Web site: http://www.
mcg.edu/som/index.html
Financial aid: (706) 721-4901
Application deadline: 11/03
In-state tuition: $9,082
Out-of-state tuition: $34,630
Room/board/expenses: $10,989
Students receiving grants: 33%
Average student indebtedness at graduation: $54,683
Enrollment: 731
men: 61%; women: 39%; minorities: 27%; underrepresented minorities: N/A; in state: 99%
Acceptance rate: 19%
Average MCAT: 9.6
Average GPA: 3.61

Most popular undergraduate majors: biological sciences: 69%; physical sciences: 18%; non-sciences: 12%; other: 1%
Graduates entering primary-care specialties: 57.0%

Mercer University

1550 College Street
Macon, GA 31207
Private
Admissions: (478) 301-2542
E-mail: faust_ek@mercer.edu
Web site:
http://medicine.mercer.edu
Financial aid: (478) 301-2853
Application deadline: 11/01
Tuition: $25,056
Room/board/expenses: $18,625
Average student indebtedness at graduation: $135,482
Enrollment: 216
men: 56%; women: 44%; minorities: 12%; underrepresented minorities: 6%; in state: 100%
Acceptance rate: 10%
Average MCAT: 8.5
Average GPA: 3.52
Most popular undergraduate majors: biological sciences: 59%; physical sciences: 10%; non-sciences: 14%; other: 17%
Graduates entering primary-care specialties: N/A

Morehouse School of Medicine

720 Westview Drive SW
Atlanta, GA 30310
Private
Admissions: (404) 752-1650
E-mail: mdadmissions@msm.edu
Web site: http://www.msm.edu
Financial aid: (404) 752-1655
Application deadline: 12/01
Tuition: $25,376
Room/board/expenses: $10,780
Average student indebtedness at graduation: $108,844
Enrollment: 169
men: 33%; women: 67%; minorities: 92%; underrepresented minorities: 80%; in state: 61%
Acceptance rate: 6%
Most popular undergraduate majors: biological sciences: 55%; physical sciences: 5%; non-sciences: 18%; other: 23%
Graduates entering primary-care specialties: N/A

HAWAII

University of Hawaii–Manoa (Burns)[1]

1960 East-West Road
Honolulu, HI 96822
Public
Admissions: (808) 956-8300
E-mail: medadmin@hawaii.edu
Web site:
http://hawaiimed.hawaii.edu
Financial aid: (808) 956-7251
Tuition: N/A
Room/board/expenses: N/A
Enrollment: N/A

ILLINOIS

Finch University of Health Sciences–Chicago Medical School[1]

3333 Greenbay Road
North Chicago, IL 60064
Private
Admissions: (847) 578-3204
E-mail: admiss@finchcms.edu
Web site: http://www.finchcms.edu
Financial aid: (847) 578-3217
Tuition: N/A
Room/board/expenses: N/A
Enrollment: N/A

Loyola University Chicago (Stritch)

2160 S. First Avenue
Building 120
Maywood, IL 60153
Private
Admissions: (708) 216-3229
Web site:
http://www.meddean.lumc.edu
Financial aid: (708) 216-3227
Application deadline: 11/15
Tuition: $32,100
Room/board/expenses: $16,486
Students receiving grants: 52%
Average student indebtedness at graduation: $129,840
Enrollment: 527
men: 53%; women: 47%; minorities: 17%; underrepresented minorities: 5%; in state: 52%
Most popular undergraduate majors: biological sciences: N/A; physical sciences: N/A; non-sciences: N/A; other: N/A
Graduates entering primary-care specialties: 50.0%

Northwestern University (Feinberg)

303 E. Chicago Avenue
Morton Building 1-606
Chicago, IL 60611
Private
Admissions: (312) 503-8206
E-mail: med-admissions@
northwestern.edu
Web site:
http://www.nums.nwu.edu
Internet application: http://www.
med-admissions.northwestern.edu
Financial aid: (312) 503-8722
Application deadline: 11/01
Tuition: $35,616
Room/board/expenses: $11,790
Students receiving grants: 43%
Average student indebtedness at graduation: $111,005
Enrollment: 701
men: 55%; women: 45%; minorities: 53%; underrepresented minorities: 9%; in state: 30%
Acceptance rate: 8%
Average MCAT: 11.0
Average GPA: 3.67
Most popular undergraduate majors: biological sciences: 44%; physical sciences: 27%; non-sciences: 23%; other: 7%
Graduates entering primary-care specialties: 40.0%

Rush University[1]

600 S. Paulina Street
Chicago, IL 60612
Private
Admissions: (312) 942-6913
E-mail: medcol@rush.edu
Web site: http://www.
rushu.rush.edu/medcol/

Internet application:
http://www.aamc.org
Financial aid: (312) 942-6256
Tuition: N/A
Room/board/expenses: N/A
Enrollment: N/A

Southern Illinois University–Springfield

801 N. Rutledge
PO Box 19620
Springfield, IL 62794-9620
Public
Admissions: (217) 545-6013
E-mail: admissions@siumed.edu
Web site: http://www.siumed.edu
Financial aid: (217) 545-2224
Application deadline: 11/15
In-state tuition: $16,039
Out-of-state tuition: $45,403
Room/board/expenses: $5,561
Students receiving grants: 39%
Average student indebtedness at graduation: $78,500
Enrollment: 287
men: 51%; women: 49%; minorities: 21%; underrepresented minorities: 9%; in state: 100%
Acceptance rate: 17%
Average MCAT: 9.0
Average GPA: 3.47
Most popular undergraduate majors: biological sciences: 48%; physical sciences: 17%; non-sciences: 4%; other: 3%
Graduates entering primary-care specialties: 52.5%

University of Chicago

924 E. 57th Street
BSLC 104
Chicago, IL 60637-5416
Private
Admissions: (773) 702-1937
E-mail: admissions@
pritzker.bsd.uchicago.edu
Web site: http://www.
bsd.uchicago.edu
Financial aid: (773) 702-1938
Application deadline: 10/15
Tuition: $31,238
Room/board/expenses: $9,458
Students receiving grants: 82%
Average student indebtedness at graduation: $90,834
Enrollment: 403
men: 48%; women: 52%; minorities: 38%; underrepresented minorities: 13%; in state: 38%
Acceptance rate: 4%
Average MCAT: 10.3
Average GPA: 3.62
Most popular undergraduate majors: biological sciences: 52%; physical sciences: 13%; non-sciences: 19%; other: 16%
Graduates entering primary-care specialties: 45.7%

University of Illinois–Chicago[1]

1853 W. Polk Street
M/C 784
Chicago, IL 60612
Public
Admissions: (312) 996-5635
E-mail: medadmit@uic.edu
Web site:
http://www.uic.edu/depts/mcam
Internet application: http://www.
aamc.org/students/amcas/
start.htm
Financial aid: (312) 413-0127
Tuition: N/A
Room/board/expenses: N/A
Enrollment: N/A

INDIANA

Indiana University–Indianapolis

1120 South Drive
Indianapolis, IN 46202
Public
Admissions: (317) 274-3772
E-mail: inmedadm@iupui.edu
Web site: http://www.
medicine.iu.edu/home.html
Internet application: http://www.
aamc.org/students/amcas
Financial aid: (317) 274-1967
Application deadline: 12/15
In-state tuition: $17,804
Out-of-state tuition: $35,741
Room/board/expenses: $13,078
Students receiving grants: 35%
Average student indebtedness at graduation: $91,691
Enrollment: 1,116
men: 56%; women: 44%; minorities: 17%; underrepresented minorities: 7%; in state: 94%
Acceptance rate: 22%
Average MCAT: 9.7
Average GPA: 3.72
Most popular undergraduate majors: biological sciences: 43%; physical sciences: 40%; non-sciences: 10%; other: 7%
Graduates entering primary-care specialties: 42.9%

IOWA

University of Iowa (Roy J. and Lucille A. Carver)

200 CMAB
Iowa City, IA 52242-1101
Public
Admissions: (319) 335-8052
E-mail: medical-admissions@
uiowa.edu
Web site:
http://www.medicine.uiowa.edu
Internet application:
http://www.medicine.uiowa.edu/
prospstudents.htm
Financial aid: (319) 335-8059
Application deadline: 11/01
In-state tuition: $18,508
Out-of-state tuition: $36,976
Room/board/expenses: $5,760
Students receiving grants: 50%
Average student indebtedness at graduation: $85,579
Enrollment: 589
men: 56%; women: 44%; minorities: 21%; underrepresented minorities: 10%; in state: 72%
Acceptance rate: 12%
Average MCAT: 10.3
Average GPA: 3.75
Most popular undergraduate majors: biological sciences: 57%; physical sciences: 18%; non-sciences: 15%; other: 10%
Graduates entering primary-care specialties: 45.1%

KANSAS

University of Kansas Medical Center

3901 Rainbow Boulevard
Kansas City, KS 66160
Public
Admissions: (913) 588-5283
E-mail: smccurdy@kumc.edu
Web site: http://www.
kumc.edu/som/som.html
Financial aid: (913) 588-5170
Application deadline: 10/15
In-state tuition: $12,936
Out-of-state tuition: $27,318

Room/board/expenses: $17,452
Students receiving grants: 71%
Average student indebtedness at graduation: $80,163
Enrollment: 691
men: 53%; women: 47%; minorities: 21%; underrepresented minorities: 11%; in state: 89%
Acceptance rate: 16%
Average MCAT: 9.2
Average GPA: 3.62
Most popular undergraduate majors: biological sciences: 51%; physical sciences: 26%; nonsciences: 19%; other: 3%
Graduates entering primary-care specialties: 57.8%

KENTUCKY

University of Kentucky[1]

Chandler Medical Center
800 Rose Street
Lexington, KY 40536
Public
Admissions: (859) 323-6161
E-mail: kstahlma@pop.uky.edu
Web site: http://www.mc.uky.edu/medicine/
Internet application: http://www.aamc.org/students/amcas/start.htm
Financial aid: (859) 323-6271
Tuition: N/A
Room/board/expenses: N/A
Enrollment: N/A

University of Louisville

Abell Administration Center
H.S.C.
Louisville, KY 40202
Public
Admissions: (502) 852-5193
E-mail: medadm@louisville.edu
Web site: http://www.louisville.edu
Financial aid: (502) 852-5187
Application deadline: 11/01
In-state tuition: $13,922
Out-of-state tuition: $33,848
Room/board/expenses: $6,672
Students receiving grants: 28%
Average student indebtedness at graduation: $73,192
Enrollment: 597
men: 49%; women: 51%; minorities: 18%; underrepresented minorities: 10%; in state: 85%
Acceptance rate: 19%
Average MCAT: 9.0
Average GPA: 3.62
Most popular undergraduate majors: biological sciences: 52%; physical sciences: 14%; nonsciences: 22%; other: 12%
Graduates entering primary-care specialties: 52.0%

LOUISIANA

LSU School of Medicine– New Orleans[1]

Admissions Office
1901 Perdido Street
New Orleans, LA 70112-1393
Public
Admissions: (504) 568-6262
E-mail: ms-admissions@lsumc.edu
Web site: http://www.medschool.lsumc.edu
Internet application: http://www.aamc.org/students/amcas/start.htm
Financial aid: (504) 568-4820
Tuition: N/A
Room/board/expenses: N/A
Enrollment: N/A

LSU School of Medicine–Shreveport[1]

PO Box 33932
Shreveport, LA 71130-3932
Public
Admissions: (318) 675-5190
E-mail: shvadm@lsumc.edu
Web site: http://www.sh.lsumc.edu
Internet application: http://www.aamc.org/students/start.htm
Financial aid: (318) 675-5561
Tuition: N/A
Room/board/expenses: N/A
Enrollment: N/A

Tulane University

1430 Tulane Avenue, SL67
New Orleans, LA 70112-2699
Private
Admissions: (504) 588-5187
E-mail: medsch@tulane.edu
Web site: http://www.mcl.tulane.edu
Financial aid: (504) 585-6135
Application deadline: 12/15
Tuition: $35,319
Room/board/expenses: $7,666
Students receiving grants: 53%
Average student indebtedness at graduation: $126,289
Enrollment: 620
men: 57%; women: 43%; minorities: 28%; underrepresented minorities: 10%; in state: 23%
Acceptance rate: 5%
Average MCAT: 10.5
Average GPA: 3.54
Most popular undergraduate majors: biological sciences: 42%; physical sciences: 17%; nonsciences: 25%; other: 16%
Graduates entering primary-care specialties: 41.0%

MARYLAND

Johns Hopkins University

720 Rutland Avenue
Baltimore, MD 21205
Private
Admissions: (410) 955-3182
Web site: http://www.hopkinsmedicine.org
Internet application: http://www.hopkinsmedicine.org/admissions
Financial aid: (410) 955-1324
Application deadline: 10/15
Tuition: $32,083
Room/board/expenses: $17,066
Students receiving grants: 59%
Average student indebtedness at graduation: $70,378
Enrollment: 478
men: 55%; women: 45%; minorities: 37%; underrepresented minorities: 14%; in state: 24%
Acceptance rate: 6%
Average MCAT: 11.0
Average GPA: 3.83
Most popular undergraduate majors: biological sciences: 38%; physical sciences: 37%; nonsciences: 18%; other: 7%
Graduates entering primary-care specialties: 45.7%

Uniformed Services University of the Health Sciences

4301 Jones Bridge Road
Bethesda, MD 20814
Public
Admissions: (800) 772-1743
E-mail: admissions@usuhs.mil
Web site: http://www.usuhs.mil
Financial aid: N/A
Application deadline: 11/03
In-state tuition: N/A

Out-of-state tuition: N/A
Room/board/expenses: N/A
Enrollment: 685
men: 74%; women: 26%; minorities: 22%; underrepresented minorities: 8%; in state: 7%
Acceptance rate: 16%
Average MCAT: 9.7
Average GPA: 3.49
Most popular undergraduate majors: biological sciences: 41%; physical sciences: 19%; nonsciences: 20%; other: 20%
Graduates entering primary-care specialties: 40.0%

University of Maryland

655 W. Baltimore Street
Room 14-029
Baltimore, MD 21201-1559
Public
Admissions: (410) 706-7478
E-mail: mfoxwell@som.umaryland.edu
Web site: http://medschool.umaryland.edu
Financial aid: (410) 706-7347
Application deadline: 11/01
In-state tuition: $15,316
Out-of-state tuition: $28,764
Room/board/expenses: $15,450
Students receiving grants: 78%
Average student indebtedness at graduation: $88,903
Enrollment: 582
men: 45%; women: 55%; minorities: 34%; underrepresented minorities: 12%; in state: 87%
Acceptance rate: 11%
Average MCAT: 10.0
Average GPA: 3.67
Most popular undergraduate majors: biological sciences: 56%; physical sciences: 13%; nonsciences: 21%; other: 10%
Graduates entering primary-care specialties: 55.0%

MASSACHUSETTS

Boston University

715 Albany Street
L-103
Boston, MA 02118
Private
Admissions: (617) 638-4630
E-mail: medadms@bu.edu
Web site: http://www.bumc.bu.edu
Financial aid: (617) 638-5130
Application deadline: 11/15
Tuition: $36,980
Room/board/expenses: $10,587
Students receiving grants: 26%
Average student indebtedness at graduation: $144,660
Enrollment: 621
men: 57%; women: 43%; minorities: 41%; underrepresented minorities: 11%; in state: 24%
Acceptance rate: 4%
Average MCAT: 9.6
Average GPA: 3.50
Most popular undergraduate majors: biological sciences: N/A; physical sciences: N/A; nonsciences: N/A; other: N/A
Graduates entering primary-care specialties: 42.6%

Harvard University

25 Shattuck Street
Boston, MA 02115-6092
Private
Admissions: (617) 432-1550
E-mail: admissions_office@hms.harvard.edu
Web site: http://www.hms.harvard.edu
Financial aid: (617) 432-1575
Application deadline: 10/15
Tuition: $32,708

Room/board/expenses: $15,042
Students receiving grants: 41%
Average student indebtedness at graduation: $80,829
Enrollment: 735
men: 51%; women: 49%; minorities: 48%; underrepresented minorities: 22%; in state: N/A
Acceptance rate: 5%
Average MCAT: 11.1
Average GPA: 3.78
Most popular undergraduate majors: biological sciences: N/A; physical sciences: N/A; nonsciences: 20%; other: 9%
Graduates entering primary-care specialties: 47.0%

Tufts University

136 Harrison Avenue
Boston, MA 02111
Private
Admissions: (617) 636-6571
E-mail: med-admissions@tufts.edu
Web site: http://www.tufts.edu/med
Financial aid: (617) 636-6574
Application deadline: 11/01
Tuition: $40,104
Room/board/expenses: N/A
Students receiving grants: 20%
Average student indebtedness at graduation: $139,394
Enrollment: 706
men: 54%; women: 46%; minorities: 45%; underrepresented minorities: 11%; in state: 31%
Acceptance rate: 9%
Average MCAT: 9.9
Average GPA: 3.48
Most popular undergraduate majors: biological sciences: 47%; physical sciences: 20%; nonsciences: 26%; other: 7%
Graduates entering primary-care specialties: 47.0%

University of Massachusetts– Worcester

55 Lake Avenue N
Worcester, MA 01655
Public
Admissions: (508) 856-2323
E-mail: admissions@umassmed.edu
Web site: http://www.umassmed.edu
Financial aid: (508) 856-2265
Application deadline: 11/01
In-state tuition: $11,352
Out-of-state tuition: N/A
Room/board/expenses: $8,236
Students receiving grants: 32%
Average student indebtedness at graduation: $79,379
Enrollment: 416
men: 50%; women: 50%; minorities: 17%; underrepresented minorities: 4%; in state: 100%
Acceptance rate: 28%
Average MCAT: 10.6
Average GPA: 3.60
Most popular undergraduate majors: biological sciences: 42%; physical sciences: 24%; nonsciences: 24%; other: 10%
Graduates entering primary-care specialties: 62.0%

MICHIGAN

Michigan State University

A110 E. Fee Hall
East Lansing, MI 48824
Public
Admissions: (517) 353-9620
E-mail: MDadmissions@msu.edu
Web site: http://www.chm.msu.edu

Financial aid: (517) 353-5188
Application deadline: 11/15
In-state tuition: $18,950
Out-of-state tuition: $40,550
Room/board/expenses: $10,656
Students receiving grants: 78%
Average student indebtedness at graduation: $110,850
Enrollment: 447
men: 42%; women: 58%; minorities: 36%; underrepresented minorities: 21%; in state: 78%
Acceptance rate: 8%
Average MCAT: 9.2
Average GPA: 3.51
Most popular undergraduate majors: biological sciences: 64%; physical sciences: 17%; nonsciences: 13%; other: 6%
Graduates entering primary-care specialties: 50.0%

University of Michigan–Ann Arbor

1301 Catherine Road
Ann Arbor, MI 48109-0624
Public
Admissions: (734) 764-6317
E-mail: umichmedadmiss@umich.edu
Web site: http://www.med.umich.edu/medschool/
Financial aid: (734) 763-4147
Application deadline: 11/15
In-state tuition: $19,919
Out-of-state tuition: $30,595
Room/board/expenses: $20,936
Students receiving grants: 52%
Average student indebtedness at graduation: $98,198
Enrollment: 670
men: 56%; women: 44%; minorities: 37%; underrepresented minorities: 15%; in state: 53%
Acceptance rate: 8%
Average MCAT: 11.4
Average GPA: 3.70
Most popular undergraduate majors: biological sciences: 44%; physical sciences: 22%; nonsciences: 19%; other: 16%
Graduates entering primary-care specialties: 41.9%

Wayne State University

540 E. Canfield
Detroit, MI 48201
Public
Admissions: (313) 577-1466
E-mail: admissions@med.wayne.edu
Web site: http://www.med.wayne.edu
Financial aid: (313) 577-7731
Application deadline: 12/15
In-state tuition: $16,162
Out-of-state tuition: $32,760
Room/board/expenses: $17,600
Students receiving grants: 45%
Average student indebtedness at graduation: $92,732
Enrollment: 1,041
men: 53%; women: 47%; minorities: 35%; underrepresented minorities: 14%; in state: 91%
Acceptance rate: 18%
Average MCAT: 9.4
Average GPA: 3.55
Most popular undergraduate majors: biological sciences: 49%; physical sciences: 27%; nonsciences: 12%; other: 12%
Graduates entering primary-care specialties: 44.0%

MINNESOTA

Mayo Medical School
200 First Street SW
Rochester, MN 55905
Private
Admissions: (507) 284-3671
E-mail: medschooladmissions@
mayo.edu
Web site:
http://www.mayo.edu/mgs/
Financial aid: (507) 284-4839
Application deadline: 11/01
Tuition: $10,750
Room/board/expenses: $10,945
Students receiving grants: 100%
**Average student indebtedness at
graduation:** $52,118
Enrollment: 176
men: 47%; women: 53%; minori-
ties: 26%; underrepresented
minorities: 11%; in state: 27%
Acceptance rate: 4%
Average MCAT: 10.9
Average GPA: 3.80
**Most popular undergraduate
majors:** biological sciences: N/A;
physical sciences: N/A; non-
sciences: N/A; other: N/A
**Graduates entering primary-care
specialties:** 29.0%

University of
Minnesota–Duluth
1035 University Drive
Duluth, MN 55812-3031
Public
Admissions: (218) 726-8511
E-mail: medadmis@d.umn.edu
Web site:
http://penguin.d.umn.edu
Financial aid: (218) 726-8000
Application deadline: 11/15
In-state tuition: $26,642
Out-of-state tuition: $48,150
Room/board/expenses: $12,142
Students receiving grants: 55%
**Average student indebtedness at
graduation:** $91,845
Enrollment: 109
men: 55%; women: 45%; minori-
ties: 12%; underrepresented
minorities: 7%; in state: 91%
Acceptance rate: 14%
Average MCAT: 9.5
Average GPA: 3.55
**Most popular undergraduate
majors:** biological sciences: 73%;
physical sciences: 13%; non-
sciences: 7%; other: 7%
**Graduates entering primary-care
specialties:** 70.0%

University of
Minnesota–Twin Cities
420 Delaware Street SE
MMC 293
Minneapolis, MN 55455
Public
Admissions: (612) 625-7977
E-mail: meded@umn.edu
Web site:
http://www.meded.umn.edu/
Financial aid: (612) 625-4998
Application deadline: 11/15
In-state tuition: $24,270
Out-of-state tuition: $32,651
Room/board/expenses: $10,642
**Average student indebtedness at
graduation:** $87,889
Enrollment: 806
men: 52%; women: 48%; minori-
ties: 20%; underrepresented
minorities: 8%; in state: 84%
Acceptance rate: 18%
Average MCAT: 10.3
Average GPA: 3.67

**Most popular undergraduate
majors:** biological sciences: 23%;
physical sciences: 17%; non-
sciences: 16%; other: 44%
**Graduates entering primary-care
specialties:** 55.1%

MISSISSIPPI

University of
Mississippi
2500 N. State Street
Jackson, MS 39216-4505
Public
Admissions: (601) 984-5010
Web site: http://www.umc.edu
Financial aid: (601) 984-1117
Application deadline: 10/15
In-state tuition: $6,715
Out-of-state tuition: $12,830
Room/board/expenses: $8,755
Students receiving grants: 60%
**Average student indebtedness at
graduation:** $62,000
Enrollment: 390
men: 62%; women: 38%; minori-
ties: 12%; underrepresented
minorities: 6%; in state: 100%
Acceptance rate: 24%
Average MCAT: 9.1
Average GPA: 3.67
**Most popular undergraduate
majors:** biological sciences: 54%;
physical sciences: 27%; non-
sciences: 11%; other: 8%
**Graduates entering primary-care
specialties:** 55.0%

MISSOURI

St. Louis University
1402 S. Grand Boulevard
St. Louis, MO 63104
Private
Admissions: (314) 577-8205
E-mail: medadmis@slu.edu
Web site: http://medschool.slu.edu
Financial aid: (314) 577-8617
Application deadline: 12/15
Tuition: $36,430
Room/board/expenses: $14,206
**Average student indebtedness at
graduation:** $135,008
Enrollment: 606
men: 53%; women: 47%; minori-
ties: 32%; underrepresented
minorities: 15%; in state: 42%
Acceptance rate: 15%
Average MCAT: 10.0
Average GPA: 3.60
**Most popular undergraduate
majors:** biological sciences: 23%;
physical sciences: 56%; non-
sciences: 13%; other: 8%
**Graduates entering primary-care
specialties:** 49.5%

University of
Missouri–Columbia
1 Hospital Drive
Columbia, MO 65212
Public
Admissions: (573) 882-9219
E-mail:
nolkej@health.missouri.edu
Web site: http://www.
muhealth.org/~medicine/
Financial aid: (573) 882-2923
Application deadline: 11/01
In-state tuition: $17,820
Out-of-state tuition: $34,754
Room/board/expenses: $7,900
Students receiving grants: 27%
**Average student indebtedness at
graduation:** $87,724
Enrollment: 374
men: 52%; women: 48%; minori-
ties: 14%; underrepresented
minorities: 4%; in state: 99%

Acceptance rate: 21%
Average MCAT: 9.7
Average GPA: 3.71
**Most popular undergraduate
majors:** biological sciences: 52%;
physical sciences: 25%; non-
sciences: 14%; other: 5%
**Graduates entering primary-care
specialties:** 60.6%

University of
Missouri–Kansas City[1]
2411 Holmes
Kansas City, MO 64108
Public
Admissions: (816) 235-1111
E-mail: tylerm@umkc.edu
Web site:
http://www.med.umkc.edu
Financial aid: (816) 235-1154
Tuition: N/A
Room/board/expenses: N/A
Enrollment: N/A

Washington University
in St. Louis
660 S. Euclid Avenue
St. Louis, MO 63110
Private
Admissions: (314) 362-6858
E-mail:
wumscoa@msnotes.wustl.edu
Web site:
http://medschool.wustl.edu
Internet application:
http://medschool.wustl.edu/
admissions/
Financial aid: (314) 362-6845
Application deadline: 12/01
Tuition: $35,780
Room/board/expenses: $7,980
Students receiving grants: 69%
**Average student indebtedness at
graduation:** $87,516
Enrollment: 566
men: 54%; women: 46%; minori-
ties: 34%; underrepresented
minorities: 8%; in state: 7%
Acceptance rate: 11%
Average MCAT: 12.2
Average GPA: 3.83
**Most popular undergraduate
majors:** biological sciences: 35%;
physical sciences: 42%; non-
sciences: 13%; other: 10%
**Graduates entering primary-care
specialties:** 40.6%

NEBRASKA

Creighton University
2500 California Plaza
Omaha, NE 68178
Private
Admissions: (402) 280-2799
E-mail:
medschadm@creighton.edu
Web site:
http://medicine.creighton.edu
Financial aid: (402) 280-2666
Application deadline: 12/01
Tuition: $34,202
Room/board/expenses: $10,350
Students receiving grants: 17%
**Average student indebtedness at
graduation:** $125,994
Enrollment: 460
men: 53%; women: 47%; minori-
ties: 32%; underrepresented
minorities: 9%; in state: N/A
Acceptance rate: 8%
Average MCAT: 9.5
Average GPA: 3.64
**Most popular undergraduate
majors:** biological sciences: 67%;
physical sciences: 13%; non-
sciences: 4%; other: 16%
**Graduates entering primary-care
specialties:** N/A

University of Nebraska
College of Medicine
986585 Nebraska Medical Center
Omaha, NE 68198-6585
Public
Admissions: (402) 559-2259
E-mail: grrogers@unmc.edu
Web site:
http://www.unmc.edu/UNCOM/
Financial aid: (402) 559-4199
Application deadline: 11/01
In-state tuition: $16,141
Out-of-state tuition: $35,602
Room/board/expenses: $13,500
Students receiving grants: 61%
**Average student indebtedness at
graduation:** $92,317
Enrollment: 483
men: 61%; women: 39%; minori-
ties: 11%; underrepresented
minorities: 4%; in state: 91%
Acceptance rate: 20%
Average MCAT: 9.6
Average GPA: 3.70
**Most popular undergraduate
majors:** biological sciences: 59%;
physical sciences: 20%; non-
sciences: 14%; other: 7%
**Graduates entering primary-care
specialties:** 60.6%

NEVADA

University of
Nevada–Reno[1]
Manville Building
Mailstop 357
Reno, NV 89557
Public
Admissions: (775) 784-6063
E-mail: asa@med.unr.edu
Web site: http://www.unr.edu/med/
Financial aid: (775) 784-4666
Tuition: N/A
Room/board/expenses: N/A
Enrollment: N/A

NEW HAMPSHIRE

Dartmouth Medical
School
3 Rope Ferry Road
Hanover, NH 03755-1404
Private
Admissions: (603) 650-1505
E-mail: dms.admissions@
dartmouth.edu
Web site:
http://www.dartmouth.edu/dms
Financial aid: (603) 650-1919
Application deadline: 11/03
Tuition: $32,050
Room/board/expenses: N/A
Students receiving grants: 48%
**Average student indebtedness at
graduation:** $90,040
Enrollment: 289
men: 54%; women: 46%; minori-
ties: 20%; underrepresented
minorities: 9%; in state: 11%
Acceptance rate: 5%
Average MCAT: 10.6
Average GPA: 3.70
**Most popular undergraduate
majors:** biological sciences: 36%;
physical sciences: 26%; non-
sciences: 31%; other: 7%
**Graduates entering primary-care
specialties:** 40.0%

NEW JERSEY

UMDNJ-New Jersey
Medical School
185 S. Orange Avenue
PO Box 1709
Newark, NJ 07101-1709
Public
Admissions: (973) 972-4631
E-mail: njmsadmiss@umdnj.edu
Web site:
http://www.njms.umdnj.edu
Internet application:
http://www.aamc.org
Financial aid: (973) 972-4376
Application deadline: 12/01
In-state tuition: $20,294
Out-of-state tuition: $30,543
Room/board/expenses: $10,250
Students receiving grants: 11%
**Average student indebtedness at
graduation:** $84,292
Enrollment: 700
men: 56%; women: 44%; minori-
ties: 53%; underrepresented
minorities: 22%; in state: 99%
Acceptance rate: 19%
Average MCAT: 9.9
Average GPA: 3.47
**Most popular undergraduate
majors:** biological sciences: 22%;
physical sciences: 28%; non-
sciences: 24%; other: 26%
**Graduates entering primary-care
specialties:** 39.0%

UMDNJ-
Robert Wood Johnson
Medical School
675 Hoes Lane
Piscataway, NJ 08854
Public
Admissions: (732) 235-4576
E-mail: rwjapadm@umdnj.edu
Web site: http://rwjms.umdnj.edu
Financial aid: (732) 235-4689
Application deadline: 12/01
In-state tuition: $20,344
Out-of-state tuition: $30,593
Room/board/expenses: $10,026
Students receiving grants: 30%
**Average student indebtedness at
graduation:** $89,256
Enrollment: 657
men: 53%; women: 47%; minori-
ties: 52%; underrepresented
minorities: 19%; in state: 98%
Acceptance rate: 17%
Average MCAT: 9.6
Average GPA: 3.59
**Most popular undergraduate
majors:** biological sciences: 54%;
physical sciences: 12%; non-
sciences: 20%; other: 14%
**Graduates entering primary-care
specialties:** 51.3%

NEW MEXICO

University of
New Mexico
Basic Medical Sciences Building
Room 107
Albuquerque, NM 87131
Public
Admissions: (505) 272-4766
Web site: http://hsc.unm.edu/som/
Internet application:
http://hsc.unm.edu/som/admiss
Financial aid: (505) 272-8008
Application deadline: 11/15
In-state tuition: $11,175
Out-of-state tuition: $28,844
Room/board/expenses: $8,460
Students receiving grants: 78%
**Average student indebtedness at
graduation:** $65,302

Enrollment: 303
men: 44%; women: 56%; minorities: 37%; underrepresented minorities: 31%; in state: 98%
Acceptance rate: 12%
Average MCAT: 9.0
Average GPA: 3.50
Most popular undergraduate majors: biological sciences: 21%; physical sciences: 19%; non-sciences: 21%; other: 39%
Graduates entering primary-care specialties: 57.0%

NEW YORK

Albany Medical College

47 New Scotland Avenue
Albany, NY 12208
Private
Admissions: (518) 262-5521
E-mail: admissions@mail.amc.edu
Web site: http://www.amc.edu
Financial aid: (518) 262-5435
Application deadline: 11/15
Tuition: $35,652
Room/board/expenses: N/A
Students receiving grants: 41%
Average student indebtedness at graduation: $124,364
Enrollment: 508
men: 50%; women: 50%; minorities: 34%; underrepresented minorities: 6%; in state: 39%
Average MCAT: 9.7
Average GPA: 3.50
Most popular undergraduate majors: biological sciences: 54%; physical sciences: 14%; non-sciences: 23%; other: 10%
Graduates entering primary-care specialties: N/A

Columbia University College of Physicians and Surgeons

630 W. 168th Street
New York, NY 10032
Private
Admissions: (212) 305-3595
E-mail: psadmissions@columbia.edu
Web site: http://cpmcnet.columbia.edu/dept/ps
Internet application: http://psadmissions.hs.columbia.edu
Financial aid: (212) 305-4100
Application deadline: 10/15
Tuition: $35,954
Room/board/expenses: $13,830
Students receiving grants: 55%
Average student indebtedness at graduation: $97,451
Enrollment: 624
men: 55%; women: 45%; minorities: 34%; underrepresented minorities: 11%; in state: 21%
Acceptance rate: 12%
Average MCAT: 11.8
Average GPA: 3.79
Most popular undergraduate majors: biological sciences: 39%; physical sciences: 30%; non-sciences: 28%; other: 3%
Graduates entering primary-care specialties: 37.4%

Cornell University (Weill)

1300 York Avenue at 69th Street
New York, NY 10021
Private
Admissions: (212) 746-1067
E-mail: cumc-admissions@med.cornell.edu

Web site: http://www.med.cornell.edu
Internet application: http://www.med.cornell.edu/education/admissions
Financial aid: (212) 746-1066
Application deadline: 10/15
Tuition: $30,045
Room/board/expenses: $8,865
Students receiving grants: 57%
Average student indebtedness at graduation: $72,541
Enrollment: 410
men: 51%; women: 49%; minorities: 40%; underrepresented minorities: 19%; in state: 52%
Acceptance rate: 4%
Average MCAT: 11.2
Average GPA: 3.68
Most popular undergraduate majors: biological sciences: 42%; physical sciences: 22%; non-sciences: 27%; other: 10%
Graduates entering primary-care specialties: 40.4%

Mount Sinai School of Medicine

1 Gustave L. Levy Place
Box 1475
New York, NY 10029
Public
Admissions: (212) 241-6696
E-mail: admissions@mssm.edu
Web site: http://www.mssm.edu/
Financial aid: (212) 241-5245
Application deadline: 11/01
In-state tuition: $30,700
Out-of-state tuition: $30,700
Room/board/expenses: $12,300
Students receiving grants: 48%
Average student indebtedness at graduation: $85,042
Enrollment: 450
men: 49%; women: 51%; minorities: 40%; underrepresented minorities: 18%; in state: N/A
Acceptance rate: 7%
Average MCAT: 10.6
Average GPA: 3.63
Most popular undergraduate majors: biological sciences: 21%; physical sciences: 22%; non-sciences: 55%; other: 0%
Graduates entering primary-care specialties: 47.0%

New York Medical College

Administration Building
Office of Admissions
Valhalla, NY 10595
Private
Admissions: (914) 594-4507
E-mail: mdadmit@nymc.edu
Web site: http://www.nymc.edu
Internet application: http://www.nymc.edu/admit/medical/info/proced.htm
Financial aid: (914) 594-4491
Application deadline: 12/15
Tuition: $35,556
Room/board/expenses: $15,694
Students receiving grants: 15%
Average student indebtedness at graduation: $137,000
Enrollment: 769
men: 50%; women: 50%; minorities: 42%; underrepresented minorities: 8%; in state: 36%
Acceptance rate: 13%
Average MCAT: 9.9
Average GPA: 3.50
Most popular undergraduate majors: biological sciences: 49%; physical sciences: 18%; non-sciences: 14%; other: 19%
Graduates entering primary-care specialties: 54.2%

New York University

550 First Avenue
New York, NY 10016
Private
Admissions: (212) 263-5290
Web site: http://www.med.nyu.edu/som/medsch/index.html
Internet application: http://www.med.nyu.edu/som/medsch/download.html
Financial aid: (212) 263-5286
Application deadline: 11/15
Tuition: $31,250
Room/board/expenses: $9,810
Students receiving grants: 68%
Average student indebtedness at graduation: $76,992
Enrollment: 703
men: 53%; women: 47%; minorities: 41%; underrepresented minorities: 10%; in state: 50%
Acceptance rate: 16%
Average MCAT: 11.0
Average GPA: 3.70
Most popular undergraduate majors: biological sciences: 41%; physical sciences: 40%; non-sciences: 19%; other: N/A
Graduates entering primary-care specialties: 45.0%

Stony Brook University

Office of Admissions
Health Science Center, L4
Stony Brook, NY 11794-8434
Public
Admissions: (631) 444-2113
E-mail: admissions@dean.som.sunysb.edu
Web site: http://www.hsc.sunysb.edu/som/
Financial aid: (631) 444-2341
Application deadline: 11/15
In-state tuition: $15,425
Out-of-state tuition: $28,525
Room/board/expenses: $19,350
Students receiving grants: 39%
Average student indebtedness at graduation: $93,000
Enrollment: 434
men: 47%; women: 53%; minorities: 42%; underrepresented minorities: 13%; in state: 100%
Acceptance rate: 10%
Average MCAT: 10.3
Average GPA: 3.60
Most popular undergraduate majors: biological sciences: 47%; physical sciences: 21%; non-sciences: 29%; other: 3%
Graduates entering primary-care specialties: 63.8%

SUNY–Brooklyn[1]

450 Clarkson Avenue
Box 60
Brooklyn, NY 11203
Public
Admissions: (718) 270-2446
E-mail: admissions@downstate.edu
Web site: http://www.hscbklyn.edu
Internet application: http://www.aamc.org/student/amcas
Financial aid: (718) 270-2488
Tuition: N/A
Room/board/expenses: N/A
Enrollment: N/A

SUNY–Syracuse[1]

750 E. Adams Street
Syracuse, NY 13210
Public
Admissions: (315) 464-4570
E-mail: admis@upstate.edu
Web site: http://www.hscsyr.edu
Internet application: http://www.aamc.org/audienceamcas.htm

Financial aid: (315) 464-4329
Tuition: N/A
Room/board/expenses: N/A
Enrollment: N/A

University at Buffalo

155 Biomedical Education Building
Buffalo, NY 14214
Public
Admissions: (716) 829-3466
E-mail: jjrosso@acsu.buffalo.edu
Web site: http://www.smbs.buffalo.edu/ome
Internet application: http://www.aamc.org
Financial aid: (716) 829-2186
Application deadline: 11/01
In-state tuition: $15,980
Out-of-state tuition: $28,080
Room/board/expenses: $7,912
Students receiving grants: 78%
Average student indebtedness at graduation: $87,521
Enrollment: 601
men: 48%; women: 52%; minorities: 22%; underrepresented minorities: 9%; in state: 100%
Acceptance rate: 18%
Average MCAT: 9.5
Average GPA: 3.54
Most popular undergraduate majors: biological sciences: 36%; physical sciences: 24%; non-sciences: 24%; other: 16%
Graduates entering primary-care specialties: 49.3%

University of Rochester

601 Elmwood Avenue
Box 706
Rochester, NY 14642
Private
Admissions: (585) 275-4539
E-mail: mdadmish@urmc.rochester.edu
Web site: http://www.urmc.rochester.edu/smd/
Internet application: http://www.urmc.rochester.edu/smd/admiss/secondaryapp.html
Financial aid: (585) 275-4523
Application deadline: 10/15
Tuition: $33,057
Room/board/expenses: $14,500
Students receiving grants: 36%
Average student indebtedness at graduation: $100,385
Enrollment: 411
men: 45%; women: 55%; minorities: 34%; underrepresented minorities: 13%; in state: 48%
Acceptance rate: 9%
Average MCAT: 10.3
Average GPA: 3.67
Most popular undergraduate majors: biological sciences: 48%; physical sciences: 24%; non-sciences: 26%; other: 2%
Graduates entering primary-care specialties: 48.3%

Yeshiva University (Albert Einstein)

1300 Morris Park Avenue
Bronx, NY 10461
Private
Admissions: (718) 430-2106
E-mail: admissions@aecom.yu.edu
Web site: http://www.aecom.yu.edu
Internet application: http://www.aecom.yu.edu/home/admissions/Default.htm
Financial aid: (718) 430-2336
Application deadline: 11/01
Tuition: $34,675

Room/board/expenses: $12,800
Students receiving grants: 45%
Average student indebtedness at graduation: $85,000
Enrollment: 722
men: 51%; women: 49%; minorities: 36%; underrepresented minorities: N/A; in state: 49%
Acceptance rate: 9%
Average MCAT: 10.3
Average GPA: 3.61
Most popular undergraduate majors: biological sciences: 42%; physical sciences: 22%; non-sciences: 23%; other: 13%
Graduates entering primary-care specialties: 55.0%

NORTH CAROLINA

Duke University

DUMC
Durham, NC 27710
Private
Admissions: (919) 684-2985
E-mail: armst002@onyx.mc.duke.edu
Web site: http://medschool.duke.edu
Financial aid: (919) 684-6649
Application deadline: 11/01
Tuition: $32,906
Room/board/expenses: $9,900
Students receiving grants: 64%
Average student indebtedness at graduation: $69,827
Enrollment: 454
men: 54%; women: 46%; minorities: 49%; underrepresented minorities: 19%; in state: 12%
Acceptance rate: 4%
Average MCAT: 11.6
Average GPA: 3.80
Most popular undergraduate majors: biological sciences: 55%; physical sciences: 33%; non-sciences: 10%; other: 2%
Graduates entering primary-care specialties: 36.2%

East Carolina University (Brody)

600 Moye Boulevard
Greenville, NC 27858-4354
Public
Admissions: (252) 744-2202
E-mail: somadmissions@mail.ecu.edu
Web site: http://www.ecu.edu/bsomadmissions
Financial aid: (252) 744-2278
Application deadline: 11/15
In-state tuition: $4,598
Out-of-state tuition: $28,985
Room/board/expenses: $16,000
Students receiving grants: 68%
Average student indebtedness at graduation: $65,233
Enrollment: 303
men: 52%; women: 48%; minorities: 34%; underrepresented minorities: 23%; in state: 100%
Acceptance rate: 10%
Average MCAT: 8.7
Average GPA: 3.40
Most popular undergraduate majors: biological sciences: 65%; physical sciences: 10%; non-sciences: 21%; other: 4%
Graduates entering primary-care specialties: 52.7%

University of North Carolina– Chapel Hill

CB #7000
125 MacNider Building
Chapel Hill, NC 27599-7000
Public
Admissions: (919) 962-8331
E-mail: admissions@med.unc.edu
Web site: http://www.
med.unc.edu/admit/require.htm
Financial aid: (919) 962-6118
Application deadline: 11/15
In-state tuition: $8,068
Out-of-state tuition: $33,536
Room/board/expenses: $21,082
Students receiving grants: 73%
Average student indebtedness at graduation: $46,717
Enrollment: 653
men: 50%; women: 50%; minorities: 26%; underrepresented minorities: 14%; in state: 95%
Acceptance rate: 8%
Average MCAT: 10.3
Average GPA: 3.61
Most popular undergraduate majors: biological sciences: 39%; physical sciences: 10%; nonsciences: 7%; other: 44%
Graduates entering primary-care specialties: 44.0%

Wake Forest University

Medical Center Boulevard
Winston-Salem, NC 27157
Private
Admissions: (336) 716-4264
E-mail: medadmit@wfubmc.edu
Web site: http://www.wfubmc.edu
Financial aid: (336) 716-2889
Application deadline: 11/01
Tuition: $30,529
Room/board/expenses: $9,735
Students receiving grants: 49%
Average student indebtedness at graduation: $100,905
Enrollment: 431
men: 59%; women: 41%; minorities: 28%; underrepresented minorities: 15%; in state: 43%
Acceptance rate: 5%
Average MCAT: 10.0
Average GPA: 3.60
Most popular undergraduate majors: biological sciences: 56%; physical sciences: 16%; nonsciences: 18%; other: 10%
Graduates entering primary-care specialties: 54.0%

NORTH DAKOTA

University of North Dakota

501 N. Columbia Road
Box 9037
Grand Forks, ND 58202-9037
Public
Admissions: (701) 777-4221
E-mail:
jdheit@medicine.nodak.edu
Web site:
http://www.med.und.nodak.edu
Internet application: http://www.
med.und.nodak.edu/
admissions.html
Financial aid: (701) 777-2849
Application deadline: 11/01
In-state tuition: $14,479
Out-of-state tuition: $36,935
Room/board/expenses: $7,604
Students receiving grants: 69%
Average student indebtedness at graduation: $88,290
Enrollment: 223
men: 50%; women: 50%; minorities: 13%; underrepresented minorities: 11%; in state: 83%

Acceptance rate: 38%
Average MCAT: 8.6
Average GPA: 3.65
Most popular undergraduate majors: biological sciences: 46%; physical sciences: 13%; nonsciences: 20%; other: 22%
Graduates entering primary-care specialties: 47.0%

OHIO

Case Western Reserve University

10900 Euclid Avenue
Cleveland, OH 44106
Private
Admissions: (216) 368-3450
E-mail: ack@po.cwru.edu
Web site:
http://mediswww.cwru.edu/
Financial aid: (216) 368-3666
Application deadline: 11/01
Tuition: $36,379
Room/board/expenses: $15,000
Students receiving grants: 65%
Average student indebtedness at graduation: $104,500
Enrollment: 566
men: 58%; women: 42%; minorities: 33%; underrepresented minorities: 14%; in state: 69%
Acceptance rate: 10%
Average MCAT: 10.6
Average GPA: 3.58
Most popular undergraduate majors: biological sciences: 50%; physical sciences: 37%; nonsciences: 13%; other: N/A
Graduates entering primary-care specialties: 43.0%

Medical College of Ohio

3000 Arlington Avenue
Toledo, OH 43614
Public
Admissions: (419) 383-4229
E-mail: admissions@mco.edu
Web site: http://www.mco.edu
Financial aid: (419) 383-3436
Application deadline: 12/01
In-state tuition: $18,932
Out-of-state tuition: $36,772
Room/board/expenses: N/A
Students receiving grants: 28%
Average student indebtedness at graduation: $104,079
Enrollment: 577
men: 60%; women: 40%; minorities: 24%; underrepresented minorities: 7%; in state: 98%
Acceptance rate: 15%
Average MCAT: 9.6
Average GPA: 3.60
Most popular undergraduate majors: biological sciences: 63%; physical sciences: 14%; nonsciences: 12%; other: 11%
Graduates entering primary-care specialties: 41.0%

Northeastern Ohio Universities College of Medicine

4209 State Route 44
PO Box 95
Rootstown, OH 44272-0095
Public
Admissions: (330) 325-6270
E-mail: admission@neoucom.edu
Web site:
http://www.neoucom.edu
Financial aid: (330) 325-6479
Application deadline: 11/03
In-state tuition: $16,746
Out-of-state tuition: $32,484
Room/board/expenses: $8,250

Students receiving grants: 38%
Average student indebtedness at graduation: $77,606
Enrollment: 429
men: 47%; women: 53%; minorities: 45%; underrepresented minorities: 7%; in state: 97%
Acceptance rate: 18%
Average MCAT: 9.0
Average GPA: 3.66
Most popular undergraduate majors: biological sciences: 90%; physical sciences: 5%; nonsciences: 2%; other: 4%
Graduates entering primary-care specialties: 44.0%

Ohio State University

200 Meiling Hall
370 W. Ninth Avenue
Columbus, OH 43210-1238
Public
Admissions: (614) 292-7137
E-mail: medicine@osu.edu
Web site: http://medicine.osu.edu
Financial aid: (614) 292-8771
Application deadline: 11/02
In-state tuition: $17,439
Out-of-state tuition: $23,231
Room/board/expenses: $6,850
Students receiving grants: 44%
Average student indebtedness at graduation: $79,994
Enrollment: 831
men: 57%; women: 43%; minorities: 25%; underrepresented minorities: 8%; in state: 91%
Acceptance rate: 14%
Average MCAT: 10.3
Average GPA: 3.65
Most popular undergraduate majors: biological sciences: 50%; physical sciences: 26%; nonsciences: 19%; other: 5%
Graduates entering primary-care specialties: 48.0%

University of Cincinnati

Office of Student Affairs and Admissions
Cincinnati, OH 45267-0552
Public
Admissions: (513) 558-7314
E-mail: comadmis@ucmail.uc.edu
Web site: http://www.med.uc.edu
Internet application:
http://comdows.uc.edu/
MedOneStop/
(s10fq3zqttxka2jsswt1umyo)/
home.aspx
Financial aid: (513) 558-6797
Application deadline: 12/15
In-state tuition: $17,709
Out-of-state tuition: $30,792
Room/board/expenses: $13,644
Students receiving grants: 36%
Average student indebtedness at graduation: $92,937
Enrollment: 623
men: 60%; women: 40%; minorities: 20%; underrepresented minorities: 7%; in state: 81%
Acceptance rate: 18%
Average MCAT: 10.0
Average GPA: 3.61
Most popular undergraduate majors: biological sciences: 52%; physical sciences: 23%; nonsciences: 16%; other: 9%
Graduates entering primary-care specialties: 42.3%

Wright State University

PO Box 1751
Dayton, OH 45401-1751
Public
Admissions: (937) 775-2934
E-mail: som_saa@wright.edu
Web site:
http://www.med.wright.edu
Internet application: http://www.
med.wright.edu/admiss/start.html
Financial aid: (937) 775-2934
Application deadline: 11/15
In-state tuition: $15,200
Out-of-state tuition: $21,164
Room/board/expenses: $10,560
Enrollment: 363
men: 44%; women: 56%; minorities: 27%; underrepresented minorities: 15%; in state: 97%
Acceptance rate: 9%
Average MCAT: 8.7
Average GPA: 3.45
Most popular undergraduate majors: biological sciences: 65%; physical sciences: 11%; nonsciences: 7%; other: 17%
Graduates entering primary-care specialties: 62.0%

OKLAHOMA

University of Oklahoma

PO Box 26901
BMSB 357
Oklahoma City, OK 73190
Public
Admissions: (405) 271-2331
E-mail: adminmed@ouhsc.edu
Web site:
http://www.medicine.ouhsc.edu
Financial aid: (405) 271-2118
Application deadline: 10/15
In-state tuition: $12,699
Out-of-state tuition: $31,285
Room/board/expenses: N/A
Students receiving grants: 62%
Average student indebtedness at graduation: $84,165
Enrollment: 590
men: 61%; women: 39%; minorities: 24%; underrepresented minorities: 11%; in state: 94%
Acceptance rate: 20%
Average MCAT: 9.4
Average GPA: 3.67
Most popular undergraduate majors: biological sciences: 47%; physical sciences: 21%; nonsciences: 20%; other: 12%
Graduates entering primary-care specialties: 45.0%

OREGON

Oregon Health & Science University

3181 S.W. Sam Jackson Park Road, L102
Portland, OR 97239-3098
Public
Admissions: (503) 494-2998
Web site: http://www.ohsu.edu
Financial aid: (503) 494-7800
Application deadline: 10/15
In-state tuition: $23,517
Out-of-state tuition: $33,517
Room/board/expenses: $13,000
Students receiving grants: 80%
Average student indebtedness at graduation: $113,000
Enrollment: 396
men: 47%; women: 53%; minorities: 16%; underrepresented minorities: 5%; in state: 70%
Acceptance rate: 7%
Average MCAT: 10.1
Average GPA: 3.73

Most popular undergraduate majors: biological sciences: 39%; physical sciences: 12%; nonsciences: 19%; other: 30%
Graduates entering primary-care specialties: 54.0%

PENNSYLVANIA

Drexel University

245 N. 15th Street
MS 400
Philadelphia, PA 19102
Private
Admissions: (215) 991-8202
E-mail: Medadmis@drexel.edu
Web site: http://www.drexel.edu
Internet application: http://www.
aamc.org/students/start.htm
Financial aid: (215) 991-8210
Application deadline: 12/01
Tuition: $32,622
Room/board/expenses: $8,500
Students receiving grants: 5%
Average student indebtedness at graduation: $135,518
Enrollment: 1,007
men: 48%; women: 52%; minorities: 33%; underrepresented minorities: 10%; in state: 39%
Acceptance rate: 17%
Average MCAT: 9.8
Average GPA: 3.42
Most popular undergraduate majors: biological sciences: 57%; physical sciences: 15%; nonsciences: 19%; other: 9%
Graduates entering primary-care specialties: 45.3%

Jefferson Medical College

1025 Walnut Street
Room 100
Philadelphia, PA 19107-5083
Private
Admissions: (215) 955-6983
E-mail:
jmc.admissions@mail.tju.edu
Web site: http://www.tju.edu
Internet application:
http://www.jefferson.edu
Financial aid: (215) 955-2867
Application deadline: 11/15
Tuition: $31,958
Room/board/expenses: $11,640
Students receiving grants: 42%
Average student indebtedness at graduation: $111,176
Enrollment: 908
men: 55%; women: 45%; minorities: 26%; underrepresented minorities: 5%; in state: 48%
Acceptance rate: 7%
Average MCAT: 10.4
Average GPA: 3.51
Most popular undergraduate majors: biological sciences: 59%; physical sciences: 18%; nonsciences: 8%; other: 16%
Graduates entering primary-care specialties: 44.2%

Penn State University College of Medicine[1]

500 University Drive
Hershey, PA 17033
Public
Admissions: (717) 531-8755
E-mail:
StudentAffairs@hmc.psu.edu
Web site: http://www.hmc.psu.edu
Internet application: http://www.
aamc.org/students/amcas/
Financial aid: (717) 531-4103
Tuition: N/A
Room/board/expenses: N/A
Enrollment: N/A

Temple University[1]
3400 N. Broad Street
Philadelphia, PA 19140
Public
Admissions: (215) 707-3656
E-mail: tusadm@blue.temple.edu
Web site:
http://www.medschool.temple.edu
Internet application: http://www.
medschool.temple.edu/
Admissions/procedures.html
Financial aid: (215) 707-2667
Tuition: N/A
Room/board/expenses: N/A
Enrollment: N/A

University of Pennsylvania
295 John Morgan Building
3620 Hamilton Walk
Philadelphia, PA 19104-6055
Private
Admissions: (215) 898-8001
E-mail:
admiss@mail.med.upenn.edu
Web site:
http://www.med.upenn.edu
Internet application:
http://www.med.upenn.edu/
admiss/applications.html
Financial aid: (215) 573-3423
Application deadline: 10/15
Tuition: $35,234
Room/board/expenses: $18,783
Students receiving grants: 65%
**Average student indebtedness at
graduation:** $96,760
Enrollment: 597
men: 56%; women: 44%; minorities: 37%; underrepresented
minorities: 12%; in state: 28%
Acceptance rate: 6%
Average MCAT: 11.5
Average GPA: 3.77
**Most popular undergraduate
majors:** biological sciences: 62%;
physical sciences: 9%; non-
sciences: 26%; other: 3%
**Graduates entering primary-care
specialties:** 34.0%

University of Pittsburgh
401 Scaife Hall
Pittsburgh, PA 15261
Public
Admissions: (412) 648-9891
E-mail:
admissions@medschool.pitt.edu
Web site:
http://www.medschool.pitt.edu
Financial aid: (412) 648-9891
Application deadline: 12/01
In-state tuition: $28,034
Out-of-state tuition: $34,728
Room/board/expenses: $13,100
Students receiving grants: 43%
**Average student indebtedness at
graduation:** $118,888
Enrollment: 569
men: 52%; women: 48%; minorities: 34%; underrepresented
minorities: 14%; in state: 43%
Acceptance rate: 10%
Average MCAT: 10.7
Average GPA: 3.66
**Most popular undergraduate
majors:** biological sciences: 47%;
physical sciences: 25%; non-
sciences: 16%; other: 12%
**Graduates entering primary-care
specialties:** 47.0%

PUERTO RICO

Ponce School of Medicine
PO Box 7004
Ponce, PR 00732
Private
Admissions: (787) 840-2575
E-mail: admissions@psm.edu
Web site: http://www.psm.edu
Financial aid: (787) 840-2575
Application deadline: 12/15
Tuition: $20,036
Room/board/expenses: $10,175
Students receiving grants: 49%
**Average student indebtedness at
graduation:** $99,278
Enrollment: 242
men: 58%; women: 42%; minorities: 96%; underrepresented
minorities: N/A; in state: 78%
Acceptance rate: 15%
Average MCAT: 6.0
Average GPA: 3.43
**Most popular undergraduate
majors:** biological sciences: 54%;
physical sciences: 7%; non-
sciences: 4%; other: N/A
**Graduates entering primary-care
specialties:** 40.0%

Universidad Central del Caribe[1]
PO Box 60-327
Bayamon, PR 00960-6032
Private
Admissions: (787) 740-1611
E-mail: icordero@uccaribe.edu
Web site: http://www.uccaribe.edu
Internet application: N/A
Financial aid: (787) 740-1611
Tuition: N/A
Room/board/expenses: N/A
Enrollment: N/A

University of Puerto Rico School of Medicine[1]
PO Box 365067
San Juan, PR 00936-5067
Public
Admissions: (787) 758-2525
E-mail: marrivera@rcm.upr.edu
Web site:
http://medweb.rcm.upr.edu/
Financial aid: (787) 758-2525
Tuition: N/A
Room/board/expenses: N/A
Enrollment: N/A

RHODE ISLAND

Brown University
97 Waterman Street
Box G-A212
Providence, RI 02912-9706
Private
Admissions: (401) 863-2149
E-mail: medschool_admissions@
brown.edu
Web site: http://bms.brown.edu
Financial aid: (401) 863-1142
Application deadline: N/A
Tuition: $32,524
Room/board/expenses: $12,706
Students receiving grants: 34%
**Average student indebtedness at
graduation:** $83,413
Enrollment: 323
men: 44%; women: 56%; minorities: 56%; underrepresented
minorities: 23%; in state: 15%
Acceptance rate: 8%
Average MCAT: 10.0
Average GPA: 3.60

**Most popular undergraduate
majors:** biological sciences: 27%;
physical sciences: 14%; non-
sciences: 34%; other: 25%
**Graduates entering primary-care
specialties:** 52.3%

SOUTH CAROLINA

Medical University of South Carolina
171 Ashley Avenue
Charleston, SC 29425
Public
Admissions: (843) 792-5396
E-mail: taylorwl@musc.edu
Web site: http://www.musc.edu/
Financial aid: (843) 792-2536
Application deadline: 12/01
In-state tuition: $14,115
Out-of-state tuition: $38,435
Room/board/expenses: $9,830
Students receiving grants: 21%
**Average student indebtedness at
graduation:** $85,967
Enrollment: 582
men: 55%; women: 45%; minorities: 20%; underrepresented
minorities: 12%; in state: 95%
Acceptance rate: 19%
Average MCAT: 9.4
Average GPA: 3.61
**Most popular undergraduate
majors:** biological sciences: 53%;
physical sciences: 15%; non-
sciences: 16%; other: 16%
**Graduates entering primary-care
specialties:** 41.0%

University of South Carolina
School of Medicine
Columbia, SC 29208
Public
Admissions: (803) 733-3325
E-mail: mills@med.sc.edu
Web site: http://www.med.sc.edu
Financial aid: (803) 733-3135
Application deadline: 12/01
In-state tuition: $13,010
Out-of-state tuition: $37,602
Room/board/expenses: $8,110
Students receiving grants: 55%
**Average student indebtedness at
graduation:** $69,275
Enrollment: 292
men: 55%; women: 45%; minorities: 20%; underrepresented
minorities: 8%; in state: 95%
Acceptance rate: 15%
Average MCAT: 8.7
Average GPA: 3.59
**Most popular undergraduate
majors:** biological sciences: 49%;
physical sciences: 14%; non-
sciences: 12%; other: 25%
**Graduates entering primary-care
specialties:** 58.0%

SOUTH DAKOTA

University of South Dakota
1400 W. 22nd Street
Sioux Falls, SD 57105
Public
Admissions: (605) 677-6886
E-mail: usdsmsa@usd.edu
Web site: http://med.usd.edu
Financial aid: (605) 677-5112
Application deadline: 11/15
In-state tuition: $14,438
Out-of-state tuition: $30,163
Room/board/expenses: $14,650
Students receiving grants: 80%
**Average student indebtedness at
graduation:** $98,071

Enrollment: 206
men: 60%; women: 40%; minorities: 4%; underrepresented
minorities: 2%; in state: 100%
Acceptance rate: 14%
Average MCAT: 9.2
Average GPA: 3.67
**Most popular undergraduate
majors:** biological sciences: 54%;
physical sciences: 14%; non-
sciences: 12%; other: 20%
**Graduates entering primary-care
specialties:** 40.4%

TENNESSEE

East Tennessee State University (J.H. Quillen)
PO Box 70694
Johnson City, TN 37614
Public
Admissions: (423) 439-2033
E-mail: sacom@mail.etsu.edu
Web site: http://qcom.etsu.edu/
Financial aid: (423) 439-2035
Application deadline: 12/01
In-state tuition: $14,991
Out-of-state tuition: $29,933
Room/board/expenses: $7,400
Students receiving grants: 38%
**Average student indebtedness at
graduation:** $86,000
Enrollment: 234
men: 49%; women: 51%; minorities: 20%; underrepresented
minorities: 12%; in state: 97%
Acceptance rate: 9%
Average MCAT: 9.3
Average GPA: 3.65
**Most popular undergraduate
majors:** biological sciences: 37%;
physical sciences: 15%; non-
sciences: 8%; other: 40%
**Graduates entering primary-care
specialties:** 66.7%

Meharry Medical College[1]
1005 D.B. Todd Jr. Boulevard
Nashville, TN 37208
Private
Admissions: (615) 327-6223
E-mail: aalva@mmc.edu
Web site: http://www.mmc.edu
Financial aid: (615) 327-6826
Tuition: N/A
Room/board/expenses: N/A
Enrollment: N/A

University of Tennessee–Memphis[1]
800 Madison Avenue
Memphis, TN 38163
Public
Admissions: (901) 448-5559
E-mail: diharris@utmem.edu
Web site: http://www.
utmem.edu/com_admissions/
Internet application:
http://www.utmem.edu/com_
admissions/MEDICINE_ADMS_
DIRECTORY2.html
Financial aid: (901) 448-5568
Tuition: N/A
Room/board/expenses: N/A
Enrollment: N/A

Vanderbilt University
21st Avenue S
at Garland Avenue
Nashville, TN 37232-2104
Private
Admissions: (615) 322-2145
Web site: http://www.
mc.vanderbilt.edu/medschool/

Internet application: http://www.
mc.vanderbilt.edu/medschool/
admissions/online_app.php
Financial aid: (615) 343-6310
Application deadline: 10/15
Tuition: $30,466
Room/board/expenses: $8,280
Students receiving grants: 50%
**Average student indebtedness at
graduation:** $86,800
Enrollment: 408
men: 59%; women: 41%; minorities: 28%; underrepresented
minorities: 5%; in state: 13%
Acceptance rate: 8%
Average MCAT: 11.2
Average GPA: 3.78
**Most popular undergraduate
majors:** biological sciences: 40%;
physical sciences: 26%; non-
sciences: 23%; other: 11%
**Graduates entering primary-care
specialties:** 35.5%

TEXAS

Baylor College of Medicine
1 Baylor Plaza
Houston, TX 77030
Private
Admissions: (713) 798-4842
E-mail: melodym@bcm.tmc.edu
Web site:
http://public.bcm.tmc.edu
Internet application:
http://public.bcm.tmc.
edu/admissions/
bcm-mdadmission.html
Financial aid: (713) 798-4603
Application deadline: 11/01
In-state tuition: $8,043
Out-of-state tuition: $21,143
Room/board/expenses: $17,347
Students receiving grants: 51%
**Average student indebtedness at
graduation:** $65,660
Enrollment: 669
men: 49%; women: 51%; minorities: 54%; underrepresented
minorities: 22%; in state: 86%
Acceptance rate: 8%
Average MCAT: 11.2
Average GPA: 3.80
**Most popular undergraduate
majors:** biological sciences: 41%;
physical sciences: 24%; non-
sciences: 20%; other: 15%
**Graduates entering primary-care
specialties:** 44.5%

Texas A&M University System Health Science Center
147 Joe H. Reynolds Medical
Building
College Station, TX 77843-1114
Public
Admissions: (979) 845-7743
E-mail: med-stu-aff@tamu.edu
Web site:
http://tamushsc.tamu.edu
Internet application:
http://www.utsystem.edu/tmdsas
Financial aid: (979) 845-8854
Application deadline: 11/01
In-state tuition: $7,925
Out-of-state tuition: $21,025
Room/board/expenses: $10,500
Students receiving grants: 20%
**Average student indebtedness at
graduation:** $66,275
Enrollment: 275
men: 48%; women: 52%; minorities: 37%; underrepresented
minorities: 8%; in state: 95%
Acceptance rate: 5%
Average MCAT: 9.5
Average GPA: 3.62

Most popular undergraduate majors: biological sciences: 62%; physical sciences: 16%; non-sciences: 14%; other: 8%
Graduates entering primary-care specialties: 41.0%

Texas Tech University Health Sciences Center

3601 Fourth Street
Lubbock, TX 79430
Public
Admissions: (806) 743-2297
E-mail: somadm@ttuhsc.edu
Web site: http://www.ttuhsc.edu/SOM/admissions/default.htm
Internet application: http://www.utsystem.edu/tmdsas/
Financial aid: (806) 743-3025
Application deadline: N/A
In-state tuition: $8,176
Out-of-state tuition: $21,276
Room/board/expenses: $9,638
Students receiving grants: 68%
Average student indebtedness at graduation: $92,428
Enrollment: 499
men: 62%; women: 38%; minorities: 30%; underrepresented minorities: 10%; in state: 96%
Acceptance rate: 9%
Average MCAT: 9.5
Average GPA: 3.61
Most popular undergraduate majors: biological sciences: 48%; physical sciences: 18%; non-sciences: 11%; other: 23%
Graduates entering primary-care specialties: 44.0%

University of Texas Health Science Center–Houston

6431 Fannin
MSB 1.126
Houston, TX 77030
Public
Admissions: (713) 500-5116
E-mail: msadmissions@uth.tmc.edu
Web site: http://www.med.uth.tmc.edu
Internet application: http://www.utsystem.edu/tmdsas
Financial aid: (713) 500-3860
Application deadline: 11/03
In-state tuition: $9,242
Out-of-state tuition: $22,342
Room/board/expenses: $11,940
Students receiving grants: 54%
Average student indebtedness at graduation: $74,723
Enrollment: 810
men: 53%; women: 47%; minorities: 29%; underrepresented minorities: 16%; in state: 98%
Acceptance rate: 10%
Average MCAT: 8.9
Average GPA: 3.62
Most popular undergraduate majors: biological sciences: N/A; physical sciences: N/A; non-sciences: N/A; other: N/A
Graduates entering primary-care specialties: 38.1%

University of Texas Health Science Center–San Antonio[1]

7703 Floyd Curl Drive
San Antonio, TX 78229-3900
Public
Admissions: (210) 567-2665
E-mail: msprospect@uthscsa.edu
Web site: http://www.uthscsa.edu
Financial aid: (210) 567-2635
Tuition: N/A
Room/board/expenses: N/A
Enrollment: N/A

University of Texas Medical Branch–Galveston[1]

301 University Boulevard
Galveston, TX 77555-0133
Public
Admissions: (409) 772-3517
E-mail: tsilva@utmb.edu
Web site: http://www.utmb.edu/
Internet application: https://www2.utmb.edu/utmbapp/app_options.htm
Financial aid: (409) 772-4955
Tuition: N/A
Room/board/expenses: N/A
Enrollment: N/A

University of Texas Southwestern Medical Center–Dallas

5323 Harry Hines Boulevard
Dallas, TX 75390
Public
Admissions: (214) 648-5617
E-mail: admissions@utsouthwestern.edu
Web site: http://www.utsouthwestern.edu/
Internet application: http://www.utsouthwestern.edu/medapp
Financial aid: (214) 648-3611
Application deadline: 11/03
In-state tuition: $8,192
Out-of-state tuition: $21,292
Room/board/expenses: $17,568
Students receiving grants: 63%
Average student indebtedness at graduation: $64,500
Enrollment: 843
men: 59%; women: 41%; minorities: 45%; underrepresented minorities: 17%; in state: 87%
Acceptance rate: 18%
Average MCAT: 10.7
Average GPA: 3.76
Most popular undergraduate majors: biological sciences: 43%; physical sciences: 22%; non-sciences: 15%; other: 20%
Graduates entering primary-care specialties: 42.0%

University of Utah

175 N Medical Drive E
Salt Lake City, UT 84132-2101
Public
Admissions: (801) 581-7498
E-mail: deans.admissions@hsc.utah.edu
Web site: http://www.med.utah.edu/som
Financial aid: (801) 581-6474
Application deadline: 10/15
In-state tuition: $12,507
Out-of-state tuition: $23,158
Room/board/expenses: $7,461
Students receiving grants: 65%
Average student indebtedness at graduation: $78,361
Enrollment: 416
men: 61%; women: 39%; minorities: 17%; underrepresented minorities: 6%; in state: 84%
Acceptance rate: 13%
Average MCAT: 9.9
Average GPA: 3.66
Most popular undergraduate majors: biological sciences: 43%; physical sciences: 18%; non-sciences: 15%; other: 24%
Graduates entering primary-care specialties: 42.7%

University of Vermont

E-126 Given Building
89 Beaumont Avenue
Burlington, VT 05405
Public
Admissions: (802) 656-2154
E-mail: medadmissions@uvm.edu
Web site: http://www.med.uvm.edu/
Internet application: http://www.aamc.org/students/amcas/application.htm
Financial aid: (802) 656-8293
Application deadline: 11/01
In-state tuition: $21,951
Out-of-state tuition: $37,801
Room/board/expenses: $9,550
Students receiving grants: 60%
Average student indebtedness at graduation: $128,515
Enrollment: 396
men: 41%; women: 59%; minorities: 20%; underrepresented minorities: 1%; in state: 28%
Acceptance rate: 4%
Average MCAT: 9.5
Average GPA: 3.50
Most popular undergraduate majors: biological sciences: 55%; physical sciences: 18%; non-sciences: 22%; other: 6%
Graduates entering primary-care specialties: 47.3%

Eastern Virginia Medical School

721 Fairfax Avenue
PO Box 1980
Norfolk, VA 23501-1980
Private
Admissions: (757) 446-5812
E-mail: nanezkf@evms.edu
Web site: http://www.evms.edu
Internet application: http://www.evms.edu/admissions
Financial aid: (757) 446-5813
Application deadline: 11/15
In-state tuition: $19,310
Out-of-state tuition: $33,310
Room/board/expenses: N/A
Students receiving grants: 72%
Average student indebtedness at graduation: $88,000
Enrollment: 419
men: 50%; women: 50%; minorities: 26%; underrepresented minorities: 11%; in state: 74%
Acceptance rate: 12%
Average MCAT: 9.8
Average GPA: 3.47
Most popular undergraduate majors: biological sciences: 54%; physical sciences: 18%; non-sciences: 18%; other: 10%
Graduates entering primary-care specialties: 53.7%

University of Virginia

PO Box 800793
McKim Hall, Health System
Charlottesville, VA 22908-0793
Public
Admissions: (434) 924-5571
E-mail: bab7g@virginia.edu
Web site: http://www.med.virginia.edu
Financial aid: (434) 924-0033
Application deadline: 11/01
In-state tuition: $18,285
Out-of-state tuition: $30,567
Room/board/expenses: $13,371
Students receiving grants: 58%
Average student indebtedness at graduation: $60,589
Enrollment: 547
men: 50%; women: 50%; minorities: 25%; underrepresented minorities: 9%; in state: 65%
Acceptance rate: 10%

Average MCAT: 10.6
Average GPA: 3.66
Most popular undergraduate majors: biological sciences: 51%; physical sciences: 14%; non-sciences: 20%; other: 15%
Graduates entering primary-care specialties: 46.0%

Virginia Commonwealth University-Medical College of Virginia

PO Box 980565
Richmond, VA 23298-0565
Public
Admissions: (804) 828-9629
E-mail: somume@hsc.vcu.edu
Web site: http://www.medschool.vcu.edu
Internet application: http://www.admissions.som.vcu.edu
Financial aid: (804) 828-4006
Application deadline: 11/15
In-state tuition: $13,031
Out-of-state tuition: $31,356
Room/board/expenses: $8,630
Students receiving grants: 44%
Average student indebtedness at graduation: $101,652
Enrollment: 698
men: 51%; women: 49%; minorities: 32%; underrepresented minorities: 7%; in state: 67%
Acceptance rate: 11%
Average MCAT: 9.6
Average GPA: 3.49
Most popular undergraduate majors: biological sciences: 58%; physical sciences: 19%; non-sciences: 21%; other: 2%
Graduates entering primary-care specialties: 47.0%

University of Washington

School of Medicine
Box 356340
Seattle, WA 98195
Public
Admissions: (206) 543-7212
E-mail: askuwsom@u.washington.edu
Web site: http://www.washington.edu/medical/som/
Financial aid: (206) 685-9229
Application deadline: 11/03
In-state tuition: $11,821
Out-of-state tuition: $27,947
Room/board/expenses: $11,637
Students receiving grants: 61%
Average student indebtedness at graduation: $72,827
Enrollment: 773
men: 48%; women: 52%; minorities: 23%; underrepresented minorities: 9%; in state: 88%
Acceptance rate: 8%
Average MCAT: 10.2
Average GPA: 3.67
Most popular undergraduate majors: biological sciences: 34%; physical sciences: 10%; non-sciences: 14%; other: 42%
Graduates entering primary-care specialties: 50.0%

Marshall University[1]

1600 Medical Center Drive
Huntington, WV 25701-3655
Public
Admissions: (800) 544-8514
E-mail: warren@marshall.edu
Web site: http://musom.marshall.edu
Financial aid: (304) 696-3162
Tuition: N/A
Room/board/expenses: N/A
Enrollment: N/A

West Virginia University

1146 Health Sciences N
Morgantown, WV 26506-9111
Public
Admissions: (304) 293-2408
E-mail: medadmissions@hsc.wvu.edu
Web site: http://www.hsc.wvu.edu/som/students
Financial aid: (304) 293-3706
Application deadline: 11/15
In-state tuition: $11,404
Out-of-state tuition: $28,144
Room/board/expenses: $9,620
Students receiving grants: 45%
Average student indebtedness at graduation: $85,235
Enrollment: 379
men: 59%; women: 41%; minorities: 18%; underrepresented minorities: N/A; in state: 94%
Acceptance rate: 18%
Average MCAT: 9.0
Average GPA: 3.69
Most popular undergraduate majors: biological sciences: 52%; physical sciences: 33%; non-sciences: 2%; other: 13%
Graduates entering primary-care specialties: 44.0%

Medical College of Wisconsin

8701 Watertown Plank Road
Milwaukee, WI 53226
Private
Admissions: (414) 456-8246
E-mail: medschool@mcw.edu
Web site: http://www.mcw.edu/acad/admission
Financial aid: (414) 456-8208
Application deadline: 11/03
Tuition: $20,197
Room/board/expenses: $7,500
Students receiving grants: 30%
Average student indebtedness at graduation: $108,092
Enrollment: 805
men: 60%; women: 40%; minorities: 22%; underrepresented minorities: 6%; in state: 51%
Acceptance rate: 12%
Average MCAT: 9.9
Average GPA: 3.70
Most popular undergraduate majors: biological sciences: 46%; physical sciences: 39%; non-sciences: 15%; other: N/A
Graduates entering primary-care specialties: 44.0%

University of Wisconsin–Madison

1300 University Avenue
Madison, WI 53706
Public
Admissions: (608) 265-6344
E-mail: jwaisman@facstaff.wisc.edu
Web site: http://www.med.wisc.edu/Education/
Financial aid: (608) 262-3060
Application deadline: 10/15
In-state tuition: $21,725
Out-of-state tuition: $32,849
Room/board/expenses: $11,970
Students receiving grants: 25%
Average student indebtedness at graduation: $101,400
Enrollment: 592
men: 45%; women: 55%; minorities: 19%; underrepresented minorities: 8%; in state: 86%
Acceptance rate: 11%
Average MCAT: 10.4
Average GPA: 3.68
Most popular undergraduate majors: biological sciences: 50%; physical sciences: 20%; non-sciences: 25%; other: 5%
Graduates entering primary-care specialties: 51.0%

INSTITUTIONS THAT GRANT THE DOCTOR OF OSTEOPATHY (D.O.) DEGREE

ARIZONA

Arizona College of Osteopathic Medicine

19555 N. 59th Avenue
Glendale, AZ 85308
Private
Admissions: (623) 572-3275
E-mail: admissaz@
arizona.midwestern.edu
Web site:
http://www.midwestern.edu
Internet application:
http://www.aacom.org
Financial aid: (623) 572-3321
Application deadline: 01/01
Tuition: $30,433
Room/board/expenses: $9,270
Students receiving grants: 17%
Average student indebtedness at graduation: $125,000
Enrollment: 548
men: 62%; women: 38%; minorities: 22%; underrepresented minorities: N/A; in state: 26%
Acceptance rate: 15%
Average MCAT: 8.4
Average GPA: 3.49
Most popular undergraduate majors: biological sciences: 40%; physical sciences: 15%; non-sciences: 24%; other: 21%
Graduates entering primary-care specialties: 65.0%

CALIFORNIA

College of Osteopathic Medicine of the Pacific

309 E. Second Street
Pomona, CA 91766-1854
Private
Admissions: (909) 469-5335
E-mail: admissions@westernu.edu
Web site: http://www.westernu.edu
Internet application:
http://www.aacom.org
Financial aid: (909) 469-5350
Application deadline: 01/15
Tuition: $29,450
Room/board/expenses: $10,220
Students receiving grants: 17%
Average student indebtedness at graduation: $136,165
Enrollment: 702
men: 56%; women: 44%; minorities: 48%; underrepresented minorities: 10%; in state: 82%
Acceptance rate: 20%
Average MCAT: 8.5
Average GPA: 3.38
Most popular undergraduate majors: biological sciences: 54%; physical sciences: 8%; non-sciences: 17%; other: 20%
Graduates entering primary-care specialties: 81.0%

Touro University College of Osteopathic Medicine

1310 Johnson Lane
Vallejo, CA 94592
Private
Admissions: (707) 638-5270
E-mail: haight@touro.edu
Web site: http://www.tucom.edu
Financial aid: (707) 638-5280
Application deadline: 02/14
Tuition: $29,850
Room/board/expenses: $12,750
Students receiving grants: 12%
Average student indebtedness at graduation: $149,000

Enrollment: 456
men: 56%; women: 44%; minorities: 32%; underrepresented minorities: 2%; in state: 54%
Acceptance rate: 12%
Average MCAT: 9.0
Average GPA: 3.48
Most popular undergraduate majors: biological sciences: 61%; physical sciences: 20%; non-sciences: 11%; other: 8%
Graduates entering primary-care specialties: 62.0%

FLORIDA

Nova Southeastern University College of Osteopathic Medicine

3200 S. University Drive
Fort Lauderdale, FL 33328
Private
Admissions: (954) 262-1101
E-mail: marlaf@nova.edu
Web site: http://medicine.nova.edu
Internet application:
http://hpd.nova.edu/
Financial aid: (954) 262-3380
Application deadline: 01/15
Tuition: $21,470
Room/board/expenses: $10,226
Students receiving grants: 15%
Average student indebtedness at graduation: $121,140
Enrollment: 805
men: 60%; women: 40%; minorities: 32%; underrepresented minorities: 15%; in state: 73%
Acceptance rate: 17%
Average MCAT: 8.1
Average GPA: 3.39
Most popular undergraduate majors: biological sciences: 64%; physical sciences: 7%; non-sciences: 14%; other: 15%
Graduates entering primary-care specialties: 87.9%

ILLINOIS

Chicago College of Osteopathic Medicine

555 31st Street
Downers Grove, IL 60515
Private
Admissions: (630) 515-7200
E-mail: admissil@midwestern.edu
Web site:
http://www.midwestern.edu
Financial aid: (630) 515-6035
Application deadline: 01/01
Tuition: $26,183
Room/board/expenses: $5,067
Students receiving grants: 21%
Average student indebtedness at graduation: $124,417
Enrollment: 643
men: 55%; women: 45%; minorities: 25%; underrepresented minorities: 5%; in state: 47%
Acceptance rate: 34%
Average GPA: 3.46
Most popular undergraduate majors: biological sciences: 64%; physical sciences: 15%; non-sciences: 12%; other: 9%
Graduates entering primary-care specialties: N/A

IOWA

Des Moines University Osteopathic Medical Center

3200 Grand Avenue
Des Moines, IA 50312
Private
Admissions: (515) 271-1499
E-mail: doadmit@dmu.edu
Web site: http://www.dmu.edu
Financial aid: (515) 271-1470
Application deadline: 02/02
Tuition: $25,475
Room/board/expenses: $12,112
Students receiving grants: 23%
Average student indebtedness at graduation: $142,997
Enrollment: 802
men: 56%; women: 44%; minorities: 10%; underrepresented minorities: 6%; in state: 26%
Acceptance rate: 26%
Average MCAT: 8.3
Average GPA: 3.50
Most popular undergraduate majors: biological sciences: 65%; physical sciences: 31%; non-sciences: 2%; other: 2%
Graduates entering primary-care specialties: 45.4%

KENTUCKY

Pikeville College School of Osteopathic Medicine

147 Sycamore Street
Pikeville, KY 41501
Private
Admissions: (606) 218-5406
E-mail: jkreutze@pc.edu
Web site: http://www.pc.edu
Internet application:
http://www.aacom.org
Financial aid: (606) 218-5407
Application deadline: 02/01
Tuition: $25,000
Room/board/expenses: N/A
Students receiving grants: 67%
Average student indebtedness at graduation: $119,000
Enrollment: 241
men: 71%; women: 29%; minorities: 9%; underrepresented minorities: 4%; in state: 87%
Acceptance rate: 18%
Average MCAT: 7.4
Average GPA: 3.30
Most popular undergraduate majors: biological sciences: 40%; physical sciences: 20%; non-sciences: 10%; other: 30%
Graduates entering primary-care specialties: N/A

MAINE

University of New England College of Osteopathic Medicine

11 Hills Beach Road
Biddeford, ME 04005
Private
Admissions: (800) 477-4863
E-mail: admissions@une.edu
Web site: http://www.une.edu/
Internet application: https://www.
applyweb.com/aw?une/
Financial aid: (207) 283-0171
Application deadline: N/A
Tuition: $29,415
Room/board/expenses: $10,700

Students receiving grants: 39%
Average student indebtedness at graduation: $132,000
Enrollment: 468
men: 51%; women: 49%; minorities: 9%; underrepresented minorities: 1%; in state: 17%
Acceptance rate: 11%
Average MCAT: 8.3
Average GPA: 3.17
Most popular undergraduate majors: biological sciences: 54%; physical sciences: 9%; non-sciences: 31%; other: 6%
Graduates entering primary-care specialties: 77.6%

MICHIGAN

Michigan State University College of Osteopathic Medicine

A308 E. Fee Hall
East Lansing, MI 48824
Public
Admissions: (517) 353-7740
E-mail: comadm@com.msu.edu
Web site: http://www.com.msu.edu
Internet application:
http://www.aacom.org
Financial aid: (517) 353-5188
Application deadline: 12/02
In-state tuition: $18,950
Out-of-state tuition: $40,550
Room/board/expenses: $10,656
Students receiving grants: 81%
Average student indebtedness at graduation: $117,221
Enrollment: 529
men: 54%; women: 46%; minorities: 19%; underrepresented minorities: 6%; in state: 92%
Acceptance rate: 12%
Average MCAT: 8.2
Average GPA: 3.46
Most popular undergraduate majors: biological sciences: 65%; physical sciences: 7%; non-sciences: 16%; other: 12%
Graduates entering primary-care specialties: 84.0%

MISSOURI

Kirksville College of Osteopathic Medicine

800 W. Jefferson Street
Kirksville, MO 63501
Private
Admissions: (660) 626-2237
E-mail: admissions@kcom.edu
Web site: http://www.kcom.edu
Internet application:
http://www.aacom.org
Financial aid: (660) 626-2529
Application deadline: 02/03
Tuition: $26,945
Room/board/expenses: $11,252
Students receiving grants: 18%
Average student indebtedness at graduation: $122,745
Enrollment: 631
men: 69%; women: 31%; minorities: 13%; underrepresented minorities: 2%; in state: 13%
Acceptance rate: 18%
Average MCAT: 8.7
Average GPA: 3.50
Most popular undergraduate majors: biological sciences: 54%; physical sciences: 12%; non-sciences: 9%; other: 25%
Graduates entering primary-care specialties: 66.0%

University of Health Sciences College of Osteopathic Medicine[1]

1750 Independence Avenue
Kansas City, MO 64106-1453
Private
Admissions: (800) 234-4847
E-mail: admissions@uhs.edu
Web site: http://www.uhs.edu
Financial aid: (816) 283-2000
Tuition: N/A
Room/board/expenses: N/A
Enrollment: N/A

NEW JERSEY

UMDNJ–School of Osteopathic Medicine

1 Medical Center Drive
Stratford, NJ 08084
Public
Admissions: (856) 566-7050
E-mail: somadm@umdnj.edu
Web site: http://som.umdnj.edu
Financial aid: (856) 566-6008
Application deadline: 02/03
In-state tuition: $19,939
Out-of-state tuition: $30,188
Room/board/expenses: $8,150
Students receiving grants: 44%
Average student indebtedness at graduation: $93,157
Enrollment: 329
men: 46%; women: 54%; minorities: 46%; underrepresented minorities: 22%; in state: 95%
Acceptance rate: 6%
Average MCAT: 8.6
Average GPA: 3.49
Most popular undergraduate majors: biological sciences: 59%; physical sciences: 9%; non-sciences: 15%; other: 17%
Graduates entering primary-care specialties: 45.9%

NEW YORK

New York College of Osteopathic Medicine

Old Westbury
Northern Boulevard
Long Island, NY 11568
Private
Admissions: (516) 686-3747
E-mail: mschaefer@nyit.edu
Web site: http://www.nyit.edu
Internet application:
http://www.aacom.org
Financial aid: (516) 686-7960
Application deadline: 02/04
Tuition: $28,590
Room/board/expenses: N/A
Students receiving grants: 2%
Average student indebtedness at graduation: $153,966
Enrollment: 1,135
men: 49%; women: 51%; minorities: 41%; underrepresented minorities: 13%; in state: 70%
Acceptance rate: 23%
Average MCAT: 7.9
Average GPA: 3.40
Most popular undergraduate majors: biological sciences: 48%; physical sciences: 10%; non-sciences: 19%; other: 23%
Graduates entering primary-care specialties: 62.0%

OHIO

Ohio University College of Osteopathic Medicine

Grosvenor and Irvine Halls
Athens, OH 45701
Public
Admissions: (740) 593-4313
E-mail: admissions@
exchange.oucom.ohiou.edu
Web site:
http://www.oucom.ohiou.edu
Internet application:
http://www.aacom.org
Financial aid: (740) 593-2152
Application deadline: 01/02
In-state tuition: $18,405
Out-of-state tuition: $25,929
Room/board/expenses: $9,006
Students receiving grants: 49%
Average student indebtedness at graduation: $105,600
Enrollment: 109
men: 39%; women: 61%; minorities: 24%; underrepresented minorities: 17%; in state: 85%
Acceptance rate: 27%
Average MCAT: 8.0
Average GPA: 3.49
Most popular undergraduate majors: biological sciences: 51%; physical sciences: 15%; nonsciences: 9%; other: 26%
Graduates entering primary-care specialties: 72.4%

OKLAHOMA

Oklahoma State University College of Osteopathic Medicine

1111 W. 17th Street
Tulsa, OK 74107
Public
Admissions: (918) 561-8421
E-mail: labgood@
osu-com.okstate.edu
Web site:
http://healthsciences.okstate.edu
Internet application:
http://www.aacom.org
Financial aid: (918) 561-8278
Application deadline: 01/15
In-state tuition: $12,334
Out-of-state tuition: $30,920
Room/board/expenses: $6,459
Students receiving grants: 63%
Average student indebtedness at graduation: $96,000
Enrollment: 348
men: 59%; women: 41%; minorities: 20%; underrepresented minorities: 16%; in state: 86%
Acceptance rate: 13%
Average MCAT: 8.8
Average GPA: 3.58
Most popular undergraduate majors: biological sciences: 53%; physical sciences: 14%; nonsciences: 14%; other: 19%
Graduates entering primary-care specialties: 90.0%

PENNSYLVANIA

Lake Erie College of Osteopathic Medicine[1]

1858 W. Grandview Boulevard
Erie, PA 16509
Private
Admissions: (814) 866-6641
E-mail: emorse@www.lecom.edu
Web site: http://www.lecom.edu
Internet application:
http://www.aacom.org
Financial aid: (814) 866-6641
Tuition: N/A
Room/board/expenses: N/A
Enrollment: N/A

Philadelphia College of Osteopathic Medicine

4170 City Avenue
Philadelphia, PA 19131
Private
Admissions: (215) 871-6700
E-mail: admissions@pcom.edu
Web site: http://www.pcom.edu
Internet application:
http://www.aacom.org
Financial aid: (215) 871-6170
Application deadline: 02/03
Tuition: $28,510
Room/board/expenses: $13,190
Students receiving grants: 57%
Average student indebtedness at graduation: $145,565
Enrollment: 1,016
men: 54%; women: 46%; minorities: 22%; underrepresented minorities: 11%; in state: 63%
Acceptance rate: 13%
Average MCAT: 8.0
Average GPA: 3.33

Most popular undergraduate majors: biological sciences: 65%; physical sciences: 9%; nonsciences: 19%; other: 7%
Graduates entering primary-care specialties: 58.0%

TEXAS

University of North Texas Health Science Center (Texas College of Osteopathic Medicine)

3500 Camp Bowie Boulevard
Fort Worth, TX 76107-2699
Public
Admissions: (800) 535-8266
E-mail: TCOMAdmissions@
hsc.unt.edu
Web site: http://www.hsc.unt.edu
Internet application: http://www.
hsc.unt.edu/education/
tcom/Admissions.cfm
Financial aid: (800) 346-8266
Application deadline: 10/15
In-state tuition: $7,802
Out-of-state tuition: $20,902
Room/board/expenses: $9,768
Students receiving grants: 46%
Average student indebtedness at graduation: $81,303
Enrollment: 479
men: 51%; women: 49%; minorities: 35%; underrepresented minorities: 9%; in state: 93%
Acceptance rate: 14%
Average MCAT: 8.8
Average GPA: 3.54
Most popular undergraduate majors: biological sciences: 53%; physical sciences: 9%; nonsciences: 15%; other: 23%
Graduates entering primary-care specialties: 83.2%

WEST VIRGINIA

West Virginia School of Osteopathic Medicine

400 N. Lee Street
Lewisburg, WV 24901
Public
Admissions: (800) 356-7836
E-mail: admissions@wvsom.edu
Web site: http://www.wvsom.edu
Internet application:
http://www.aacom.org
Financial aid: (800) 356-7836
Application deadline: 01/03
In-state tuition: $14,206
Out-of-state tuition: $35,158
Room/board/expenses: N/A
Students receiving grants: 7%
Average student indebtedness at graduation: $120,061
Enrollment: 306
men: 52%; women: 48%; minorities: 6%; underrepresented minorities: 1%; in state: 69%
Acceptance rate: 13%
Average MCAT: 7.3
Average GPA: 3.46
Most popular undergraduate majors: biological sciences: 53%; physical sciences: 7%; nonsciences: 17%; other: 22%
Graduates entering primary-care specialties: 85.0%

BUSINESS

ENGINEERING

OSTEOPATHY